An Introduction
to Probability Theory
and Its Applications

About the book . . .

Like its predecessor, the second edition of *An Introduction to Probability Theory and Its Applications* serves a dual purpose. It develops probability theory rigorously as a mathematical discipline, and, at the same time, illustrates the broad variety of practical problems with modern techniques used in their solution. For his illustrative material and examples, the author draws from a great many fields, including engineering, genetics, physics, and statistics. He includes new results concerning fluctuation theory developed by elementary methods.

In addition to new material in many of the chapters, the text includes two new chapters. One of these covers by elementary methods surprising phenomena of random walks and general fluctuation theory. An extended treatment of compound distributions and branching processes is offered in the other new chapter.

In order to present the intuitive background, and the basic concepts of probability theory unhampered by analytical formalism, the first volume is restricted to discrete sample spaces. The restricted coverage allows the author to treat many typical problems in great detail and to explain the probabilistic approach to them.

About the author . . .

William Feller received his M. S. from the University of Zagreb (Yugoslavia) in 1925 and his Ph.D. from the University of Gottingen one year later. After pursuing an academic career at the Universities of Gottingen, Kiel, Copenhagen, and Stockholm, he came in 1939 to the United States. Until 1945 he was an Associate Professor of Mathematics at Brown University and Executive Editor of Mathematical Reviews.

From 1945 to 1950, Dr. Feller was Professor of Mathematics at Cornell University. He is, at present, Eugene Higgins Professor of Mathematics at Princeton University.

A WILEY PUBLICATION IN MATHEMATICAL STATISTICS

An Introduction
to Probability Theory
and Its Applications.

WILLIAM FELLER

Eugene Higgins Professor of Mathematics

Princeton University

VOLUME I

SECOND EDITION

John Wiley & Sons, Inc.

New York · London

Library of Congress Catalog Card Number: 57–10805

PRINTED IN THE UNITED STATES OF AMERICA

To

O. E. Neugebauer

Preface to the Second Edition

THE FAVORABLE RECEPTION OF THE FIRST EDITION SURPASSED the most daring anticipation and, in addition to an unexpected number of users, the book seems to have found friends who read it merely for fun; it is most heartening that they range from pure mathematicians to pure amateurs. Although I cannot here express individual thanks to all readers to whom I am indebted for useful critical comments, their communications stimulated me during six years to think of improvements and to collect better examples and exercises. I hope that these will make for easier reading and teaching from the book.

The general plan, as described in the preface to the first edition, remains unchanged. To accommodate the manifold needs of readers with divergent backgrounds, interests, and degrees of mathematical sophistication, it was necessary frequently to deviate from the main path. The exposition therefore does not always progress from the easy to the difficult; comparatively technical sections appear at the beginning and easy sections in chapters XV and XVII. Inexperienced readers should not attempt to follow many side lines lest they lose sight of the forest for too many trees. To facilitate orientation and the choice of desirable omissions, stars are used more systematically than in the first edition. *The unstarred sections form a self-contained whole in which the starred sections are not used.*

A first introduction to the basic notions of probability is contained in chapters I, V, VI, IX; beginners should cover these with as few digressions as possible. Chapter II is designed to develop the student's technique and probabilistic intuition; some experience in its contents is desirable, but it is not necessary to cover the chapter systematically: it may prove more profitable to return to the elementary illustrations as occasion arises at later stages. For the purposes of a first introduction, the restriction to discrete distributions should not be a serious handicap since the elementary theory of continuous distributions requires only a few words of supplementary explanation.

From chapter IX an introductory course may proceed directly to chapter XI, considering generating functions as an example of more general transforms. Chapter XI should be followed by some applications in chapters XIII (recurrent events) or XII (chain reactions, infinitely divisible distributions). Without generating functions it is possible to turn in one of the following directions: limit theorems and fluctuation theory (chapters VIII, X, III); stochastic processes (chapter XVII); random walks (chapter III and the main part of XIV). These chapters are almost independent of each other. The Markov chains of chapter XV depend conceptually on recurrent events, but they may be studied independently if the reader is willing to accept without proof the basic ergodic theorem.

Space saved by streamlining made it possible to add new material and to integrate the old third chapter with chapter II. New emphasis is laid on waiting times, a topic now serving as a unifying thread throughout the book. This emphasis is reflected in the early introduction of waiting times in chapter II and in the several independent treatments of the first-passage times in random walks.

Chapter III is entirely new. It illustrates the power of combinatorial methods by deriving in an elementary way important results previously obtained by advanced analytical tools. The results concerning fluctuations in coin tossing show that widely held beliefs about the law of large numbers are fallacious. These results are so amazing and so at variance with common intuition that even sophisticated colleagues doubted that coins actually misbehave as theory predicts. The record of a simulated experiment is therefore included in section 7.

A new stress on the essential unity of recurrent events and Markov chains permitted improvements and simplifications, but at the cost of a change from the terminology of the first edition. I am deeply apologetic for the confusion which is bound to ensue.

Great care has been taken to render the index usable, but it cannot serve as a *Who's Who* in probability: the proper balance is destroyed by references to all papers that chanced to lead, often indirectly, to the construction of an example or exercise. I regret that sometimes important contributions are quoted in an irrelevant context not indicative of their value.

This edition was prepared under ideal working conditions without interruptions by routine duties. For this ease I must thank the Air Force Office of Scientific Research, Princeton University, and the stimulating hospitality of J. Wolfowitz. I have continued to benefit from the helpful criticism of J. L. Doob. The careful checking of manuscript and proofs by my wife has removed many errors and effects of chance.

WILLIAM FELLER

August 1957

Preface to the First Edition

IT WAS THE AUTHOR'S ORIGINAL INTENTION TO WRITE A BOOK ON analytical methods in probability theory in which the latter was to be treated as a topic in pure mathematics. Such a treatment would have been more uniform and hence more satisfactory from an aesthetic point of view; it would also have been more appealing to pure mathematicians. However, the generous support by the Office of Naval Research of work in probability theory at Cornell University led the author to a more ambitious and less thankful undertaking of satisfying heterogeneous needs.

It is the purpose of this book to treat probability theory as a self-contained mathematical subject rigorously, avoiding non-mathematical concepts. At the same time, the book tries to describe the empirical background and to develop a feeling for the great variety of practical applications. This purpose is served by many special problems, numerical estimates, and examples which interrupt the main flow of the text. They are clearly set apart in print and are treated in a more picturesque language and with less formality. A number of special topics have been included in order to exhibit the power of general methods and to increase the usefulness of the book to specialists in various fields. To facilitate reading, detours from the main path are indicated by stars. The knowledge of starred sections is not assumed in the remainder.

A serious attempt has been made to unify methods. The specialist will find many simplifications of existing proofs and also new results. In particular, the theory of recurrent events has been developed for the purpose of this book. It leads to a new treatment of Markov chains which permits simplification even in the finite case.

The examples are accompanied by about 340 problems mostly with complete solutions. Some of them are simple exercises, but most of them serve as additional illustrative material to the text or contain various complements. One purpose of the examples and problems is to develop the reader's intuition and art of probabilistic formulation. Several previously treated examples show that apparently difficult

ix

problems may become almost trite once they are formulated in a natural way and put into the proper context.

There is a tendency in teaching to reduce probability problems to pure analysis as soon as possible and to forget the specific characteristics of probability theory itself. Such treatments are based on a poorly defined notion of random variables usually introduced at the outset. This book goes to the other extreme and dwells on the notion of sample space, without which random variables remain an artifice.

In order to present the true background unhampered by measurability questions and other purely analytic difficulties this volume is restricted to *discrete sample spaces*. This restriction is severe, but should be welcome to non-mathematical users. It permits the inclusion of special topics which are not easily accessible in the literature. At the same time, this arrangement makes it possible to begin in an elementary way and yet to include a fairly exhaustive treatment of such advanced topics as random walks and Markov chains. The general theory of random variables and their distributions, limit theorems, diffusion theory, etc., is deferred to a succeeding volume.

This book would not have been written without the support of the Office of Naval Research. One consequence of this support was a fairly regular personal contact with J. L. Doob, whose constant criticism and encouragement were invaluable. To him go my foremost thanks. The next thanks for help are due to John Riordan, who followed the manuscript through two versions. Numerous corrections and improvements were suggested by my wife who read both the manuscript and proof.

The author is also indebted to K. L. Chung, M. Donsker, and S. Goldberg, who read the manuscript and corrected various mistakes; the solutions to the majority of the problems were prepared by S. Goldberg. Finally, thanks are due to Kathryn Hollenbach for patient and expert typing help; to E. Elyash, W. Hoffman, and J. R. Kinney for help in proofreading.

WILLIAM FELLER

Cornell University
January 1950

Contents

* Starred sections are not required for the understanding of the sequel and should be omitted at first reading.

The Nature
of Probability Theory

1. THE BACKGROUND

Probability is a mathematical discipline with aims akin to those, for example, of geometry or analytical mechanics. In each field we must carefully distinguish three aspects of the theory: (a) the formal logical content, (b) the intuitive background, (c) the applications. The character, and the charm, of the whole structure cannot be appreciated without considering all three aspects in their proper relation.

(a) Formal Logical Content

Axiomatically, mathematics is concerned solely with relations among undefined things. *This property* is well illustrated by the game of chess. It is impossible to "define" chess otherwise than by stating a set of rules. The conventional shape of the pieces may be described to some extent, but it will not always be obvious which piece is intended for "king." The chessboard and the pieces are helpful, but they can be dispensed with. The essential thing is to know how the pieces move and act. It is meaningless to talk about the "definition" or the "true nature" of a pawn or a king. Similarly, geometry does not care what a point and a straight line "really are." They remain undefined notions, and the axioms of geometry specify the relations among them: two points determine a line, etc. These are the rules, and there is nothing sacred about them. We change the axioms to study different forms of geometry, and the logical structure of the several non-Euclidean geometries is independent of their relation to reality. Physicists have studied the motion of bodies under laws of attraction different from Newton's, and such studies are meaningful even if Newton's law of attraction is accepted as true in nature.

1

(b) Intuitive Background

In contrast to chess, the axioms of geometry and of mechanics refer to an existing intuitive background. In fact, geometrical intuition is so strong that it is prone to run ahead of logical reasoning. The extent to which logic, intuition, and physical experience are interdependent is a problem into which we need not enter. Certainly intuition can be trained and developed. The bewildered novice in chess moves cautiously, recalling individual rules, whereas the experienced player absorbs a complicated situation at a glance and is unable to account rationally for his intuition. In like manner mathematical intuition grows with experience, and it is possible to develop a natural feeling for concepts such as a four-dimensional space.

Even the collective intuition of mankind appears to progress. Newton's notions of a field of force and of action at a distance and Maxwell's concept of electromagnetic "waves" were at first decried as "unthinkable" and "contrary to intuition." Modern technology and radio in the homes have popularized these notions to such an extent that they form part of the ordinary vocabulary. Similarly, the modern student has no appreciation of the modes of thinking, the prejudices, and other difficulties against which the theory of probability had to struggle when it was new. Nowadays newspapers report on samples of public opinion, and the magic of statistics embraces all phases of life to the extent that young girls watch the statistics of their chances to get married. Thus everyone has acquired a feeling for the meaning of statements such as "the chances are three in five." Vague as it is, this intuition serves as background and guide for the first step. It will be developed as the theory progresses and acquaintance is made with more sophisticated applications.

(c) Applications

The concepts of geometry and mechanics are in practice identified with certain physical objects, but the process is so flexible and variable that no general rules can be given. The notion of a rigid body is fundamental and useful, even though no physical object is rigid. Whether a given body can be treated as if it were rigid depends on the circumstances and the desired degree of approximation. Rubber is certainly not rigid, but in discussing the motion of automobiles textbooks treat the rubber tires as rigid bodies. Depending on the purpose of the theory, we disregard the atomic structure of matter and treat the sun now as a ball of continuous matter, now as a single mass point.

In applications, the abstract mathematical models serve as tools, and different models can describe the same empirical situation. *The manner in which mathematical theories are applied does not depend on preconceived ideas; it is a purposeful technique depending on, and changing with, experience.* A philosophical analysis of such techniques is a legitimate study, but it is not within the realm of mathematics, physics, or statistics. The philosophy of the foundations of probability must be divorced from mathematics and statistics, exactly as the discussion of our intuitive space concept is now divorced from geometry.

2. PROCEDURE

The history of probability (and of mathematics in general) shows a stimulating interplay of theory and applications; theoretical progress opens new fields of applications, and in turn applications lead to new problems and fruitful research. The theory of probability is now applied in many diverse fields, and we require the flexibility of a general theory to provide appropriate tools for so great a variety of needs. We must therefore withstand the temptation (and the pressure) to build the theory, its terminology, and its arsenal too close to one particular sphere of interest. We wish instead to develop a mathematical theory in the established way which has proved so successful in geometry and mechanics.

We shall start from the simplest experiences such as tossing a coin or throwing dice, where all statements have an obvious intuitive meaning. This intuition will be translated into an abstract model to be generalized gradually and by degrees. Illustrative examples will be provided to explain the empirical background of the several models and to develop the reader's intuition, but the theory itself will be of a mathematical character. We shall no more attempt to explain the "true meaning" of probability than the modern physicist dwells on the "real meaning" of mass and energy or the geometer discusses the nature of a point. Instead, we shall prove theorems and show how they are applied.

At the outset the purpose of the theory of probability was to describe the exceedingly narrow domain of experience connected with games of chance, the main effort being directed to the calculation of certain probabilities. In the opening chapters we too shall calculate a few typical probabilities, but it should be borne in mind that numerical probabilities are not the principal object of the theory. Its aim is to discover general laws and to construct satisfactory theoretical models.

Probabilities play for us the same role as masses in mechanics. The motion of the planetary system can be discussed without knowledge of the individual masses and without contemplating methods for their actual measurements. Even non-existent planetary systems may be the object of a profitable and illuminating study. Similarly, practical and *useful probability models may refer to non-observable worlds*. For example, billions of dollars have been invested in automatic telephone exchanges. These are based on simple probability models in which various possible systems are compared. The theoretically best system is built and the others will never exist. In insurance, probability theory is used to calculate the probability of ruin; that is, the theory is used to avoid certain undesirable situations, and consequently it applies to situations that are not actually observed. Probability theory would be effective and useful even if not a single numerical value were accessible.

3. "STATISTICAL" PROBABILITY

The success of the modern mathematical theory of probability is bought at a price: the theory is limited to one particular aspect of "chance." The intuitive notion of probability is connected with inductive reasoning and with judgments such as "Paul is probably a happy man," "Probably this book will be a failure," "Fermat's conjecture is probably false." Judgments of this sort are of interest to the philosopher and the logician, and they are a legitimate object of a mathematical theory.[1] It must be understood, however, that we are concerned not with modes of inductive reasoning but with something that might be called physical or *statistical probability*. In a rough way we may characterize this concept by saying that our probabilities do not refer to judgments but to possible outcomes of a *conceptual experiment*. Before we speak of probabilities, we must agree on an idealized model of a particular conceptual experiment such as tossing a coin, sampling kangaroos on the moon, observing a particle under diffusion, counting the number of telephone calls. At the outset we must agree on the possible outcomes of this experiment (our *sample space*) and the probabilities associated with them. This is analogous to the procedure in mechanics where fictitious models involving two, three, or seventeen mass points are introduced, these points being devoid of individual properties. Similarly, in analyzing the coin tossing game we are not concerned with the accidental circumstances of an actual experiment: the object of our theory are sequences (or arrangements) of symbols such as "head, head, tail, head, ..." There is no place in our system for speculations concerning the probability that the sun will rise tomorrow. Before speaking of it we should have to agree on an (idealized)

---

[1] B. O. Koopman, The axioms and algebra of intuitive probability, *Annals of Mathematics* (2), vol. 41 (1940), pp. 269–292, and The bases of probability, *Bulletin of the American Mathematical Society*, vol. 46 (1940), pp. 763–774.

model which would presumably run along the lines "out of infinitely many worlds one is selected at random. . . ." Little imagination is required to construct such a model, but it appears both uninteresting and meaningless.

The astronomer speaks of measuring the temperature at the center of the sun or of travel to Sirius. These operations seem impossible, and yet it is not senseless to contemplate them. By the same token, we shall not worry whether or not our conceptual experiments can be performed; we shall analyze abstract models. In the back of our minds we keep an intuitive interpretation of probability which gains operational meaning in certain applications. We *imagine* the experiment performed a great many times. An event with probability 0.6 should be expected, in the long run, to occur sixty times out of a hundred. This description is deliberately vague but supplies a picturesque intuitive background sufficient for the more elementary applications. As the theory proceeds and grows more elaborate, the operational meaning and the intuitive picture will become more concrete.

4. SUMMARY

We shall be concerned with theoretical models in which probabilities enter as free parameters in much the same way as masses in mechanics. They are applied in many and variable ways. The technique of applications and the intuition develop with the theory.

This is the standard procedure accepted and fruitful in other mathematical disciplines. No alternative has been devised which could conceivably fill the manifold needs and requirements of *all* branches of the growing entity called probability theory and its applications.

We may fairly lament that intuitive probability is insufficient for scientific purposes, but it is a historical fact. In example I(6.*b*), we shall discuss random distributions of particles in compartments. The appropriate, or "natural," probability distribution seemed perfectly clear to everyone and had been accepted without hesitation by physicists. It turned out, however, that physical particles are not trained in human common sense, and the "natural" (or Boltzmann) distribution had to be given up for the Einstein-Bose distribution in some cases, for the Fermi-Dirac distribution in others. No intuitive argument has been offered why photons should behave differently from protons and why they do not obey the "a priori" laws. *If* a justification could now be found, it would only show that intuition develops with theory. At any rate, even for applications freedom and flexibility are essential, and it would be pernicious to fetter the theory to fixed poles.

It has also been claimed that the modern theory of probability is too abstract and too general to be useful. This is the battle cry once raised by practical-minded people against Maxwell's field theory. The argument could be countered by pointing to the unexpected new applications opened by the abstract theory of stochastic processes or to the new insights offered by the modern fluctuation theory which once more belies intuition and is leading to a revision of practical attitudes. However, the discussion is useless; it is too easy to condemn. Only yesterday the practical things of today were decried as impractical, and the theories which will be practical tomorrow will always be branded as valueless games by the practical men of today.

5. HISTORICAL NOTE

The statistical, or empirical, attitude toward probability has been developed mainly by R. A. Fisher and R. von Mises. The notion of sample space [2] comes from von Mises. This notion made it possible to build up a strictly mathematical theory of probability based on measure theory. Such an approach has emerged gradually in the 'twenties under the influence of many authors. An axiomatic treatment representing the modern development was given by A. Kolmogorov.[3] We shall follow this line, but the term axiom appears too solemn inasmuch as the present volume deals only with the simple case of discrete probabilities.

---

[2] See his book, *Wahrscheinlichkeitsrechnung*, Leipzig and Wien, 1931, with references to his original papers dating back to about 1921. The German word is *Merkmalraum* (label space).

[3] A. Kolmogoroff, Grundbegriffe der Wahrscheinlichkeitsrechnung, fasc. 3 of vol. 2 of *Ergebnisse der Mathematik*, Berlin, 1933.

CHAPTER I

The Sample Space

1. THE EMPIRICAL BACKGROUND

The mathematical theory of probability gains practical value and an intuitive meaning in connection with real or conceptual experiments such as tossing a coin once, tossing a coin 100 times, throwing three dice, arranging a deck of cards, matching two decks of cards, playing roulette, observing the life span of a radioactive atom or a person, selecting a random sample of people and observing the number of left-handers in it, crossing two species of plants and observing the phenotypes of the offspring; or with phenomena such as the sex of a newborn baby, the number of busy trunklines in a telephone exchange, the number of calls on a telephone, random noise in an electrical communication system, routine quality control of a production process, frequency of accidents, the number of double stars in a region of the skies, the position of a particle under diffusion. All these descriptions are rather vague, and, in order to render the theory meaningful, we have to agree on what we mean by *possible results of the experiment or observation in question.*

When a coin is tossed, it does not necessarily fall heads or tails; it can roll away or stand on its edge. Nevertheless, we shall agree to regard "head" and "tail" as the only possible outcomes of the experiment. This convention simplifies the theory without affecting its applicability. Idealizations of this type are standard practice. It is impossible to measure the life span of an atom or a person without some error, but for theoretical purposes it is expedient to imagine that these quantities are exact numbers. The question then arises as to which numbers can actually represent the life span of a person. Is there a maximal age beyond which life is impossible, or is any age conceivable? We hesitate to admit that man can grow 1000 years old, and yet current actuarial practice admits no bounds to the possible duration of life. According to formulas on which modern mortality tables are based, the proportion of men surviving 1000 years is of the order of magnitude of one in $10^{10^{36}}$—a number with 10^{27} billions of zeros. This statement does not make sense from a biological or sociological point of view, but considered exclusively from a statistical standpoint it certainly does not contradict any experience. There are fewer than 10^{10} people born in a century. To test the contention statistically, more than $10^{10^{35}}$ centuries would be required, which is considerably more than $10^{10^{34}}$ lifetimes of the earth. Obviously, such extremely small probabilities are compatible with our notion of impossibility. Their use may appear utterly absurd, but it does no harm and is convenient in simplifying many formulas. Moreover, if we were seriously to discard the possibility of living 1000 years, we should have to accept the existence of a maximum age, and the assumption that it should be possible to live x years and impossible to live x years and two seconds is as unappealing as the idea of unlimited life.

Any theory necessarily involves idealization, and our first idealization concerns the possible outcomes of an "experiment" or "observation." If we want to construct an abstract model, we must at the outset reach a decision about what constitutes a possible outcome of the (idealized) experiment.

For uniform terminology, the results of experiments or observations will be called *events*. Thus we shall speak of the event that of five coins tossed more than three fell heads. Similarly, the "experiment" of distributing the cards in bridge [1] may result in the "event" that North has two aces. The composition of a sample ("two left-handers in a sample of 85") and the result of a measurement ("temperature 120°," "seven trunklines busy") will each be called an event.

We shall distinguish between *compound* (or decomposable) and *simple* (or indecomposable) *events*. For example, saying that a throw with two dice resulted in "sum six" amounts to saying that it resulted in "(1, 5) or (2, 4) or (3, 3) or (4, 2) or (5, 1)," and this enumeration decomposes the event "sum six" into five simple events. Similarly, the event "two odd faces" admits of the decomposition "(1, 1) or (1, 3) or ... or (5, 5)" into nine simple events. Note that if a throw results in

---

[1] *Definition of bridge and poker.* A deck of bridge cards consists of 52 cards arranged in four suits of thirteen each. There are thirteen face values (2, 3, ..., 10, jack, queen, king, ace) in each suit. The four suits are called spades, clubs, hearts, diamonds. The last two are red, the first two black. Cards of the same face value are called of the same kind. For our purposes, playing bridge means distributing the cards to four players, to be called North, South, East, and West (or N, S, E, W, for short) so that each receives thirteen cards. Playing poker, by definition, means selecting five cards out of the pack.

(3, 3), then *the same throw* results also in the events "sum six" and "two odd faces"; these events are not mutually exclusive and hence may occur simultaneously. As a second example consider the age of a person. Every particular value x represents a *simple* event, whereas the statement that a person is in his fifties describes the compound event that x lies between 50 and 60. In this way every compound event can be decomposed into simple events, that is to say, a compound event is an *aggregate of certain simple events*.

If we want to speak about "experiments" or "observations" in a theoretical way and without ambiguity, we must first agree on the simple events representing the thinkable outcomes; *they define the idealized experiment*. It is usual to refer to these simple events as *sample points*, or *points* for short. By definition, *every indecomposable result of the (idealized) experiment is represented by one, and only one, sample point*. The aggregate of all sample points will be called the *sample space*. All events connected with a given (idealized) experiment can be described in terms of sample points.

Before formalizing these basic conventions, we proceed to discuss a few typical examples which will play a role further on.

2. EXAMPLES

(a) *Distribution of three balls in three cells.* Table 1 describes all possible outcomes of the "experiment" of placing three balls into three cells.

TABLE 1

1. $\{abc\| - \| - \}$	10. $\{a \| bc \| - \}$	19. $\{ - \|a \| bc\}$
2. $\{ - \|abc\| - \}$	11. $\{ b \|a c\| - \}$	20. $\{ - \| b \|a c\}$
3. $\{ - \| - \|abc\}$	12. $\{ c\|ab \| - \}$	21. $\{ - \| c\|ab \}$
4. $\{ab \| c\| - \}$	13. $\{a \| - \| bc\}$	22. $\{a \| b \| c\}$
5. $\{a c\| b \| - \}$	14. $\{ b \| - \|a c\}$	23. $\{a \| c\| b \}$
6. $\{ bc\|a \| - \}$	15. $\{ c\| - \|ab \}$	24. $\{ b \|a \| c\}$
7. $\{ab \| - \| c\}$	16. $\{ - \|ab \| c\}$	25. $\{ b \| c\|a \}$
8. $\{a c\| - \| b \}$	17. $\{ - \|a c\| b \}$	26. $\{ c\|a \| b \}$
9. $\{ bc\| - \|a \}$	18. $\{ - \| bc\|a \}$	27. $\{ c\| b \|a \}$.

Each of these arrangements represents a simple event, that is, a sample point. The event A "one cell is multiply occupied" is realized in the arrangements numbered 1–21, and we express this by saying that the event A is the aggregate of the sample points 1–21. Similarly, the event B "first cell is not empty" is the aggregate of the sample points 1, 4–15, 22–27. The event C defined by "both A and B occur" is the aggregate of the thirteen sample points 1, 4–15. In this particular example it so happens that each of the 27 points belongs to either A or B (or to both); therefore the event "either A or B or both occur" is the entire sample space and occurs with absolute certainty. The event D defined by "A does not occur" consists of the points 22–27 and can be described by the condition that no cell remains empty. The event "first cell empty and no cell multiply occupied" is impossible (does not occur) since no sample point satisfies these specifications.

(b) *Distribution of r balls in n cells.* The more general case of r balls in n cells can be studied in the same manner, except that the number of possible arrangements increases rapidly with r and n. For $r = 3$ balls in $n = 4$ cells, the sample space contains already 64 points, and for $r = n = 10$ there are 10^{10} sample points; a complete tabulation would require some hundred thousand big volumes.

We use this example to illustrate the important fact that the nature of the sample points is irrelevant for our theory. To us the sample space (together with the probability distribution defined in it) *defines* the idealized experiment. We use the picturesque language of balls and cells, but the same sample space admits of a great variety of different practical interpretations. To clarify this point, and also for further reference, *we list here a number of situations in which the intuitive background varies; all are, however, abstractly equivalent to the scheme of placing r balls into n cells, in the sense that the outcomes differ only in their verbal description.* The appropriate assignment of probabilities is not the same in all cases and will be discussed later on.

(b, 1). *Birthdays.* The possible configurations of the birthdays of r people correspond to the different arrangements of r balls in $n = 365$ cells (assuming the year to have 365 days).

(b, 2). *Accidents.* Classifying r accidents according to the weekdays when they occurred is equivalent to placing r balls into $n = 7$ cells.

(b, 3). *In firing* at n targets, the hits correspond to balls, the targets to cells.

(b, 4). *Sampling.* Let a group of r people be classified according to, say, age or profession. The classes play the role of our cells, the people that of balls.

(b, 5). *Irradiation in biology.* When the cells in the retina of the eye are exposed to light, the light particles play the role of balls, and the actual cells are the "cells" of our model. Similarly, in the study of the genetic effect of irradiation, the chromosomes correspond to the cells of our model and α-particles to the balls.

(b, 6). In *cosmic ray experiments* the particles hitting the Geiger counters represent the balls, and the counters function as cells.

(b, 7). *An elevator* starts with r passengers and stops at n floors. The different arrangements of discharging the passengers are replicas of the different distributions of r balls in n cells.

(b, 8). *Dice.* The possible outcomes of a throw with r dice correspond to placing r balls into $n = 6$ cells. When *tossing a coin* we are in effect dealing with only $n = 2$ cells.

(b, 9). *Random digits.* The possible orderings of a sequence of r digits correspond to the distribution of r balls (= places) into ten cells called 0, 1, ..., 9.

(b, 10). The *sex distribution* of r persons. Here we have $n = 2$ cells and r balls.

(b, 11). *Coupon collecting.* The different kinds of coupons represent the cells; the coupons collected represent the balls.

(b, 12). *Aces in bridge.* The four players represent four cells, and we have $r = 4$ balls.

(b, 13). *Gene distributions.* Each descendant of an individual (person, plant, or animal) inherits from the progenitor certain genes. If a particular gene can appear in n forms $A_1, \ldots, A_n$, then the descendants may be classified according to the type of the gene. The descendants correspond to the balls, the genotypes $A_1, \ldots, A_n$ to the cells.

(b, 14). *Chemistry.* Suppose that a long chain polymer reacts with oxygen. An individual chain may react with 0, 1, 2, ... oxygen molecules. Here the reacting oxygen molecules play the role of balls and the polymer chains the role of cells into which the balls are put.

(b, 15). *Theory of photographic emulsions.* A photographic plate is covered with grains sensitive to light quanta: a grain reacts if it is hit by a certain number, r, of quanta. For the theory of black-white contrast we must know how many cells are likely to be hit by the r quanta. We have here an occupancy problem where the grains correspond to cells, and the light quanta to balls. (Actually the situation is more complicated since a plate usually contains grains of different sensitivity.)

(b, 16). *Misprints.* The possible distributions of r misprints in the n pages of a book correspond to all the different distributions of r balls in n cells, provided r is smaller than the number of letters per page.

(c) *The case of indistinguishable balls.* Let us return to example (a) and suppose that the three balls are not distinguishable. This means that we no longer distinguish between three arrangements such as 4, 5, 6, and thus table 1 reduces to table 2. The latter *defines* the sample

TABLE 2

1. {***	–	– }	6. { *	**	– }
2. { –	***	– }	7. { *	–	** }
3. { –	–	***}	8. { –	**	* }
4. {**	*	– }	9. { –	*	** }
5. {**	–	* }	10. { *	*	* }.

space of the ideal experiment which we call *"placing three indistinguishable balls into three cells,"* and a similar procedure applies to the case of r balls in n cells.

Whether or not actual balls are in practice distinguishable is irrelevant for our theory. Even if they are, we may decide to treat them as indistinguishable. The aces in bridge [example $(b, 12)$] or the people in an elevator [example $(b, 7)$] certainly are distinguishable and yet it is often preferable to treat them as indistinguishable. The dice of example $(b, 8)$ may be colored to make them distinguishable, but whether in discussing a particular problem we use the model of distinguishable or indistinguishable balls is purely a matter of purpose and convenience. The nature of a concrete problem may dictate the choice, but under any circumstances our theory begins only after the appropriate model has been chosen, that is, after the sample space has been defined.

In the scheme above we have considered indistinguishable balls, but table 2 still refers to a first, second, third cell, and their order is essential. We can go a step further and assume that even the cells are indistinguishable (for example, the cell may be chosen at random without regard to its contents). With both balls and cells indistinguishable, only three different arrangements are possible, namely {*** | – | – }, {** | * | – }, { * | * | * }.

(d) Sampling. Suppose that a sample of 100 people is taken in order to estimate how many people smoke. The only property of the sample of interest in this connection is the number x of smokers; this may be any integer between 0 and 100. In this case we may agree that our sample space consists of the 101 "points" 0, 1, ..., 100. Every particular sample or observation is completely described by stating the corresponding point x. An example of a compound event is the result that "the majority of the people sampled are smokers." This means that the experiment resulted in one of the fifty simple events 51, 52, ..., 100, but it is not stated in which. Similarly, every property of the sample can be described in enumerating the corresponding cases

or sample points. For uniform terminology we speak of events rather than properties of the sample. Mathematically, an event is simply the aggregate of the corresponding sample points.

(e) *Sampling* (*continued*). Suppose now that the 100 people in our sample are classified not only as smokers or non-smokers but also as males or females. The sample may now be characterized by a quadruple (M_s, F_s, M_n, F_n) of integers giving in order the number of male and female smokers, male and female non-smokers. We can take for sample points the quadruples of integers lying between 0 and 100 and adding to 100. There are 176,851 such quadruples, and they constitute the sample space (cf. chapter II, section 5). The event "relatively more males than females smoke" means that in our sample the ratio M_s/M_n is greater than F_s/F_n. The point (73, 2, 8, 17) has this property, but (0, 1, 50, 49) has not. Our event can be described in principle by enumerating all quadruples with the desired property.

(f) *Coin tossing*. For the experiment of tossing a coin three times, the sample space consists of eight points which may conveniently be represented by $HHH, HHT, HTH, THH, HTT, THT, TTH, TTT$. The event A, "two or more heads," is the aggregate of the first four points. The event B, "just one tail," means either HHT, or HTH, or THH; we say that B contains these three points.

(g) *Ages of a couple*. An insurance company is interested in the age distribution of couples. Let x stand for the age of the husband, y for the age of the wife. Each observation results in a number-pair (x, y). For the sample space corresponding to a single observation we take the first quadrant of the x, y-plane so that each point $x > 0$, $y > 0$ is a sample point. The event A, "husband is older than 40," is represented by all points to the right of the line $x = 40$; the event B, "husband is older than wife," is represented by the angular region between the x-axis and the bisector $y = x$, that is to say, by the aggregate of points with $x > y$; the event C, "wife is older than 40," is represented by the portion of the first quadrant above the line $y = 40$. For a geometric representation of the joint age distributions of two couples we would require a four-dimensional space.

(h) *Phase space*. In statistical mechanics, each possible "state" of a system is called a "point in phase space." This is only a difference in terminology. The phase space is simply our sample space; its points are our sample points.

3. THE SAMPLE SPACE. EVENTS

It should be clear from the preceding that we shall never speak of probabilities except in relation to a given sample space (or, physically, in relation to a certain conceptual experiment). *We start with the notion of a sample space and its points; from now on they will be considered given. They are the primitive and undefined notions of the theory* precisely as the notions of "points" and "straight line" remain undefined in an axiomatic treatment of Euclidean geometry. The nature of the sample points does not enter our theory. The sample space provides a model of an ideal experiment in the sense that, by definition, *every thinkable outcome of the experiment is completely described by one, and only one, sample point.* It is meaningful to talk about an event A only when it is clear for *every* outcome of the experiment whether the event A has or has not occurred. The collection of all those sample points representing outcomes where A has occurred completely describes the event. Conversely, any given aggregate A containing one or more sample points can be called an event; this event does, or does not, occur according as the outcome of the experiment is, or is not, represented by a point of the aggregate A. We therefore define the word *event to mean the same as an aggregate of sample points.* We shall say that an *event A consists of* (*or contains*) *certain points*, namely those representing outcomes of the ideal experiment in which A occurs.

Example. In the sample space of example (2.a) consider the event U consisting of the points number 1, 7, 13. This is a formal and straightforward definition, but U can be described in many equivalent ways. For example, U may be defined as the event that the following three conditions are satisfied: (1) the second cell is empty, (2) the ball a is in the first cell, (3) the ball b does not appear after c. Each of these conditions itself describes an event. The event U_1 defined by the condition (1) alone consists of points 1, 3, 7–9, 13–15. The event U_2 defined by (2) consists of points 1, 4, 5, 7, 8, 10, 13, 22, 23, and the event U_3 defined by (3) contains the points 1–4, 6, 7, 9–11, 13, 14, 16, 18–20, 22, 24, 25. The event U can also be described as the *simultaneous realization* of all three events U_1, U_2, U_3.

The terms "sample point" and "event" have an intuitive appeal, but they refer to the notions of point and point set common to all parts of mathematics.

We have seen in the preceding example and in (2.a) that new events can be defined in terms of two or more given events. With these examples in mind we now proceed to introduce the notation of the formal *algebra of events* (that is, algebra of point sets).

4. RELATIONS AMONG EVENTS

We shall now suppose that an arbitrary, but fixed, sample space $\mathfrak{S}$ is given.

Definition 1. *We shall use the notation* $A = 0$ *to express that the event A contains no sample points (is impossible).* The zero must be interpreted in a symbolic sense and not as the numeral.

To every event A there corresponds another event defined by the condition "*A* does not occur." It contains all points not contained in A.

Definition 2. *The event consisting of all points not contained in the event A will be called the complementary event (or negation) of A and will be denoted by* A'. *In particular,* $\mathfrak{S}' = 0$.

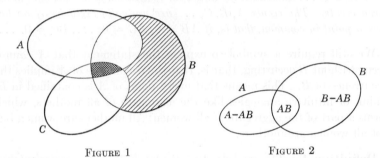

FIGURE 1　　　　　　　　　　　　FIGURE 2

FIGURES 1 AND 2. Illustrating relations among events. In Figure 1 the domain within heavy boundaries is the union $A \cup B \cup C$. The triangular (*heavily shaded*) domain is the intersection ABC. The moon-shaped (*lightly shaded*) domain is the intersection of B with the complement of $A \cup C$.

With any two events A and B we can associate two new events defined by the conditions "*both A and B occur*" and "*either A or B or both occur*." These events will be denoted by AB and $A \cup B$, respectively. The event AB contains all sample points which are common to A and B. If A and B exclude each other, then there are no points common to A and B and the event AB is impossible; analytically, this situation is described by the equation

$$(4.1) \qquad\qquad AB = 0$$

which should be read "*A and B are mutually exclusive.*" The event AB' means that both A and B' occur or, in other words, that A but not B occurs. Similarly, $A'B'$ means that neither A nor B occurs. The event $A \cup B$ means that at least one of the events A and B occurs; it contains all sample points except those that belong neither to A nor to B.

In the theory of probability we can describe the event AB as the simultaneous occurrence of A and B. In standard mathematical terminology AB is called the (logical) intersection of A and B. Similarly, $A \cup B$ is the union of A and B. Our notion carries over to the case of events $A, B, C, D, \ldots$.

Definition 3. *To every collection $A, B, C, \ldots$ of events we define two new events as follows. The aggregate of the sample points which belong to all the given sets will be denoted by $ABC \ldots$ and called the intersection [2] (or simultaneous realization) of $A, B, C, \ldots$. The aggregate of sample points which belong to at least one of the given sets will be denoted by $A \cup B \cup C \ldots$ and called the union (or realization of at least one) of the given events. The events $A, B, C, \ldots$ are mutually exclusive if no two have a point in common, that is, if $AB = 0$, $AC = 0$, $\ldots$, $BC = 0$, $\ldots$.*

We still require a symbol to express the statement that A cannot occur without B occurring, that is, that the occurrence of A implies the occurrence of B. This means that every point of A is contained in B. Think of intuitive analogies like the aggregate of all mothers, which forms a part of the aggregate of all women: All mothers are women but not all women are mothers.

Definition 4. *The symbols $A \subset B$ and $B \supset A$ are equivalent and signify that every point of A is contained in B; they are read, respectively, "A implies B" and "B is implied by A". If this is the case, we shall also write $B - A$ instead of BA' to denote the event that B but not A occurs.*

The event $B - A$ contains all those points which are in B but not in A. With this notation we can write $A' = \mathfrak{S} - A$ and $A - A = 0$.

Examples. (a) If A and B are mutually exclusive, then the occurrence of A implies the non-occurrence of B and vice versa. Thus $AB = 0$ means the same as $A \subset B'$ and as $B \subset A'$.

(b) The event $A - AB$ means the occurrence of A but not of both A and B. Thus $A - AB = AB'$.

(c) In the example (2.g), the event AB means that the husband is older than 40 *and* older than his wife; AB' means that he is older than 40 but *not* older than his wife. AB is represented by the infinite trape-

---

[2] The standard mathematical notation for the intersection of two or more sets is $A \cap B$ or $A \cap B \cap C$, etc. This notation is more suitable for certain specific purposes and is to be adopted in the second volume. At present we use the notation AB, ABC, etc., since it is less clumsy in print.

zoidal region between the x-axis and the lines $x = 40$ and $y = x$, and the event AB' is represented by the angular domain between the lines $x = 40$ and $y = x$, the latter boundary included. The event AC means that both husband and wife are older than 40. The event $A \cup C$ means that at least one of them is older than 40, and $A \cup B$ means that the husband is either older than 40 or, if not that, at least older than his wife (in official language, "husband's age exceeds 40 years or wife's age, whichever is smaller").

(d) In example (2.a) let E_i be the event that the cell number i is empty (here $i = 1, 2, 3$). Similarly, let S_i, D_i, T_i, respectively, denote the event that the cell number i is occupied simply, doubly, or triply. Then $E_1 E_2 = T_3$, and $S_1 S_2 \subset S_3$, and $D_1 D_2 = 0$. Note also that $T_1 \subset E_2$, etc. The event $D_1 \cup D_2 \cup D_3$ is defined by the condition that there exist at least one doubly occupied cell.

(e) *Bridge* (cf. footnote 1). Let A, B, C, D be the events, respectively, that North, South, East, West have at least one ace. It is clear that at least one player has an ace, so that one or more of the four events must occur. Hence $A \cup B \cup C \cup D = \mathfrak{S}$ is the whole sample space. The event $ABCD$ occurs if, and only if, each player has an ace. The event "West has all four aces" means that none of the three events A, B, C has occurred; this is the same as the simultaneous occurrence of A' and B' and C' or the event $A'B'C'$.

(f) In the example (2.g) we have $BC \subset A$; in words "if husband is older than wife (B) and wife is older than 40 (C), then husband is older than 40 (A)." How can the event $A - BC$ be described in words?

5. DISCRETE SAMPLE SPACES

The simplest sample spaces are those containing only a finite number, n, of points. If n is fairly small (as in the case of tossing a few coins), it is easy to visualize the space. The space of distributions of cards in bridge is more complicated. However, we may imagine each sample point represented on a chip and may then consider the collection of these chips as representing the sample space. An event A (like "North has two aces") is represented by a certain set of chips, the complement A' by the remaining ones. It takes only one step from here to imagine a bowl with infinitely many chips or a sample space with an infinite sequence of points $E_1, E_2, E_3, \ldots$.

Examples. (a) Let us toss a coin as often as necessary to turn up one head. The points of the sample space are then $E_1 = H$, $E_2 = TH$, $E_3 = TTH$, $E_4 = TTTH$, etc. We may or may not consider as thinkable the possibility that H never appears. If we do, this possibility should be represented by a point E_0.

(b) Three players a, b, c take turns at a game, such as chess, according to the following rules. At the start a and b play while c is out. The loser is replaced by c and at the second trial the winner plays against c while the loser is out. The game continues in this way until a player wins twice in succession, thus becoming the winner of the game. For simplicity we disregard the possibility of ties at the individual trials. The possible outcomes of our game are indicated by the following scheme:

$$(*) \quad \begin{matrix} aa, & acc, & acbb, & acbaa, & acbacc, & acbacbb, & acbacbaa, & \ldots \\ bb, & bcc, & bcaa, & bcabb, & bcabcc, & bcabcaa, & bcabcabb, & \ldots . \end{matrix}$$

In addition, it is thinkable that no player ever wins twice in succession, which means that the play continues indefinitely according to one of the patterns

$$(**) \qquad acbacbacbacb \ldots, \qquad bcabcabcabca \ldots .$$

The sample space corresponding to our ideal "experiment" is defined by (*) and (**) and is infinite. It is clear that the sample points can be arranged in a simple sequence by taking first the two points (**) and continuing with the points of (*) in the order aa, bb, acc, bcc, ... (This example is continued in problems 5 and 6; example V(2.a); problem XV, 5.)

Definition. *A sample space is called discrete if it contains only finitely many points or infinitely many points which can be arranged into a simple sequence $E_1, E_2, \ldots .$*

Not every sample space is discrete. It is a known theorem (due to G. Cantor) that the sample space consisting of all positive numbers is not discrete. We are here confronted with a distinction familiar in mechanics. There it is usual first to consider discrete mass points with each individual point carrying a finite mass, and then to pass to the notion of a continuous mass distribution, where each individual point has zero mass. In the first case, the mass of a system is obtained simply by adding the masses of the individual points; in the second case, masses are computed by integration over mass densities. Quite similarly, the probabilities of events in discrete sample spaces are obtained by mere additions, whereas in other spaces integrations are necessary. Except for the technical tools required, there is no essential difference between the two cases. In order to present actual probability considerations unhampered by technical difficulties, we shall take up only discrete sample spaces. It will be seen that even this special case leads to many interesting and important results.

In this volume we shall consider only discrete sample spaces.

6. PROBABILITIES IN DISCRETE SAMPLE SPACES: PREPARATIONS

The probabilities of the various events are numbers of the same nature as distances in geometry or masses in mechanics. The theory assumes that they are given but need assume nothing about their actual numerical values or how they are measured in practice. Some of the most important applications are of a qualitative nature and independent of numerical values; the general conclusions of the theory are applied in many ways exactly as the theorems of geometry serve as a basis for physical theories and engineering applications. In the relatively few instances where numerical values for probabilities are required, the methods of procedure vary as widely as do the methods of determining distances. There is little in common in the practices of the carpenter, the practical surveyor, the pilot, and the astronomer when they measure distances. In our context, we may consider the diffusion constant, which is a notion of the theory of probability. To find its numerical value, physical considerations relating it to other theories are required; a direct measurement is impossible. By contrast, mortality tables are constructed from rather crude observations. In most actual applications the determination of probabilities, or the comparison of theory and observation, requires rather sophisticated statistical methods, which in turn are based on a refined probability theory. In other words, the intuitive meaning of probability is clear, but only as the theory proceeds shall we be able to see how it is applied. All possible "definitions" of probability fall far short of the actual practice.

When tossing a "good" coin we do not hesitate to associate probability $\frac{1}{2}$ with either head or tail. This amounts to saying that when a coin is tossed n times all 2^n possible results have the same probability. From a theoretical standpoint, this is a *convention*. Frequently, it has been contended that this convention is logically unavoidable and the only possible one. Yet there have been philosophers and statisticians defying the convention and starting from contradictory assumptions (uniformity or non-uniformity in nature). It has also been claimed that the probabilities $\frac{1}{2}$ are due to experience. As a matter of fact, whenever refined statistical methods have been used to check on actual coin tossing, the result has been invariably that head and tail are *not* equally likely. And yet we stick to our model of an "ideal" coin, even though no good coins exist. We preserve the model not merely for its logical simplicity, but essentially for its usefulness and applicability. In many applications it is sufficiently accurate to describe reality. More important is the empirical fact that departures from our scheme are always coupled with phenomena such as an eccentric position of the center of gravity. In this way our idealized model can be extremely useful even if it never applies exactly. For example, in modern statistical quality control based on Shewhart's methods, idealized probability models are used to discover "assignable causes" for flagrant departures from these models and thus to remove impending machine troubles and process irregularities at an early stage.

Similar remarks apply to other cases. The number of possible distributions of cards in bridge is almost 10^{30}. Usually we agree to consider them as equally probable. For a check of this convention more than 10^{30} experiments would be required—thousands of billions of years if every living person played one game every second, day and night. However, consequences of the assumption can be verified experimentally, for example, by observing the frequency of multiple aces in the hands at bridge. It turns out that for crude purposes the idealized model describes experience sufficiently well, provided the card shuffling is done better than is usual. It is more important that the idealized scheme, when it does not apply, permits the discovery of "assignable causes" for the discrepancies, for example, the reconstruction of the mode of shuffling. These are examples of limited importance, but they indicate the usefulness of assumed models. More interesting cases will appear only as the theory proceeds.

Examples. (a) *Distinguishable balls.* In example (2.a) it appears natural to assume that all sample points are *equally probable,* that is, that *each sample point has probability* $\frac{1}{27}$. We can start from this *definition* and investigate its consequences. Whether or not our model will come reasonably close to actual experience will depend on the type of phenomena to which it is applied. In some applications the assumption of equal probabilities is imposed by physical considerations; in others it is introduced to serve as the simplest model for a general orientation, even though it quite obviously represents only a crude first approximation (e.g., consider the examples (2.b, 1), birthdays; (2.b, 7), elevator problem; or (2.b, 11) coupon collecting).

(b) *Indistinguishable balls: Bose-Einstein statistics.* We now turn to the example (2.c) of three indistinguishable balls in three cells. It is possible to argue that the actual physical experiment is unaffected by our failure to distinguish between the balls; physically there remain 27 different possibilities, even though only ten different forms are distinguishable. This consideration leads us to attribute the following probabilities to the ten points of table 2.

Point number:	1	2	3	4	5	6	7	8	9	10
Probability:	$\frac{1}{27}$	$\frac{1}{27}$	$\frac{1}{27}$	$\frac{1}{9}$	$\frac{1}{9}$	$\frac{1}{9}$	$\frac{1}{9}$	$\frac{1}{9}$	$\frac{1}{9}$	$\frac{2}{9}$.

It must be admitted that for most applications listed in example (2.*b*) this argument appears sound and the assignment of probabilities reasonable. Historically, our argument was accepted for a long time without question and served in statistical mechanics as the basis for the derivation of the *Maxwell-Boltzmann statistics* for the distribution of r balls in n cells. The greater was the general surprise when Bose and Einstein showed that certain particles are subject to the *Bose-Einstein* statistics (for details see chapter II, section 5). In our case with $r = n = 3$, the Bose-Einstein model attributes *probability* $\frac{1}{10}$ *to each of the ten sample points.*

This example will show that different assignments of probabilities are compatible with the same sample space and will illustrate the intricate interrelation between theory and experience. In particular, it teaches us not to rely too much on a priori arguments and to be prepared to accept new and unforeseen schemes.

(*c*) *Coin tossing.* A frequency interpretation of the postulate of equal probabilities requires records of actual experiments. Now in reality every coin is biased, and it is possible to devise physical experiments which come much closer to the ideal model of coin tossing than

TABLE 3

Trials number	Numbers of heads										Total
0– 1,000	54	46	53	55	46	54	41	48	51	53	501
– 2,000	48	46	40	53	49	49	48	54	53	45	485
– 3,000	43	52	58	51	51	50	52	50	53	49	509
– 4,000	58	60	54	55	50	48	47	57	52	55	536
– 5,000	48	51	51	49	44	52	50	46	53	41	485
– 6,000	49	50	45	52	52	48	47	47	47	51	488
– 7,000	45	47	41	51	49	59	50	55	53	50	500
– 8,000	53	52	46	52	44	51	48	51	46	54	497
– 9,000	45	47	46	52	47	48	59	57	45	48	494
–10,000	47	41	51	48	59	51	52	55	39	41	484

real coins ever do. To give an idea of the fluctuations to be expected, we give the record of such a simulated experiment corresponding to 10,000 trials with a coin.[3] Table 3 contains the number of occurrences

---

[3] The table actually records the frequency of even digits in a section of *A Million Random Digits with* 100,000 *Normal Deviates*, by The RAND Corporation, The Free Press, Glenese, Illinois, 1955.

of "heads" in a series of 100 experiments each corresponding to a sequence of 100 trials with a coin. The grand total is 4979. Looking at these figures the reader is very probably left with a vague feeling of: So what? The truth is that a more advanced theory is necessary to judge to what extent such empirical data agree with our abstract model. (Incidentally, we shall return to this material in chapter III, section 7.)

7. THE BASIC DEFINITIONS AND RULES

Fundamental Convention. *Given a discrete sample space $\mathfrak{S}$ with the sample points $E_1, E_2, \ldots$, we shall assume that with each point E_j there is associated a number, called the probability of E_j and denoted by $\mathbf{P}\{E_j\}$. It is to be non-negative and such that*

$$(7.1) \qquad \mathbf{P}\{E_1\} + \mathbf{P}\{E_2\} + \ldots = 1.$$

Note that we do not exclude the possibility that a point has probability zero. This convention may appear artificial but is necessary to avoid complications. In discrete sample spaces probability zero is in practice interpreted as an impossibility, and any sample point known to have probability zero can, with impunity, be eliminated from the sample space. However, frequently the numerical values of the probabilities are not known in advance, and involved considerations are required to decide whether or not a certain sample point has positive probability.

Definition. *The probability $\mathbf{P}\{A\}$ of any event A is the sum of the probabilities of all sample points in it.*

The fundamental equation (7.1) states that the probability of the entire sample space $\mathfrak{S}$ is unity, or $\mathbf{P}\{\mathfrak{S}\} = 1$. It follows that for any event A

$$(7.2) \qquad 0 \leq \mathbf{P}\{A\} \leq 1.$$

Consider now two arbitrary events A_1 and A_2. To compute the probability $\mathbf{P}\{A_1 \cup A_2\}$ that either A_1 or A_2 or both occur, we have to add the probabilities of all sample points contained either in A_1 or in A_2, but each point is to be counted only once. We have, therefore,

$$(7.3) \qquad \mathbf{P}\{A_1 \cup A_2\} \leq \mathbf{P}\{A_1\} + \mathbf{P}\{A_2\}.$$

Now, if E is any point contained both in A_1 and in A_2, then $\mathbf{P}\{E\}$ occurs twice in the right-hand member but only once in the left-hand member. Therefore, the right side exceeds the left side by the amount $\mathbf{P}\{A_1A_2\}$, and we have the simple but important

Theorem. *For any two events A_1 and A_2 the probability that either A_1 or A_2 or both occur is given by*

(7.4) $$\mathbf{P}\{A_1 \cup A_2\} = \mathbf{P}\{A_1\} + \mathbf{P}\{A_2\} - \mathbf{P}\{A_1 A_2\}.$$

If $A_1 A_2 = 0$, that is, if A_1 and A_2 are mutually exclusive, then (7.4) *reduces to*

(7.5) $$\mathbf{P}\{A_1 \cup A_2\} = \mathbf{P}\{A_1\} + \mathbf{P}\{A_2\}.$$

Example. A coin is tossed twice. For sample space we take the four points HH, HT, TH, TT, and associate with each probability $\frac{1}{4}$. Let A_1 and A_2 be, respectively, the events "head at first and second trial." Then A_1 consists of HH and HT, and A_2 of TH and HH. Furthermore $A = A_1 \cup A_2$ contains the three points HH, HT, and TH, whereas $A_1 A_2$ consists of the single point HH. Thus

$$\mathbf{P}\{A_1 \cup A_2\} = \tfrac{1}{2} + \tfrac{1}{2} - \tfrac{1}{4} = \tfrac{3}{4}.$$

The probability $\mathbf{P}\{A_1 \cup A_2 \cup \ldots \cup A_n\}$ of the realization of at least one among n events can be computed by a formula analogous to (7.4); this will be taken up in chapter IV, section 1. Here we note only that the inequality (7.3) obviously holds in general. Thus *for arbitrary events A_1, A_2, ... the inequality*

(7.6) $$\mathbf{P}\{A_1 \cup A_2 \cup \ldots\} \leq \mathbf{P}\{A_1\} + \mathbf{P}\{A_2\} + \ldots$$

holds. In the special case where the events A_1, A_2, ... are mutually exclusive, we have

(7.7) $$\mathbf{P}\{A_1 \cup A_2 \cup \ldots\} = \mathbf{P}\{A_1\} + \mathbf{P}\{A_2\} + \ldots.$$

Occasionally (7.6) is referred to as *Boole's inequality*.

We shall first investigate the simple special case where the sample space has a finite number, N, of points each having probability $1/N$. In this case, the probability of any event A equals the number of points in A divided by N. In the older literature, the points of the sample space were called "cases," and the points of A "favorable" cases (favorable for A). *If all points have the same probability, then the probability of an event A is the ratio of the number of favorable cases to the total number of cases.* Unfortunately, this statement has been much abused to provide a "definition" of probability. It is often contended that in *every* finite sample space probabilities of all points are equal. This is not so. For a single throw of an untrue coin, the sample space still contains only the two points, head and tail, but they may have arbitrary probabilities p and q, with $p + q = 1$. A newborn baby is a boy or girl, but in applications we have to admit that the two possibilities are not equally likely. A further counterexample is provided by (6.b). The usefulness of sample spaces in which all sample points have the same probability is restricted almost entirely to the study of games of chance and to combinatorial analysis.

8. PROBLEMS FOR SOLUTION

1. Among the digits 1, 2, 3, 4, 5 first one is chosen, and then a second selection is made among the remaining four digits. Assume that all twenty possible results have the same probability. Find the probability that an odd digit will be selected (a) the first time, (b) the second time, (c) both times.

2. In the sample space of example (2.a) attach equal probabilities to all 27 points. Using the notation of example (4.d), verify formula (7.4) for the two events $A_1 = S_1$ and $A_2 = S_2$. How many points does $S_1 S_2$ contain?

3. Consider the 24 possible arrangements (permutations) of the symbols 1234 and attach to each probability $\frac{1}{24}$. Let A_i be the event that the digit i appears at its natural place (where $i = 1, 2, 3, 4$). Verify formula (7.4).

4. A coin is tossed until for the first time the same result appears twice in succession. To every possible outcome requiring n tosses attribute probability $1/2^{n-1}$. Describe the sample space. Find the probability of the following events: (a) the experiment ends before the sixth toss, (b) an *even* number of tosses is required.

5. In the sample space of example (5.b) let us attribute to each point of (∗) containing exactly k letters probability $1/2^k$. (In other words, aa and bb carry probability $\frac{1}{4}$, acb has probability $\frac{1}{8}$, etc.) (a) Show that the probabilities of the points of (∗) add up to unity, whence the two points (∗∗) receive probability zero. (b) Show that the probability that a wins is $\frac{5}{14}$. The probability of b winning is the same, and c has probability $\frac{2}{7}$ of winning. (c) The probability that no decision is reached at or before the kth turn (game) is $1/2^{k-1}$.

6. Modify example (5.b) to take account of the possibility of ties at the individual games. Describe the appropriate sample space. How would you define probabilities?

7. In problem 3 show that $A_1 A_2 A_3 \subset A_4$ and $A_1 A_2 A'_3 \subset A'_4$.

8. Using the notations of example (4.d) show that (a) $S_1 S_2 D_3 = 0$; (b) $S_1 D_2 \subset E_3$; (c) $E_3 - D_2 S_1 \supset S_2 D_1$.

9. Two dice are thrown. Let A be the event that the sum of the faces is odd, B the event of at least one ace. Describe the events AB, $A \cup B$, AB'. Find their probabilities assuming that all 36 sample points have equal probabilities.

10. In example (2.g), discuss the meaning of the following events: (a) ABC, (b) $A - AB$, (c) $AB'C$.

11. In example (2.g), verify that $AC' \subset B$.

12. *Bridge* (cf. footnote 1). For $k = 1, 2, 3, 4$ let N_k be the event that North has at least k aces. Let S_k, E_k, W_k be the analogous events for South, East, West. What can be said about the number x of aces in West's possession in the events (a) W'_1, (b) $N_2 S_2$, (c) $N'_1 S'_1 E'_1$, (d) $W_2 - W_3$, (e) $N_1 S_1 E_1 W_1$, (f) $N_3 W_1$, (g) $(N_2 \cup S_2) E_2$?

13. In the preceding problem verify that (a) $S_3 \subset S_2$, (b) $S_3W_2 = 0$, (c) $N_2S_1E_1W_1 = 0$, (d) $N_2S_2 \subset W'_1$, (e) $(N_2 \cup S_2)W_3 = 0$, (f) $W_4 = N'_1S'_1E'_1$.

14. Verify the following relations.[4]

(a) $(A \cup B)' = A'B'$.

(b) $(A \cup B) - B = A - AB = AB'$.

(c) $AA = A \cup A = A$.

(d) $(A - AB) \cup B = A \cup B$.

(e) $(A \cup B) - AB = AB' \cup A'B$.

(f) $A' \cup B' = (AB)'$.

(g) $(A \cup B)C = AC \cup BC$.

15. Find simple expressions for

(a) $(A \cup B)(A \cup B')$, (b) $(A \cup B)(A' \cup B)(A \cup B')$, (c) $(A \cup B)(B \cup C)$.

16. State which of the following relations are correct and which incorrect:

(a) $(A \cup B) - C = A \cup (B - C)$.

(b) $ABC = AB(C \cup B)$.

(c) $A \cup B \cup C = A \cup (B - AB) \cup (C - AC)$.

(d) $A \cup B = (A - AB) \cup B$.

(e) $AB \cup BC \cup CA \supset ABC$.

(f) $(AB \cup BC \cup CA) \subset (A \cup B \cup C)$.

(g) $(A \cup B) - A = B$.

(h) $AB'C \subset A \cup B$.

(i) $(A \cup B \cup C)' = A'B'C'$.

(j) $(A \cup B)'C = A'C \cup B'C$.

(k) $(A \cup B)'C = A'B'C$.

(l) $(A \cup B)'C = C - C(A \cup B)$.

17. Let A, B, C be three arbitrary events. Find expressions for the events that of A, B, C:

(a) Only A occurs.

(b) Both A and B, but not C, occur.

(c) All three events occur.

(d) At least one occurs.

(e) At least two occur.

(f) One and no more occurs.

(g) Two and no more occur.

(h) None occurs.

(i) Not more than two occur.

18. The union $A \cup B$ of two events can be expressed as the union of two mutually exclusive events, thus: $A \cup B = A \cup (B - AB)$. Express in a similar way the union of three events A, B, C.

19. Using the result of problem 18 prove that

$$\mathbf{P}\{A \cup B \cup C\} = \mathbf{P}\{A\} + \mathbf{P}\{B\} +$$
$$+ \mathbf{P}\{C\} - \mathbf{P}\{AB\} - \mathbf{P}\{AC\} - \mathbf{P}\{BC\} + \mathbf{P}\{ABC\}.$$

[This formula is a special case of IV(1.5).]

---

[4] Notice that $(A \cup B)'$ denotes the complement of $A \cup B$ which is not the same as $A' \cup B'$. Similarly, $(AB)'$ is not the same as $A'B'$.

CHAPTER II

Elements
of Combinatorial Analysis

The purpose of this chapter is to derive a few basic formulas and to develop the corresponding probabilistic background. A more advanced reader may pass directly to chapter V where the main theoretical thread of chapter I is taken up again.

In the study of simple games of chance, sampling procedures, occupancy and order problems, etc., we are usually dealing with finite sample spaces in which the same probability is attributed to all points. To compute the probability of an event A we have then to divide the number of sample points in A ("favorable cases") by the total number of sample points ("possible cases"). This is facilitated by a systematic use of a few rules which we shall now proceed to review. Simplicity and economy of thought can be achieved by adhering to a few standard tools, and we shall follow this procedure instead of describing the shortest computational method in each special case.[1]

1. PRELIMINARIES

Pairs. *With m elements $a_1, \ldots, a_m$ and n elements $b_1, \ldots, b_n$, it is possible to form mn pairs (a_j, b_k) containing one element from each group.*

Proof. Arrange the pairs in a rectangular array in the form of a multiplication table with m rows and n columns so that (a_j, b_k) stands at the intersection of the jth row and kth column. Then each pair appears once and only once, and the assertion becomes obvious.

Examples. (*a*) *Bridge cards* (cf. footnote 1 to chapter I, section 1). As sets of elements take the four suits and the thirteen face values,

---

[1] The interested reader will find many topics of elementary combinatorial analysis treated in the classical textbook, *Choice and chance*, by W. A. Whitworth, fifth edition, London, 1901, reprinted by G. E. Stechert, New York, 1942. The companion volume by the same author, *DCC exercises*, reprinted New York, 1945, contains 700 problems with complete solutions.

respectively. Each card is defined by its suit and its face value, and there exist $4 \cdot 13 = 52$ such combinations, or cards.

(b) *"Seven-way lamps."* Some floor lamps so advertised contain 3 ordinary bulbs and also an indirect lighting fixture which can be operated on three levels but need not be used at all. Each of these four possibilities can be combined with 0, 1, 2, or 3 bulbs. Hence there are $4 \cdot 4 = 16$ possible combinations of which one, namely $(0, 0)$, means that no bulb is on. There remain fifteen (not seven) ways of operating the lamps.

Multiplets. *Given n_1 elements $a_1, \ldots, a_{n_1}$, and n_2 elements $b_1, \ldots, b_{n_2}$, etc., up to n_r elements $x_1, \ldots, x_{n_r}$; it is possible to form $n_1 \cdot n_2 \cdots n_r$ ordered r-tuplets $(a_{j_1}, b_{j_2}, \ldots, x_{j_r})$ containing one element of each kind.*

Proof. If $r = 2$, the assertion reduces to the first rule. If $r = 3$, take the pair (a_i, b_j) as element of a new kind. There are $n_1 n_2$ such pairs and n_3 elements c_k. Each triple (a_i, b_j, c_k) is itself a pair consisting of (a_i, b_j) and an element c_k; the number of triplets is therefore $n_1 n_2 n_3$. Proceeding by induction, the assertion follows for every r.

Perhaps the simplest and most useful way of describing the last theorem is as follows. To form an r-tuplet $(a_{j_1}, b_{j_2}, \ldots, x_{j_r})$ we have to choose one a, one b, etc. We have to perform r selections in all and have in succession $n_1, n_2, \ldots, n_r$ possibilities to choose from. It is asserted that this procedure can lead to $n_1 \cdot n_2 \cdots n_r$ different results.

Examples. (c) *Multiple classifications.* Suppose that people are classified according to sex, marital status, and profession. The various categories play the role of elements. If there are 17 professions, then we have $2 \cdot 2 \cdot 17 = 68$ classes in all.

(d) In an agricultural experiment three different treatments are to be tested (for example, the application of a fertilizer, a spray, and temperature). If these treatments can be applied on r_1, r_2, and r_3 levels or concentrations, respectively, then there exist a total of $r_1 r_2 r_3$ combinations, or ways of treatment.

(e) *"Placing balls into cells"* amounts to choosing one cell for each ball. With r balls we have r independent choices, and therefore *r balls can be placed into n cells in n^r different ways.* It will be recalled from example I(2.b) that a great variety of conceptual experiments are abstractly equivalent to that of placing balls into cells. For example, considering the faces of a die as "cells," the last proposition implies that the experiment of throwing a die r times has 6^r possible outcomes, of which 5^r satisfy the condition that no ace turns up. Assuming that all outcomes are equally probable, the event "no ace in r throws" has therefore probability $(\frac{5}{6})^r$. We might expect naively that in six throws "an ace should turn up," but the probability of this event is only $1 - (\frac{5}{6})^6$ or less than $\frac{2}{3}$. [Cf. example (3.b).]

2. ORDERED SAMPLES

Consider the set or "population" of n elements $a_1, a_2, \ldots, a_n$. Any ordered arrangement $a_{j_1}, a_{j_2}, \ldots, a_{j_r}$ of r symbols is called *an ordered sample of size r* drawn from our population. For an intuitive picture we can imagine that the elements are selected one by one. Two procedures are then possible. First, *sampling with replacement;* here each selection is made from the entire population, so that the same element can be drawn more than once. The samples are then arrangements in which repetitions are permitted. Second, *sampling without replacement;* here an element once chosen is removed from the population, so that the sample becomes an arrangement without repetitions. Obviously, in this case, the sample size r cannot exceed the population size n.

In sampling with replacement each of the r elements can be chosen in n ways: the number of possible samples is therefore n^r, as can be seen from the last theorem with $n_1 = n_2 = \ldots = n$. In sampling without replacement we have n possible choices for the first element, but only $n - 1$ for the second, $n - 2$ for the third, etc. Using the same rule, we see that in this case we have $n(n - 1) \cdots (n - r + 1)$ choices in all. Products of this type appear so often that it is convenient to introduce the notation [2]

(2.1) $(n)_r = n(n - 1) \cdots (n - r + 1).$

Clearly $(n)_r = 0$ for integers $r > n$. We have thus the following

Theorem. *For a population of n elements and a prescribed sample size r, there exist n^r different samples with replacement and $(n)_r$ samples without replacement.*

We note the special case where $r = n$. In sampling without replacement a sample of size n includes the whole population and represents a reordering (or *permutation*) of its elements. Accordingly, n elements $a_1, \ldots, a_n$ can be ordered in $(n)_n = n \cdot (n - 1) \cdots 2 \cdot 1$ different ways. Instead of $(n)_n$ we write $n!$, which is the more usual notation. We see that our theorem has the following

Corollary. *The number of different orderings of n elements is*

---

[2] The notation $(n)_r$ is not standard, but it will be used consistently in this book, *even if n is not an integer.*

$$n! = n \cdot (n - 1) \cdots 2 \cdot 1.$$

Mr. and Mrs. Smith form a sample of size two drawn from the human population; at the same time, they form a sample of size one drawn from the population of all couples. This example shows that the sample size is defined only in relation to a given population. Tossing a coin r times is one way of obtaining a sample of size r drawn from the population of the two letters, H and T. The same arrangement of r letters H and T is a single sample point in the space corresponding to the experiment of tossing a coin r times.

Drawing r elements from a population of size n is an experiment whose possible outcomes are samples of size r. Their number is n^r or $(n)_r$, depending on whether or not replacement is used. In either case, our conceptual experiment is described by a sample space in which each individual point represents a sample of size r.

So far we have not spoken of probabilities associated with our samples. Usually we shall assign equal probabilities to all of them and then speak of random samples. The word "random" is not well defined, but when applied to samples or selections it has a unique meaning. Whenever we speak of *random samples of fixed size r, the adjective random is to imply that all possible samples have the same probability*, namely, n^{-r} in sampling with replacement and $1/(n)_r$ in sampling without replacement, n denoting the size of the population from which the sample is drawn. If n is large and r relatively small, the ratio $(n)_r/n^r$ is near unity. This leads us to expect that, for large populations and relatively small samples, the two ways of sampling are practically equivalent [cf. problems 11.1, 11.2, and VI, 35].

We have introduced a practical terminology but have made no statements about the applicability of our model of random sampling to reality. Tossing coins, throwing dice, and similar activities may be interpreted as experiments in practical random sampling with replacements, and our probabilities are numerically close to frequencies observed in long-run experiments, even though perfectly balanced coins or dice do not exist. Random sampling without replacement is typified by successive drawings of cards from a shuffled deck (provided shuffling is done much better than is usual). In sampling human populations the statistician encounters considerable and often unpredictable difficulties, and bitter experience has shown that it is difficult to obtain even a crude image of randomness.

Exercise. In sampling without replacement the probability for any fixed element of the population to be included in a random sample of size r is

$$1 - (n - 1)_r \div (n)_r = 1 - (n - r)/n = r/n.$$

In sampling with replacement the corresponding probability is $1 - \{(n - 1)/n\}^r$.

3. EXAMPLES

We consider random samples of size r *with replacement* taken from a population of the n elements $a_1, \ldots, a_n$. We are interested in the event A that in such a sample $(a_{j_1}, \ldots, a_{j_r})$ no element appears twice, that is, that our sample could have been obtained also by sampling without replacement. The last theorem shows that there exist n^r different samples in all, of which $(n)_r$ satisfy the stipulated condition. Assuming that all arrangements have equal probability, we conclude that *the probability of no repetition in our sample is*

$$(3.1) \qquad p = \frac{(n)_r}{n^r} = \frac{n(n-1) \cdots (n-r+1)}{n^r}.$$

The following concrete interpretations of this formula will reveal surprising features.

(a) *Random sampling numbers.* Let the population consist of the ten digits 0, 1, $\ldots$, 9. Every succession of five digits represents a sample of size $r = 5$, and we assume that each such arrangement has probability 10^{-5}. By (3.1), *the probability that five consecutive random digits are all different is* $p = (10)_5 10^{-5} = 0.3024$.

We expect intuitively that in large mathematical tables having many decimal places the last five digits will have many properties of randomness. (In ordinary logarithmic and many other tables the tabular difference is nearly constant, and the last digit therefore varies regularly.) As an experiment, sixteen-place tables [3] were selected and the entries were counted whose last five digits are all different. In the first twelve batches of a hundred entries each, the number of entries with five different digits varied as follows: 30, 27, 30, 34, 26, 32, 37, 36, 26, 31, 36, 32. Small-sample theory shows that the magnitude of the fluctuations is well within the expected limits. The average frequency is 0.3142, which is rather close to the theoretical probability, 0.3024 [cf. example VII(3.f)].

Consider next the number $e = 2.71828\ldots$. The first 800 decimals [4] form 160 groups of five digits each, which we arrange in sixteen batches of ten each. In these sixteen batches the numbers of groups in which all five digits are different are as follows:

3,   1,   3,   4,   4,   1,   4,   4,   4,   2,   3,   1,   5,   4,   6,   3.

The frequencies again oscillate around the value 0.3024, and small-

---

[3] *Tables of probability functions*, vol. I, National Bureau of Standards, 1941.
[4] *Intermédiaire des recherches mathématiques*, vol. 2, 1946, p. 112.

sample theory confirms that the magnitude of the fluctuations is not larger than should be expected. The overall frequency of our event in the 160 groups is $\frac{52}{160} = 0.325$, which is reasonably close to $p = 0.3024$.

(b) *If n balls are randomly placed into n cells, the probability that each cell will be occupied is* $n!/n^n$. This probability is surprisingly small: for $n = 7$ it is only 0.00612.... This means that *if in a city seven accidents occur each week, then (assuming that all possible distributions are equally likely) practically all weeks will contain days with two or more accidents, and on the average only one week out of 165 will show a uniform distribution of one accident per day.* This example shows an unexpected characteristic of pure randomness. (All possible configurations of seven balls in seven cells are exhibited in table 1, section 5. With probability about 0.87 it will be observed that two or more cells remain empty.) For $n = 6$ the probability $n!n^{-n}$ equals 0.01543.... This shows how extremely improbable it is that in six throws with a perfect die *all* faces turn up. [The probability that a particular face does not turn up is about $\frac{1}{3}$; cf. example (1.e).]

(c) *Elevator.* An elevator starts with $r = 7$ passengers and stops at $n = 10$ floors. What is the probability p that no two passengers leave at the same floor? To render the question precise, we assume that all arrangements of discharging the passengers have the same probability (which is a crude approximation). Then

$$p = 10^{-7}(10)_7 = (10 \cdot 9 \cdot 8 \cdot 7 \cdot 6 \cdot 5 \cdot 4)10^{-7} = 0.06048.$$

When the event was once observed, the occurrence was deemed remarkable and odds of 1000 to 1 were offered against a repetition. (Cf. the answer to problem 10.43.)

(d) *Birthdays.* The birthdays of r people form a sample of size r from the population of all days in the year. The years are not of equal length, and we know that the birth rates are not quite constant throughout the year. However, in a first approximation, we may take a random selection of people as equivalent to a random selection of birthdays and consider the year as consisting of 365 days.

With these conventions we can interpret equation (3.1) to the effect *that the probability, p, that all r birthdays are different is* [5]

$$(3.2) \quad p = \frac{(365)_r}{365^r} = \left(1 - \frac{1}{365}\right)\left(1 - \frac{2}{365}\right) \cdots \left(1 - \frac{r-1}{365}\right).$$

---

[5] Cf. R. von Mises, Ueber Aufteilungs- und Besetzungs-Wahrscheinlichkeiten, *Revue de la Faculté des Sciences de l'Université d'Istanbul,* N.S. vol. 4 (1938–1939), pp. 145–163.

Again the numerical consequences are astounding. Thus for $r = 23$ people we have $p < \frac{1}{2}$, that is, *for 23 people the probability that at least two people have a common birthday exceeds $\frac{1}{2}$.*

Formula (3.2) looks forbidding, but it is easy to derive good numerical approximations to p. If r is small, we can neglect all cross products and have in a crude approximation [6]

$$(3.3) \qquad p \approx 1 - \frac{1 + 2 + \ldots + (r - 1)}{365} = 1 - \frac{r(r-1)}{730}.$$

For $r = 10$ the correct value is $p = 0.883\ldots$; equation (3.3) gives the approximation 0.877.

For larger r we obtain a much better approximation by passing to logarithms. For small positive x we have $\log(1 - x) \approx -x$, and thus from (3.2)

$$(3.4) \qquad \log p \approx - \frac{1 + 2 + \ldots + (r - 1)}{365} = - \frac{r(r-1)}{730}.$$

For $r = 30$ this leads to the approximation 0.3037 whereas the correct value is $p = 0.294$. For $r \leq 40$ the error in (3.4) is less than 0.08. (For a continuation see section 7. See also answer to problem 10.44.)

4. SUBPOPULATIONS AND PARTITIONS

As before, we use the term *population of size n* to denote an aggregate of n elements *without regard to their order*. Two populations are considered different if one contains an element not contained in the other. Choosing r elements out of a given population of size n means forming a subpopulation of size r. In how many ways can this be done? Each subpopulation of size r can be arranged in $r!$ different orders and in this way produces $r!$ different samples without repetition. Conversely, each such sample of size r contains r different elements and thus defines a subpopulation of size r. We know that there exist $(n)_r$ samples of the described sort. If x is the number of subpopulations of size r, then obviously the number of ordered samples is $x \cdot r!$, and we conclude that $x = (n)_r/r!$. Numbers of this kind are known as *binomial coefficients*, and the standard notation for them is

$$(4.1) \qquad \binom{n}{r} = \frac{(n)_r}{r!} = \frac{n(n-1)\cdots(n-r+1)}{1 \cdot 2 \cdots (r-1) \cdot r}.$$

---

[6] The sign $\approx$ signifies that the equality is only approximate.

We have now proved

Theorem 1. *A population of n elements possesses* $\binom{n}{r}$ *different sub-populations of size* $r \leq n$.

In other words, out of n elements, we can choose a group of r elements in $\binom{n}{r}$ different ways. Now choosing the r elements to be taken out of the given population amounts to the same as choosing the $n - r$ elements which are to stay in. It is therefore clear that for each $r \leq n$ we must have

(4.2)
$$\binom{n}{r} = \binom{n}{n-r}.$$

To prove equation (4.2) directly we observe that an alternative way of writing the binomial coefficient (4.1) is

(4.3)
$$\binom{n}{r} = \frac{n!}{r!(n-r)!}.$$

[This follows on multiplying numerator and denominator of (4.1) by $(n - r)!$.] Note that the left side in equation (4.2) is not defined for $r = 0$, but the right side is. In order to make equation (4.2) valid for all integers r such that $0 \leq r \leq n$, *we now define*

(4.4)
$$\binom{n}{0} = 1, \qquad 0! = 1,$$

and $(n)_0 = 1$.

Examples. (a) *Bridge and poker* (cf. footnote 1 of chapter I). Since the order of the cards in a hand is irrelevant, the last theorem shows that there exist $\binom{52}{13} = 635{,}013{,}559{,}600$ different hands at bridge, and $\binom{52}{5} = 2{,}598{,}960$ hands at poker. Let us calculate the probability, x, that a hand at poker contains five different face values. These face values can be chosen in $\binom{13}{5}$ ways, and corresponding to each card we are free to choose one of the four suits. It follows that $x = 4^5 \cdot \binom{13}{5} \div \binom{52}{5}$, which is approximately 0.5071. For bridge the probability of thirteen different face values is $4^{13} \div \binom{52}{13}$ or, approximately, 0.0001057.

(b) Each of the 48 states has two senators. We consider the events that in a committee of 48 senators chosen at random: (1) a given state is represented, (2) all states are represented.

In the first case it is better to calculate the probability q of the complementary event, namely, that the given state is *not* represented. There are 96 senators, and 94 not from the given state. Hence,

$$q = \binom{94}{48} \div \binom{96}{48} = \frac{48 \cdot 47}{96 \cdot 95} = 0.24737\ldots.$$

Next, the theorem of section 2 shows that a committee including one senator from each state can be chosen in 2^{48} different ways. The probability that *all* states are included in the committee is, therefore, $p = 2^{48} \div \binom{96}{48}$. Using Stirling's formula (cf. section 9), it can be shown that $p \approx (3\pi)^{\frac{1}{2}} 2^{-46} \approx 4 \cdot 10^{-14}$.

(c) *An occupancy problem.* Consider once more a random distribution of r balls in n cells (i.e., each of the n^r possible arrangements has probability n^{-r}). To find *the probability, p_k, that a specified cell contains exactly k balls* ($k = 0, 1, \ldots, r$) we note that the k balls can be chosen in $\binom{r}{k}$ ways, and the remaining $r - k$ balls can be placed into the remaining $n - 1$ cells in $(n - 1)^{r-k}$ ways. It follows that

$$(4.5) \qquad p_k = \binom{r}{k} \cdot \frac{1}{n^r} \cdot (n - 1)^{r-k} = \binom{r}{k} \cdot \frac{1}{n^k} \cdot \left(1 - \frac{1}{n}\right)^{r-k}.$$

This is a special case of the so-called *binomial distribution* which will be taken up in chapter VI. Numerical values will be found in table 3 of chapter IV.

(d) *Orderings involving two kinds of elements.* Consider a population of $n = a + b$ elements, of which a are of one kind and b of another kind. For convenience we denote the elements by $\alpha_1, \alpha_2, \ldots, \alpha_a, \beta_1, \beta_2, \ldots, \beta_b$. These elements can be ordered in $n!$ different ways. However, if we agree to treat both the alphas and the betas as *indistinguishable* among themselves (that is, if we omit their subscripts), then certain orderings become indistinguishable. In fact, an ordering is now completely described by specifying the a places occupied by the alphas, and these a places can be chosen in $\binom{a+b}{a} = \binom{a+b}{b}$ different ways.

Accordingly, *a population of a indistinguishable alphas and b indistin-*

guishable betas can be arranged in $\begin{pmatrix} a+b \\ a \end{pmatrix} = \begin{pmatrix} a+b \\ b \end{pmatrix}$ *distinguishable*
orders. (For example, the sequence $\alpha\alpha\alpha\beta\beta$ can be ordered in ten distinguishable ways.) Any permutation among the alphas, or among the betas, will leave the outer appearance unchanged so that $a!b!$ permutations have the same outer appearance. It follows that *if we attribute to each of the* $(a+b)!$ *permutations the same probability* $1 \div (a+b)!$, *then all distinguishable arrangements are equally probable,* each having probability $a!b! \div (a+b)!$. Thus, if we speak about equally probable arrangements, the term applies both to distinguishable arrangements and to the aggregate of all permutations of the elements. (This stands in marked contrast to the case of random placements of balls into cells— see section 5.)

Theorem 2. *Let* $r_1, \ldots, r_k$ *be integers such that*

(4.6) $r_1 + r_2 + \ldots + r_k = n,$ $r_i \geq 0.$

The number of ways in which a population of n elements can be divided into k ordered parts (partitioned into k subpopulations) of which the first contains r_1 *elements, the second* r_2 *elements, etc. is*

(4.7)
$$\frac{n!}{r_1!r_2! \cdots r_k!}.$$

(The numbers (4.7) are called multinomial coefficients.)

[Note that the order of the subpopulations is essential in the sense that $(r_1 = 2, r_2 = 3)$ and $(r_1 = 3, r_2 = 2)$ represent different partitions; however, no attention is paid to the order within the groups. Note also that $0! = 1$ so that the vanishing r_i in no way affect formula (4.7).]

Proof. A repeated use of (4.3) will show that the number (4.7) may be rewritten in the form

(4.8) $\begin{pmatrix} n \\ r_1 \end{pmatrix} \begin{pmatrix} n-r_1 \\ r_2 \end{pmatrix} \begin{pmatrix} n-r_1-r_2 \\ r_3 \end{pmatrix} \ldots \begin{pmatrix} n-r_1-\ldots-r_{k-2} \\ r_{k-1} \end{pmatrix}$

On the other hand, in order to effect the desired partition, we have first to select r_1 elements out of the given n; of the remaining $n-r_1$ elements we select a second group of size r_2, etc. After forming the $(k-1)$st group there remain $n - r_1 - r_2 - \ldots - r_{k-1} = r_k$ elements, and these form the last group. We conclude that (4.8) indeed represents the number of ways in which the operation can be performed.

Examples. (*e*) *Bridge.* At a bridge table the 52 cards are partitioned into four equal groups and therefore the number of different situations is $52! \cdot (13!)^{-4} = (5.36\ldots) \cdot 10^{28}$. Let us now calculate the probability that each player has an ace. The four aces can be ordered in $4! = 24$ ways, and each order represents one possibility of giving one ace to each player. The remaining 48 cards can be distributed in $(48!)(12!)^{-4}$ ways. Hence the required probability is

$$24 \cdot 48! \cdot (13)^4 \div 52! = 0.105\ldots.$$

(*f*) *Dice.* A throw of twelve dice can result in 6^{12} different outcomes, to all of which we attribute equal probabilities. The event that each face appears twice can occur in as many ways as twelve dice can be arranged in six groups of two each. Hence the probability of the event is $12!/(2^6 \cdot 6^{12}) = 0.003438\ldots.$

(In theorem 2 it is permitted that $r_i = 0$ so that in reality the n elements are divided into k *or fewer* subpopulations. The case $r_i > 0$ of partitions into *exactly* k classes is treated in problem 11.7.)

*5. APPLICATION TO OCCUPANCY PROBLEMS

The examples of chapter I, section 2, indicate the wide applicability of the model of placing randomly r balls into n cells. We now turn to a discussion of this model, assuming, of course, that each of the n^r possible distributions has probability n^{-r}. The most important properties of a particular distribution are expressed by its *occupancy numbers* $r_1, \ldots, r_n$ where r_i is the number of balls in the ith cell. Here

$$(5.1) \qquad\qquad r_1 + r_2 + \ldots + r_n = r, \qquad\qquad r_i \geq 0.$$

We agree to treat the balls as indistinguishable. The distribution of balls is then completely described by its occupancy numbers, and two distributions are distinguishable only if the corresponding *ordered* n-tuples $(r_1, \ldots, r_n)$ are not identical. Our first aim is to prove the

Lemma. *The number of distinguishable distributions [i.e. the number of different solutions of equation (5.1)] is* [7]

$$(5.2) \qquad\qquad A_{r,n} = \binom{n+r-1}{r} = \binom{n+r-1}{n-1}.$$

---

[7] The special case $r = 100$, $n = 4$ has been used in example I (2.*e*).

The number of distinguishable distributions in which no cell remains empty is $\binom{r-1}{n-1}$.

Proof. We use the artifice of representing the n cells by the space between $n+1$ bars and the balls by stars. Thus $|\!*\!*\!*|\!*|\,|\,|\,|\!*\!*\!*\!*|$ is used as a symbol for a distribution of $r = 8$ balls in $n = 6$ cells with occupancy numbers 3, 1, 0, 0, 0, 4. Such a symbol necessarily starts and ends with a bar, but the remaining $n-1$ bars and r stars can appear in an arbitrary order. In this way it becomes apparent that the number of distinguishable distributions equals the number of ways of selecting r places out of $n + r - 1$. The condition that no cell be empty imposes the restriction that no two bars be adjacent. The r stars leave $r - 1$ spaces of which $n - 1$ are to be occupied by bars: thus we have $\binom{r-1}{n-1}$ choices and the lemma is proved.

Examples. (a) There are $\binom{r+5}{5}$ distinguishable results of a throw with r indistinguishable dice.

(b) *Partial derivatives.* The partial derivatives of order r of an analytic function $f(x_1, \ldots, x_n)$ of n variables do not depend on the order of differentiation but only on the number of times that each variable appears. Thus each variable corresponds to a cell, and hence *there exist* $\binom{n+r-1}{r}$ *different partial derivatives of rth order.* A function of three variables has fifteen derivatives of fourth order and 21 derivatives of fifth order.

Placing r balls into n cells is one way of partitioning the population of r balls. By theorem 2 of section 4 *there exist* $r! \div (r_1! \cdot r_2! \cdots r_n!)$ *distributions with given occupancy numbers* $r_1, \ldots, r_n$. This formula still involves the *order* in which the occupancy numbers, or cells, appear, but frequently this order is immaterial. The following example is intended to illustrate an exceedingly simple and routine method of solving many elementary combinatorial problems.

Example. (c) *Configurations of $r = 7$ balls in $n = 7$ cells.* (The cells may be interpreted as days of the week, the balls as calls, letters, accidents, etc.) For the sake of definiteness let us consider the distributions with occupancy numbers 2, 2, 1, 1, 1, 0, 0 *appearing in an arbitrary order.* These seven occupancy numbers induce a partition of the *seven cells* into three subpopulations (categories) consisting, respectively, of the two doubly occupied, the three simply occupied, and the two empty cells. Such a partition into three groups of size 2, 3, and 2 can be effected in $7! \div (2! \cdot 3! \cdot 2!)$ ways. To each particular assignment of our occupancy numbers to the seven cells there correspond $7! \div (2! \cdot 2! \cdot 1! \cdot 1! \cdot 1! \cdot 0! \cdot 0!) = 7! \div (2! \cdot 2!)$ different distributions of the $r = 7$ balls into the seven cells. Accordingly, *the total number of distributions such that the occupancy numbers coincide with* 2, 2, 1, 1, 1, 0, 0 *in some order is*

$$(5.3) \qquad \frac{7!}{2! 3! 2!} \times \frac{7!}{2! 2!}.$$

It will be noticed that this result has been derived by a *double application of* (4.7), namely to balls and to cells. The same result can be derived and rewritten in many ways, but the present method provides the simplest routine technique for a great variety of problems. (Cf. problems 43–45 of section 10.) Table 1 contains the analogue to (5.3) and the probabilities for all possible configurations of occupancy numbers in the case $r = n = 7$.

TABLE 1

RANDOM DISTRIBUTIONS OF 7 BALLS IN 7 CELLS

Occupancy Numbers	Number of Arrangements Equals $7! \times 7!$ Divided by	Probability (Number of Arrangements Divided by 7^7)
1, 1, 1, 1, 1, 1, 1	$7! \times 1!$	0.006 120
2, 1, 1, 1, 1, 1, 0	$5! \times 2!$	.128 518
2, 2, 1, 1, 1, 0, 0	$2! 3! 2! \times 2! 2!$	.321 295
2, 2, 2, 1, 0, 0, 0	$3! 3! \times 2! 2! 2!$	.107 098
3, 1, 1, 1, 1, 0, 0	$4! 2! \times 3!$	.107 098
3, 2, 1, 1, 0, 0, 0	$2! 3! \times 3! 2!$	.214 197
3, 2, 2, 0, 0, 0, 0	$2! 4! \times 3! 2! 2!$	.026 775
3, 3, 1, 0, 0, 0, 0	$2! 4! \times 3! 3!$	.017 850
4, 1, 1, 1, 0, 0, 0	$3! 3! \times 4!$	.035 699
4, 2, 1, 0, 0, 0, 0	$4! \times 4! 2!$	.026 775
4, 3, 0, 0, 0, 0, 0	$5! \times 4! 3!$	.001 785
5, 1, 1, 0, 0, 0, 0	$2! 4! \times 5!$	.005 355
5, 2, 0, 0, 0, 0, 0	$5! \times 5! 2!$	.001 071
6, 1, 0, 0, 0, 0, 0	$5! \times 6!$	.000 357
7, 0, 0, 0, 0, 0, 0	$6! \times 7!$	.000 008

Note on Bose-Einstein and Fermi-Dirac statistics. Up to now we have assumed that each of the n^r possible distributions has probability n^{-r}. It is of interest that facts and experience have compelled physicists to abandon this hypothesis and to assign probabilities in different ways.

Consider a mechanical system of r indistinguishable particles. In statistical mechanics it is usual to subdivide the phase space into a large number, n, of small regions or cells so that each particle is assigned to one cell. In this way the state of the entire system is described in terms of a random distribution of the r particles in n cells. Offhand it would seem that (at least with an appropriate definition of the n cells) all n^r arrangements should have equal probabilities. If this is true, the physicist speaks of *Maxwell-Boltzmann statistics* (the term "statistics" is here used in a sense peculiar to physics). Numerous attempts have been made to prove that physical particles behave in accordance with Maxwell-Boltzmann statistics, but modern theory has shown beyond doubt that this statistics *does not apply to any known particles;* in no case are all n^r arrangements approximately equally probable. Two different probability models have been introduced, and each describes satisfactorily the behavior of one type of particle. The justification of either model depends on its success. Neither claims universality, and it is possible that some day a third model may be introduced for certain kinds of particles.

Remember that we are here concerned only with *indistinguishable* particles. We have r particles and n cells. *By Bose-Einstein statistics we mean that only distinguishable arrangements are considered and that each is assigned probability*

(5.4)
$$\binom{n + r - 1}{r}^{-1}.$$

It is shown in statistical mechanics that this assumption holds true for photons, nuclei, and atoms containing an even number of elementary particles.[8] To describe other particles a third possible assignment of probabilities must be introduced. *Fermi-Dirac statistics* is based on these hypotheses: (1) *it is impossible for two or more particles to be in the same cell, and* (2) *all distinguishable arrangements satisfying the first condition have equal probabilities.* The first hypothesis requires that $r \leq n$. An arrangement is then completely described by stating which of the n cells contain a particle; and since there are r particles, the corresponding cells can be chosen in $\binom{n}{r}$ ways. Hence, with *Fermi-Dirac statistics there are in all* $\binom{n}{r}$ *possible arrangements, each having probability* $\binom{n}{r}^{-1}$. This model applies to electrons, neutrons, and protons. We have here an instructive example of the impossibility of selecting or justifying probability models by *a priori* arguments. In fact, no pure reasoning could tell that photons and protons would not obey the same probability laws. (Essential differences between Maxwell-Boltzmann and Bose-Einstein statistics are discussed in section 11, problems 14–19.)

To sum up: *the probability that cells number* 1, 2, $\ldots$, n *contain* r_1, r_2, $\ldots$, r_n *balls, respectively (where* $r_1 + \ldots + r_n = r$) *equals*

(5.5)
$$\frac{r!}{r_1! r_2! \cdots r_n!} n^{-r}$$

under Maxwell-Boltzmann statistics; it is given by (5.4) *under Bose-Einstein statistics;*

---

[8] Cf. H. Margenau and G. M. Murphy, *The mathematics of physics and chemistry*, New York, 1943, Chapter 12.

and it equals $\begin{pmatrix} n \\ r \end{pmatrix}^{-1}$ *under Fermi-Dirac statistics provided each* r_j *equals* 0 *or* 1.
Note that "Maxwell-Boltzmann statistics" is the physicist's term for what we call random placement of balls into cells.

Examples. (a) Let $n = 5, r = 3$. The arrangement $(*|-|*|*|-)$ has probability $\frac{6}{125}, \frac{1}{35},$ or $\frac{1}{10},$ according to whether Maxwell-Boltzmann, Bose-Einstein, or Fermi-Dirac statistics is used. See also example I(6.b).

(b) *Misprints.* A book contains n symbols (letters), of which r are misprinted. The distribution of misprints corresponds to a distribution of r balls in n cells with no cell containing more than one ball. It is therefore reasonable to suppose that, approximately, *the misprints obey the Fermi-Dirac statistics.* (Cf. problem 10.38.)

5a. Application to Runs. In any ordered sequence of elements of two kinds, each maximal subsequence of elements of like kind is called *a run.* For example, the sequence $\alpha\alpha\alpha\beta\alpha\alpha\beta\beta\beta\alpha$ opens with an alpha run of length 3; it is followed by runs of length 1, 2, 3, 1, respectively. The alpha and beta runs alternate so that the total number of runs is always one plus the number of *unlike neighbors* in the given sequence.

Examples of applications. The theory of runs is applied in statistics in many ways, but its principal uses are connected with tests of randomness or tests of homogeneity.

(a) In *testing randomness*, the problem is to decide whether a given observation is attributable to chance or whether a search for assignable causes is indicated. As a simple example suppose that an observation [9] yielded the following arrangement of empty and occupied seats along a lunch counter: *EOEEOEEEEOEEEEOEOE.* Note that no two occupied seats are adjacent. Can this be due to chance? With five occupied and eleven empty seats it is impossible to get more than eleven runs, and this number was actually observed. It will be shown later that if all arrangements were equally probable the probability of eleven runs would be 0.0578.... This small probability to some extent confirms the hunch that the separations observed were intentional. This suspicion cannot be proved by statistical methods, but further evidence could be collected from continued observation. If the lunch counter were frequented by families, there would be a tendency for occupants to cluster together, and this would lead to relatively small numbers of runs. Similarly, counting runs of boys and girls in a classroom might disclose the mixing to be better or worse than random. Improbable arrangements give clues to assignable causes; *an excess of runs points to intentional mixing, a paucity of runs to intentional clustering.* It is true that these conclusions are never foolproof, but efficient statistical techniques have been developed which in actual practice minimize the risk of incorrect conclusions.

The theory of runs is also useful in industrial quality control as introduced by Shewhart. As washers are produced, they will vary in thickness. Long runs of thick washers may suggest imperfections in the production process and lead to the removal of the causes; thus oncoming trouble may be forestalled and greater homogeneity of product achieved.

In biological field experiments successions of healthy and diseased plants are

---

[9] F. S. Swed and C. Eisenhart, Tables for testing randomness of grouping in a sequence of alternatives, *Annals of Mathematical Statistics*, vol. 14 (1943), pp. 66–87.

counted, and long runs are suggestive of contagion. The meteorologist watches successions of dry and wet months [10] to discover clues to a tendency of the weather to persist.

(b) To understand a typical problem of *homogeneity*, suppose that two drugs have been applied to two sets of patients, or that we are interested in comparing the efficiency of two treatments (medical, agricultural, or industrial). In practice, we shall have two sets of observations, say, $\alpha_1, \alpha_2, \ldots, \alpha_a$ and $\beta_1, \beta_2, \ldots, \beta_b$ corresponding to the two treatments or representing a certain characteristic (such as weight) of the elements of two populations. The alphas and betas are *numbers* which we imagine ordered in increasing order of magnitude: $\alpha_1 \leq \alpha_2 \leq \ldots \leq \alpha_a$ and $\beta_1 \leq \beta_2 \leq \ldots \leq \beta_b$. We now pool the two sets into one sequence ordered according to magnitude. An extreme case is that all alphas precede all betas, and this may be taken as indicative of a significant difference between the two treatments or populations. On the other hand, if the two treatments are identical, the alphas and betas should appear more or less in random order. Wald and Wolfowitz [11] have shown that the theory of runs can be often advantageously applied to discover small systematic differences. (An illustrative example, treated by a different method, will be found in chapter III, section 1.)

Many problems concerning runs can be solved in an exceedingly simple manner. Given a indistinguishable alphas and b indistinguishable betas, we know from example (4.d) that there are $\binom{a+b}{a}$ distinguishable orderings. If there are n_1 alpha runs, the number of beta runs is necessarily one of the numbers $n_1 \pm 1$ or n_1. Arranging the a alphas in n_1 runs is equivalent to arranging them into n_1 cells, none of which is empty. By the last lemma this can be done in $\binom{a-1}{n_1-1}$ distinguishable ways. It follows, for example, that there are $\binom{a-1}{n_1-1}\binom{b-1}{n_1}$ arrangements with n_1 alpha runs and $n_1 + 1$ beta runs (continued in problems 20–25 of section 11).

(c) In physics, the theory of runs is used in the study of cooperative phenomena. In Ising's theory of one-dimensional lattices the energy depends on the number of unlike neighbors, that is, the number of runs.

6. THE HYPERGEOMETRIC DISTRIBUTION

Many combinatorial problems can be reduced to the following form. In a population of n elements n_1 are red and $n_2 = n - n_1$ are black. A group of r elements is chosen at random. We seek the probability q_k that the group so chosen will contain exactly k red elements. Here k can be any integer between zero and n_1 or r, whichever is smaller.

---

[10] W. G. Cochran, An extension of Gold's method of examining the apparent persistence of one type of weather, *Quarterly Journal of the Royal Meteorological Society*, vol. 64, No. 277 (1938), pp. 631–634.

[11] A. Wald and J. Wolfowitz, On a test whether two samples are from the same population, *Annals of Mathematical Statistics*, vol. 2 (1940), pp. 147–162.

To find q_k, we note that the chosen group contains k red and $r - k$ black elements. The red ones can be chosen in $\binom{n_1}{k}$ different ways and the black ones in $\binom{n - n_1}{r - k}$ ways. Since any choice of k red elements may be combined with any choice of black ones, we find

$$(6.1) \qquad q_k = \frac{\binom{n_1}{k}\binom{n - n_1}{r - k}}{\binom{n}{r}}.$$

The system of probabilities so defined is called the *hypergeometric distribution*.[12] Using formula (4.3), it is possible to rewrite (6.1) in the form

$$(6.2) \qquad q_k = \frac{\binom{r}{k}\binom{n - r}{n_1 - k}}{\binom{n}{n_1}}.$$

Note. The probabilities q_k are defined only for k not exceeding r or n_1. However, from the definition (4.1) it follows that $\binom{a}{b} = 0$ whenever $b > a$. Therefore, formulas (6.1) and (6.2) give $q_k = 0$ if either $k > n_1$ or $k > r$. Accordingly, the definitions (6.1) and (6.2) may be used for all $k \geq 0$, provided the relation $q_k = 0$ is interpreted as impossibility.

Examples. (a) *Quality inspection.* In industrial quality control, lots of size n are subjected to sampling inspection. The defective items in the lot play the role of "red" elements. Their number n_1 is, of course, unknown. A sample of size r is taken, and the number k of defective items in it is determined. Formula (6.1) then permits us to draw inferences about the likely magnitude of n_1; this is a typical problem of statistical estimation and is beyond the scope of the present book.

(b) In example (4.b), the population consists of $n = 96$ senators of whom $n_1 = 2$ represent the given state (are "red"). A group of

---

[12] The name is explained by the fact that the generating function (cf. chapter XI) of $\{q_k\}$ can be expressed in terms of hypergeometric functions.

$r = 48$ senators is chosen at random. It may include $k = 0, 1,$ or 2 senators from the given state. From (6.2) we find, remembering (4.4),

$$q_0 = q_2 = \frac{48 \cdot 47}{96 \cdot 95} = 0.24737\ldots, \qquad q_1 = \frac{48}{95} = 0.50527\ldots.$$

The value q_0 was obtained in a different way in example (4.b).

(c) *Estimation of the size of an animal population from recapture data.*[13] Suppose that 1000 fish caught in a lake are marked by red spots and released. After a while a new catch of 1000 fish is made, and it is found that 100 among them have red spots. What conclusions can be drawn concerning the number of fish in the lake? This is a typical problem of *statistical estimation.* It would lead us too far to describe the various methods that a modern statistician might use, but we shall show how the hypergeometric distribution gives us a clue to the solution of the problem. We assume naturally that the two catches may be considered as random samples from the population of all fish in the lake. (In practice this assumption excludes situations where the two catches are made at one locality and within a short time.) We also suppose that the number of fish in the lake does not change between the two catches.

We generalize the problem by admitting arbitrary sample sizes. Let

$n =$ the (unknown) number of fish in the lake.

$n_1 =$ the number of fish in the first catch. They play the role of red balls.

$r =$ the number of fish in the second catch.

$k =$ the number of red fish in the second catch.

$q_k(n) =$ the probability that the second catch contains exactly k red fish.

In this formulation it is rather obvious that $q_k(n)$ is given by (6.1). In practice n_1, r, and k can be observed, but n is unknown. Notice, incidentally, that n is a fixed number which in no way depends on chance. It is, therefore, meaningless to ask for the probability that n is greater than, say, 6000. We know that $n_1 + r - k$ different fish were caught, and therefore $n \geq n_1 + r - k$. This is all that can be

---

[13] This example was used in the first edition without knowledge that the method is widely used in practice. Newer contributions to the literature include N. T. J. Bailey, On estimating the size of mobile populations from recapture data, *Biometrika*, vol. 38 (1951), pp. 293–306, and D. G. Chapman, Some properties of the hypergeometric distribution with applications to zoological sample censuses, *University of California Publications in Statistics*, vol. 1 (1951), pp. 131–160.

said with certainty. In our example we had $n_1 = r = 1000$ and $k = 100$, and it is conceivable that the lake contains only 1900 fish. However, starting from this hypothesis, we are led to the conclusion that an event of a fantastically small probability has occurred. In fact, assuming that there are $n = 1900$ fish in all, the probability that two samples of size 1000 each will between them exhaust the entire population is by (6.1),

$$\binom{1000}{100}\binom{900}{900}\binom{1900}{1000}^{-1} = \frac{(1000!)^2}{100!\,1900!}.$$

Stirling's formula (cf. section 9) shows this probability to be of the order of magnitude 10^{-430}, and in this situation common sense bids us to reject our hypothesis as unreasonable. A similar reasoning would induce us to reject the hypothesis that n is very large, say, a million. This consideration leads us to seek the particular value of n for which $q_k(n)$ attains its largest value, since for that n our observation would have the greatest probability. For any particular set of observations n_1, r, k, the value of n for which $q_k(n)$ is largest is denoted by $\hat{n}$ and is called the *maximum likelihood estimate* of n. This notion was introduced by R. A. Fisher. To find $\hat{n}$ consider the ratio

$$(6.3) \qquad \frac{q_k(n)}{q_k(n-1)} = \frac{(n-n_1)(n-r)}{(n-n_1-r+k)n}.$$

A simple calculation shows that this ratio is greater than or smaller than unity, according as $nk < n_1 r$ or $nk > n_1 r$. This means that with increasing n the sequence $q_k(n)$ first increases and then decreases; it reaches its maximum when n is the largest integer short of $n_1 r/k$, so that $\hat{n}$ equals about $n_1 r/k$. In our particular example the maximum likelihood estimate of the number of fish is $\hat{n} = 10,000$.

The true number n may be larger or smaller, and we may ask for limits within which we may reasonably expect n to lie. For this purpose let us test the hypothesis that n is smaller than 8500. We substitute in (6.1) $n = 8500$, $n_1 = r = 1000$, and calculate the probability that the second sample contains 100 or fewer red fish. This probability is $x = q_0 + q_1 + \ldots + q_{100}$. A direct evaluation is cumbersome, but using the normal approximation of chapter VII, we find easily that $x = 0.04$. Similarly, if $n = 12,000$, the probability that the second sample contains 100 or more red fish is about 0.03. These figures would justify a bet that the true number n of fish lies somewhere between 8500 and 12,000. There exist other ways of formulating these conclusions and other methods of estimation, but we do not propose to discuss the details.

From the definition of the probabilities q_k it follows that $q_0 + q_1 + q_2 + \ldots = 1$. Formula (6.2) therefore implies that for any positive integers n, n_1, and r

$$(6.4) \quad \binom{r}{0}\binom{n-r}{n_1} + \binom{r}{1}\binom{n-r}{n_1-1} + \ldots + \binom{r}{n_1}\binom{n-r}{0} = \binom{n}{n_1}.$$

This identity is frequently useful. We have proved it only for positive integers n and r, but it holds true without this restriction for arbitrary positive or negative numbers n and r (it is meaningless if n_1 is not a positive integer). (An indication of two proofs is given in section 12, problems 8 and 9.)

The hypergeometric distribution can easily be generalized to the case where the original population of size n contains several classes of elements. For example, let the population contain three classes of sizes n_1, n_2, and $n - n_1 - n_2$, respectively. If a sample of size r is taken, the probability that it contains k_1 elements of the first, k_2 elements of the second, and $r - k_1 - k_2$ elements of the last class is, by analogy with (6.1),

$$(6.5) \quad \binom{n_1}{k_1}\binom{n_2}{k_2}\binom{n-n_1-n_2}{r-k_1-k_2} \div \binom{n}{r}$$

It is, of course, necessary that $k_1 \leq n_1$, $k_2 \leq n_2$, and $r - k_1 - k_2 \leq n - n_1 - n_2$.

Example. (d) *Bridge.* The population of 52 cards consists of four classes, each of thirteen elements. The probability that a hand of thirteen cards consists of five spades, four hearts, three diamonds, and one club is $\binom{13}{5}\binom{13}{4}\binom{13}{3}\binom{13}{1} \div \binom{52}{13}$.

7. EXAMPLES FOR WAITING TIMES

In this section we shall depart from the straight path of combinatorial analysis in order to consider some sample spaces of a novel type to which we are led by a simple variation of our occupancy problems. Consider once more the conceptual "experiment" of placing balls randomly into n cells. This time, however, we do not fix in advance the number r of balls but let the balls be placed one by one as long as necessary for a prescribed situation to arise. Two such possible situations will be discussed explicitly: (i) *The random placing of balls continues until for the first time a ball is placed into a cell already occupied.* The process terminates when the first duplication of this type occurs. (ii) *We fix a cell (say cell number 1) and continue the procedure of placing balls as long as this cell remains empty.* The process terminates when a ball is placed into the prescribed cell.

A few interpretations of this model will elucidate the problem.

Examples. (*a*) *Birthdays.* In the birthday example (3.*d*), the $n = 365$ days of the year correspond to cells, and people to balls. Our model (i) now amounts to this: If we select people at random one by one, how many people shall we have to sample in order to find a pair with a common birthday? Model (ii) corresponds to waiting for *my* birthday to turn up in the sample.

(*b*) *Key problem.* A man wants to open his door. He has n keys, of which only one fits the door. For reasons which can only be surmised, he tries the keys at random so that at each try each key has probability n^{-1} of being tried and all possible outcomes involving the same number of trials are equally likely. What is the probability that the man will succeed exactly at the rth trial? This is a special case of model (ii). It is interesting to compare this random search for the key with a more systematic approach (problem (10.11); see also problem V, 5).

(*c*) In the preceding example we can replace the sampling of keys by a sampling from an arbitrary population, say by the *collecting of coupons*. Again we ask when the first duplication is to be expected and when a prescribed element will show up for the first time.

(*d*) *Coins and dice.* In example I(5.*a*) a coin is tossed as often as necessary to turn up one head. This is a special case of model (ii) with $n = 2$. When a die is thrown until an ace turns up for the first time, the same question applies with $n = 6$. (Other waiting times are treated in problems 21, 22, and 36 of section 10, and 12 of section 11.)

We begin with the conceptually simpler model (i). It is convenient to use symbols of the form $(j_1, j_2, \ldots, j_r)$ to indicate that the first, second, ..., rth ball are placed in cells number $j_1, j_2, \ldots, j_r$ and that the process terminates at the rth step. This means that the j_i are integers between 1 and n; furthermore, $j_1, \ldots, j_{r-1}$ are all different, but j_r equals one among them. Every arrangement of this type represents a sample point. For r only the values 2, 3, ..., $n+1$ are possible, since a doubly occupied cell cannot appear before the second ball or after the $(n+1)$st ball is placed. The connection of our present problem with the old model of placing a fixed number of balls into the n cells leads us to attribute to each sample point $(j_1, \ldots, j_r)$ involving exactly r

balls the probability n^{-r}. We proceed to show that this convention is permissible (i.e., that our probabilities add to unity) and that it leads to reasonable results.

For a fixed r the aggregate of all sample points $(j_1, \ldots, j_r)$ represents *the event that the process terminates at the rth step.* According to (3.1) the numbers $j_1, \ldots, j_{r-1}$ can be chosen in $(n)_{r-1}$ different ways; for j_r we have the choice of the $r - 1$ numbers $j_1, \ldots, j_{r-1}$. It follows that *the probability of the process terminating at the rth step is*

$$(7.1) \quad q_r = \frac{(n)_{r-1} \cdot (r-1)}{n^r} = \left(1 - \frac{1}{n}\right) \cdots \left(1 - \frac{r-2}{n}\right) \cdot \frac{r-1}{n},$$

with $q_1 = 0$ *and* $q_2 = 1/n$. *The probability that the process lasts for more than r steps is* $p_r = 1 - (q_1 + q_2 + \ldots + q_r)$ *or* $p_1 = 1$ *and*

$$(7.2) \qquad p_r = \frac{(n)_r}{n^r} = \left(1 - \frac{1}{n}\right) \cdots \left(1 - \frac{r-1}{n}\right)$$

as can be seen by simple induction. In particular, $p_{n+1} = 0$ and $q_1 + \ldots + q_{n+1} = 1$, as is proper. Furthermore, when $n = 365$, formula (7.2) reduces to (3.2), and in general our new model leads to the same quantitative results as the previous model involving a fixed number of balls.

The model (ii) differs from (i) in that it depends on *an infinite sample space.* The sequences $(j_1, \ldots, j_r)$ are now subjected to the condition that the numbers $j_1, \ldots, j_{r-1}$ are different from a prescribed number $a \leq n$, but $j_r = a$. Moreover, there is no a priori reason why the process should ever terminate. For a fixed r we attribute again to each sample point of the form $(j_1, \ldots, j_r)$ probability n^{-r}. For $j_1, \ldots, j_{r-1}$ we have $n - 1$ choices each, and for j_r no choice at all. For *the probability that the process terminates at the rth step* we get therefore

$$(7.3) \qquad q_r{}^* = \left(\frac{n-1}{n}\right)^{r-1} \cdot \frac{1}{n}, \qquad r = 1, 2, \ldots.$$

Summing this geometric series we find $q_1{}^* + q_2{}^* + \ldots = 1$. Thus the probabilities add to unity, and there is no necessity of introducing a sample point to represent the possibility that no ball will ever be placed into the prescribed cell number a. For *the probability*

$$p_r{}^* = 1 - (q_1{}^* + \ldots + q_r{}^*)$$

that the process lasts for more than r steps we get

$$(7.4) \qquad\qquad p_r^* = \left(1 - \frac{1}{n}\right)^r, \qquad\qquad r = 1, 2, \ldots$$

as was to be expected.

The medians for the distributions $\{p_r\}$ *and* $\{p_r^*\}$ *are defined as those* values of r for which p_r and p_r^* come closest to $\frac{1}{2}$; it is about as likely that the process continues beyond the median as that it stops before. (In the *birthday* example (3.d) the median is $r = 23$.) To calculate the median for $\{p_r\}$ we pass to logarithms as we did in (3.4). When r is small as compared to n, we see that $-\log p_r$ is close to $r^2/2n$. It follows that *the median to* $\{p_r\}$ *is close to* $(n \cdot 2 \cdot \log 2)^{\frac{1}{2}}$ or, approximately, $\frac{6}{5}n^{\frac{1}{2}}$. It is interesting that the median increases with the square root of the population size. By contrast, *the median for* $\{p_r^*\}$ *is close to* $n \cdot \log 2$ or $0.7n$ and increases linearly with n. The probability of the waiting time in model (ii) to exceed n is $(1 - n^{-1})^n$ or, approximately, $e^{-1} = 0.36788\ldots$.

8. BINOMIAL COEFFICIENTS

We have used binomial coefficients $\binom{n}{r}$ only when n is a positive integer, but it is very convenient to extend their definition. The number $(x)_r$ introduced in equation (2.1), namely

$$(8.1) \qquad\qquad (x)_r = x(x - 1) \cdots (x - r + 1)$$

is well defined for all real x provided only that r is a positive integer. For $r = 0$ we put $(x)_0 = 1$. Then

$$(8.2) \qquad \binom{x}{r} = \frac{(x)_r}{r!} = \frac{x(x - 1) \cdots (x - r + 1)}{r!}.$$

defines the binomial coefficients for all values of x and all positive integers r. For $r = 0$ we put, as in (4.4), $\binom{x}{0} = 1$ and $0! = 1$. *For negative integers* r *we define*

$$(8.3) \qquad\qquad\qquad \binom{x}{r} = 0 \qquad\qquad\qquad (r < 0).$$

We shall never use the symbol $\binom{x}{r}$ *if r is not an integer.*

It is easily verified that with this definition we have, for example,

$$(8.4) \qquad \binom{-1}{r} = (-1)^r \qquad \binom{-2}{r} = (-1)^r(r+1).$$

Three important properties will be used in the sequel. First, for *any positive integer n*

$$(8.5) \qquad \binom{n}{r} = 0 \qquad \text{if either } r > n \text{ or } r < 0.$$

Second, *for any number x and any integer r*

$$(8.6) \qquad \binom{x}{r-1} + \binom{x}{r} = \binom{x+1}{r}.$$

These relations are easily verified from the definition. The proof of the next relation can be found in calculus textbooks: *for any number a and all values* $-1 < t < 1$, *we have Newton's binomial formula*

$$(8.7) \qquad (1+t)^a = 1 + \binom{a}{1}t + \binom{a}{2}t^2 + \binom{a}{3}t^3 + \ldots.$$

If a is a positive integer, all terms to the right containing powers higher than t^a vanish automatically and the formula is correct for all t. If a is not a positive integer, the right side represents an *infinite* series.

Using equation (8.4), we see that for $a = -1$ the expansion (8.7) reduces to the *geometric series*

$$(8.8) \qquad \frac{1}{1+t} = 1 - t + t^2 - t^3 + t^4 - + \ldots, \quad -1 < t < 1.$$

Integrating (8.8), we obtain another formula which will be useful in the sequel, namely, the *Taylor expansion of the natural logarithm*

$$(8.9) \qquad \log(1+t) = t - \tfrac{1}{2}t^2 + \tfrac{1}{3}t^3 - \tfrac{1}{4}t^4 + \ldots, \quad -1 < t < 1.$$

Two alternative forms for (8.9) are frequently used. Replacing t by $-t$ we get

$$(8.10) \qquad \log\frac{1}{1-t} = t + \tfrac{1}{2}t^2 + \tfrac{1}{3}t^3 + \tfrac{1}{4}t^4 + \ldots, \quad -1 < t < 1.$$

Adding the last two formulas we find

$$(8.11) \qquad \tfrac{1}{2}\log\frac{1+t}{1-t} = t + \tfrac{1}{3}t^3 + \tfrac{1}{5}t^5 + \ldots, \qquad -1 < t < 1.$$

For $0 < t < 1$, the right-hand member of (8.10) exceeds t but is smaller than $t + t^2 + t^3 + \ldots = t/(1 - t)$. Hence we have *the double inequality*

$$(8.12) \qquad e^{-\frac{t}{1-t}} < 1 - t < e^{-t}, \qquad\qquad 0 < t < 1.$$

Many useful relations and identities will be derived from (8.7) in section 12. Here we mention only that for any positive integer n we find, letting $t = 1$,

$$(8.13) \qquad \binom{n}{0} + \binom{n}{1} + \binom{n}{2} + \ldots + \binom{n}{n} = 2^n$$

Incidentally, this formula admits of a simple combinatorial interpretation: The left side represents the number of ways in which a population of n elements can be divided into two subpopulations if the size of the first group is permitted to be any number $k = 0, 1, \ldots, n$. On the other hand, such a division can be effected directly by deciding for each element whether it is to belong to the first or second group. (A similar argument shows that the multinomial coefficients (4.7) add up to k^n.)

9. STIRLING'S FORMULA

An important tool of analytical probability theory is contained in a classical theorem [14] known as

Stirling's Formula:

$$(9.1) \qquad n! \sim (2\pi)^{\frac{1}{2}} n^{n+\frac{1}{2}} e^{-n}$$

where the sign $\sim$ is used to indicate that the ratio of the two sides tends to unity as $n \to \infty$.

This formula is invaluable for many theoretical purposes and can be used also to obtain excellent numerical approximations. It is true that the difference of the two sides in (9.1) increases over all bounds, but it is the percentage error which really matters. It decreases steadily, and Stirling's approximation is remarkably accurate even for small n. In fact, the right side of (9.1) approximates 1! by 0.9221 and 2! by 1.919 and 5! = 120 by 118.019. The percentage errors are 8 and 4 and 2, respectively. For 10! = 3,628,800 the approximation is 3,598,600 with an error of 0.8 per cent. For 100! the error is only 0.08 per cent.

Proof of Stirling's formula. We consider

$$(9.2) \qquad a_n = \log 2 + \log 3 + \ldots + \log (n - 1) + \tfrac{1}{2} \log n$$

---

[14] James Stirling, *Methodus differentialis*, 1730.

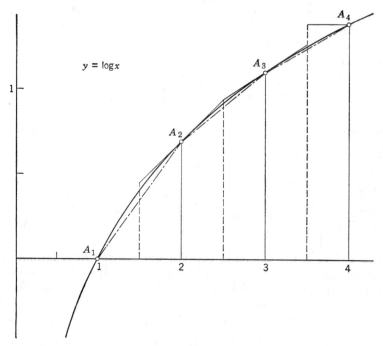

FIGURE 1. Illustrating the derivation of Stirling's formula and, more generally, the approximation of sums by integrals.

which differs from $\log n!$ only by the factor $\frac{1}{2}$ in the last term to the right. We shall show that a_n represents the areas of two different polygons, and this remark will lead to two bounds for $\log n!$. Figure 1 illustrates the situation for the special case $n = 4$. On writing

$$(9.3) \quad a_n = \tfrac{1}{2}\{\log 1 + \log 2\} + \tfrac{1}{2}\{\log 2 + \log 3\} + \ldots +$$

$$+ \tfrac{1}{2}\{\log (n - 1) + \log n\}$$

it becomes apparent that a_n equals the area of the trapezoid whose vertices are the points $A_1, A_2, \ldots, A_n$ of the curve $y = \log x$ with abscissas $1, 2, \ldots, n$ and the point $(n, 0)$ of the x-axis. This trapezoid being inside the curve, its area is *smaller* than the area of the domain bounded by the curve, the x-axis, and the line $x = n$.

On the other hand, $\log k$ equals the area of the trapezoid with basis $k - \frac{1}{2} < x < k + \frac{1}{2}$ and bounded above by the tangent to the curve at the point $A_k = (k, \log k)$. It follows that $\log (n - 1)!$ is *greater* than the area of the domain bounded by $y = \log x$, the x-axis, and the vertical lines $x = \frac{3}{2}$ and $x = n - \frac{1}{2}$. Now $\frac{1}{2} \log n$ quite obviously exceeds the area of the strip $n - \frac{1}{2} < x < n$ under the curve, and hence a_n *exceeds* the area under the curve and between $x = \frac{3}{2}$ and $x = n$. In other words, we have shown that

(9.4)
$$\int_{\frac{3}{2}}^{n} \log x \cdot dx < a_n < \int_{1}^{n} \log x \cdot dx.$$

The indefinite integral of $\log x$ is given by $x \log x - x$, and equation (9.4) reduces to the double inequality

(9.5) $(n + \frac{1}{2}) \log n - n + \frac{3}{2}(1 - \log \frac{3}{2}) <$
$$< \log n! < (n + \tfrac{1}{2}) \log n - n + 1.$$

    Put for abbreviation

(9.6) $\delta_n = \log n! - (n + \frac{1}{2}) \log n + n.$

Then $1 - \delta_n$ is the difference between the extreme right member of (9.5) and $\log n!$, that is, $1 - \delta_n$ equals the area of the domain between the curve $y = \log x$ and the polygon $A_1 A_2 \ldots A_n$. It follows that δ_n *decreases monotonically.* But by (9.5) we have $\frac{3}{2}(1 - \log \frac{3}{2}) < \delta_n < 1$. We conclude that δ_n tends to a limit comprised between 1 and $\frac{3}{2}(1 - \log \frac{3}{2})$. Denoting this limit by $\log c$ we have

(9.7) $\delta_n \to \log c$ where $2.45 < c < 2.72.$

In logarithmic notation Stirling's formula reduces to (9.7) with $c = (2\pi)^{\frac{1}{2}}$ (or 2.507, approximately). Now π can be defined in many ways, and for our purposes it is simplest and most natural to *define* $\pi = c^2/2$. With this definition we have Stirling's formula, but it remains to show that the constant so defined agrees with the more familiar π of other formulas. This fact will develop as a by-product of other calculations in chapter VII, and so the proof of Stirling's formula will be completed there.

    Refinements. Stirling's formula can be improved by the addition of further terms. Although we shall never make use of such refinements, we shall here indicate the proof of the following *double inequality* [15]

(9.8) $(2\pi)^{\frac{1}{2}} n^{n+\frac{1}{2}} e^{-n+1/(12n+1)} < n! < (2\pi)^{\frac{1}{2}} n^{n+\frac{1}{2}} e^{-n+1/(12n)}.$

    To prove (9.8) note that

(9.9) $\delta_n - \delta_{n+1} = \left(n + \frac{1}{2}\right) \log \frac{n+1}{n} - 1 = \frac{1}{3(2n+1)^2} + \frac{1}{5(2n+1)^5} + \cdots$

---

[15] H. Robbins, A remark on Stirling's formula, *American Mathematical Monthly*, vol. 62 (1955), pp. 26–29.

[the last expansion follows from (8.11) on setting $t = 1/(2n + 1)$]. We *increase* the extreme right member in (9.9) by replacing the coefficients $\frac{1}{5}, \frac{1}{7}, \frac{1}{9}, \ldots$ by $\frac{1}{3}$; this leads to a geometric series with ratio $(2n + 1)^{-2}$, and thus

$$(9.10) \qquad \delta_n - \delta_{n+1} < \frac{1}{3[(2n + 1)^2 - 1]} = \frac{1}{12n} - \frac{1}{12(n + 1)}.$$

Accordingly, $\delta_n - 1/12n$ *increases* monotonically. Now the limit of this sequence is given by Stirling's formula, and passing to antilogarithms we have the second inequality in (9.8). The first inequality follows similarly from (9.9) on noticing that

$$(9.11) \qquad \delta_n - \delta_{n+1} > \frac{1}{3(2n + 1)^2} > \frac{1}{12n + 1} - \frac{1}{12(n + 1) + 1}.$$

The accuracy of the approximations (9.8) is remarkable; even for $n = 1$ the formula leads to the two bounds $0.9958\ldots$ and $1.0023\ldots$. The upper bound provided in (9.8) is slightly better [cf. (12.28)]. For $n = 2$ it yields 2.0007, for $n = 5$ we get $120.01\ldots$, and for $n = 10$ the first five significant figures are correct.

PROBLEMS FOR SOLUTION

Note: Sections 11 and 12 contain problems of a different character and diverse complements to the text.

10. EXERCISES AND EXAMPLES

Note: *Assume in each case that all arrangements have the same probability.*

1. How many different sets of initials can be formed if every person has one surname and (*a*) exactly two given names, (*b*) at most two given names, (*c*) at most three given names?

2. In how many ways can two rooks of different colors be put on a chessboard so that they can take each other?

3. Letters in the Morse code are formed by a succession of dashes and dots with repetitions permitted. How many letters is it possible to form with ten symbols or less?

4. Each domino piece is marked by two numbers. The pieces are symmetrical so that the number-pair is not ordered. How many different pieces can be made using the numbers $1, 2, \ldots, n$?

5. The numbers $1, 2, \ldots, n$ are arranged in random order. Find the probability that the digits (*a*) 1 and 2, (*b*) 1, 2, and 3, appear as neighbors in the order named.

6. (*a*) Find the probability that among three random digits there occur 2, 1, or 0 repetitions. (*b*) Do the same for four random digits.

7. Find the probabilities p_r that in a sample of r random digits no two are equal. Estimate the numerical value of p_{10}, using Stirling's formula.

8. What is the probability that among k random digits (*a*) 0 does not appear; (*b*) 1 does not appear; (*c*) neither 0 nor 1 appears; (*d*) at least one of the two digits 0 and 1 does not appear? Let A and B represent the events in (*a*) and (*b*). Express the other events in terms of A and B.

9. If n balls are placed at random into n cells, find the probability that exactly one cell remains empty.

10. At a parking lot there are twelve places arranged in a row. A man observed that there were eight cars parked, and that the four empty places were adjacent to each other (formed *one* run). Given that there are four empty places, is this arrangement surprising (indicative of non-randomness)?

11. A man is given n keys of which only one fits his door. He tries them successively (sampling without replacement). This procedure may require 1, 2, ..., n trials. Show that each of these n outcomes has probability n^{-1}.

12. Suppose that each of n sticks is broken into one long and one short part. The $2n$ parts are arranged into n pairs from which new sticks are formed. Find the probability (a) that the parts will be joined in the original order, (b) that all long parts are paired with short parts.[16]

13. *Testing a statistical hypothesis.* A Cornell professor got a ticket twelve times for illegal overnight parking. All twelve tickets were given either Tuesdays or Thursdays. Find the probability of this event. (Was his renting a garage only for Tuesdays and Thursdays justified?)

14. *Continuation.* Of twelve police tickets none was given on Sunday. Is this evidence that no tickets are given on Sundays?

15. A box contains ninety good and ten defective screws. If ten screws are used, what is the probability that none is defective?

16. From the population of five symbols a, b, c, d, e, a sample of size 25 is taken. Find the probability that the sample will contain five symbols of each kind. Check the result in tables of random numbers,[17] identifying the digits 0 and 1 with a, the digits 2 and 3 with b, etc.

17. If n men, among whom are A and B, stand in a row, what is the probability that there will be exactly r men between A and B? If they stand in a ring instead of in a row, show that the probability is independent of r and hence $1/(n-1)$. (In the circular arrangement consider only the arc leading from A to B in the positive direction.)

18. What is the probability that two throws with three dice each will show the same configuration if (a) the dice are distinguishable, (b) they are not?

19. Show that it is more probable to get at least one ace with four dice than at least one double ace in 24 throws of two dice. (The answer is known as de Méré's paradox. Chevalier de Méré, a gambler, thought that the two probabilities ought to be equal and blamed mathematics for his losses.)

20. From a population of n elements a sample of size r is taken. Find the probability that none of N prescribed elements will be included in the sample,

---

[16] When cells are exposed to harmful radiation, some chromosomes break and play the role of our "sticks." The "long" side is the one containing the so-called centromere. If two "long" or two "short" parts unite, the cell dies. See D. G. Catcheside, The effect of X-ray dosage upon the frequency of induced structural changes in the chromosomes of *Drosophila Melanogaster, Journal of Genetics*, vol. 36 (1938), pp. 307–320.

[17] They are occasionally extraordinarily obliging: see J. A. Greenwood and E. E. Stuart, Review of Dr. Feller's critique, *Journal for Parapsychology*, vol. 4 (1940), pp. 298–319, in particular p. 306.

assuming the sampling to be (a) without, (b) with replacement. Compare the numerical values for the two methods when (i) $n = 100$, $r = N = 3$, and (ii) $n = 100$, $r = N = 10$.

21. *Spread of rumors.* In a town of $n + 1$ inhabitants, a person tells a rumor to a second person, who in turn repeats it to a third person, etc. At each step the recipient of the rumor is chosen at random from the n people available. Find the probability that the rumor will be told r times without: (a) returning to the originator, (b) being repeated to any person. Do the same problem when at each step the rumor is told by one person to a gathering of N randomly chosen people. (The first question is the special case $N = 1$.)

22. *Chain letters.* In a population of $n + 1$ people a man, the "progenitor," sends out letters to two persons, the "first generation." These repeat the performance and, generally, each member of the rth generation sends out letters to two persons chosen at random. Find the probability that the generations number 1, 2, $\ldots$, r will not include the progenitor. Find the median of the distribution, supposing n to be large.

23. *A familiar problem.* In a certain family four girls take turns at washing dishes. Out of a total of four breakages, three were caused by the youngest girl, and she was thereafter called clumsy. Was she justified in attributing the frequency of her breakages to chance? Discuss the connection with random placements of balls.

24. What is the probability that (a) the birthdays of twelve people will fall in twelve different calendar months (assume equal probabilities for the twelve months), (b) the birthdays of six people will fall in exactly two calendar months?

25. Given thirty people, find the probability that among the twelve months there are six containing two birthdays and six containing three.

26. A closet contains n pairs of shoes. If $2r$ shoes are chosen at random (with $2r < n$), what is the probability that there will be (a) no complete pair, (b) exactly one complete pair, (c) exactly two complete pairs among them?

27. A car is parked among N cars in a row, not at either end. On his return the owner finds that exactly r of the N places are still occupied. What is the probability that both neighboring places are empty?

28. A group of $2N$ boys and $2N$ girls is divided into two equal groups. Find the probability p that each group will be equally divided into boys and girls. Estimate p, using Stirling's formula.

29. In bridge, prove that the probability p of West's receiving exactly k aces is the same as the probability that an arbitrary hand of thirteen cards contains exactly k aces. (This is intuitively clear. Note, however, that the two probabilities refer to two different experiments, since in the second case thirteen cards are chosen at random and in the first case all 52 are distributed.)

30. The probability that in a bridge game East receives m and South n spades is the same as the probability that of two hands of thirteen cards each, drawn at random from a deck of bridge cards, the first contains m and the second n spades.

31. What is the probability that the bridge hands of North and South together contain exactly k aces, where $k = 0, 1, 2, 3, 4$?

32. Let a, b, c, d be four non-negative integers such that $a + b + c + d = 13$. Find the probability $p(a, b, c, d)$ that in a bridge game the players North, East,

South, West have a, b, c, d spades, respectively. Formulate a scheme of placing red and black balls into cells that contains the problem as a special case.

33. Using the result of problem 32, find the probability that some player receives a, another b, a third c, and the last d spades if (a) $a = 5$, $b = 4$, $c = 3$, $d = 1$; (b) $a = b = c = 4$, $d = 1$; (c) $a = b = 4$, $c = 3$, $d = 2$. Note that the three cases are essentially different.

34. Let a, b, c, d be integers with $a + b + c + d = 13$. Find the probability $q(a, b, c, d)$ that a hand at bridge will consist of a spades, b hearts, c diamonds, and d clubs and show that the problem does *not* reduce to one of placing, at random, thirteen balls into four cells. Why?

35. *Distribution of aces among r bridge cards.* Calculate the probabilities $p_0(r)$, $p_1(r)$, ..., $p_4(r)$ that among r bridge cards drawn at random there are 0, 1, ..., 4 aces, respectively. Verify that $p_0(r) = p_4(52 - r)$.

36. *Continuation: waiting times.* If the cards are drawn one by one, find the probabilities $f_1(r)$, ..., $f_4(r)$ that the first, ..., fourth ace turns up at the rth trial. *Guess* at the *medians* of the waiting times for the first, ..., fourth ace and then calculate them.

37. Find the probability that each of two hands contains exactly k aces if the two hands are composed of r bridge cards each, and are drawn (a) from the same deck, (b) from two decks. Show that when $r = 13$ the probability in part (a) is the probability that two preassigned bridge players receive exactly k aces each.

38. *Misprints.* Each page of a book contains N symbols, possibly misprints. The book contains $n = 500$ pages and $r = 50$ misprints. Show that (a) the probability that pages number 1, 2, ..., n contain, respectively, r_1, r_2, ..., r_n misprints equals

$$\binom{N}{r_1} \binom{N}{r_2} \cdots \binom{N}{r_n} \div \binom{nN}{r} ;$$

(b) for large N this probability may be approximated by (5.5). Conclude that *the r misprints are distributed in the n pages approximately in accordance with a random distribution of r balls in n cells.* (*Note.* This may be restated as a general limiting property of Fermi-Dirac statistics. Cf. section 5.)

Note: *The following problems refer to the material of section 5.*

39. If r_1 indistinguishable things of one kind and r_2 indistinguishable things of a second kind are placed into n cells, find the number of distinguishable arrangements.

40. If r_1 dice and r_2 coins are thrown, how many results can be distinguished?

41. In how many different distinguishable ways can r_1 white, r_2 black, and r_3 red balls be arranged?

42. Find the probability that in a random arrangement of 52 bridge cards no two aces are adjacent.

43. *Elevator.* In the example (3.c) the elevator starts with seven passengers and stops at ten floors. The various arrangements of discharge may be denoted by symbols like (3, 2, 2), to be interpreted as the event that three passengers leave together at a certain floor, two other passengers at another

floor, and the last two at still another floor. Find the probabilities of the fifteen possible arrangements ranging from (7) to (1, 1, 1, 1, 1, 1, 1).

44. *Birthdays.* Find the probabilities for the various configurations of the birthdays of 22 people.

45. Find the probability for a *poker* hand to be a (*a*) royal flush (ten, jack, queen, king, ace in a single suit); (*b*) four of a kind (four cards of equal face values); (*c*) full house (one pair and one triple of cards with equal face values); (*d*) straight (five cards in sequence regardless of suit); (*e*) three of a kind (three equal face values plus two extra cards); (*f*) two pairs (two pairs of equal face values plus one other card); (*g*) one pair (one pair of equal face values plus three different cards).

11. PROBLEMS AND COMPLEMENTS OF A THEORETICAL CHARACTER

1. A population of n elements includes np red ones and nq black ones ($p + q = 1$). A random sample of size r is taken with replacement. Show that the probability of its including exactly k red elements is

$$(11.1) \qquad \binom{r}{k} p^k q^{r-k}.$$

2. *A limit theorem for the hypergeometric distribution.* If n is large and $n_1/n = p$, then the probability q_k given by (6.1) and (6.2) is close to (11.1). More precisely,

$$(11.2) \quad \binom{r}{k}\left(p - \frac{k}{n}\right)^k \left(q - \frac{r-k}{n}\right)^{r-k} < q_k < \binom{r}{k} p^k q^{r-k} \left(1 - \frac{r}{n}\right)^{-r}$$

A comparison of this and the preceding problem shows: *For large populations there is practically no difference between sampling with or without replacement.*

3. A random sample of size r *without replacement* is taken from a population of n elements. The probability u_r that N given elements will all be included in the sample is

$$(11.3) \qquad u_r = \binom{n-N}{r-N} \div \binom{n}{r}.$$

(The corresponding formula for sampling *with replacement* is given by (11.10) and cannot be derived by a direct argument. For an alternative form of (11.3) cf. problem IV, 9.)

4. *Limiting form.* If $n \to \infty$ and $r \to \infty$ so that $r/n \to p$, then $u_r \to p^N$ (cf. problem 13).

Note: *Problems 5–13 refer to the classical occupancy problem (Maxwell-Boltzmann statistics): That is, r balls are distributed among n cells and each of the n^r possible distributions has probability n^{-r}.*[18]

---

[18] Problems 5–19 play a role in quantum statistics, the theory of photographic plates, G-M counters, etc. The formulas are therefore frequently discussed and discovered in the physical literature, usually without a realization of their classical and essentially elementary character. Probably all the problems occur (although in modified form) in the book by Whitworth quoted at the opening of this chapter.

5. The probability p_k that a given cell contains exactly k balls is given by the binomial distribution (4.5). The most probable number is the integer ν such that $(r - n + 1)/n < \nu \leq (r + 1)/n$. (In other words, it is asserted that $p_0 < p_1 < \ldots < p_{\nu-1} \leq p_\nu > p_{\nu+1} > \ldots > p_r$; cf. problem 15.)

6. *Limiting form.* If $n \to \infty$ and $r \to \infty$ so that the average number $\lambda = r/n$ of balls per cell remains constant, then

$$(11.4) \qquad p_k \to e^{-\lambda} \lambda^k / k!.$$

This is the *Poisson distribution,* discussed in chapter VI; see problem 16.

7. Let $A(r, n)$ be the number of distributions leaving *none of the n cells empty.* Show by a combinatorial argument that

$$(11.5) \qquad A(r, n+1) = \sum_{k=1}^{r} \binom{r}{k} A(r-k, n).$$

Conclude that

$$(11.6) \qquad A(r, n) = \sum_{\nu=0}^{n} (-1)^\nu \binom{n}{\nu} (n - \nu)^r.$$

Hint: Use induction; assume (11.6) to hold and express $A(r-k, n)$ in (11.5) accordingly. Change the order of summation and use the binomial formula to express $A(r, n+1)$ as the difference of two simple sums. Replace in the second sum $\nu + 1$ by a new index of summation and use (8.6).

Note: *Formula (11.6) provides a theoretical solution to an old problem but obviously it would be a thankless task to use it for the calculation of the probability x, say, that in a village of $r = 1900$ people every day of the year is a birthday. In chapter IV, section 2, we shall derive (11.6) by another method and obtain a simple approximation formula (showing, e.g., that $x = 0.135$, approximately).*

8. Show that *the number of distributions leaving exactly m cells empty is*

$$(11.7) \quad E_m(r, n) = \binom{n}{m} A(r, n-m) = \binom{n}{m} \sum_{\nu=0}^{n-m} (-1)^\nu \binom{n - m}{\nu} (n - m - \nu)^r.$$

9. Show without using the preceding results that *the probability*

$$p_m(r, n) = n^{-r} E_m(r, n)$$

of finding exactly m cells empty satisfies

$$(11.8) \qquad p_m(r+1, n) = p_m(r, n) \frac{n - m}{n} + p_{m-1}(r, n) \frac{m - 1}{n}.$$

10. Using the results of problems 7 and 8, show by direct calculation that (11.8) holds. Show that this method provides *a new derivation (by induction on r) of (11.6).*

11. From (11.6) and problem 8 conclude that *the probability of finding m or more cells empty is*

$$(11.9) \qquad \binom{n}{m} \sum_{\nu=0}^{n-m} (-1)^\nu \binom{n - m}{\nu} \left(1 - \frac{m + \nu}{n}\right)^r \frac{m}{m + \nu}.$$

(For $m \geq n$ this expression reduces to zero, as is proper.)

12. *The probability that each of N given cells is occupied is*

(11.10) $$u(r, n) = n^{-r} \sum_{k=0}^{r} \binom{r}{k} A(k, N)(n - N)^{r-k}$$

Conclude that

(11.11) $$u(r, n) = \sum_{\nu=0}^{N} (-1)^{\nu} \binom{N}{\nu} \left(1 - \frac{\nu}{n}\right)^{r}.$$

(Use the binomial theorem. For $N = n$ we have $u(r, n) = n^{-r} A(r, n)$. Note that (11.11) is the analogue of (11.3) for *sampling with replacement*.[19] For an alternative derivation see problem IV, 8.)

13. *Limiting form.* For the passage to the limit described in problem 4 one has $u(r, n) \to (1 - e^{-p})^{N}$.

Note: *In problems 14–19 r and n have the same meaning as above, but we assume that the balls are indistinguishable and that all distinguishable arrangements have equal probabilities (Bose-Einstein statistics).*

14. The probability that a given cell contains exactly k balls is

(11.12) $$q_k = \binom{n + r - k - 2}{r - k} \div \binom{n + r - 1}{r}.$$

15. Show that when $n > 2$ zero is the most probable number of balls in any specified cell, or more precisely, $q_0 > q_1 > \ldots$ (cf. problem 5).

16. *Limit theorem.* Let $n \to \infty$ and $r \to \infty$, so that the average number of particles per cell, r/n, tends to λ. Then

(11.13) $$q_k \to \frac{\lambda^k}{(1 + \lambda)^{k+1}}.$$

(The right side is known as the *geometric distribution.*)

17. The probability that exactly m cells remain empty is

(11.14) $$p_m = \binom{n}{m} \binom{r - 1}{n - m - 1} \div \binom{n + r - 1}{r}.$$

---

[19] Note that $u(r, n)$ may be interpreted as the probability that the *waiting time* up to the moment when the Nth element joins the sample is less than r. The result may be applied to *random sampling digits:* here $u(r, 10) - u(r - 1, 10)$ is the probability that a sequence of r elements must be observed to include the complete set of all ten digits. This can be used as a test of randomness. R. E. Greenwood (Coupon collector's test for random digits, *Mathematical Tables and Other Aids to Computation*, vol. 9 (1955), pp. 1–5) has tabulated the distribution and compared it to actual counts for the corresponding waiting times for the first 2035 decimals of π and the first 2486 decimals of e. The median of the waiting time for a complete set of all ten digits is **27**. The probability that this waiting time exceeds 50 is greater than 0.05, and the probability of the waiting time exceeding **75** is about 0.0037.

18. The probability that a group of m prescribed cells contains a total of exactly j balls is

$$(11.15) \quad q_j(m) = \binom{m+j-1}{m-1} \binom{n-m+r-j-1}{r-j} \div \binom{n+r-1}{r}.$$

19. *Limiting form.* For the passage to the limit of problem 4 we have

$$(11.16) \qquad\qquad q_j(m) \rightarrow \binom{m+j-1}{m-1} \frac{p^j}{(1+p)^{m+j}}.$$

(The right side is a special case of the *negative binomial distribution* to be introduced in chapter VI.)

Theorems on Runs. *In problems 20–25 we consider arrangements of r_1 alphas and r_2 betas and assume that all arrangements are equally probable [see example (4.d)]. This group of problems refers to section 5a.*

20. The probability that the arrangement contains exactly k runs of either kind is

$$(11.17) \qquad\qquad P_{2\nu} = 2 \binom{r_1-1}{\nu-1} \binom{r_2-1}{\nu-1} \div \binom{r_1+r_2}{r_1}$$

when $k = 2\nu$ is even, and

$$(11.18) \quad P_{2\nu+1} = \left\{ \binom{r_1-1}{\nu} \binom{r_2-1}{\nu-1} + \binom{r_1-1}{\nu-1} \binom{r_2-1}{\nu} \right\} \div \binom{r_1+r_2}{r_1}$$

when $k = 2\nu + 1$ is odd.

21. *Continuation.* Conclude that the most probable number of runs is an integer k such that $\dfrac{2r_1r_2}{r_1+r_2} < k < \dfrac{2r_1r_2}{r_1+r_2} + 3$. (*Hint:* Consider the ratios $P_{2\nu+2} \div P_{2\nu}$ and $P_{2\nu+1} \div P_{2\nu-1}$.)

22. The probability that the arrangement starts with an alpha run of length $\nu \geq 0$ is $(r_1)_\nu r_2 \div (r_1 + r_2)_{\nu+1}$. (*Hint:* Choose the ν alphas and the beta which must follow it.) What does the theorem imply for $\nu = 0$?

23. The probability of having exactly k runs of alphas is

$$(11.19) \qquad\qquad \pi_k = \binom{r_1-1}{k-1} \binom{r_2+1}{k} \div \binom{r_1+r_2}{r_1}.$$

Hint: This follows easily from the second part of the lemma of section 5. Alternatively, equation (11.19) may be derived from (11.17) and (11.18), but this procedure is more laborious.

24. The probability that the nth alpha is preceded by exactly m betas is

$$(11.20) \qquad \binom{r_1+r_2-n-m}{r_2-m} \binom{m+n-1}{m} \div \binom{r_1+r_2}{r_1}.$$

25. The probability for the alphas to be arranged in k runs of which k_1 are of length 1, k_2 of length 2, ..., k_ν of length ν (with $k_1 + \ldots + k_\nu = k$) is

$$(11.21) \qquad\qquad \frac{k!}{k_1!k_2!\ldots k_\nu!} \binom{r_2+1}{k} \div \binom{r_1+r_2}{r_1}.$$

12. PROBLEMS AND IDENTITIES INVOLVING BINOMIAL COEFFICIENTS

1. For integral $n \geq 2$

$$1 - \binom{n}{1} + \binom{n}{2} - + \ldots = 0$$

$$\binom{n}{1} + 2\binom{n}{2} + 3\binom{n}{3} + \ldots = n2^{n-1}$$

(12.1)

$$\binom{n}{1} - 2\binom{n}{2} + 3\binom{n}{3} - + \ldots = 0,$$

$$2 \cdot 1 \binom{n}{2} + 3 \cdot 2 \binom{n}{3} + 4 \cdot 3 \binom{n}{4} + \ldots = n(n-1)2^{n-2}$$

(*Hint:* Use the binomial formula.)

2. Prove that for positive integers n, k

(12.2) $\binom{n}{0}\binom{n}{k} - \binom{n}{1}\binom{n-1}{k-1} + \binom{n}{2}\binom{n-2}{k-2} \cdots \pm \binom{n}{k}\binom{n-k}{0} = 0.$

More generally [20]

(12.3) $$\Sigma \binom{n}{\nu}\binom{n-\nu}{k-\nu} t^\nu = \binom{n}{k}(1+t)^k.$$

3. For any $a > 0$

(12.4) $$\binom{-a}{k} = (-1)^k \binom{a+k-1}{k}.$$

If a is an integer, this can be proved also by differentiation of the geometric series $\Sigma x^k = (1-x)^{-1}$.

4. Prove that

(12.5) $$\binom{2n}{n} 2^{-2n} = (-1)^n \binom{-\frac{1}{2}}{n}.$$

5. For integral non-negative n and r and all real a

'12.6) $$\sum_{\nu=0}^{n} \binom{a-\nu}{r} = \binom{a+1}{r+1} - \binom{a-n}{r+1}.$$

(*Hint:* Use equation (8.6). The special case $n = a$ is frequently used.)

6. For arbitrary a and integral $n \geq 0$

(12.7) $$\sum_{\nu=0}^{n} (-1)^\nu \binom{a}{\nu} = (-1)^n \binom{a-1}{n}.$$

[*Hint:* Use equation (8.6).]

---

[20] The reader is reminded of the convention (8.5): if ν runs through *all* integers, only finitely many terms in the sum in (12.3) are different from zero.

7. For positive integers r, k

(12.8)
$$\sum_{\nu=0}^{r} \binom{\nu + k - 1}{k - 1} = \binom{r + k}{k}.$$

(*a*) Prove this using (8.6). (*b*) Show that (12.8) is a special case of (12.7). (*c*) Show by an inductive argument that (12.8) leads to a new proof of the first part of the lemma of section 5.

8. In section 6 we remarked that the terms of the hypergeometric distribution should add to unity. This amounts to saying that for any positive integers a, b, n,

(12.9)
$$\binom{a}{0}\binom{b}{n} + \binom{a}{1}\binom{b}{n-1} + \ldots + \binom{a}{n}\binom{b}{0} = \binom{a + b}{n}.$$

Prove this by induction. (*Hint:* Prove first that equation (12.9) holds for $a = 1$ and all b.)

9. *Continuation.* By a comparison of the coefficients of t^n on both sides of

(12.10)
$$(1 + t)^a(1 + t)^b = (1 + t)^{a+b}$$

prove more generally that (12.9) is true for arbitrary numbers a, b (and integral n).

10. Using equation (12.9), prove that

(12.11)
$$\binom{n}{0}^2 + \binom{n}{1}^2 + \binom{n}{2}^2 + \ldots + \binom{n}{n}^2 = \binom{2n}{n}.$$

11. Using equation (12.11), prove that

(12.12)
$$\sum_{\nu=0}^{n} \frac{(2n)!}{(\nu!)^2(n - \nu)!^2} = \binom{2n}{n}^2.$$

12. Prove that for integers $0 < a < b$

(12.13)
$$\sum_{k=1}^{a} (-1)^{a-k} \binom{a}{k}\binom{b + k}{b + 1} = \binom{b}{a - 1}.$$

Hint: Using (12.4) show that (12.11) is a special case of (12.9). Alternatively, compare coefficients of t^{a-1} in $(1 - t)^a(1 - t)^{-b-2} = (1 - t)^{a-b-2}$.

13. By specialization derive from (12.9) the identities

(12.14)
$$\binom{a}{k} - \binom{a}{k-1} + - \ldots \mp \binom{a}{1} \pm 1 = \binom{a - 1}{k}$$

and

(12.15)
$$\sum_{\nu} (-1)^{\nu} \binom{a}{\nu}\binom{n - \nu}{r} = \binom{n - a}{n - r},$$

valid if k, n, and r are positive integers. [*Hint:* Use (12.4).]

14. Using equation (12.9), prove that

(12.16)
$$\sum_{j=0}^{k} \binom{a + k - j - 1}{k - j}\binom{b + j - 1}{j} = \binom{a + b + k - 1}{k}.$$

(*Hint:* Apply equation (12.4) back and forth.) Note the important special cases $b = 1, 2$.

15. Referring to the problems of section 11, notice that equations (11.12), (11.14), (11,15), and (11.16) define probabilities. In each the quantities should therefore add to unity. Show that this is implied, respectively, by (12.8), (12.9), (12.16), and the binomial theorem.

16. From the definition of $A(r, n)$ in problem 7 of section 11 it follows that $A(r, n) = 0$ if $r < n$ and $A(n, n) = n!$. In other words

$$(12.17) \qquad \sum_{k=0}^{n} (-1)^{n-k} \binom{n}{k} k^r = \begin{matrix} 0 & \text{if } r < n \\ n! & \text{if } r = n. \end{matrix}$$

(*a*) Prove (12.17) directly by reduction from n to $n - 1$. (*b*) Next prove (12.17) by considering the rth derivative of $(1 - e^t)^n$ at $t = 0$. (*c*) Generalize (12.17) by starting from (11.11) instead of (11.6).

17. If $0 \leq N \leq n$ prove by induction that for each integer $r \geq 0$

$$(12.18) \qquad \sum_{\nu=0}^{N} (-1)^\nu \binom{N}{\nu} (n - \nu)_r = \binom{n - N}{r - N} r!.$$

(Note that the right-hand member vanishes when $r < N$ and when $r > n$.) Verify (12.18) by considering the rth derivative of $t^{n-N}(t - 1)^N$ at $t = 1$.

18. Prove by induction (using the binomial theorem)

$$(12.19) \qquad \binom{n}{1}\frac{1}{1} - \binom{n}{2}\frac{1}{2} + \ldots + (-1)^{n-1} \binom{n}{n}\frac{1}{n} = 1 + \frac{1}{2} + \frac{1}{3} + \ldots + \frac{1}{n}.$$

Verify (12.19) by integrating the identity $\sum_{0}^{n-1} (1 - t)^\nu = \{1 - (1 - t)^n\} t^{-1}$.

19. Show that for any positive integer m

$$(12.20) \qquad (x + y + z)^m = \sum \frac{m!}{a!b!c!} x^a y^b z^c$$

where the summation extends over all non-negative integers a, b, c, such that $a + b + c = m$.

20. Using Stirling's formula, prove that

$$(12.21) \qquad \binom{2n}{n} \sim (\pi n)^{-\frac{1}{2}} 2^{2n}.$$

21. Prove that for any positive integers a and b

$$(12.22) \qquad \frac{(a + 1)(a + 2)\cdots(a + n)}{(b + 1)(b + 2)\cdots(b + n)} \sim \frac{b!}{a!} n^{a-b}.$$

22. The *gamma function* is defined by

$$(12.23) \qquad \Gamma(x) = \int_0^\infty z^{x-1} e^{-z}\, dz$$

where $x > 0$. Show that $\Gamma(x) \sim (2\pi)^{\frac{1}{2}} e^{-x} x^{x-\frac{1}{2}}$. (Notice that if $x = n$ is an integer, $\Gamma(n) = (n - 1)!$.)

23. Let a and r be arbitrary positive numbers and n a positive integer. Show that

(12.24) $$a(a + r)(a + 2r)\cdots(a + nr) \sim Cr^{n+1}n^{n+(a/r)+\frac{1}{2}}e^{-n}.$$

[The constant C is equal to $(2\pi)^{\frac{1}{2}}/\Gamma(a/r)$.]

24. Using the results of the preceding problem, show that

(12.25) $$\frac{a(a + r)(a + 2r)\cdots(a + nr)}{b(b + r)(b + 2r)\cdots(b + nr)} \sim \frac{\Gamma(b/r)}{\Gamma(a/r)}n^{(a-b)/r}.$$

25. Prove the following *alternative form of Stirling's formula:*

(12.26) $$n! \sim (2\pi)^{\frac{1}{2}}(n + \tfrac{1}{2})^{n+\frac{1}{2}}e^{-(n+\frac{1}{2})}.$$

26. *Continuation.* Using the method of the text, show that

(12.27) $$(2\pi)^{\frac{1}{2}}(n + \tfrac{1}{2})^{n+\frac{1}{2}}e^{-(n+\frac{1}{2})-1/24(n+\frac{1}{2})} < n! < (2\pi)^{\frac{1}{2}}(n + \tfrac{1}{2})^{n+\frac{1}{2}}e^{-(n+\frac{1}{2})}.$$

27. Extending Stirling's formula, prove that

(12.28) $$n! \sim (2\pi)^{\frac{1}{2}}n^{n+\frac{1}{2}}\exp\left\{-n + \frac{1}{12n} - \frac{1}{360n^3} + \cdots\right\}.$$

CHAPTER III

Fluctuations in Coin Tossing
and Random Walks

This chapter serves two purposes. First, it will show that exceedingly simple methods may lead to far-reaching and important results. Second, in it we shall for the first time encounter theoretical conclusions which not only are unexpected but actually come as a shock to intuition and common sense. They will reveal that commonly accepted notions concerning chance fluctuations are without foundation and that the implications of the law of large numbers are widely misconstrued.[1]

The discussion is inserted at this place only because of its elementary character; the main topic of the book continues in chapter V. The entire book is independent of the present chapter. Some of the formulas will reappear later in connection with first passages and recurrence, but they will be derived anew by analytical methods. A comparison of methods should prove instructive and interesting. *Accordingly, the present chapter should be read at the reader's discretion independently of, or parallel to, the remainder of the book.* To facilitate such a procedure, this chapter may be read in *two versions:* the main text appears in ordinary type. Passages in small type cover additional topics (referring mainly to first passage and recurrence phenomena) and should be omitted at first reading. Section 7 contains an empirical illustration.

---

* This chapter may be omitted or read in conjunction with the following chapters. Reference to its contents will be made in chapters X (laws of large numbers), XI (first-passage times), XIII (recurrent events), XIV (random walks), but the contents will not be used explicitly in the sequel.

[1] Although we are dealing formally only with coin tossing, the basic conclusions are widely applicable. In fact, E. Sparre Andersen has made the surprising discovery that many facets of the fluctuation theory of sums of independent random variables are of a purely combinatorial nature and are common to a huge class of such variables. This is true, in particular, of the two arc sine laws. See *Mathematica Scandinavica*, vol. 1 (1953), pp. 263–285, and vol. 2 (1954), pp. 195–223.

1. GENERAL ORIENTATION

A surprising wealth of information concerning chance fluctuations in general will be derived from the following inconspicuous lemma announced in 1887 by Bertrand. Similar problems of arrangements have attracted the interest of students of combinatorial analysis under the name of *ballot problems*.[2] *Suppose that, in a ballot, candidate P scores p votes and candidate Q scores q votes, where $p > q$. The probability that throughout the counting there are always more votes for P than for Q equals $(p - q)/(p + q)$.*

In mathematical language we are here concerned with arrangements of $x = p + q$ symbols $\epsilon_1, \epsilon_2, \ldots, \epsilon_x$ consisting of p plus ones (votes for *P*) and q minus ones (votes for *Q*). The partial sum $s_k = \epsilon_1 + \epsilon_2 + \ldots + \epsilon_k$ is the number of votes by which *P* leads, or trails, just after the kth vote is cast. Clearly $s_x = p - q$ and

$$(1.1) \qquad s_i - s_{i-1} = \epsilon_i = \pm 1, \qquad s_0 = 0 \qquad (i = 1, 2, \ldots, x).$$

Conversely, every arrangement $\{s_1, s_2, \ldots, s_x\}$ of integers satisfying (1.1) represents a potential voting record. We shall use a geometrical terminology and represent such an arrangement by a polygonal line whose ith side has slope ϵ_i and whose ith vertex has ordinate s_i. Such lines will be called paths.

Definition. *Let $x > 0$ and y be integers. A path $\{s_1, s_2, \ldots, s_x\}$ from the origin to the point (x, y) is a polygonal line whose vertices have abscissas 0, 1, 2, $\ldots$, x and ordinates $s_0, s_1, s_2, \ldots, s_x$ satisfying (1.1) with $s_x = y$.*

If p among the ϵ_i are positive and q negative, then

$$(1.2) \qquad\qquad x = p + q, \qquad y = p - q.$$

An arbitrary point (x, y) can be joined to the origin by a path only if x and y are of the form (1.2). In this case the p places for the positive

---

[2] For the history and literature see A. Dvoretzky and T. Motzkin, A problem of arrangements, *Duke Mathematical Journal*, vol. 14 (1947), pp. 305–313. As these authors point out, most of the formally different proofs in reality use the reflection principle (lemma 1 of section 2), but without the geometric interpretation this principle loses its simplicity and appears as a curious trick. Dvoretzky and Motzkin give a new proof of great simplicity and elegance. They generalize the ballot problem by requiring that at each instant *P* have at least α times the votes scored by *Q*. This work has been continued by M. T. L. Bizley, Derivation of a new formula for the number of minimal lattice paths, etc., *The Journal of the Institute of Actuaries*, vol. 80, Part 1, No. 354 (1954), pp. 55–62.

ε_i can be chosen from the $x = p + q$ available places in

(1.3)
$$N_{x,y} = \binom{p + q}{p} = \binom{p + q}{q}$$

different ways. It is convenient to *define* $N_{x,y} = 0$ *whenever* x, y *are not of the form* (1.2). Then *there exist exactly* $N_{x,y}$ *different paths from the origin to the point* (x, y). Bertrand's ballot theorem asserts that when $y > 0$ there exist exactly $(y/x)N_{x,y}$ paths satisfying the conditions $s_1 > 0$, $s_2 > 0$, ..., $s_{x-1} > 0$, $s_x = y$. It will be proved in section 2.

Example. Figure 1 exhibits a path to the point $N_1 = (5,1)$. There exist ten such paths of which two satisfy the conditions $s_i > 0$. The path in the graph is $\{1, 2, 1, 2, 1\}$, and the other is $\{1, 2, 3, 2, 1\}$.

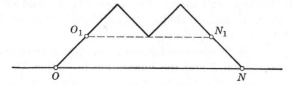

FIGURE 1. Illustrating positive paths and the proof of theorem 2 in section 2.

We can draw the most interesting conclusions from the ballot theorem if we drop the convention that the terminal point (x, y) of the path be fixed in advance. There exist 2^n different paths from the origin to points (n, y) with an arbitrary ordinate y. As explained in section 3, these 2^n paths may be taken to represent the 2^n possible outcomes of the ideal experiment consisting in n successive tossings of a perfect coin. The classical description introduces the fictitious gambler Peter who at each trial wins or loses a unit amount. The sequence $\{s_1, s_2, \ldots, s_n\}$ *then represents Peter's successive cumulative gains*, that is, the excess of the accumulated number of heads over tails.

If $s_n = 0$, the net gain at the conclusion of the nth trial is zero: there exists a *tie*. Ties occur so infrequently that they do not affect the picture, but repeated references to them are disturbing. We shall therefore agree to say that *at the nth trial Peter leads if either $s_n > 0$ or $s_n = 0$ but $s_{n-1} > 0$* (i.e., in case of a tie that player leads who led at the preceding trial). "Peter leads at the nth trial" is but a description for "the nth side of the path is above the x-axis."

The ballot theorem refers to paths situated entirely above the x-axis, that is, to games in which the lead never changes. This topic may be pursued further by investigating how often the lead is likely to change for an arbitrary path. In this connection we reach conclusions that play havoc with our intuition. It is generally expected that in a prolonged series of coin tossings Peter should lead about half the time and Paul the other half. This is entirely wrong, however. *In 20,000 tossings it is about 88 times more probable that Peter leads in all 20,000 trials than that each player leads in 10,000 trials*. In general, the lead changes at such infrequent intervals that intuition is defied. No matter how long the series of tossings, the *most probable number of changes of lead is zero;* exactly one change of lead is more probable than two, two changes are more probable than three, etc. In short, if a modern educator or psychologist were to describe the long-run case histories of individual coin-tossing games, he would classify the majority of coins as maladjusted. If many coins are tossed n times each, a surprisingly large proportion of them will leave one player in the lead almost all the time; and in very few cases will the lead change sides and fluctuate in the manner that is generally expected of a well-behaved coin.

This is a sample of the conclusions to be drawn from the first arc sine law (see section 5 and the illustration in section 7). E. Sparre Andersen has shown that this law has a wide field of applicability, and the situation here described for coin tossings is typical for chance fluctuations involving cumulative effects. Most stochastic processes in physics, economics, and education are of this nature, and our findings should serve as a warning to those who are prone to discern secular trends and deviations from average norms.

The same situation may be viewed from a somewhat different angle. If the coin tossing proceeds at a uniform rate, common sense expects that, with due allowance for chance fluctuations, a two-day game should produce twice as many ties as a one-day game. In other words, we expect intuitively the number of ties to increase roughly in proportion to the duration of the game. Paradoxically this is not so: *The number of ties increases about as the square root of time.* In 10,000 tossings the median number of ties is 67, but in 1,000,000 tossings it increases only to 674; the typical *"wavelength"* increases from about 150 to about 1500. *The average wavelength increases with time* (sections 6 and 8). The formulas on which these conclusions are based play an important role for first passage and recurrence times in general random walks and diffusion theory.

Theorem 3 of section 2 stands apart from the remainder and is not used elsewhere. It concerns a variant of the ballot problem for the case where the two candidates score the same number, n, of votes. Then P leads an even number, $2k$, of times and Q leads in the remaining $2n - 2k$ trials. Again we have the false intuition that each candidate is likely to lead about half the time, that is, we expect $2k$ to be close to n. Actually, if the ballot ended in a tie $n:n$, the $n + 1$ *possible divisions of leads (namely $2n:0$, $2n-2:2$, $2n-4:4$, ..., $2:2n-2$, $0:2n$) have the same probability*

$(n + 1)^{-1}$. This result stands in a marked contrast to the situation described above where the end result was not prescribed in advance; there the extreme divisions $2n:0$ and $0:2n$ are most probable.

It has been pointed out by J. L. Hodges [3] that this theorem has statistical applications to *rank-order* tests. We illustrate this point by the

Example. Suppose that a quantity (e.g. the height of plants) is measured on each of n treated subjects and also on each of n control subjects, obtaining measurements $a_1, \ldots, a_n$ and $b_1, \ldots, b_n$. To fix ideas, suppose that each group is arranged in decreasing order: $a_1 > a_2 > \ldots$ and $b_1 > b_2 > \ldots$. Let us combine the two sequences and write the $2n$ letters $a_1, \ldots, b_n$ in decreasing order. The resulting arrangement of n letters a and n letters b may be interpreted as the record of a ballot in which each candidate received n votes. For an extremely successful treatment all the a's should precede the b's; a completely ineffectual treatment should produce a random order. In our arrangement the a's lead exactly $2k$ times if k different a's precede the b's of same rank, that is, if the inequality $a_i > b_i$ holds for exactly k subscripts. Assuming randomness, the probability that this happens equals $1/(n + 1)$ and therefore the probability that the a's lead $2k$ times *or more* is $(n - k + 1)/(n + 1)$. The classical example for this argument (used qualitatively without knowledge of the theoretical probabilities) is due to Galton who used it in 1876 for data referred to him by Charles Darwin. In his example $2n$ was 30 and the a's were in the lead 26 times. Galton concluded that the treatment *was* efficient, but on the hypothesis of mere randomness even an ineffectual treatment would produce 26 or more leads in three out of sixteen similar experiments. This shows that a qualitative analysis may be a valuable supplement to our rather shaky intuition. (For related tests based on the theory of runs see chapter II, section 5a.)

2. PROBLEMS OF ARRANGEMENTS

Let $A = (a, \alpha)$ and $B = (b, \beta)$ be integral points in the positive quadrant: $b > a \geq 0$, $\alpha > 0$, $\beta > 0$. By *reflection of A on the x-axis is*

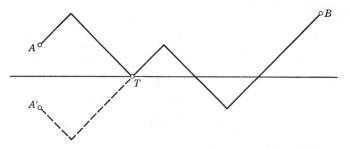

FIGURE 2.   Illustrating the reflection principle.

meant the point $A' = (a, -\alpha)$. (See figure 2.)   A *path from A to B* is defined as in section 1, with A playing the role of the origin.

[3] Galton's rank-order test, *Biometrika*, vol. 42 (1955), pp. 261–262.

Lemma.[4] (*Reflection principle.*)   *The number of paths from A to B which touch or cross the x-axis equals the number of all paths from A' to B.*

Proof.   Consider a path $\{s_a = \alpha,\ s_{a+1},\ \ldots,\ s_b = \beta\}$ from A to B having one or more vertices on the x-axis. Let t be the abscissa of the *first* such vertex (see figure 2); that is, choose t so that $s_a > 0,\ \ldots,$ $s_{t-1} > 0,\ s_t = 0$. Then $\{-s_a,\ -s_{a+1},\ \ldots,\ -s_{t-1},\ s_t = 0,\ s_{t+1},\ s_{t+2},$ $\ldots,\ s_b\}$ is a path leading from A' to B and having $T = (t, 0)$ as its first vertex on the x-axis. The sections AT and $A'T$ being reflections of each other, there exists a one-to-one correspondence between all paths from A' to B and such paths from A to B as have a vertex on the x-axis. The lemma is proved.

Theorem 1.   (*Ballot theorem.*)   *Let $x > 0,\ y > 0$; the number of paths $\{s_1, s_2, \ldots, s_x = y\}$ from the origin to (x, y) such that $s_1 > 0,\ s_2 > 0,$ $\ldots,\ s_x > 0$ equals $(y/x)N_{x,y}$.*

Proof.   Since $s_1 = \pm 1$, we have $s_1 = 1$ for each admissible path. It follows that there exist as many admissible paths as there are paths leading from the point $(1, 1)$ to (x, y) which neither touch nor cross the x-axis. By the last lemma the number of such paths equals

$$(2.1) \quad N_{x-1,y-1} - N_{x-1,y+1} = \binom{p+q-1}{p-1} - \binom{p+q-1}{q-1}$$

$$= \frac{p-q}{p+q}\binom{p+q}{p} = \frac{y}{x}N_{x,y}.$$

The Duality Principle.   Almost every theorem on paths can be reformulated to obtain a formally different theorem.   Consider $\{s_1, \ldots, s_x\}$ and the path obtained from it by reversing the order of the ϵ_i, that is, the path $\{s_1{}^*, s_2{}^*, \ldots, s_x{}^*\}$

where $s_1{}^* = \epsilon_x,$ $s_2{}^* = \epsilon_x + \epsilon_{x-1},$ $s_3{}^* = \epsilon_x + \epsilon_{x-1} + \epsilon_{x-2}, \ldots$ or

$$(2.2) \quad s_0{}^* = 0, \quad s_1{}^* = s_x - s_{x-1}, \quad \ldots, \quad s_i{}^* = s_x - s_{x-i}, \quad \ldots, \quad s_x{}^* = s_x.$$

The two paths (1.1) and (2.2) are congruent and are obtained from each other by a rotation through 180 degrees; they join the same endpoints. *To each theorem on paths there corresponds a dual theorem obtained by applying it to the reversed path* (2.2).

For example, the ballot theorem gives us the number of reversed paths $\{s_1{}^*, \ldots,$ $\ldots, s_x{}^*\}$ joining the origin to (x, y) such that $s_i{}^* > 0$ for $i = 1, 2, \ldots, x$. But this is

---

[4] The probability literature attributes this method to D. André (1887). The text reduces it to a lemma on random walks. The classical difference equations of random walks (chapter XIV) closely resemble differential equations, and the reflection principle (even a stronger form of it) is familiar in that theory under the name of *Lord Kelvin's method of images.*

the same as $s_x > s_{x-i}$ for $i = 1, 2, \ldots, x-1$ and hence we have as an alternative form of the ballot theorem

Theorem 1*. *The number of paths* $\{s_1, s_2, \ldots, s_x\}$ *from* $(0, 0)$ *to* (x, y) *such that* $s_1 < s_x$, $s_2 < s_x$, $\ldots$, $s_{x-1} < s_x$ *(where* $s_x = y > 0$*) equals* $(y/x)N_{x,y}$.

Geometrically speaking, theorem 1 is concerned with paths whose left endpoint is the lowest vertex, whereas the dual theorem 1* refers to paths whose last vertex is highest. (See figure 3.) Theorem 1* has implications for first-passage times in random walks.

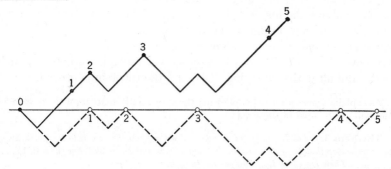

Figure 3.   Illustrating first passages and returns to the origin.

We turn to a study of paths joining the origin to a point $N = (2n, 0)$ of the x-axis (an odd vertex on the x-axis is impossible). Put for abbreviation

$$(2.3) \qquad\qquad L_{2n} = \frac{1}{n+1}\binom{2n}{n}.$$

Theorem 2. *Among the* $\binom{2n}{n}$ *paths joining the origin to the point* $2n$ *of the* x-*axis there are*

(a) *exactly* L_{2n-2} *paths such that*

$$(2.4) \qquad\qquad s_1 > 0, \quad s_2 > 0, \quad \ldots, \quad s_{2n-1} > 0, \qquad (s_{2n} = 0)$$

(b) *exactly* L_{2n} *paths such that*

$$(2.5) \qquad\qquad s_1 \geq 0, \quad s_2 \geq 0, \quad \ldots, \quad s_{2n-1} \geq 0, \qquad (s_{2n} = 0).$$

(*That is, there are as many paths to* $2n$ *with all inner vertices above the* x-*axis as there are paths to* $2n - 2$ *with no vertex below the* x-*axis.*)

Proof. (See figure 1.) Each path satisfying condition (2.4) passes through the point $N_1 = (2n-1, 1)$ and by theorem 1 the number of paths to N_1 such that $s_1 > 0, \ldots, s_{2n-2} > 0$ equals

(2.6) $$\frac{1}{2n-1}\binom{2n-1}{n-1} = \frac{1}{n}\binom{2n-2}{n-1} = L_{2n-2}.$$

This proves (a). Again, let a path satisfy condition (2.4). Omitting the first and the last side we get a path that joins the point $O_1 = (1, 1)$ to $N_1 = (2n-1, 1)$ and at the same time is such that all its vertices lie on or above the line $y = 1$. Translating the origin to O_1, we get a path from the new origin to the point N_1 (which has the new coordinates $2n-2$ and 0), none of whose vertices lies below the new x-axis. We have thus established a one-to-one correspondence between such paths and all paths satisfying (2.4), and the theorem is proved.

As explained in section 1 the following theorem stands apart from the remainder and will not be used in the sequel.

Theorem 3.[5] *Let $L_{2k,2n}$ be the number of paths from the origin to the point $2n$ of the x-axis such that $2k$ of its sides lie above the x-axis and $2n - 2k$ below $(k = 0, 1, \ldots,$ $\ldots, n)$. Then $L_{2k,2n} = L_{2n}$, independently of k.*

Proof. The assertion is trivially true for $n = 1$ and we assume by induction that $L_{2k,2\nu} = L_{2\nu}$ for $\nu = 1, 2, \ldots, n-1$ and $0 \leq k \leq \nu$. We propose to count the number of paths $\{s_1, s_2, \ldots, s_{2n} = 0\}$ with exactly $2k$ sides above the x-axis. First assume $1 \leq k \leq n - 1$. Such a path crosses the x-axis and we denote by $2r$ the abscissa of its *first* vertex on the x-axis. We have then to consider two classes of paths.

A path of the first class is positive between 0 and $2r$, and its section between $2r$ and $2n$ contains exactly $2k - 2r$ sides above the axis. Here $k \geq r$. By theorem 2(a) there exist L_{2r-2} paths $\{s_1, \ldots, s_{2r-1}, s_{2r} = 0\}$ with $s_1 > 0, \ldots, s_{2r-1} > 0$, and by the induction hypothesis there exist $L_{2k-2r,2n-2r} = L_{2n-2r}$ paths joining $(2r, 0)$ to $(2n, 0)$ and having $2k - 2r$ sides above the x-axis. Accordingly, there exists a total of $L_{2r-2}L_{2n-2r}$ paths of this class.

A path of the second class is negative between 0 and $2r$; its section between $2r$ and $2n$ then contains $2k$ sides above the x-axis. By the argument above there exist again $L_{2r-2}L_{2n-2r}$ paths of this class, but this time $n - r \geq k$. It follows that for $k = 1, \ldots, n-1$

(2.7) $$L_{2k,2n} = \sum_{r=1}^{k} L_{2r-2}L_{2n-2r} + \sum_{r=1}^{n-k} L_{2r-2}L_{2n-2r}.$$

By changing the summation index to $\rho = n - r + 1$, the terms of the second

---

[5] First proved by complicated analytical methods by K. L. Chung and W. Feller, Fluctuations in coin tossing, *Proceedings National Academy of Sciences USA*, vol. 35 (1949), pp. 605–608 (see also the first edition of the present book, chapter XII, problem 4). An elegant combinatorial proof was given by J. L. Hodges (see footnote 3).

sum become $L_{2r-2}L_{2n-2r} = L_{2\rho-2}L_{2n-2\rho}$ with ρ running from $k+1$ to n. Thus

$$(2.8) \qquad L_{2k,2n} = \sum_{\rho=1}^{n} L_{2\rho-2}L_{2n-2\rho},$$

which is *independent of k*.

A path with all $2n$ sides above the x-axis is a path of the sort described in theorem 2(*b*), and hence $L_{2n,2n} = L_{2n}$. For reasons of symmetry we have also $L_{0,2n} = L_{2n}$. The total number of paths from the origin to $(2n, 0)$ being $(n + 1)L_{2n}$, it follows that $L_{2k,2n} = L_{2n}$ for $k = 0, 1, \ldots, n$.

As a *corollary* we find the identity

$$(2.9) \qquad L_{2n} = \sum_{\rho=1}^{n} L_{2\rho-2}L_{2n-2\rho}.$$

For a direct analytic verification see section 8(*a*).

3. RANDOM WALKS AND COIN TOSSING

In a sequence of N tossings of an ideal coin let $\epsilon_k = +1$ if the kth trial results in heads and $\epsilon_k = -1$ otherwise. Then $s_k = \epsilon_1 + \epsilon_2 + +\ldots + \epsilon_k$ is the cumulative excess of heads over tails at the conclusion of the kth trial. In classical betting language s_k is "Peter's accumulated net gain." Each possible outcome of the N successive tossings is represented by a path of N sides starting at the origin, and conversely each such path may be taken as representing the outcome of N-tossings.

This consideration leads us to *take for our sample space the aggregate of the 2^N paths* $\{s_1, \ldots, s_N\}$ *starting at the origin and to attribute probability* 2^{-N} *to each*.

An event such as "heads at the first two trials" must be interpreted as the aggregate of all sequences starting with $s_1 = 1$, $s_2 = 2$. There are 2^{N-2} such sequences and the probability of this event is therefore 2^{-2}, as is proper. More generally, if $k < N$ there exist exactly 2^{N-k} different paths $\{s_1, s_2, \ldots, s_N\}$ such that their first k vertices lie on a preassigned path $\{s_1, s_2, \ldots, s_k\}$. It follows that *an event determined by the outcome of the first $k < N$ trials has a probability independent of N*. In practice, therefore, the number N plays no role, provided it is sufficiently large. Conceptually and formally it is best to consider each finite sequence of tossings as the beginning of a potentially infinite sequence, but this would lead us into non-denumerable sample spaces. We shall therefore consider finite sequences with N larger than the number of trials occurring in the formulas; except for this we shall be permitted, and be glad, to forget about N.

For the probabilistic background and the connection with related topics it is desirable to supplement the geometric language by an alternative terminology. We imagine the coin tossings performed at a uniform rate, so that the nth trial occurs at *time n*. Peter may mark his cumulative gain at all times by an indicator which we shall call "particle." This particle, then, moves on a vertical axis starting from the origin. It moves at times 1, 2, ... one unit step upward if the coin lands heads, one unit step downward if the coin lands tails. We say that *the particle performs a symmetric random walk.* (The physicist takes it as the simplest model for one-dimensional diffusion; see chapter XIV.)

At time n the position of the particle is the point s_n of the vertical axis. *The path* $\{s_1, s_2, \ldots, s_N\}$ *represents the space-time diagram of the random walk,* the x-axis playing the role of the time axis.

Guided by this background we introduce the following

Terminology. *We shall say that at time n there takes place:*
A return to the origin if $s_n = 0.$
A first return to the origin if

$$(3.1) \qquad s_1 \neq 0, \quad s_2 \neq 0, \quad \ldots, \quad s_{n-1} \neq 0, \quad s_n = 0.$$

A first passage through $r > 0$ if

$$(3.2) \qquad s_1 < r, \quad s_2 < r, \quad \ldots, \quad s_{n-1} < r, \quad s_n = r.$$

A second, third, ... return to the origin and a first passage through $r < 0$ are defined in an obvious way. Note that passages through the origin can take place only at *even* times, and we shall frequently restrict the formulas to even times. In betting language a return to the origin represents an *equalization of the accumulated numbers of heads and tails.* (Figure 3 exhibits two paths in which the first passages and returns to the origin, respectively, are marked; the second path has the peculiarity of keeping to the negative side.)

4. REFORMULATION OF THE COMBINATORIAL THEOREMS

In the following sections we shall use the notations

$$(4.1) \qquad u_{2n} = \binom{2n}{n} 2^{-2n}, \qquad n = 0, 1, 2, \ldots$$

and

$$(4.2) \qquad f_0 = 0, \quad f_{2n} = \frac{1}{2n} u_{2n-2}, \qquad n = 1, 2, \ldots$$

It is easily verified that

$$(4.3) \qquad f_{2n} = u_{2n-2} - u_{2n}, \qquad n = 1, 2, \ldots.$$

Theorem 1. *For each $n \geq 1$:*

$$(4.4) \qquad u_{2n} = \mathbf{P}\{s_{2n} = 0\}$$

(4.5) $u_{2n} = \mathbf{P}\{s_1 \neq 0,\, s_2 \neq 0,\, \ldots,\, s_{2n} \neq 0\}$

(4.6) $u_{2n} = \mathbf{P}\{s_1 \geq 0,\, s_2 \geq 0,\, \ldots,\, s_{2n} \geq 0\}$

or in words: The three events, (a) a return to the origin takes place at time 2n, (b) no return occurs up to and including time 2n, and (c) the path is non-negative between 0 and 2n, have the common probability u_{2n}.
  Furthermore,

(4.7) $f_{2n} = \mathbf{P}\{s_1 \neq 0,\, s_2 \neq 0,\, \ldots,\, s_{2n-1} \neq 0,\, s_{2n} = 0\}$

(4.8) $f_{2n} = \mathbf{P}\{s_1 \geq 0,\, s_2 \geq 0,\, \ldots,\, s_{2n-2} \geq 0,\, s_{2n-1} < 0\}$

that is: the two events (a) the first return to the origin takes place at time 2n, and (b) the first passage through −1 occurs at time 2n − 1, have the common probability f_{2n}.

  Proof. As was observed in section 3 it suffices to consider the sample space of paths of the fixed length $2n$. By (1.3) there exist $\binom{2n}{n}$ paths joining the origin to the point $(2n, 0)$, and this proves (4.4).

  By theorem 2(a) in section 2 there exist L_{2n-2} paths joining the origin to $(2n, 0)$ such that $s_1 > 0,\, \ldots,\, s_{2n-1} > 0$. Therefore there are twice as many paths satisfying the condition in (4.7), and the corresponding probability is $2L_{2n-2} \cdot 2^{-2n} = f_{2n}$. Theorem 2(b) in section 2 implies in the same way (4.8).

  The probability that no zero occurs up to and including time $2n$ equals one minus the probability of a first return to the origin at a time $\leq 2n$. Using (4.7) this difference is

(4.9) $1 - f_2 - f_4 - \ldots - f_{2n} =$

$$1 - (1 - u_2) - (u_2 - u_4) - \ldots - (u_{2n-2} - u_{2n}) = u_{2n}$$

which proves (4.5). Similarly, the right side in (4.6) equals one minus the probability of a first passage through −1 before time $2n$, and using (4.8) this difference is again given by (4.9). This accomplishes the proof.

  Corollary. *It follows that for $n \geq 1$*

(4.10) $$u_{2n} = \sum_{r=1}^{n} f_{2r} u_{2n-2r}.$$

Proof. If a return to the origin takes place at time $2n$, then the *first* return must take place at some time $2r \leq 2n$. We have just seen that the number of paths from the origin to $(2n, 0)$ with the first return to the origin taking place at time $2r \leq 2n$ equals $2^{2r}f_{2r} \cdot 2^{2n-2r}u_{2n-2r}$. Summing over r, we get equation (4.10). (For a direct analytic proof see section 8(a). In chapter XIII, section 3, we shall see that (4.10) is a special case of the basic equation for recurrent events.)

Theorem 1* in section 2 enumerates the paths in which a first passage through y occurs at time x. The sum $x + y$ must be even, and for our purposes it is convenient to put $x = 2n - y$. The content of theorem 1* may then be restated as follows.

Theorem 2. *The probability that a first passage through $y > 0$ takes place at time $2n - y$ is given by*

$$(4.11) \qquad f_{2n}^{(y)} = \frac{y}{2n - y} \binom{2n - y}{n} 2^{-2n+y}, \qquad n \geq y > 0.$$

The simplicity with which the duality principle delivered this important formula as a direct consequence of the ballot theorem is truly remarkable. A direct analytic derivation of (4.11) is difficult and requires special tricks.

In principle, the probabilities $f_{2n}^{(y)}$ can be calculated by induction on y. A path of length $2n - y - 1$ in which a first passage through $y + 1$ occurs at the terminal point may be decomposed into two segments (see figure 3 for $y = 4$). The first segment is the path from the origin up to the point of the first passage through y; it occurs at some time $2\nu - y < 2n - y - 1$. This section is followed by the second, a section of length $2n - 2\nu - 1$ in which the terminal endpoint is the only one lying above the left endpoint. In other words, if its left endpoint is taken as the origin, the second section represents a path with a first passage through 1 at the endpoint. By definition there exist $2^{2\nu-y}f_{2\nu}^{(y)}$ sections of the first type and $2^{2n-2\nu-1}f_{2n-2\nu}^{(1)}$ of the second, and any two can be combined to give a path with first passage through $y + 1$ at time $2n - y - 1$. Therefore

$$(4.12) \qquad f_{2n}^{(y+1)} = \sum_{\nu=y}^{n-1} f_{2\nu}^{(y)} f_{2n-2\nu}^{(1)}, \qquad n \geq y + 1.$$

Formula (4.8) states that a first passage through -1 (and hence also through $+1$) at time $2n - 1$ has probability f_{2n}, that is,

$$(4.13) \qquad f_{2n}^{(1)} = f_{2n} \qquad\qquad n \geq 1.$$

Equations (4.12) and (4.13) determine recursively all $f_{2n}^{(y)}$, but it is not easy to verify that (4.11) satisfies (4.12), and it is not at all clear how the explicit formula (4.11) could be derived from (4.12).

Formulas (4.12)–(4.13) permit a novel conclusion. We see from (4.13) that $f_{2n}^{(1)}$ is the probability that the first return to zero occurs at time $2n$. Forgetting about the preceding theorem, let us now define $f_{2n}^{(y)}$ as the probability that the yth return to zero takes place at time $2n$. The argument used in the last proof applies without change: Splitting a path from the origin to the $(y+1)$st return into the initial section leading to the yth return and the terminal section between the yth and the $(y+1)$st return, we see again that (4.12) holds. Since this relation uniquely determines all $f_{2n}^{(y)}$ we have

Theorem 3. *The probability that the yth return to zero takes place at time $2n$ is given by* (4.11).

Alternative geometric proof. Consider a path leading from the origin to a first passage through y at time $2n - y$. (Figure 3 exhibits the case $y = 5$, $2n - y = 15$.) Construct a new path by inserting into this path y new sides each of slope -1 and having left endpoints, respectively, at the origin and the $y - 1$ vertices at which a first passage through $1, 2, \ldots, y-1$ takes place. The new path, say $\{\sigma_1, \sigma_2, \ldots, \sigma_{2n}\}$, has length $2n$. Clearly $\sigma_1 \leq 0, \ldots, \sigma_{2n-1} \leq 0$, $\sigma_{2n} = 0$, and exactly $y - 1$ interior vertices lie on the x-axis. Conversely, each path $\{\sigma_1, \ldots, \sigma_{2n}\}$ with this property is obtained, in the manner described, from a path with first passage through y at time $2n - y$. If $f_{2n}^{(y)}$ is defined as in theorem 2, we see that there exist exactly $2^{2n-y}f_{2n}^{(y)}$ paths $\{\sigma_1, \ldots, \sigma_{2n}\}$ such that $\sigma_i \leq 0$, $\sigma_{2n} = 0$, and exactly $y - 1$ interior vertices lie on the x-axis. Such a path consists of y sections with endpoints on the x-axis, and we can produce 2^y different paths by changing the signs of all σ_i of one or more such sections. In this way we obtain *all* paths of length $2n$ with $s_{2n} = 0$ and exactly $y - 1$ inner vertices on the x-axis, and their number is therefore $2^{2n}f_{2n}^{(y)}$, as asserted.

5. PROBABILITY OF LONG LEADS: THE FIRST ARC SINE LAW

We shall say that *the particle spends the time from $k - 1$ to k on the positive side if the kth side of its path lies above the x-axis*, that is, if at least one of the two vertices s_{k-1} and s_k is positive (in which case the other is positive or zero). In the betting terminology this means that at both the $(k-1)$st and the kth trial Peter's accumulated gain was non-negative.

The paradoxical properties of the paths mentioned in section 1 will be derived from the following

Theorem 1.[6] *Let $p_{2k,2n}$ be the probability that in the time interval from 0 to $2n$ the particle spends $2k$ time units on the positive side and $2n - 2k$ time units on the negative side. Then*

$$(5.1) \qquad\qquad p_{2k,2n} = u_{2k}u_{2n-2k}.$$

(Note that the total time spent on the positive side is necessarily even.)

Proof. The probability that the particle keeps to the positive side during the entire time interval from 0 to $2n$ is given by formula (4.6),

---

[6] First proved by complicated analytical methods by K. L. Chung and W. Feller (see footnote 5 and the first edition of the present book, chapter XII, sections 5 and 6). The theorem was suggested by the work of E. Sparre Andersen (see footnote 1).

and we see that $p_{2n,2n} = u_{2n}$ as asserted. For reasons of symmetry we have also $p_{0,2n} = u_{2n}$, and it remains only to prove (5.1) for $1 \leq k \leq n - 1$. For that purpose we repeat the argument which led to (2.7). A particle that keeps for $2k > 0$ time units to the positive side and for $2n - 2k > 0$ time units to the negative side necessarily passes through zero. Let $2r$ be the moment of its *first* return to zero. Then the path belongs to one of the following two classes.

In the first class, up to time $2r$ the particle stays on the positive side, and during the time interval from $2r$ to $2n$ it spends exactly $2k - 2r \geq 0$ time units on the positive side. There exist $2^{2r}f_{2r}$ paths of length $2r$ which return to the origin for the first time at $2r$, and half of them keep to the positive side. Furthermore, by definition, there are $2^{2n-2r}p_{2k-2r,2n-2r}$ paths of length $2n - 2r$ starting at $(2r, 0)$ and having exactly $2k - 2r$ sides above the x-axis. Thus the total number of paths of length $2n$ in the first class equals

$$\tfrac{1}{2} \cdot 2^{2r}f_{2r} \cdot 2^{2n-2r}p_{2k-2r,2n-2r} = 2^{2n-1}f_{2r}p_{2k-2r,2n-2r}.$$

In the second class, from 0 to $2r$ the particle keeps to the negative side, and between $2r$ and $2n$ it spends $2k$ time units on the positive side. Here $2k \leq 2n - 2r$ and the argument above shows that the number of paths in this class equals $2^{2n-1}f_{2r}p_{2k,2n-2r}$.

It follows that for $1 \leq k \leq n - 1$

$$(5.2) \qquad p_{2k,2n} = \tfrac{1}{2} \sum_{r=1}^{k} f_{2r}p_{2k-2r,2n-2r} + \tfrac{1}{2} \sum_{r=1}^{n-k} f_{2r}p_{2k,2n-2r}.$$

Suppose now by induction that $p_{2k,2\nu} = u_{2k}u_{2\nu-2k}$ for $\nu = 1, 2, \ldots, n-1$ (this relation being trivially true for $\nu = 1$). Then formula (5.2) reduces to

$$(5.3) \qquad p_{2k,2n} = \tfrac{1}{2} u_{2n-2k} \sum_{r=1}^{k} f_{2r}u_{2k-2r} + \tfrac{1}{2} u_{2k} \sum_{r=1}^{n-k} f_{2r}u_{2n-2k-2r}.$$

In view of equation (4.10), the first sum equals u_{2k} and the second equals u_{2n-2k} and therefore (5.1) holds.

We feel intuitively that the *fraction k/n of the total time spent on the positive side* is most likely to be close to $\tfrac{1}{2}$. However, the opposite is true: *The possible values close to $\tfrac{1}{2}$ are least probable and the extreme values $k/n = 0$ and $k/n = 1$ have the greatest probability.* This assertion can be verified using a ratio test on (5.1).

Table 1 illustrates the paradox. In betting terminology it reveals the startling fact that in $2n = 20$ tossings of a perfect coin *with proba-*

bility 0.3524 *the less fortunate player will never be in the lead.* In most cases (with probability 0.5379) the accumulated gain of the less fortunate player will be positive just once or never. By contrast, an equal division 10:10 of the leads has a probability of only 0.0606.

TABLE 1

DISTRIBUTION OF LEADS IN 20 TOSSES OF A COIN

	$k = 0$ $k = 20$	$k = 2$ $k = 18$	$k = 4$ $k = 16$	$k = 6$ $k = 14$	$k = 8$ $k = 12$	$k = 10$
$p_{k,20} =$	0.1762	0.0927	0.0736	0.0655	0.0617	0.0606
$P_{k,20} =$	0.3524	0.5379	0.6851	0.8160	0.9394	1

$p_{k,20} = u_k u_{20}$ is the probability that k sides of the path are above the axis, i.e., "Peter leads during exactly k out of the 20 trials."

$P_{k,20}$ is the probability that one of the players is in the lead for at least k trials, the other for at most $20 - k$ trials.

Formula (5.1), although exact, is not very revealing, and it is preferable to replace it by a simpler approximation. An easy application of Stirling's formula II(9.1) shows that $u_{2n}(\pi n)^{\frac{1}{2}} \to 1$ as $n \to \infty$. [This is the content of problem II(12.20).] It follows that

$$(5.4) \qquad p_{2k,2n} \sim \frac{1}{\pi k^{\frac{1}{2}}(n - k)^{\frac{1}{2}}}$$

where the ratio of the two sides tends rapidly to unity as $k \to \infty$ and $n - k \to \infty$. The probability that the fraction k/n of the time spent on the positive side lies between $\frac{1}{2}$ and α ($\frac{1}{2} < \alpha < 1$) is given by

$$(5.5) \qquad \sum_{\frac{1}{2}n < k < \alpha n} p_{2k,2n} \sim \frac{1}{\pi n} \sum_{\frac{1}{2}n < k < \alpha n} \left\{ \frac{k}{n}\left(1 - \frac{k}{n}\right) \right\}^{-\frac{1}{2}}$$

On the right side we recognize the Riemann sum approximating the integral

$$(5.6) \qquad \pi^{-1} \int_{\frac{1}{2}}^{\alpha} \frac{dx}{\{x(1 - x)\}^{\frac{1}{2}}} = 2\pi^{-1} \arcsin \alpha^{\frac{1}{2}} - \frac{1}{2}.$$

For reasons of symmetry the probability that $k/n \leq \frac{1}{2}$ tends to $\frac{1}{2}$ as $n \to \infty$. Adding this probability to (5.5), we get

Theorem 2.[7] (*The first arc sine law.*) *For fixed α $(0 < \alpha < 1)$ and $n \to \infty$ the probability that the fraction k/n of time spent on the positive side be $< \alpha$ tends to*

$$(5.7) \qquad \pi^{-1} \int_0^\alpha \frac{dx}{\{x(1-x)\}^{\frac{1}{2}}} = 2\pi^{-1} \arc\sin \alpha^{\frac{1}{2}}.$$

In practice formula (5.7) provides an excellent approximation even for values of n as small as 20. The integrand in (5.7) is represented by a U-shaped curve tending to infinity at the endpoints 0 and 1. This

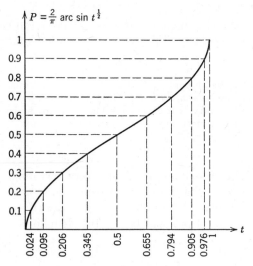

FIGURE 4.   The arc sine law.

shows in a striking fashion that the fraction of time spent on the positive side is much more likely to be close to zero or to one than to the "expected" or "normal" value $\frac{1}{2}$. Figure 4 will reveal:

---

[7] Paul Lévy (Sur certains processus stochastiques homogènes, *Compositio Mathematica*, vol. 7 (1939), pp. 283–339) found the arc sine law for certain continuous diffusion processes and referred to the connection with the coin-tossing game. A general arc sine law for the number of positive partial sums in a sequence of mutually independent random variables was proved by P. Erdös and M. Kac, On the number of positive sums of independent random variables, *Bulletin of the American Mathematical Society*, vol. 53 (1947), pp. 1011–1020. It was E. Sparre Andersen who discovered the combinatorial nature of the arc sine law and its validity for general classes of random variables.

With probability 0.20 *the particle stays for about* 97.6 *per cent of the time on the same side of the origin. In one out of* 10 *cases the particle will spend* 99.4 *per cent of the time on the same side.* Another illustration is given in table 2.

TABLE 2

ILLUSTRATING THE ARC SINE LAW

p	t_p
0.9	153.95 days
.8	126.10 days
.7	99.65 days
.6	75.23 days
.5	53.45 days
.4	34.85 days
.3	19.89 days
.2	8.93 days
.1	2.24 days
.05	13.5 hours
.02	2.16 hours
.01	32.4 minutes

A coin is tossed once per second for a total of 365 days; let **Z** be the fraction of time during which the less fortunate player is in the lead. Then t_p is a number such that the event **Z** $< t_p$ has probability p, approximately.

This table shows the probability p that the less fortunate player will be in the lead for a total of less than t_p days of a full year. Using, for example, the significance level $p = 0.05$ dear to statisticians, we see that *in one out of* 20 *cases the more fortunate player will be in the lead for more than* 364 *days and* 10 *hours.* Few people will believe that a perfect coin will produce preposterous sequences in which no change of lead occurs for millions of trials in succession, and yet this is what a good coin will do rather regularly.

In the next section we shall treat another aspect of the same phenomenon, and in section 7 we shall illustrate the theory by empirical material.

6. THE NUMBER OF RETURNS TO THE ORIGIN

The explanation of the arc sine law lies in the fact that frequently enormously many trials are required before the particle returns to the origin. Geometrically speaking, the path crosses the x-axis very rarely.

We feel intuitively that if Peter and Paul toss a coin for a long time $2n$, *the number of ties* (moments when the cumulative scores are equal) *should be roughly proportional to* $2n$. *But this is not so.* Actually the number of ties increases in probability only as $(2n)^{\frac{1}{2}}$; that is, with increasing duration of the game the frequency of ties decreases rapidly, and the "waves" increase in length. In analyzing this situation we shall consider the number of returns to zero. It should be borne in mind that the number of times when the particle actually crosses from the positive side into the negative or conversely is roughly *one-half* the number of returns.

Theorem 1. *Let $z_{2n}^{(r)}$ be the probability that up to and including time $2n$ the particle returns to zero exactly r times.   Then*

$$(6.1) \qquad z_{2n}^{(r)} = \frac{1}{2^{2n-r}} \binom{2n-r}{n}, \qquad\qquad n \geq 1.$$

In particular $z_{2n}^{(0)} = z_{2n}^{(1)} = u_{2n}$ and

$$(6.2) \qquad z_{2n}^{(0)} = z_{2n}^{(1)} > z_{2n}^{(2)} > z_{2n}^{(3)} > \dots.$$

In words (6.2) states that, *independently of the duration $2n$ of the game, it is more likely that no return or exactly one return to zero has occurred than any other number.*

Proof. We recall that by formulas (4.4) and (4.5) there exist exactly as many paths of length 2ν with no return to zero as there are paths with a return to zero at the last step.   Consider now paths of length $2n$ in which the rth *and last* return occurred at some time $2n - 2\nu < 2n$. The section of length 2ν starting at this last return can be chosen in as many ways as we can choose an alternative section starting at the same point $(2n-2\nu, 0)$ of the x-axis and leading to $(2n, 0)$.   In other words: *The probability that exactly r returns to zero occur before time $2n$ equals the probability that a return occurs at time $2n$ and that it is preceded by at least r returns.* By theorem 3 of section 4 this means that

$$(6.3) \qquad z_{2n}^{(r)} = f_{2n}^{(r)} + f_{2n}^{(r+1)} + f_{2n}^{(r+2)} + \dots.$$

with $f_{2n}^{(y)}$ given by (4.11).   It is easily verified that

$$(6.4) \qquad f_{2n}^{(y)} = \frac{1}{2^{2n-y}} \binom{2n-y}{n} - \frac{1}{2^{2n-y-1}} \binom{2n-y-1}{n},$$

and adding for $y = r, r+1, \dots$ we get equation (6.1) as asserted. The assertion (6.2) being a trivial consequence, the theorem is proved.

It is again desirable to replace the exact formula (6.1) by a simpler approximation.   For that purpose we rewrite (6.1) in the form

$$(6.5) \qquad z_{2n}^{(r)} = u_{2n} \frac{\left(1 - \frac{1}{n}\right)\left(1 - \frac{2}{n}\right) \dots \left(1 - \frac{r-1}{n}\right)}{\left(1 - \frac{1}{2n}\right)\left(1 - \frac{2}{2n}\right) \dots \left(1 - \frac{r-1}{2n}\right)}.$$

As was pointed out in the proof of the arc sine law, we have $u_{2n}(\pi n)^{\frac{1}{2}} \to 1$ as $n \to \infty$. From the Taylor expansion of the logarithm, II(8.10), we see that $\log (1 - \nu/n)$ may be approximated by $-\nu/n$ with an error of the order of magnitude $(\nu/n)^2$.   It follows that with an error of the magnitude r^3/n^2 we have the approximation

$$(6.6) \qquad \log \{z_{2n}^{(r)} \pi^{\frac{1}{2}} n^{\frac{1}{2}}\} \approx -\frac{1}{2n}\sum_{\nu=1}^{r-1} \nu \approx -\frac{r^2}{4n}$$

or

$$(6.7) \qquad z_{2n}^{(r)} \approx \pi^{-\frac{1}{2}} n^{-\frac{1}{2}} e^{-r^2/4n}.$$

The probability of fewer than k returns, namely $z_{2n}^{(0)} + z_{2n}^{(1)} + \ldots + z_{2n}^{(k-1)}$, is thus approximated by a Riemann sum to the integral over $\pi^{-1} e^{-\frac{1}{4}x^2}$ extended from 0 to k/n, the relative (or percentage) error involved being of the order of magnitude k^3/n^2. We have thus

Theorem 2. *For each fixed $\alpha > 0$ the probability that up to and including time $2n$ the particle returns to the origin fewer than $\alpha(2n)^{\frac{1}{2}}$ times tends as $n \to \infty$ to* [8]

$$(6.8) \qquad f(\alpha) = (2/\pi)^{\frac{1}{2}} \int_0^\alpha e^{-\frac{1}{2}s^2}\, ds.$$

In particular, the probability that there occur fewer than $0.6745(2n)^{\frac{1}{2}}$ returns is, for large n, approximately $\frac{1}{2}$.

In chapter VII, section 1, the reader will find a table of the normal distribution function $\Phi(\alpha) = \frac{1}{2}\{1 + f(\alpha)\}$; from it the values $f(\alpha)$ may be obtained using $f(\alpha) = 2\{\Phi(\alpha) - \frac{1}{2}\}$ for $\alpha > 0$.

Let a coin be tossed 10,000 times: with probability $\frac{1}{2}$ there will be fewer than 68 returns to zero, of which only one-half represent actual changes of the lead. In other words, with probability $\frac{1}{2}$ the mean duration of a "wave" between two consecutive changes of lead is about 300. For 1,000,000 tossings the median number of returns has increased only by a factor 10, and the *mean* duration of a wave has increased to about 3000. The longer the series of trials, the rarer the returns to zero and the longer the waves.

The probability that in 10,000 *tossings of a coin the lead never changes* is about 0.0085, and with the same probability there will be fewer than 10 changes of lead in 1,000,000 tossings.

7. AN EXPERIMENTAL ILLUSTRATION

Figure 5 represents the result of an experiment simulating 10,000 tosses of a coin; it is the material tabulated in example I(6.c). The top line contains the graph of the first 550 trials, and the next two lines represent the entire record of 10,000 trials on a smaller scale in the x-direction. The scale in the y-direction is the same on the two graphs.

When looking at the graph most people feel surprised by the length of the waves between successive crossings of the x-axis (i.e., successive changes of lead). Nevertheless, the graph represents a comparatively mild case history and was chosen as the mildest among three available records. The reader is asked to look at the *same graph in the reverse direction*, that is, to take the terminal point as origin. [Analytically, the reversed path is given by (2.2).] Theoretically, the series as graphed and the reversed series are equivalent, and each represents a

---

[8] Readers acquainted with the central limit theorem are warned that the number of returns is *not* normally distributed. In (6.8) there appears a *truncated* normal distribution with mean $(2/\pi)^{\frac{1}{2}}$ and variance $1 - 2/\pi$.

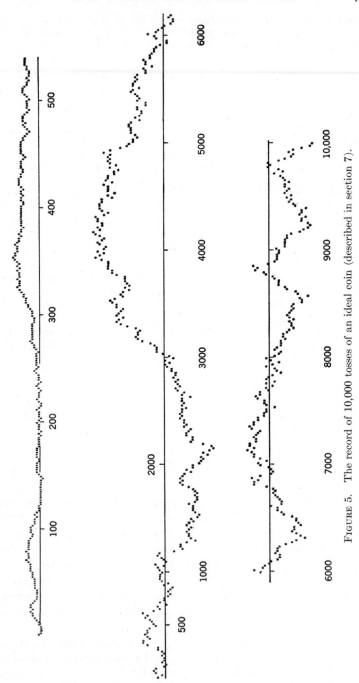

FIGURE 5.   The record of 10,000 tosses of an ideal coin (described in section 7).

random walk.   The reversed random walk has the following characteristics.   Starting from the origin

the "particle" stays at the

	negative side		*positive side*
first	7804 *steps*	*next*	8 *steps*
next	2 *steps*	*next*	54 *steps*
next	30 *steps*	*next*	2 *steps*
next	48 *steps*	*next*	6 *steps*
next	2046 *steps*		
	total of 9930 *steps*		*total of* 70 *steps*
	fraction of time: 0.9930		*fraction of time:* 0.007

This *looks* absurd, and yet the probability that in 10,000 tosses of a
perfect coin the lead is on one side for more than 9930 trials and at
the other for fewer than 70 trials is slightly greater than 0.1.   In other
words, on the average *more than one record out of ten will look worse
than the one just described*.   By contrast, the probability of a record
showing a better balance of leads than that of figure 5 is smaller,
namely about 0.072.

The record of figure 5 contains 142 returns to the origin among which
there are 78 actual changes of lead.   The reversed series described
above contains 14 returns of which 8 are changes of lead.   Sampling
of expert opinion has revealed that even trained statisticians feel that
142 equalizations in 10,000 tosses of a coin is a surprisingly small number, and 14 appears quite out of bounds.   Actually *the probability of
more than* 140 *equalizations is about* 0.157 *while the probability of fewer
than* 14 *equalizations is about* 0.115.   Thus, contrary to intuition, finding only 14 equalizations is not surprising at all; as far as the number
of changes of lead is concerned, the reversed series stands on a par with
the original series of figure 5.

8. MISCELLANEOUS COMPLEMENTS

(a) Analytical Verification of Identities

It is easily verified that

$$(8.1) \qquad u_{2n} = (-1)^n \binom{-\frac{1}{2}}{n}, \qquad f_{2n} = (-1)^{n+1} \binom{\frac{1}{2}}{n}.$$

The basic identity (4.10) can now be regarded as a special case of equa-

tion II(12.9) for $a = \frac{1}{2}$, $b = -\frac{1}{2}$. The same formula shows in addition
that $\sum\limits_{r=0}^{n} u_{2r} u_{2n-2r} = 1$.

Formula (2.8) may be rewritten in terms of f_{2k} instead of L_{2k+2} and reduces to the special case of II(12.9) for $a = b = \frac{1}{2}$. Alternatively, formula (2.8) may be derived from (4.10) using the identity $nr^{-1}(n-r)^{-1} = r^{-1} + (n-r)^{-1}$.

(b) The Position of the Maxima: The Second Arc Sine Law

We shall say that *the path* $\{s_1, s_2, \ldots, s_x\}$ *has its first maximum at the place* k *if*

$$(8.2) \qquad s_k > 0, \quad s_k > s_1, \quad \ldots, \quad s_k > s_{k-1}, \quad s_k \geq s_{k+1}, \quad \ldots, \quad s_k \geq s_x.$$

In particular, the first maximum is at the place 0 if $s_j \leq 0$ for $1 \leq j \leq x$. By formula (4.6) the probability that a path of length $x = 2n$ has its first maximum at 0 equals u_{2n}. It follows that also for a path of length $x = 2n - 1$ the probability of the first maximum at 0 equals u_{2n}.

The event "first maximum at the *last* place" is the same as $s_j < s_x$ for $j = 0, 1, \ldots, x-1$. For the reversed path (2.2) this means $s_1{}^* > 0$, $s_2{}^* > 0$, $\ldots$, $s_x{}^* > 0$, and the probability of this is given by (4.5), namely $\frac{1}{2} u_{2n}$ for $x = 2n$ and also for $x = 2n + 1$.

A path of length $2n$ with a first maximum at k consists of two sections: The initial section has its first maximum at the last, or kth, place, and the second section has its first maximum at the initial, or zero-th, place. Conversely, any two sections with the stated properties may be combined to give a path with its first maximum at the kth place. We have thus the

Theorem. *The probability that a path of length* $2n$ *has its first maximum at the place* ν *equals*

$$(8.3) \qquad \frac{1}{2} u_{2k} u_{2n-2k} \qquad \begin{array}{ll} \text{if} \quad \nu = 2k & (k = 1, 2, \ldots, n) \\ \text{or} \quad \nu = 2k + 1 & (k = 0, 1, \ldots, n-1) \end{array}$$

and u_{2n} *if* $\nu = 0$.

The remarkable fact is that *the probability of finding the first maximum at either* $2k$ *or* $2k + 1$ *equals the probability* $p_{2k,2n}$ in (5.1) that the particle spends $2k$ out of $2n$ time units on the positive side. It follows that the arc sine approximation applies and we can conclude that there is a *strong tendency for the maxima to occur near one or the other of the endpoints.*

The surprising circumstance that the probability distribution $\{p_{2k,2n}\}$ of leads and the distribution of the position of the maxima are practically the same is no peculiarity of the coin-tossing game. An analogous theorem has been proved by E. Sparre Andersen for a large class of random variables, and the combinatorial basis of his proof is similar to the argument used above.

(c) A Limit Theorem for First Passages and Returns to the Origin [9]

The estimates used in section 6 may be used to show that for fixed $y > 0$ the probability $f_{2n}^{(y)}$ of (4.11) satisfies the asymptotic relation

$$(8.4) \qquad f_{2n}^{(y)} \sim \left(\frac{2}{\pi}\right)^{\frac{1}{2}} \frac{y}{(2n - y)^{\frac{3}{2}}} e^{-\frac{1}{2}y^2/(2n - y)},$$

the sign $\sim$ indicating that the ratio of the two sides tends to unity as $n \to \infty$. The methods employed for the limit theorems in sections 5 and 6 now lead to the following conclusion: *The probability that the yth return to zero (or the first passage through y) takes place before time ty^2 tends, with increasing y, to $1 - f(t^{-\frac{1}{2}})$ with $f(\alpha)$ defined in equation (6.8).*

It follows that *with probability near $\frac{1}{2}$ the yth return to zero will occur after time* $(2.21 \ldots)y^2$, so that *the average time between consecutive returns is bound to increase roughly linearly with y*. This should come as a surprise to physicists accustomed to taking the average of y "measurements on the same quantity" as approximation to the "true" value. In the present case a closer analysis reveals that in all likelihood one among the y measurements will be of the same order of magnitude as the whole sum, namely y^2.

---

[9] This is theorem 3 of chapter XII, section 5, in the first edition. Advanced readers are advised that $1 - f(t^{-\frac{1}{2}})$ is the so-called positive stable distribution of order $\frac{1}{2}$.

CHAPTER IV

Combination of Events

This chapter is concerned with events which are defined in terms of certain other events A_1, A_2, ..., A_N. Thus in bridge the event A, "at least one player has a complete suit," is the union of the four events A_k, "player number k has a complete suit" ($k = 1$, 2, 3, 4). Of the events A_k one, two, or more can occur simultaneously, and, because of this overlap, the probability of A is not the sum of the four probabilities $\mathbf{P}\{A_k\}$. Given a set of events A_1, ..., A_N, we shall show how to compute the probabilities that 0, 1, 2, 3, ... among them occur.

The material of this chapter is covered in a monograph by M. Fréchet,[1] to which the reader is referred for further information.

1. UNION OF EVENTS

If A_1 and A_2 are two events, then $A = A_1 \cup A_2$ denotes the event that either A_1 or A_2 or both occur. By formula I (7.4) we have

(1.1) $$\mathbf{P}\{A\} = \mathbf{P}\{A_1\} + \mathbf{P}\{A_2\} - \mathbf{P}\{A_1 A_2\}.$$

We want to generalize this formula to the case of N events A_1, A_2, ..., A_N; that is, we wish to compute the probability of the event that at least one among the A_k occurs. In symbols this event is $A = A_1 \cup A_2 \cup \ldots \cup A_N$. For our purpose it is not sufficient to know the probabilities of the individual events A_k, but we must be given complete information concerning all possible overlaps. This means that for every pair (i, j), every triple (i, j, k), etc., we must know the probability of A_i and A_j, or A_i, A_j, and A_k, etc., occurring simultaneously. For convenience of notation we shall denote these

---

* The material of this chapter will not be used explicitly in the sequel. Only the first theorem is of considerable importance.

[1] Les probabilités associées à un système d'événements compatibles et dépendants, *Actualités scientifiques et industrielles*, nos. 859 and 942, Paris, 1940 and 1943.

probabilities by the letter p with appropriate subscripts. Thus

(1.2) $p_i = \mathbf{P}\{A_i\}$, $p_{i,j} = \mathbf{P}\{A_iA_j\}$, $p_{i,j,k} = \mathbf{P}\{A_iA_jA_k\}$, ...

The order of the subscripts is irrelevant, but for uniqueness we shall always *write the subscripts in increasing order;* thus, we write $p_{3,7,11}$ and not $p_{7,3,11}$. Two subscripts are never equal. For the sum of all p's with r subscripts we shall write S_r, that is, we define

(1.3) $S_1 = \Sigma p_i$, $S_2 = \Sigma p_{i,j}$, $S_3 = \Sigma p_{i,j,k}$, ...

Here $i < j < k < \ldots \leq N$, so that in the sums each combination appears once and only once; hence S_r has $\binom{N}{r}$ terms. The last sum, S_N, reduces to the single term $p_{1,2,3,\ldots,N}$, which is the probability of the simultaneous realization of all N events. For $N = 2$ we have only the two terms S_1 and S_2, and formula (1.1) can be written

(1.4) $\mathbf{P}\{A\} = S_1 - S_2$.

The generalization to an arbitrary number N of events is given in the following

Theorem. *The probability P_1 of the realization of at least one among the events $A_1, A_2, \ldots, A_N$ is given by*

(1.5) $P_1 = S_1 - S_2 + S_3 - S_4 + - \ldots \pm S_N$.

Proof. We prove (1.5) by the so-called method of inclusion and exclusion (cf. problem 26). To compute P_1 we should add the probabilities of all sample points which are contained in at least one of the A_i, but each point should be taken only once. To proceed systematically we first take the points which are contained in only one A_i, then those contained in exactly two events A_i, and so forth, and finally the points (if any) contained in all A_i. Now let E be any sample point contained in exactly n among our N events A_i. Without loss of generality we may number the events so that E is contained in $A_1, A_2, \ldots, A_n$ but not contained in $A_{n+1}, A_{n+2}, \ldots, A_N$. Then $\mathbf{P}\{E\}$ appears as a contribution to those $p_i, p_{ij}, p_{ijk}, \ldots$ whose subscripts range from 1 to n. Hence $\mathbf{P}\{E\}$ appears n times as a contribution to S_1, and $\binom{n}{2}$ times as a contribution to S_2, etc. In all, when the right-hand side of (1.5) is expressed in terms of the probabilities of sample points we find $\mathbf{P}\{E\}$ with the factor

(1.6) $n - \binom{n}{2} + \binom{n}{3} - + \ldots \pm \binom{n}{n}$.

To prove the theorem we have to show that this number equals 1. This follows at once on comparing (1.6) with the binomial expansion of $(1 - 1)^n$ [cf. formula II(8.7)]. The latter starts with 1, and the terms of (1.6) follow with reversed sign. Hence for every $n \geq 1$ the expression (1.6) equals 1, and this proves the theorem.

Examples. (a) In a game of bridge let A_i be the event "player number i has a complete suit." Then $p_i = 4/\binom{52}{13}$; the event that both player i and player j have complete suits can occur in $4 \cdot 3$ ways and has probability $p_{i,j} = 12/\binom{52}{13}\binom{39}{13}$; similarly we find

$$p_{i,j,k} = 24/\binom{52}{13}\binom{39}{13}\binom{26}{13}.$$

Finally, $p_{1,2,3,4} = p_{1,2,3}$, since whenever three players have a complete suit so does the fourth. The probability that *some* player has a complete suit is therefore $P_1 = 4p_1 - 6p_{1,2} + 4p_{1,2,3} - p_{1,2,3,4}$. Using Stirling's formula, we see that $P_1 = \frac{1}{4} 10^{-10}$ approximately. In this particular case P_1 is very nearly the sum of the probabilities of A_i, but this is the exception rather than the rule.

(b) *Matches (coincidences).* The following problem with many variants and a surprising solution goes back to Montmort (1708). It has been generalized by Laplace and many other authors.

Two equivalent decks of N different cards each are put into random order and matched against each other. If a card occupies the same place in both decks, we speak of a *match* (*coincidence* or *rencontre*). Matches may occur at any of the N places and at several places simultaneously. This experiment may be described in more amusing forms. For example, the two decks may be represented by a set of N letters and their envelopes, and a capricious secretary may perform the random matching. Alternatively we may imagine the hats in a checkroom mixed and distributed at random to the guests. A match occurs if a person gets his own hat. It is instructive to venture guesses as to how the probability of a match depends on N: How does the probability of a match of hats in a diner with 8 guests compare with the corresponding probability at a gathering of 10,000 people? It seems surprising that the probability is practically independent of N and roughly $\frac{2}{3}$. (For less frivolous applications cf. problems 10 and 11.)

The probabilities of having exactly 0, 1, 2, 3, ... matches will be calculated in section 4. Here we shall derive only the probability P_1 of at least 1 match. For simplicity of expression let us renumber the cards $1, 2, \ldots, N$ in such a way that one deck appears in its natural order, and assume that each permutation of the second deck has probability $1/N!$. Let A_k be the event that a match occurs at the kth place. This means that card number k is at the kth place, and the remaining $N - 1$ cards may be in an arbitrary order. Clearly $p_k = (N - 1)!/N! = 1/N$. Similarly, for every combination i, j, we have $p_{i,j} = (N - 2)!/N! = 1/N(N - 1)$, etc. The sum S_r contains $\binom{N}{r}$ terms, each of which equals $(N - r)!/N!$. Hence $S_r = 1/r!$, and from (1.5) we find the required probability to be

$$(1.7) \qquad P_1 = 1 - \frac{1}{2!} + \frac{1}{3!} - + \ldots \pm \frac{1}{N!}.$$

Note that $1 - P_1$ represents the first $N + 1$ terms in the expansion

$$(1.8) \qquad e^{-1} = 1 - 1 + \frac{1}{2!} - \frac{1}{3!} + \frac{1}{4!} - + \ldots.$$

Therefore we have with a good approximation

$$(1.9) \qquad P_1 \approx 1 - e^{-1} = 0.63212\ldots.$$

The degree of approximation is shown in the following table of correct values of P_1:

$N =$	3	4	5	6	7
$P_1 =$	0.66667	0.62500	0.63333	0.63196	0.63214

2. APPLICATION TO THE CLASSICAL OCCUPANCY PROBLEM

We now return to the problem of a random distribution of r balls in n cells, assuming that each arrangement has probability n^{-r}. We seek the probability $p_m(r, n)$ of finding exactly m cells empty.[2]

Let A_k be the event that cell number k is empty $(k = 1, 2, \ldots, n)$. In this event all r balls are placed in the remaining $n - 1$ cells, and this can be done in $(n - 1)^r$ different ways. Similarly, there are $(n - 2)^r$ arrangements, leaving two preassigned cells empty, etc. Accordingly

$$(2.1) \quad p_i = \left(1 - \frac{1}{n}\right)^r, \quad p_{ij} = \left(1 - \frac{2}{n}\right)^r, \quad p_{ijk} = \left(1 - \frac{3}{n}\right)^r, \ldots$$

---

[2] This probability has been derived, by an entirely different method, in problem II (11.8). Compare also the example in section 3.

and hence for every $\nu \le n$

$$(2.2) \qquad S_\nu = \binom{n}{\nu}\left(1 - \frac{\nu}{n}\right)^r.$$

The probability that at least one cell is empty is given by (1.5), and hence the *probability that all cells are occupied is* $1 - S_1 + S_2 - + \ldots$ or

$$(2.3) \qquad p_0(r, n) = \sum_{\nu=0}^{n} (-1)^\nu \binom{n}{\nu}\left(1 - \frac{\nu}{n}\right)^r.$$

Consider now a distribution in which exactly m cells are empty. These m cells can be chosen in $\binom{n}{m}$ ways. The r balls are distributed among the remaining $n - m$ cells so that each of these cells is occupied; the number of such distributions is $(n - m)^r p_0(r, n-m)$. Dividing by n^r we find for the *probability that exactly* m *cells remain empty*

$$(2.4) \qquad p_m(r, n) = \binom{n}{m}\left(1 - \frac{m}{n}\right)^r p_0(r, n-m) =$$

$$= \binom{n}{m}\sum_{\nu=0}^{n-m}(-1)^\nu \binom{n-m}{\nu}\left(1 - \frac{m+\nu}{n}\right)^r.$$

We have already used the model of r random digits to illustrate the random distribution of r things in $n = 10$ cells. Empty cells correspond in this case to missing digits: if m cells are empty, $10 - m$ different digits appear in the given sequence. Table 1 provides a numerical illustration.

TABLE 1

PROBABILITIES $p_m(r, 10)$ ACCORDING TO (2.4)

m	$r = 10$	$r = 18$
0	0.000 363	0.134 673
1	.016 330	.385 289
2	.136 080	.342 987
3	.355 622	.119 425
4	.345 144	.016 736
5	.128 596	.000 876
6	.017 189	.000 014
7	.000 672	.000 000
8	.000 005	.000 000
9	.000 000	.000 000

$p_m(r, 10)$ is the probability that exactly m of the digits $0, 1, \ldots, 9$ will *not* appear in a sequence of r random digits.

It is clear that a direct numerical evaluation of (2.4) is limited to the case of relatively small n and r. On the other hand, the occupancy problem is of particular interest when n is large. If 10,000 balls are distributed in 1000 cells, is there any chance of finding an empty cell? In a group of 2000 people, is there any chance of finding a day in the year which is not a birthday? Fortunately, questions of this kind can be answered by means of a remarkably simple approximation with an error which tends to zero as $n \to \infty$. This approximation and the argument leading to it are typical of many *limit theorems* in probability.

Our purpose, then, is to discuss the limiting form of the formula (2.4) as $n \to \infty$ and $r \to \infty$. The relation between r and n is, in principle, arbitrary. However, the ratio r/n represents the average number of things per cell. If it is excessively large, then we cannot expect any empty cells; in this case $p_0(r, n)$ is near unity and all $p_m(r, n)$ with $m \geq 1$ are small. On the other hand, if r/n tends to zero, then practically all cells must be empty, and in this case $p_m(r, n) \to 0$ for every fixed m. Therefore only the intermediate case is of real interest.

We begin by estimating the quantity S_ν of formula (2.2). Since $(n - \nu)^\nu < (n)_\nu < n^\nu$, we have clearly

$$(2.5) \qquad n^\nu \left(1 - \frac{\nu}{n} \right)^{\nu + r} < \nu! S_\nu < n^\nu \left(1 - \frac{\nu}{n} \right)^r.$$

Using the double inequality II(8.12) with $t = \nu/n$, we get

$$(2.6) \qquad \{ ne^{-(\nu+r)/(n-\nu)} \}^\nu < \nu! S_\nu < \{ ne^{-r/n} \}^\nu.$$

Now put for abbreviation

$$(2.7) \qquad ne^{-r/n} = \lambda$$

and suppose that r and n increase in such a way that λ *remains bounded*. Then, for each fixed ν, the ratio of the extreme members in (2.6) tends to unity, and we conclude that

$$(2.8) \qquad S_\nu < \frac{\lambda^\nu}{\nu!} \quad \text{and} \quad \frac{1}{\nu!} \lambda^\nu - S_\nu \to 0.$$

It follows that

$$(2.9) \qquad p_0(r, n) - \sum_{\nu=0}^{\infty} (-1)^\nu \frac{\lambda^\nu}{\nu!} \to 0$$

or $p_0(r, n) - e^{-\lambda} \to 0$. Now the factor of $p_0(r, n-m)$ in (2.4) may be rewritten as S_m, and we have therefore for each fixed m

$$(2.10) \qquad\qquad p_m(r, n) - e^{-\lambda} \frac{\lambda^m}{m!} \to 0.$$

This completes the proof of the

Theorem.[3] *If n and r tend to infinity so that $\lambda = ne^{-r/n}$ remains bounded, then* (2.10) *holds for each fixed m.*

The approximating expressions

$$(2.11) \qquad\qquad p(m; \lambda) = e^{-\lambda} \frac{\lambda^m}{m!}$$

define the so-called *Poisson distribution,* which is of great importance and describes a variety of phenomena; it will be studied in chapter VI.

In practice we may use $p(m; \lambda)$ as an approximation whenever n is great. For moderate values of n an estimate of the error is required, but we shall not enter into it.

Examples. (*a*) Table 2 gives the approximate probabilities of finding m cells empty when the number of cells is 1000 and the number of balls varies from 5000 to 9000. For $r = 5000$ the median value of the number of empty cells is six: seven or more empty cells are about as probable as six or fewer. Even with 9000 balls in 1000 cells we have about one chance in nine to find an empty cell.

(*b*) In birthday statistics [example II(3.*d*)] $n = 365$, and r is the number of people. For $r = 1900$ we find $\lambda = 2$, approximately. *In a village of 1900 people the probabilities $P_{[m]}$ of finding m days of the year which are not birthdays are approximately as follows:*

$$P_{[0]} = 0.135, \quad P_{[1]} = 0.271, \quad P_{[2]} = 0.271, \quad P_{[3]} = 0.180,$$

$$P_{[4]} = 0.090, \quad P_{[5]} = 0.036, \quad P_{[6]} = 0.012, \quad P_{[7]} = 0.003.$$

The probability of finding exactly m cells each containing exactly k balls can be derived in the same way. As von Mises has shown, this probability can again be approximated by the Poisson expression (2.11), only this time λ must be defined by

$$(2.12) \qquad\qquad \lambda = ne^{-r/n} \left(\frac{r}{n}\right)^k /k!.$$

---

[3] Due (with a different proof) to R. von Mises, Über Aufteilungs- und Besetzungs-wahrscheinlichkeiten, *Revue de la Faculté des Sciences de l'Université d'Istanbul,* N.S., vol. 4 (1939), pp. 145–163.

TABLE 2

POISSON APPROXIMATION (2.11) TO THE PROBABILITIES OF FINDING EXACTLY m EMPTY CELLS WHEN r BALLS ARE RANDOMLY DISTRIBUTED IN $n = 1000$ CELLS

$p(m; \lambda)$

r	λ	$m = 0$	$m = 1$	$m = 2$	$m = 3$	$m = 4$	$m = 5$	$m = 6$	$m = 7$	$m = 8$	$m = 9$	$m = 10$	$m = 11$
5000	6.74	0.0012	0.0080	0.0269	0.0604	0.1017	0.1371	0.1540	0.1482	0.1249	0.0935	0.0630	0.0386
5500	4.09	.0167	.0685	.1400	.1909	.1951	.1596	.1088	.0636	.0325	.0148	.0060	.0023
6000	2.48	.0838	.2077	.2575	.2128	.1320	.0655	.0271	.0096	.0030	.0008	.0002	
6500	1.50	.2231	.3347	.2510	.1255	.0471	.0141	.0035	.0008	.0001			
7000	0.91	.4027	.3661	.1666	.0506	.0115	.0021	.0003					
7500	0.55	.5777	.3163	.0873	.0162	.0023	.0003						
8000	0.34	.7126	.2406	.0414	.0049	.0004							
8500	0.20	.8187	.1637	.0164	.0011	.0001							
9000	0.12	.8869	.1064	.0064	.0003								

3. THE REALIZATION OF *m* AMONG *N* EVENTS

The theorem of section 1 can be strengthened as follows.

Theorem. *For any integer m with $1 \leq m \leq N$ the probability $P_{[m]}$ that exactly m among the N events $A_1, \ldots, A_N$ occur simultaneously is given by*

$$(3.1) \quad P_{[m]} = S_m - \binom{m+1}{m} S_{m+1} +$$

$$+ \binom{m+2}{m} S_{m+2} - + \ldots \pm \binom{N}{m} S_N.$$

Note: According to (1.5), the probability $P_{[0]}$ that none among the A_j occurs is

$$(3.2) \qquad P_{[0]} = 1 - P_1 = 1 - S_1 + S_2 - S_3 \pm \ldots \mp S_N.$$

This shows that (3.1) gives the correct value also for $m = 0$ provided we put $S_0 = 1$.

Proof. We proceed as in the proof of (1.5). Let E be an arbitrary sample point, and suppose that it is contained in exactly n among the N events A_j. Then $\mathbf{P}\{E\}$ appears as a contribution to $P_{[m]}$ only if $n = m$. To investigate how $\mathbf{P}\{E\}$ contributes to the right side of (3.1), note that $\mathbf{P}\{E\}$ appears in the sums $S_1, S_2, \ldots, S_n$ but not in $S_{n+1}, \ldots, S_N$. It follows that $\mathbf{P}\{E\}$ does not contribute to the right side in (3.1) if $n < m$. If $n = m$, then $\mathbf{P}\{E\}$ appears in one and only one term of S_m. To complete the proof of the theorem it remains to show that for $n > m$ the contributions of $\mathbf{P}\{E\}$ to the terms $S_m, S_{m+1}, \ldots, S_n$ on the right in (3.1) cancel. Now out of the n events containing E we can form $\binom{n}{k}$ k-tuplets; hence $\mathbf{P}\{E\}$ appears in S_k with the factor $\binom{n}{k}$. For $n > m$ the total contribution of $\mathbf{P}\{E\}$ to the right side in (3.1) is therefore

$$(3.3) \quad \binom{n}{m} - \binom{m+1}{m}\binom{n}{m+1} + \binom{m+2}{m}\binom{n}{m+2} - + \ldots.$$

However, $\binom{m+\nu}{m}\binom{n}{m+\nu} = \binom{n}{m}\binom{n-m}{\nu}$, and hence (3.3) reduces to

$$(3.4) \quad \binom{n}{m}\left\{\binom{n-m}{0} - \binom{n-m}{1} + - \ldots \pm \binom{n-m}{n-m}\right\}.$$

Within the braces we have the binomial expansion of $(1 - 1)^{n-m}$ so that (3.3) vanishes, as asserted.

Example. The reader is asked to verify that a substitution from formula (2.2) into (3.1) leads *directly* to formula (2.4).

4. APPLICATION TO MATCHING AND GUESSING

In example (1.b) we considered the matching of two decks of cards and found that $S_k = 1/k!$. Substituting into (3.1), we find the following result.

In a random matching of two equivalent decks of N distinct cards the probability $P_{[m]}$ of having exactly m matches is given by

$$P_{[0]} = 1 - 1 + \frac{1}{2!} - \frac{1}{3!} + - \ldots \pm \frac{1}{(N-2)!} \mp \frac{1}{(N-1)!} \pm \frac{1}{N!}$$

$$(4.1) \quad P_{[1]} = 1 - 1 + \frac{1}{2!} - \frac{1}{3!} + - \ldots \pm \frac{1}{(N-2)!} \mp \frac{1}{(N-1)!}$$

$$P_{[2]} = \frac{1}{2!}\left\{1 - 1 + \frac{1}{2!} - \frac{1}{3!} + - \ldots \pm \frac{1}{(N-3)!} \mp \frac{1}{(N-2)!}\right\}$$

$$P_{[3]} = \frac{1}{3!}\left\{1 - 1 + \frac{1}{2!} - \frac{1}{3!} + - \ldots \pm \frac{1}{(N-3)!}\right\}$$

$$\cdots \cdots \cdots \cdots \cdots \cdots \cdots \cdots$$

$$\cdots \cdots \cdots \cdots \cdots \cdots \cdots \cdots$$

$$P_{[N-2]} = \frac{1}{(N-2)!}\left\{1 - 1 + \frac{1}{2!}\right\}$$

$$P_{[N-1]} = \frac{1}{(N-1)!}\{1 - 1\} = 0 \qquad P_{[N]} = \frac{1}{N!}.$$

The last relation is obvious. The vanishing of $P_{[N-1]}$ expresses the impossibility of having $N - 1$ matches without having all N cards in the same order.

The braces on the right in (4.1) contain the initial terms of the expansion of e^{-1}. *For large N we have therefore approximately*

$$(4.2) \qquad\qquad P_{[m]} \approx \frac{1}{m!} e^{-1}.$$

Table 3

Probabilities of m Correct Guesses in Calling a Deck of N Distinct Cards

	N = 3		N = 4		N = 5		N = 6		N = 10		p_m
	$P_{[m]}$	b_m	$P_{[m]}$	b_m	$P_{[m]}$	b_m	$P_{[m]}$	b_m	$P_{[m]}$	b_m	
0	0.333	0.296	0.375	0.316	0.367	0.328	0.368	0.335	0.36788	0.34868	0.367879
1	.500	.444	.333	.422	.375	.410	.367	.402	.36788	.38742	.367879
2	...	.222	.250	.211	.167	.205	.187	.201	.18394	.19371	.183940
3	.167	.037	...	.047	.083	.051	.056	.053	.06131	.05740	.061313
4			.042	.004	...	.006	.021	.008	.01534	.01116	.015328
5					.008	.000	...	.001	.00306	.00149	.003066
6							.001	.000	.00052	.00014	.000511
7									.00007	.00001	.000073
8									.00001	.....	.000009
9									.....	.....	.000001
10									.....	.....	.000000

The $P_{[m]}$ are given by (4.1), the b_m by (4.4). The last column gives the Poisson limits (4.3).

In table 3 the columns headed $P_{[m]}$ give the exact values of $P_{[m]}$ for $N = 3, 4, 5, 6, 10$. The last column gives the limiting values

$$(4.3) \qquad p_m = \frac{e^{-1}}{m!}.$$

The approximation of p_m to $P_{[m]}$ is rather good even for moderate values of N.

For the numbers p_m defined by (4.3) we have $\Sigma p_k = e^{-1}(1 + 1 + \frac{1}{2!} + \frac{1}{3!} + \ldots) = e^{-1}e = 1$. Accordingly, the p_k may be interpreted as probabilities. Note that (4.3) represents the special case $\lambda = 1$ of the *Poisson distribution* (2.11).

Formulas (4.1) are useful in testing *guessing abilities*. In wine tasting, psychic experiments, etc., the subject is asked to call an unknown order of N things, say, cards. Any actual insight on the part of the subject will appear as a departure from randomness. To judge the amount of insight we must appraise the probability of turns of good luck. Now chance guesses can be made according to several systems among which we mention three extreme possibilities. (1) The subject sticks to one card and keeps calling it. With this system he is sure to have one, and only one, correct guess in each series; chance fluctuations are eliminated. (2) The subject calls each card once so that each series of N guesses corresponds to a rearrangement of the deck. If this system is applied without insight, formulas (4.1) should apply. (3) A third possibility is that N guesses are made absolutely independently of each other. There are N^N possible arrangements. It is true that every person has fixed mental habits and is prone to call certain patterns more frequently than others, but in first approximation we may assume all N^N arrangements to be equally probable. Since m correct and $N - m$ incorrect guesses can be arranged in $\binom{N}{m}(N - 1)^{N-m}$ different ways, the probability of exactly m correct guesses is now

$$(4.4) \qquad b_m = \binom{N}{m}\frac{(N - 1)^{N-m}}{N^N}.$$

[This is a special case of the binomial distribution and has been derived in example II(4.c).]

Table 3 gives a comparison of the probabilities of success when guesses are made in accordance with system (2) or (3). To judge the merits of the two methods we require the theory of mean values and probable fluctuations. It turns out that the average number of correct chance guesses is one under all systems; the chance fluctuations are somewhat larger under system (2) than (3). A glance at table 3 will show that in practice the differences will not be excessive.

5. MISCELLANY

(a) The Realization of at Least m Events

With the notations of section 3 *the probability P_m that m or more of the events $A_1, \ldots, A_N$ occur simultaneously is given by*

$$(5.1) \qquad P_m = P_{[m]} + P_{[m+1]} + \ldots + P_{[N]}.$$

To find a formula for P_m in terms of S_k it is simplest to proceed by induction, starting with formula (1.5) and using the recurrence relation $P_{m+1} = P_m - P_{[m]}$. We get for $m \geq 1$

$$(5.2) \quad P_m = S_m - \binom{m}{m-1}S_{m+1} +$$

$$+ \binom{m+1}{m-1}S_{m+2} - \binom{m+2}{m-1}S_{m+3} + \ldots \pm \binom{N-1}{m-1}S_N.$$

It is also possible to derive (5.2) directly, using the argument which led to (3.1).

(b) Further Identities

The coefficients S_ν can be expressed in terms of either $P_{[k]}$ or P_k as follows

$$(5.3) \qquad S_\nu = \sum_{k=\nu}^{N} \binom{k}{\nu} P_{[k]}$$

and

$$(5.4) \qquad S_\nu = \sum_{k=\nu}^{N} \binom{k-1}{\nu-1} P_k.$$

Indication of proof. For given values of $P_{[m]}$ the equations (3.1) may be taken as linear equations in the unknowns S_ν, and we have to prove that (5.3) represents the unique solution. If (5.3) is introduced into the expression (3.1) for $P_{[m]}$, the coefficient of $P_{[k]}$ ($m \leq k \leq N$) to the right is found to be

$$(5.5) \quad \sum_{\nu=m}^{k} (-1)^{\nu-m} \binom{\nu}{m}\binom{k}{\nu} = \binom{k}{m} \sum_{\nu=m}^{k} (-1)^{\nu-m} \binom{k-m}{\nu-m}.$$

If $k = m$ this expression reduces to 1. If $k > m$ the sum is the binomial expansion of $(1-1)^{k-m}$ and therefore vanishes. Hence the substitution (5.3) reduces (3.1) to the identity $P_{[m]} = P_{[m]}$. The uniqueness of the solution of (3.1) follows from the fact that each equation introduces only one new unknown, so that the S_ν can be computed recursively. The truth of (5.4) can be proved in a similar way.

(c) Bonferroni's Inequalities

A string of inequalities both for $P_{[m]}$ and for P_m can be obtained in the following way. *If in either (3.1) or (5.2) only the terms involving S_m, S_{m+1}, ..., S_{m+r-1} are retained while the terms involving S_{m+r}, S_{m+r+1}, ..., S_N are dropped, then the error (i.e., true value minus approximation) has the sign of the first omitted term [namely, $(-1)^r$] and is smaller in absolute value.* Thus, for $r = 1$ and $r = 2$:

$$(5.6) \qquad S_m - (m+1)S_{m+1} \leq P_{[m]} \leq S_m$$

and

$$(5.7) \qquad S_m - mS_{m+1} \leq P_m \leq S_m.$$

Indication of proof. To prove the statement for (3.1) it must be shown that

(5.8) $$\sum_{\nu=t}^{N} (-1)^{\nu-t} \binom{\nu}{m} S_\nu \geq 0,$$

for every t. Now use (5.3) to write the left side as a linear combination of the $P_{[k]}$. For $t \leq k \leq N$ the coefficient of $P_{[k]}$ equals

$$\sum_{\nu=t}^{k} (-1)^{\nu-t} \binom{\nu}{m}\binom{k}{\nu} = \binom{k}{m} \sum_{\nu=t}^{k} (-1)^{\nu-t} \binom{k-m}{\nu-m}.$$

The last sum equals $\binom{k-m-1}{t-m-1}$ and is therefore positive [problem II(12.13)]. For further inequalities the reader is referred to Fréchet's monograph cited at the beginning of the chapter.

6. PROBLEMS FOR SOLUTION

Note: *Assume in each case that all possible arrangements have the same probability.*

1. Ten pairs of shoes are in a closet. Four shoes are selected at random. Find the probability that there will be at least one pair among the four shoes selected.

2. Five dice are thrown. Find the probability that at least three of them show the same face. (Verify by the methods of chapter II, section 5.)

3. Find the probability that in five tossings a coin falls heads at least three times in succession.

4. Solve problem 3 for a head-run of at least length five in ten tossings.

5. Solve problems 3 and 4 for ace runs when a die is used instead of a coin.

6. Two dice are thrown r times. Find the probability p_r that each of the six combinations $(1, 1), \ldots, (6, 6)$ appears at least once.

7. *Quadruples in a bridge hand.* By a quadruple we shall understand four cards of the same face value, so that a bridge hand of thirteen cards may contain 0, 1, 2, or 3 quadruples. Calculate the corresponding probabilities.

8. *Sampling with replacement.* A sample of size r is taken from a population of n people. Find the probability u_r that N given people will all be included in the sample. [This is problem II(11.12).]

9. *Sampling without replacement.* Answer problem 8 for this case and show that 8 holds with $u_r \to p^N$. (This is problem II(11.3), but the present method leads to an entirely different formula.)

10. In the general expansion of a determinant of order N the number of terms containing one or more diagonal elements is $N!P_1$ with P_1 defined by (1.7).

11. The number of ways in which 8 rooks can be placed on a chessboard so that none can take another and that none stands on the white diagonal is $8!(1 - P_1)$, where P_1 is defined by (1.7) with $N = 8$.

12. *A sampling (coupon collector's) problem.* A pack of cards consists of s identical series, each containing n cards numbered 1, 2, ..., n. A random sample of $r \geq n$ cards is drawn from the pack without replacement. Calculate the probability u_r that each number is represented in the sample. (Applied to a deck of bridge cards we get for $s = 4$, $n = 13$ the probability that a hand of r cards contains all 13 values; and for $s = 13$, $n = 4$ we get the probability that all four suits are represented.)

13. *Continuation.* Show that as $s \to \infty$ one has $u_r \to p_0(r, n)$ where the latter expression is defined in (2.3). This means that in the limit our sampling becomes random sampling with replacement from the population of the numbers 1, 2, ..., n.

14. *Continuation.* From the result of problem 12 conclude that

$$\sum_{k=0}^{n} (-1)^k \binom{n}{k} (ns - ks)_r = 0$$

if $r < n$ and for $r = n$

$$\sum_{k=0}^{n} (-1)^k \binom{n}{k} (ns - ks)_n = s^n n!.$$

Verify this by evaluating the rth derivative, at $x = 0$, of

$$\frac{1}{(1 - x)^{ns - r + 1}} \{1 - (1 - x)^s\}^n.$$

15. In the sampling problem 12 find the probability that it will take exactly r drawings to get a sample containing all numbers. Pass to the limit as $s \to \infty$.

16. A cell contains N chromosomes, between any two of which an interchange of parts may occur. If r interchanges occur (which can happen in $\binom{N}{2}^r$ distinct ways), find the probability that exactly m chromosomes will be involved.[4]

17. Find the probability that exactly k suits will be missing in a poker hand.

18. Find the probability that a hand of thirteen bridge cards contains the ace-king pairs of exactly k suits.

19. *Multiple matching.* Two similar decks of N distinct cards each are matched simultaneously against a similar target deck. Find the probability u_m of having exactly m double matches. Show that $u_0 \to 1$ as $N \to \infty$ (which implies that $u_m \to 0$ for $m \geq 1$).

20. *Multiple matching.* The procedure of the preceding problem is modified as follows. Out of the $2N$ cards N are chosen at random, and only these N are matched against the target deck. Find the probability of no match. Prove that it tends to $1/e$ as $N \to \infty$.

21. *Multiple matching.* Answer problem 20 if r decks are used instead of two.

---

[4] For $N = 6$ see D. G. Catcheside, D. E. Lea, and J. M. Thoday, Types of chromosome structural change introduced by the irradiation of *tradescantia* microspores, *Journal of Genetics*, vol. 47 (1945–46), pp. 113–149.

22. In the classical occupancy problem, the probability $P_{[m]}(k)$ of finding exactly m cells occupied by exactly k things is

$$P_{[m]}(k) = \frac{(-1)^m n!r!}{m!n^r} \sum_j (-1)^j \frac{(n-j)^{r-jk}}{(j-m)!(n-j)!(r-jk)!(k!)^j},$$

the summation extending over those $j \geq m$ for which $j \leq n$ and $kj \leq r$.

23. Prove the last statement of section 2 for the case $k = 1$.

24. Using (3.1), derive the probability of finding exactly m empty cells in the case of Bose-Einstein statistics.

25. Verify that the formula obtained in 24 checks with formula II(11.14).

26. Prove formula (1.5) by induction on N.

CHAPTER V

Conditional Probability.
Stochastic Independence

1. CONDITIONAL PROBABILITY

The notion of conditional probability is a basic tool of probability theory, and it is unfortunate that its great simplicity is somewhat obscured by a singularly clumsy terminology. The following considerations lead in a natural way to the formal definition.

Preparatory Examples

Suppose a population of N people includes N_A colorblind people and N_H females. Let the events that a person chosen at random is colorblind and a female be A and H, respectively. Then (cf. the definition of random choice, chapter II, section 2)

$$(1.1) \qquad \mathbf{P}\{A\} = \frac{N_A}{N}, \qquad \mathbf{P}\{H\} = \frac{N_H}{N}.$$

Instead of the entire population, we may investigate the female subpopulation and require the probability that a female chosen at random be colorblind. This probability is N_{HA}/N_H, where N_{HA} is the number of colorblind females. We have here no new notion, but we need a new notation to designate which particular subpopulation is under investigation. The most widely adopted symbol is $\mathbf{P}\{A \mid H\}$; it may be read "the probability of the event A (colorblindness), assuming the event H (that the person chosen is female)." In symbols:

$$(1.2) \qquad \mathbf{P}\{A \mid H\} = \frac{N_{AH}}{N_H} = \frac{\mathbf{P}\{AH\}}{\mathbf{P}\{H\}}.$$

Obviously every subpopulation may be considered as a population in its own right; we speak of a subpopulation merely for convenience of language to indicate that we have a larger population in the back of our minds. An insurance company may be interested in the frequency of damages of a fixed amount caused by lightning (event A). Presumably this company has several categories of insured objects such as industrial, urban, rural, etc. Studying separately the damages to industrial objects means to study the event A only in conjunction with the event H—"Damage is to an industrial object." Formula (1.2) again applies in an obvious manner. Note, however, that for an insurance company specializing in industrial objects the category H coincides with the whole sample space, and $\mathbf{P}\{A\,|\,H\}$ reduces to $\mathbf{P}\{A\}$.

Finally consider the bridge player North. Once the cards are dealt, he knows his hand and is interested only in the distribution of the remaining 39 cards. It is legitimate to introduce the aggregate of all possible distributions of these 39 cards as a new sample space, but it is obviously more convenient to consider them in conjunction with the 13 cards in North's hand (event H) and to speak of the probability of an event A (say South's having two aces) assuming the event H. Formula (1.2) again applies.

By analogy with (1.2) we now introduce the formal

Definition. *Let H be an event with positive probability. For an arbitrary event A we shall write*

$$(1.3) \qquad\qquad \mathbf{P}\{A\,|\,H\} = \frac{\mathbf{P}\{AH\}}{\mathbf{P}\{H\}}.$$

The quantity so defined will be called the conditional probability of A on the hypothesis H (or for given H). When all sample points have equal probabilities, $\mathbf{P}\{A\,|\,H\}$ is the ratio N_{AH}/N_H of the number of sample points common to A and H, to the number of points in H.

Conditional probabilities remain undefined when the hypothesis has zero probability. This is of no consequence in the case of discrete sample spaces but is important in the general theory.

Though the symbol $\mathbf{P}\{A\,|\,H\}$ itself is practical, its phrasing in words is so unwieldy that in practice less formal descriptions are used. Thus in our introductory example we referred to the probability of a female's being colorblind instead of saying "the conditional probability of a randomly chosen person's being colorblind on the hypothesis that the person is a female." Often the phrase "on the hypothesis H" is replaced by "if it is known that H occurred." In short, our formulas and symbols are unequivocal, but phrasings in words are often informal and must be properly interpreted.

Sometimes for stylistic clarity probabilities in sample space are called *absolute probabilities* in contradistinction to conditional ones. Strictly speaking, the adjective "absolute" is redundant and will be omitted.

Taking conditional probabilities of various events with respect to a particular hypothesis H amounts to choosing H as a new sample space; we have to multiply all probabilities by the constant factor $1/\mathbf{P}\{H\}$ in order to reduce the total probability of the new sample space to unity. This formulation shows that *all general theorems on probabilities are valid also for conditional probabilities with respect to any particular hypothesis H*. As an example we mention the fundamental relation for the probability of the occurrence of either A or B or both. We have

$$(1.4) \qquad \mathbf{P}\{A \cup B \,|\, H\} = \mathbf{P}\{A \,|\, H\} + \mathbf{P}\{B \,|\, H\} - \mathbf{P}\{AB \,|\, H\}.$$

Similarly, all theorems of chapter IV concerning probabilities of the realization of m among N events carry over to conditional probabilities, but we shall not need them.

Formula (1.3) is often used in the form

$$(1.5) \qquad\qquad \mathbf{P}\{AH\} = \mathbf{P}\{A \,|\, H\} \cdot \mathbf{P}\{H\}.$$

This is the so-called theorem on compound probabilities. To generalize it to three events A, B, C we first take $H = BC$ as hypothesis and then apply (1.5) once more; it follows that

$$(1.6) \qquad\qquad \mathbf{P}\{ABC\} = \mathbf{P}\{A \,|\, BC\} \cdot \mathbf{P}\{B \,|\, C\} \cdot \mathbf{P}\{C\}.$$

A further generalization to four or more events is straightforward.

We conclude with a simple formula which is frequently useful. Let $H_1, \ldots, H_n$ be a set of mutually exclusive events of which one necessarily occurs (that is, the union of $H_1, \ldots, H_n$ is the entire sample space). Then any event A can occur only in conjunction with some H_j, or in symbols,

$$(1.7) \qquad\qquad A = AH_1 \cup AH_2 \cup \ldots \cup AH_n.$$

Since the AH_j are mutually exclusive, their probabilities add. Applying (1.5) to $H = H_j$ and adding, we get

$$(1.8) \qquad\qquad \mathbf{P}\{A\} = \Sigma \mathbf{P}\{A \,|\, H_j\} \cdot \mathbf{P}\{H_j\}.$$

This formula is useful because an evaluation of the conditional probabilities $\mathbf{P}\{A \,|\, H_j\}$ is sometimes easier than a direct calculation of $\mathbf{P}\{A\}$.

Examples. (a) *Sampling without replacement.* From a population of the n elements $1, 2, \ldots, n$ an ordered sample is taken. Let i and j be two different elements. Assuming that i is the first element drawn (event H), what is the probability that the second element is j (event

A)? Clearly $\mathbf{P}\{AH\} = 1/n(n-1)$ and $\mathbf{P}\{A\,|\,H\} = 1/(n-1)$. This expresses the fact that the second choice refers to a population of $n-1$ elements, each of which has the same probability of being chosen. In fact, the most natural *definition* of random sampling is: "*Whatever the first r choices, at the $(r+1)$st step each of the remaining $n-r$ elements has probability $1/(n-r)$ to be chosen.*" This definition is equivalent to that given in chapter II, but we could not have stated it earlier since it involves the notion of conditional probability.

(b) Four balls are placed successively into four cells, all 4^4 arrangements being equally probable. Given that the first two balls are in different cells (event H), what is the probability that one cell contains exactly three balls (event A)? Given H, the event A can occur in two ways, and so $\mathbf{P}\{A\,|\,H\} = 2\cdot4^{-2} = \frac{1}{8}$. (It is easy to verify directly that the events H and AH contain $12\cdot4^2$ and $12\cdot2$ points, respectively.)

(c) *Distribution of sexes.* Consider families with exactly two children. Letting b and g stand for boy and girl, respectively, and the first letter for the older child, we have four possibilities: bb, bg, gb, gg. These are the four sample points, and we associate probability $\frac{1}{4}$ with each. Given that a family has a boy (event H), what is the probability that both children are boys (event A)? The event AH means bb, and H means bb, or bg, or gb. Therefore, $\mathbf{P}\{A\,|\,H\} = \frac{1}{3}$; in about one-third of the families with the characteristic H we can expect that A also will occur. It is interesting that most people expect the answer to be $\frac{1}{2}$. This is the correct answer to a different question, namely: A boy is chosen at random and found to come from a family with two children; what is the probability that the other child is a boy? The difference may be explained empirically. With our original problem we might refer to a card file of families, with the second to a file of males. In the latter, each family with two boys will be represented twice, and this explains the difference between the two results.

(d) *Stratified populations.* Suppose a human population consists of subpopulations or strata $H_1, H_2, \ldots$. These may be races, age groups, professions, etc. Let p_j be the probability that an individual chosen at random belongs to H_j. Saying "the probability that an individual in H_j is left-handed is q_j" is short for "the conditional probability of the event A (left-handedness) on the hypothesis that an individual belongs to H_j is q_j." The probability that an individual chosen at random is left-handed is $p_1q_1 + p_2q_2 + p_3q_3 + \ldots$, which is a special case of (1.8). Given that an individual is left-handed, the conditional probability of his belonging to stratum H_j is

$$(1.9) \qquad \mathbf{P}\{H_j\,|\,A\} = \frac{p_jq_j}{p_1q_1 + p_2q_2 + \ldots}.$$

2. PROBABILITIES DEFINED BY CONDITIONAL PROBABILITIES.   URN MODELS

In the preceding section we have taken the probabilities in the sample space for granted and merely calculated a few conditional probabilities. In applications, many experiments are described by specifying certain conditional probabilities (although the adjective "conditional" is usually omitted). Theoretically this means that the probabilities in sample space are to be derived from the given conditional probabilities. It has already been pointed out [example (1.a)] that sampling without replacement is best defined by saying that whatever the result of the r first selections, at the $(r+1)$st step each of the remaining elements has the same probability of being selected. Similarly, in example (1.d) our stratified population is completely described by stating the absolute probabilities p_j of the several strata, and the conditional probability q_j of the characteristic "left-handed" within each stratum. A few more examples will reveal the general scheme more effectively than a direct description could.

Examples. (a) In example I(5.b) we have considered three players a, b, c taking turns at a game; we have described the points of the sample space but have not assigned probabilities to them. Suppose now that the game is such that at each trial each of the two partners has probability $\frac{1}{2}$ of winning. This statement does not contain the word "conditional probability" but refers to it nonetheless. For it says that if player a participates in the rth round (event H), his probability of winning that particular round is $\frac{1}{2}$. It follows from equation (1.5) that the probability of a winning at the first and second try is $\frac{1}{4}$, in symbols, $\mathbf{P}\{aa\} = \frac{1}{4}$. A repeated application of (1.5) shows that $\mathbf{P}\{acc\} = \frac{1}{8}$, $\mathbf{P}\{acbb\} = \frac{1}{16}$, etc.; that is, a sample point of the scheme (∗) involving r letters has probability 2^{-r}. This is the assignment of probabilities used in problem I,5, but now the description is more intuitive. (Continued in problem 14.)

(b) *Families.* We want to interpret the following statement. "The probability of a family with exactly k children is p_k (where $p_0 + p_1 + +\ldots = 1$). For any family size all sex distributions have equal probabilities." Letting b stand for boy and g for girl, our sample space consists of the points 0 (no children), b, g, bb, bg, gb, gg, bbb, $\ldots$. The second assumption in quotation marks can be stated more formally thus: If it is known that the family has exactly n children, each of the 2^n possible sex distributions has conditional probability 2^{-n}. The probability of the hypothesis is p_n, and we see from (1.5) that the absolute probability of any arrangement of n letters b and g is $p_n \cdot 2^{-n}$.

Note that this is an example of a *stratified population*, the families of size j forming the stratum H_j. As an exercise let A stand for the event "the family has boys but no girls." Its probability is obviously $\mathbf{P}\{A\} = p_1 \cdot 2^{-1} + p_2 \cdot 2^{-2} + \ldots$ which is a special case of (1.8). The hypothesis H_j in this case is "family has j children." We now ask the question: If it is known that a family has no girls, what is the (conditional) probability that it has only one child? Here A is the hypothesis. Let H be the event "only one child." Then AH means "one child and no girl," and

$$(2.1) \quad \mathbf{P}\{H \mid A\} = \frac{\mathbf{P}\{AH\}}{\mathbf{P}\{A\}} = \frac{p_1 2^{-1}}{p_1 2^{-1} + p_2 2^{-2} + p_3 2^{-3} + \ldots},$$

which is a special case of (1.9).

(c) *Urn models for aftereffect.* For the sake of definiteness consider an industrial plant liable to accidents. The occurrence of an accident might be pictured as the result of a superhuman game of chance: Fate has in storage an urn containing red and black balls; at regular time intervals a ball is drawn at random, a red ball signifying an accident. If the chance of an accident remains constant in time, the composition of the urn is always the same. But it is conceivable that each accident has an *aftereffect* in that it either increases or decreases the chance of new accidents. This corresponds to an urn whose composition changes according to certain rules that depend on the outcome of the successive drawings. It is easy to invent a variety of such rules to cover various situations, but we shall be content with a discussion of the following[1]

Urn model: An urn contains b black and r red balls. A ball is drawn at random. It is replaced and, moreover, c balls of the color drawn and d balls of the opposite color are added. A new random drawing is made from the urn (now containing $r + b + c + d$ balls), and this procedure is repeated. Here c and d are arbitrary integers. They may be chosen *negative*, except that in this case the procedure may terminate after finitely many drawings for lack of balls. In particular, choosing $c = -1$ and $d = 0$ we have the model of *random drawings without replacement* which terminates after $r + b$ steps.

---

[1] The idea to use urn models to describe aftereffects (contagious diseases) seems to be due to Polya. His scheme (first introduced in F. Eggenberger and G. Polya, *Über die Statistik verketteter Vorgänge, Zeitschrift für Angewandte Mathematik and Mechanik*, vol. 3 (1923), pp. 279–289) served as a prototype for many models discussed in the literature. The model described in the text and its three special cases were proposed by B. Friedman, A simple urn model, *Communications on Pure and Applied Mathematics*, vol. 2 (1949), pp. 59–70.

To turn our picturesque description into mathematics, note that it specifies conditional probabilities from which certain basic probabilities are to be calculated. A typical point of the sample space corresponding to n drawings may be represented by a sequence of n letters B and R. The event "black at first drawing" (i.e., the aggregate of all sequences starting with B) has probability $b/(b + r)$. *If the first ball is black, the (conditional) probability of a black ball at the second drawing is $(b + c)/(b + r + c + d)$.* The (absolute) probability of the sequence black, black (i.e., the aggregate of the sample points starting with BB) is therefore, by (1.5),

$$(2.2) \qquad \frac{b}{b + r} \cdot \frac{b + c}{b + r + c + d}.$$

The probability of the sequence black, black, black is (2.2) multiplied by $(b + 2c)/(b + r + 2c + 2d)$, etc. It is clear that in this way the probabilities of all sample points can be calculated. (Of course, in the case of a negative c or d the number n of drawings should be chosen small enough to avoid negative numbers of balls.) It is easily verified by induction that the probabilities of all sample points indeed add to unity.

Explicit expressions for the probabilities are not readily obtainable except in the most important and best-known special case, that of

Polya's urn scheme which is characterized by $d = 0$, $c > 0$. Here after each drawing the number of balls of the color drawn increases, whereas the balls of opposite color remain unchanged in number. In effect the drawing of either color increases the probability of the same color at the next drawing, and we have a rough model of phenomena such as *contagious diseases*, where each occurrence increases the probability of further occurrences. The analytical simplicity of the Polya model is due to the following obvious property: Any sequence of n drawings resulting in n_1 black and n_2 red balls ($n_1 + n_2 = n$) has the same probability as the event of extracting *first* n_1 black and *then* n_2 red balls, namely,

$$(2.3) \qquad p_{n_1,n} =$$

$$= \frac{b(b + c)(b + 2c) \cdots (b + n_1 c - c) \cdot r(r + c) \cdots (r + n_2 c - c)}{(b + r)(b + r + c)(b + r + 2c) \cdots (b + r + nc - c)}.$$

On dividing numerator and denominator by c and using the notation II(2.1), this formula may be rewritten in the following ways:

$$(2.4) \quad p_{n_1,n} = \frac{\left(\dfrac{b}{c} + n_1 - 1\right)_{n_1} \left(\dfrac{r}{c} + n_2 - 1\right)_{n_2}}{\left(\dfrac{b+r}{c} + n - 1\right)_n} = \frac{\left(-\dfrac{b}{c}\right)_{n_1} \left(-\dfrac{r}{c}\right)_{n_2}}{\left(-\dfrac{b+r}{c}\right)_n}.$$

(The Polya scheme is discussed in problems 18–24.)

In addition to the Polya scheme our urn model contains another special case of interest, namely the

Ehrenfest model[2] *of heat exchange* between two isolated bodies. In the original description, as used by physicists, the Ehrenfest model envisages *two* containers I and II and k particles distributed in them. A particle is chosen at random and moved from its container into the other container. This procedure is repeated. What is the distribution of the particles after n steps? To reduce this to an urn model it suffices to call the particles in container I red, the others black. Then at each drawing the ball drawn is replaced by a ball of the opposite color, that is, we have $c = -1$, $d = 1$. It is clear that in this case the process can continue as long as we please (if there are no red balls, a black ball is drawn automatically and replaced by a red one). [We shall discuss the Ehrenfest model in another way in example XV$(2.f)$.]

The special case $c = 0$, $d > 0$ has been proposed by Friedman as a model of a *safety campaign*. Every time an accident occurs (i.e., a red ball is drawn), the safety campaign is pushed harder; whenever no accident occurs, the campaign slackens and the probability of an accident increases.

(d) Urn models for stratification. Spurious contagion. To continue in the vein of the preceding example, suppose that each person is liable to accidents and that their occurrence is determined by random drawings from an urn. This time, however, we shall suppose that no aftereffect exists, so that the composition of the urn remains unchanged throughout the process. Now the chance of an accident or proneness to accidents may vary from person to person or from profession to profession, and we imagine that each person (or each profession) has his own urn. In order not to complicate matters unnecessarily, let us suppose that there are just two types of people (two professions) and that their numbers in the total population stand in the ratio 1:5. We consider then an urn I containing r_1 red and b_1 black balls, and an urn II

---

[2] P. and T. Ehrenfest, Über zwei bekannte Einwände gegen das Boltzmannsche H-Theorem, *Physikalische Zeitschrift*, vol. 8 (1907), pp. 311–314. For a mathematical discussion see M. Kac, Random walk and the theory of Brownian motion, *American Mathematical Monthly*, vol. 54 (1947), pp. 369–391.

containing r_2 red and b_2 black balls. The experiment "choose a person at random and observe how many accidents he has during n time units" has the following counterpart: *A die is thrown; if ace appears, choose urn* I, *otherwise urn* II. *In each case n random drawings with replacement are selected from the urn.* Our experiment describes the situation of an insurance company accepting a new subscriber.

By using (1.8) it is seen that the probability of red at the first drawing is

$$(2.5) \qquad \mathbf{P}\{R\} = \frac{1}{6} \cdot \frac{r_1}{b_1 + r_1} + \frac{5}{6} \cdot \frac{r_2}{b_2 + r_2}$$

and the probability of a sequence red, red

$$(2.6) \qquad \mathbf{P}\{RR\} = \frac{1}{6} \cdot \left(\frac{r_1}{b_1 + r_1}\right)^2 + \frac{5}{6} \cdot \left(\frac{r_2}{b_2 + r_2}\right)^2.$$

No mathematical problem is involved in our model, but it has an interesting feature which has caused great confusion in applications. Suppose our insurance company observes that a new subscriber has an accident during the first year, and is interested in the probability of a further accident during the second year. In other words, given that the first drawing resulted in red, we ask for the (conditional) probability of a sequence red, red. This is clearly the ratio $\mathbf{P}\{RR\}/\mathbf{P}\{R\}$ and is *different* from $\mathbf{P}\{R\}$. For the sake of illustration suppose that $r_1/(b_1 + r_1) = 0.6$ and $r_2/(b_2 + r_2) = 0.06$. The probability of red at any drawing is 0.15, but if the first drawing resulted in red, the chances that the next drawing also results in red are 0.42. Note that our model involves *no aftereffect* in the total population, and yet the occurrence of an accident for a person chosen at random increases the odds that *this same person* will have a second accident. We have here an effect of sampling; the occurrence of an accident does not have a real effect, but it is an indication that the person chosen at random has a high proneness to accidents.

In the statistical literature it has become customary to use the word *contagion* instead of aftereffect. The *apparent* aftereffect of sampling was at first misinterpreted as an effect of true contagion, and so statisticians now speak of contagion (or contagious probability distributions) in a vague and misleading manner. Take, for example, the ecologist searching for insects in a field. If after an unsuccessful period he finds an insect, he might conclude that the litter is likely close by and that his chances of finding another insect are good. Obviously no aftereffect is involved, and yet the statistician speaks of contagion.

(e) The following example is famous and illustrative but somewhat artificial. Imagine a population of $N + 1$ urns, each containing N red and white balls; the urn number k contains k red and $N - k$ white balls ($k = 0, 1, 2, \ldots, N$). An urn is chosen at random and n random drawings are made from it, the ball drawn being replaced each time. Suppose that all n balls turn out to be red (event A). We seek the (conditional) probability that the next drawing will also yield a red ball (event B). If the first choice falls on urn number k, then the probability of extracting in succession n red balls is $(k/N)^n$. Hence, by (1.8),

$$(2.7) \qquad \mathbf{P}\{A\} = \frac{1^n + 2^n + \ldots + N^n}{N^n(N + 1)}.$$

The event AB means that $n + 1$ drawings yield red balls, and therefore

$$(2.8) \qquad \mathbf{P}\{AB\} = \mathbf{P}\{B\} = \frac{1^{n+1} + 2^{n+1} + \ldots + N^{n+1}}{N^{n+1}(N + 1)}.$$

The required probability is $\mathbf{P}\{B|A\} = \mathbf{P}\{B\}/\mathbf{P}\{A\}$.

The sums in (2.7) and (2.8) can be considered Riemann sums approximating integrals, so that when N is large

$$(2.9) \qquad N^{-1} \sum_{k=1}^{N} \left(\frac{k}{N}\right)^n \sim \int_0^1 x^n \, dx = \frac{1}{n + 1}.$$

We have therefore for large N approximately

$$(2.10) \qquad \mathbf{P}\{B|A\} \approx \frac{n + 1}{n + 2}.$$

This formula can be interpreted roughly as follows: If all compositions of an urn are equally probable, and if n trials yielded red balls, the probability of a red ball at the next trial is $(n + 1)/(n + 2)$. This is the so-called law of succession of Laplace (1812).

Before the ascendance of the modern theory, the notion of equal probabilities was often used as synonymous for "no advance knowledge." Laplace himself has illustrated the use of (2.10) by computing the probability that the sun will rise tomorrow, given that it has risen daily for 5000 years or $n = 1,826,213$ days. It is said that Laplace was ready to bet 1,826,214 to 1 in favor of regular habits of the sun, and we should be in a position to better the odds since regular service has followed for another century. A historical study would be necessary to render justice to Laplace and to understand his intentions. His successors, however, used similar arguments in routine work and recommended methods of this kind to physicists and engineers in cases where the formulas have no operational meaning. We should have to reject the method even if, for sake of argument, we were to concede that our universe was chosen at random from a collection in which all conceivable possibilities were equally likely. In fact, it pretends to judge the chances of the sun's rising tomorrow from the *assumed* risings in the past. But the assumed rising of the sun on February 5, 3123 B.C., is by no means more certain than that the sun will rise tomorrow. We believe in both for the same reasons.

Note on Bayes's Rule. In (1.9) and (2.2) we have calculated certain conditional probabilities directly from the definition. The beginner is advised always to do so and not to memorize the formula (2.12), which we shall now derive. It retraces in a general way what we did in special cases, but it is only a way of rewriting (1.3). We had a collection of events H_1, H_2, ... which are mutually exclusive and exhaustive, that is, every sample point belongs to one, and only one, among the H_j. We were interested in

$$(2.11) \qquad\qquad \mathbf{P}\{H_k | A\} = \frac{\mathbf{P}\{AH_k\}}{\mathbf{P}\{A\}}.$$

If (1.5) and (1.8) are introduced into (2.11), it takes the form

$$(2.12) \qquad\qquad \mathbf{P}\{H_k | A\} = \frac{\mathbf{P}\{A | H_k\} \mathbf{P}\{H_k\}}{\sum_j \mathbf{P}\{A | H_j\} \mathbf{P}\{H_j\}}.$$

If the events H_k are called causes, then (2.12) becomes "Bayes's rule for the probability of causes." Mathematically, (2.12) is a special way of writing (1.3) and nothing more. The formula is useful in many statistical applications of the type described in examples (*b*) and (*d*), and we have used it there. Unfortunately, Bayes's rule has been somewhat discredited by metaphysical applications of the type described in example (*e*). In routine practice this kind of argument can be dangerous. A quality control engineer is concerned with one particular machine and not with an infinite population of machines from which one was chosen at random. He has been advised to use Bayes's rule on the grounds that it is logically acceptable and corresponds to our way of thinking. Plato used this type of argument to prove the existence of Atlantis, and philosophers used it to prove the absurdity of Newton's mechanics. But for our engineer the argument overlooks the circumstance that he desires success and that he will do better by estimating and minimizing the sources of various types of errors in prediction and guessing. The modern method of statistical tests and estimation is less intuitive but more realistic. It may be not only defended but also applied.

3. STOCHASTIC INDEPENDENCE

In the examples above the conditional probability $\mathbf{P}\{A | H\}$ generally does not equal the absolute probability $\mathbf{P}\{A\}$. Popularly speaking, the information whether H has occurred changes our way of betting on the event A. Only when $\mathbf{P}\{A | H\} = \mathbf{P}\{A\}$ this information does not permit any inference about the occurrence of A. In this case we shall say that A is stochastically independent of H. Now (1.5) shows that the condition $\mathbf{P}\{A \mid H\} = \mathbf{P}\{A\}$ can be written in the form

$$(3.1) \qquad\qquad \mathbf{P}\{AH\} = \mathbf{P}\{A\} \cdot \mathbf{P}\{H\}.$$

This equation is symmetric in A and H and shows that whenever A is stochastically independent of H, so is H of A. It is therefore preferable to start from the following symmetric

Definition 1. *Two events A and H are said to be stochastically independent (or independent, for short) if equation (3.1) holds.* This definition is accepted also if $\mathbf{P}\{H\} = 0$, in which case $\mathbf{P}\{A \mid H\}$ is not defined. The term *statistically* independent is synonymous with stochastically independent.

Examples. (a) A card is chosen at random from a deck of playing cards. For reasons of symmetry we expect the events "spade" and "ace" to be independent. As a matter of fact, their probabilities are $\frac{1}{4}$ and $\frac{1}{13}$, and the probability of their simultaneous realization is $\frac{1}{52}$.

(b) Two true dice are thrown. The events "ace with first die" and "even face with second" are independent since the probability of their simultaneous realization, $\frac{3}{36} = \frac{1}{12}$, is the product of their probabilities, namely $\frac{1}{6}$ and $\frac{1}{2}$.

(c) In a random permutation of the four letters (a, b, c, d) the events "a precedes b" and "c precedes d" are independent. This is intuitively clear and easily verified.

(d) *Sex distribution.* We return to example (1.c) but now consider families with three children. We assume that each of the eight possibilities $bbb, bbg, \ldots, ggg$ has probability $\frac{1}{8}$. Let H be the event "the family has children of both sexes," and A the event "there is at most one girl." Then $\mathbf{P}\{H\} = \frac{6}{8}$, and $\mathbf{P}\{A\} = \frac{4}{8}$. The simultaneous realization of A and H means one of the possibilities bbg, bgb, gbb, and therefore $\mathbf{P}\{AH\} = \frac{3}{8} = \mathbf{P}\{A\} \cdot \mathbf{P}\{H\}$. Thus in families with three children the two events are independent. Note that this is not true for families with two or four children. This shows that it is not always obvious whether or not we have independence.

If H occurs, the complementary event H' does not occur, and vice versa. Stochastic independence implies that no inference can be drawn from the occurrence of H to that of A; therefore stochastic independence of A and H should mean the same as independence of A and H' (and, because of symmetry, also of A' and H, and of A' and H'). This assertion is easily verified, using the relation $\mathbf{P}\{H'\} = 1 - \mathbf{P}\{H\}$. If

(3.1) holds, then (since $AH' = A - AH$)

(3.2) $\quad \mathbf{P}\{AH'\} = \mathbf{P}\{A\} - \mathbf{P}\{AH\} = \mathbf{P}\{A\} - \mathbf{P}\{A\} \cdot \mathbf{P}\{H\} =$
$$= \mathbf{P}\{A\} \cdot \mathbf{P}\{H'\},$$

as expected.

Suppose now that three events A, B, and C are pairwise independent so that

$$\mathbf{P}\{AB\} = \mathbf{P}\{A\} \cdot \mathbf{P}\{B\}$$

(3.3) $$\mathbf{P}\{AC\} = \mathbf{P}\{A\} \cdot \mathbf{P}\{C\}$$

$$\mathbf{P}\{BC\} = \mathbf{P}\{B\} \cdot \mathbf{P}\{C\}.$$

We might think that this always implies the independence of such pairs of events as AB and C. Unfortunately this is *not* necessarily so. We shall exhibit an example in which (3.3) is true but the simultaneous occurrence of A, B, and C is impossible, so that AB and C cannot be independent.

Example. (*e*) Two dice are thrown and three events are defined as follows: A means "odd face with first die"; B means "odd face with second die"; finally, C means "odd sum" (one face even, the other odd). If each of the 36 sample points has probability $\frac{1}{36}$, then any two of the events are clearly independent. The probability of each is $\frac{1}{2}$, and so is its conditional probability, assuming that *one* of the other two events has occurred. Nevertheless, the three events cannot occur simultaneously. The information that A but not B has occurred assures that C has occurred, and a similar statement holds for all other combinations.

It is desirable to reserve the term stochastic independence for the case where no such inference is possible. Then not only (3.3) must hold but in addition

(3.4) $$\mathbf{P}\{ABC\} = \mathbf{P}\{A\}\mathbf{P}\{B\}\mathbf{P}\{C\}.$$

This equation insures that A and BC are independent and also that the same is true of B and AC, and C and AB. Furthermore, it can now be proved also that $A \cup B$ and C are independent. In fact, by the fundamental relation I(7.4) we have

(3.5) $\quad \mathbf{P}\{(A \cup B)C\} = \mathbf{P}\{AC\} + \mathbf{P}\{BC\} - \mathbf{P}\{ABC\}.$

Now, applying (3.3) and (3.4) to the right side, we can factor out $\mathbf{P}\{C\}$. The other factor is $\mathbf{P}\{A\} + \mathbf{P}\{B\} - \mathbf{P}\{AB\} = \mathbf{P}\{A \cup B\}$ so that

(3.6) $\quad \mathbf{P}\{A \cup B)C\} = \mathbf{P}\{(A \cup B)\} \, \mathbf{P}\{C\}.$

This makes it plausible that the conditions (3.3) and (3.4) together suffice to avoid embarrassment; any event expressible in terms of A and B will be independent of C.

In the general case of n events the following definition proves satisfactory.

Definition 2. *The events A_1, A_2, ..., A_n are called mutually independent if for all combinations $1 \leq i < j < k < \ldots \leq n$ the multiplication rules*

$$\mathbf{P}\{A_iA_j\} = \mathbf{P}\{A_i\} \, \mathbf{P}\{A_j\}$$

$$\mathbf{P}\{A_iA_jA_k\} = \mathbf{P}\{A_i\} \, \mathbf{P}\{A_j\} \, \mathbf{P}\{A_k\}$$

(3.7)   . . . .

               . . . .

$$\mathbf{P}\{A_1A_2 \ldots A_n\} = \mathbf{P}\{A_1\} \, \mathbf{P}\{A_2\} \, \cdots \, \mathbf{P}\{A_n\}$$

apply.

The first line stands for $\binom{n}{2}$ equations, the second for $\binom{n}{3}$, etc. We have, therefore,

$$\binom{n}{2} + \binom{n}{3} + \ldots + \binom{n}{n} = (1 + 1)^n - \binom{n}{1} - \binom{n}{0} = 2^n - n - 1$$

conditions which must be satisfied. On the other hand, the $\binom{n}{2}$ conditions stated in the first line suffice to insure *pairwise independence*. The whole system (3.7) looks like a complicated set of conditions, but it will soon become apparent that its validity is usually obvious and requires no checking. It is readily seen by induction [starting with $n = 2$ and (3.2)] that

In definition 2 the system (3.7) may be replaced by the system of the 2^n equations obtained from the last equation in (3.7) on replacing an arbitrary number of events A_j by their complements A'_j.

The distinction between mutual and pairwise independence is of theoretical rather than practical interest. Practical examples of pairwise independent events that are not mutually independent apparently do not exist. The possibility of such an occurrence was discovered by S. Bernstein.

4. REPEATED TRIALS

The notion of stochastic independence finally enables us to formulate analytically the intuitive concept of experiments "repeated under identical conditions."

Consider the sample space $\mathfrak{S}$ representing a certain conceptual experiment. Let the sample points be E_1, E_2, ... and denote their probabilities by p_1, p_2, ... The possible results of a succession of two similar experiments are the pairs (E_j, E_k), and they form a new sample space. In it probabilities can be assigned in many ways. However, if the experimentalist says that two measurements are performed under identical conditions, he implies independence; the first outcome should have no influence on the second. This means that the two events "first outcome is E_j" and "second outcome is E_k" should be stochastically independent or that

$$(4.1) \qquad \mathbf{P}\{E_j, E_k\} = p_j p_k.$$

This equation assigns a probability to every pair (E_j, E_k). Before we can use (4.1) as a definition of probabilities in the new sample space, we must show that the quantities $p_j p_k$ add to unity. Now, in the sum $\Sigma\Sigma p_j p_k$ each term appears once, and only once, so that $\Sigma\Sigma p_j p_k = (p_1 + p_2 + \ldots)(p_1 + p_2 + \ldots) = 1$. Hence (4.1) is acceptable as a definition of probabilities.

Let A and B be two arbitrary events in the original sample space $\mathfrak{S}$. We denote the event "A occurred at first trial and B at second" by (A, B). Suppose A contains the points E_{a_1}, E_{a_2}, ... and B the points E_{b_1}, E_{b_2}, ... Then (A, B) is the union of all pairs (E_{a_j}, E_{b_k}), and as before we see that

$$(4.2) \qquad \mathbf{P}\{(A, B)\} = \Sigma\Sigma p_{a_j} p_{b_k} = (\Sigma p_{a_j})(\Sigma p_{b_k}) = \mathbf{P}\{A\}\mathbf{P}\{B\}.$$

Hence the events A and B are independent. We see that the definition (4.1) entails that all events at the second trial be independent of events at the first trial. For the purposes of probability theory this describes "identical experiments."

These considerations obviously also apply to a succession of r experiments and lead to the

Definition 1. *Let $\mathfrak{S}$ be a sample space with sample points E_1, E_2, ... and corresponding probabilities p_1, p_2, ... By r independent trials corresponding to $\mathfrak{S}$ we mean the sample space whose points are the r-tuples $(E_{j_1}, E_{j_2}, \ldots, E_{j_r})$ to which the probabilities*

$$(4.3) \qquad \mathbf{P}\{(E_{j_1}, E_{j_2}, \ldots, E_{j_r})\} = p_{j_1} p_{j_2} \cdots p_{j_r}$$

are assigned.

In other words, each point of the new space is a sample of size r (with possible repetitions) of points of the original space, and probabilities are defined by the multiplication rule (4.3). The reader is reminded that (4.3) is *not* the only possible definition of probabilities. In other words, repeated trials are not necessarily independent. For example, the Polya urn scheme [example (2.c)] defines *dependent* trials. Equation (4.3) defines independent trials or, in physical terms, trials repeated under identical conditions.

The argument which led to (4.2) shows more generally the truth of the following theorem concerning independent trials.

Theorem. *Suppose that a system of events A_1, A_2, ..., A_r is such that the jth trial alone decides whether or not A_j occurs; then the events A_1, ..., A_r are mutually independent if the trials are independent, that is, if (4.3) holds.*

If $\mathfrak{S}$ contains a finite number, N, of points, then there are N^r sample points $(E_{j_1}, \ldots, E_{j_r})$. If each point of $\mathfrak{S}$ has probability $1/N$, then (4.3) assigns probability N^{-r} to each point $(E_{j_1}, \ldots, E_{j_r})$. The new approach is conceptually preferable to a formal assignment of equal probabilities because it applies to sample spaces with unequal probabilities and also to infinite sample spaces. It is indispensable for the general theory of probability where we consider even a single trial as the first in a potentially infinite sequence. We are then dealing only with infinite sequences $(E_{j_1}, E_{j_2}, \ldots)$ of possible outcomes, and in this new space probabilities are defined in a way consistent with (4.3). Unfortunately this leads beyond the theory of discrete sample spaces, to which the present volume is restricted. We have a more elementary theory but pay for it by the necessity of changing the sample space according to the number of trials.

In the preceding discussion we have considered only repetitions of the same experiment, but successions of unlike experiments can be treated in the same way. If we first toss a coin, then throw a die, we naturally assume that the two experiments are independent. This amounts to assigning probabilities by the product rule. Thus $\mathbf{P}\{(\text{heads, ace})\} = \frac{1}{2} \cdot \frac{1}{6}$, etc. In this particular case this is equivalent to assigning equal probabilities to all twelve sample points, but in general we must proceed as in (4.3).

Definition 2. *Let $\mathfrak{S}'$ and $\mathfrak{S}''$ be two sample spaces and denote their points by E'_1, E'_2, ... and E''_1, E''_2, ... Let the corresponding probabilities be p'_1, p'_2, ... and p''_1, p''_2, ... The succession of the two experiments is described by the space with points (E'_j, E''_k). Saying that* *the two successive experiments are independent means defining probabilities by*

(4.4) $$\mathbf{P}\{(E'_j, E''_k)\} = p'_j p''_k.$$

[The notions which were just introduced are by no means peculiar to probability theory. Given two spaces $\mathfrak{S}'$ and $\mathfrak{S}''$ with generic points E' and E'', *the set of all pairs* (E', E'') *is called the combinatorial product* of $\mathfrak{S}'$ and $\mathfrak{S}''$ and is usually denoted by $\mathfrak{S}' \times \mathfrak{S}''$. For example, the Cartesian plane, that is the set of pairs (x, y), is the combinatorial product of the x-axis and the y-axis. (The three dimensional space may be viewed either as triple product or as product of the x, y-plane and the z-axis.) The equation (4.4) defines what is usually called the *product measure* of the probabilities in $\mathfrak{S}'$ and $\mathfrak{S}''$. We used the word *experiment* as equivalent to a sample space with a probability defined in it. Similarly, *succession of two independent experiments is short for combinatorial product of the corresponding sample spaces with probabilities defined by* (4.4).

These notions carry over in an obvious way to products of any number of spaces. For example, in (4.3) there figures the r-tuple combinatorial product of $\mathfrak{S}$ with itself. Where the student of probability speaks of the first, second, ..., trial, other mathematicians use the term: first, second, ..., *coordinate space*. (An event which depends only on the outcome of the first trial is also called a cylindrical set over the first coordinate space.)]

The aggregate of all pairs (i, j) where i, j are positive integers between 1 and n forms the product of the set of integers $1, 2, \ldots, n$ with itself. In sampling without replacement pairs of the form (i, i) are forbidden, and therefore taking a sample of size two without replacement does not *directly* lead to a product space. Nevertheless, as the following examples will show, it is possible to represent it in a different way as a succession of independent experiments, and the same method applies to more complicated cases.

Examples. (*a*) *Permutations.* We have considered the $n!$ permutations of $a_1, a_2, \ldots, a_n$ as points of a sample space and attributed probability $1/n!$ to each. We may consider the *same sample space* as representing $n - 1$ successive experiments as follows. Begin by writing down a_1. The first experiment consists in putting a_2 either before or after a_1. This done, we have three places for a_3 and the second experiment consists of a choice among them, deciding on the relative order of a_1, a_2, and a_3. In general, when $a_1, \ldots, a_k$ are put into some relative order, we proceed with experiment number k, which consists in selecting one of the $k + 1$ places for a_{k+1}. In other words, we have a succession of $n - 1$ experiments of which the kth can result in k different choices (sample points), each having probability $1/k$. The experiments are independent, that is, the probabilities are multiplicative. Each permutation of the n elements has probability $\frac{1}{2} \cdot \frac{1}{3} \cdots 1/n$, in accordance with the original definition.

(*b*) *Sampling without replacement.* Let the population be $(a_1, \ldots, a_n)$. In sampling without replacement each choice removes an element.

After k steps there remain $n - k$ elements, and the next choice can be described by specifying the number ν of the place of the element chosen ($\nu = 1, 2, \ldots, n-k$). In this way the taking of a sample of size r without replacement becomes a succession of r experiments where the first has n possible results, the second $n - 1$, the third $n - 2$, etc. We attribute equal probabilities to all results of the individual experiments and postulate that the r experiments are independent. This amounts to attributing probability $1/(n)_r$ to each sample in accordance with our definition of random samples. (Note that for $n = 100$, $r = 3$, the sample (a_{13}, a_{40}, a_{81}) means choices number 13, 39, 79, respectively. We must say that at the third experiment the seventy-ninth element of the reduced population of $n - 2$ was chosen, for with the original numbering the outcomes of the third experiment would depend on the first two choices.) We see that the notion of repeated independent experiments permits us to study sampling as a succession of individual operations.

* 5. APPLICATIONS TO GENETICS

The theory of heredity, originated by G. Mendel (1822–1884), provides instructive illustrations for the applicability of simple probability models. We shall restrict ourselves to indications concerning the most elementary problems. In describing the biological background, we shall necessarily oversimplify and concentrate on such facts as are pertinent to the mathematical treatment.

Heritable characters depend on special carriers, called *genes*. All cells of the body, except the reproductive cells or gametes, carry exact replicas of the same gene structure. The salient fact is that genes appear in pairs. The reader may picture them as a vast collection of beads on short pieces of string, the chromosomes. These also appear in pairs, and paired genes occupy the same position on paired chromosomes. In the simplest case each gene of a particular pair can assume two forms (alleles), A and a. Then three different pairs can be formed, and, with respect to this particular pair, the organism belongs to one of the three *genotypes* AA, Aa, aa (there is no distinction between Aa and aA). For example, peas carry a pair of genes such that A causes red blossom color and a causes white. The three genotypes are in this case distinguishable as red, pink, and white. Each pair of genes determines one heritable factor, but the majority of observable properties of organisms depend on several factors. For some characteristics (e.g., eye color and left-handedness) the influence of one particular pair of genes is pre-

---

* This section treats a special subject and may be omitted.

dominant, and in such cases the effects of Mendelian laws are readily observable. Other characteristics, such as height, can be understood as the cumulative effect of a very large number of genes [cf. example X(5.c)]. Here we shall study genotypes and inheritance for only one particular pair of genes with respect to which we have the three genotypes AA, Aa, aa. Frequently there are N different forms $A_1, \ldots, A_N$ for the two genes and, accordingly, $\binom{N+1}{2}$ genotypes A_1A_1, A_1A_2, $\ldots$, A_NA_N. The theory applies to this case with obvious modifications (cf. problem 27). The following calculations apply also to the case where A is *dominant* and a *recessive*. By this is meant that Aa-individuals have the same observable properties as AA, so that only the pure aa-type shows an observable influence of the a-gene. All shades of partial dominance appear in nature. Typical partially recessive properties are blue eyes, left-handedness, etc.

The reproductive cells, or gametes, are formed by a splitting process and receive *one* gene only. Organisms of the pure AA- and aa-genotypes (or homozygotes) produce therefore gametes of only one kind, but Aa-organisms (hybrids or heterozygotes) produce A- and a-gametes in equal numbers. New organisms are derived from two parental gametes from which they receive their genes. Therefore each pair includes a paternal and a maternal gene, and any gene can be traced back to one particular ancestor in any generation, however remote.

The genotypes of offspring depend on a chance process. At every occasion, each parental gene has probability $\frac{1}{2}$ to be transmitted, and the successive trials are independent. In other words, we conceive of the genotypes of n offspring as the result of n independent trials, each of which corresponds to the tossing of two coins. For example, the genotypes of descendants of an $Aa \times Aa$ pairing are AA, Aa, aa with respective probabilities $\frac{1}{4}$, $\frac{1}{2}$, $\frac{1}{4}$. An $AA \times aa$ union can have only Aa-offspring, etc.

Looking at the population as a whole, we conceive of the pairing of parents as the result of a second chance process. We shall investigate only the so-called *random mating*, which is defined by this condition: If r descendants in the first filial generation are chosen at random, then their parents form a random sample of size r, with possible repetitions, from the aggregate of all possible parental pairs. In other words, each descendant is to be regarded as the product of a random selection of parents, and all selections are mutually independent. Random mating is an idealized model of the conditions prevailing in many natural populations and in field experiments. However, if red peas are sown in one corner of the field and white peas in another, parents of like color will unite more often than under random mating. Preferential selectivity (such as blonde preferring blondes) also violates the condition of random mating. Extreme non-random mating is represented by self-fertilizing plants and artificial inbreeding. Some such assortative mating systems will be analyzed mathematically, but for the most part we shall restrict our attention to random mating.

The genotype of an offspring is the result of four independent random choices. The genotypes of the two parents can be selected in $3 \cdot 3$ ways, their genes in $2 \cdot 2$ ways. However, we may combine two selections and describe the process as one of double selection thus: The paternal and maternal gene are each selected independently and at random from the population of all genes carried by males or females of the parental population.

Suppose that the three genotypes AA, Aa, aa occur among males and females in the same ratios, $u : 2v : w$. We shall suppose $u + 2v + + w = 1$ and call u, $2v$, w, the *genotype frequencies*. Put

$$(5.1) \qquad p = u + v, \qquad q = v + w.$$

Clearly the numbers of A- and a-genes are as $p : q$, and since $p + q = 1$ we shall call p and q the *gene frequencies* of A and a. In each of the two selections an A-gene is selected with probability p, and, because of the assumed independence, the probability of an offspring being AA is p^2. The genotype Aa can occur in two ways, and its probability is therefore $2pq$. Thus, under random mating conditions *an offspring belongs to the genotypes AA, Aa, or aa with probabilities*

$$(5.2) \qquad u_1 = p^2, \qquad 2v_1 = 2pq, \qquad w_1 = q^2.$$

Examples. (*a*) All parents are Aa (heterozygotes); then $u = w = 0$, $2v = 1$, and $p = q = \frac{1}{2}$. (*b*) AA- and aa-parents are mixed in equal proportions; then $u = w = \frac{1}{2}$, $v = 0$, and again $p = q = \frac{1}{2}$. (*c*) Finally, $u = w = \frac{1}{4}$, $2v = \frac{1}{2}$; again $p = q = \frac{1}{2}$. In all three cases we have for the filial generation $u_1 = \frac{1}{4}$, $2v_1 = \frac{1}{2}$, $w_1 = \frac{1}{4}$.

For a better understanding of the implications of (5.2) let us fix the gene frequencies p and q ($p + q = 1$) and consider all systems of genotype frequencies u, $2v$, w for which $u + v = p$ and $v + w = q$. They all lead to the same probabilities (5.2) for the first filial generation. Among them there is the particular distribution

$$(5.3) \qquad u = p^2, \qquad 2v = 2pq, \qquad w = q^2.$$

If the frequencies u, v, w in the original generation stand in the particular relation (5.3)—as in example *c*—then we find for the genotype probabilities in the first filial generation $u_1 = u$, $v_1 = v$, and $w_1 = w$. Therefore we call genotype distributions of the form (5.3) *stationary*. To every ratio $p:q$ there corresponds a stationary distribution, or equilibrium.

Equations (5.2) give the genotype probabilities for a randomly selected individual of the second generation. In a large population we must expect the actual genotype frequencies to be close to the theoretical distribution.[3] Now, whatever the distribution $u:2v:w$ in the parental generation, equations (5.2) define a stationary distribution; in it the genes A and a appear with frequencies [cf. (5.1)] $u_1 + v_1 = u + v = p$ and $v_1 + w_1 = v + w = q$. In other words, if the observed frequencies coincided exactly with the calculated probabilities, then the first filial generation would have a stationary genotype distribution which would perpetuate itself without change in all succeeding generations. In practice, deviations will be observed, but for large populations we can say: *Whatever the composition of the parent population may be, random mating will within one generation produce an approximately stationary genotype distribution with unchanged gene frequencies.* From the second generation on, there is no tendency toward a systematic change; a steady state is reached with the first filial generation. This was first noticed by G. H. Hardy,[4] who thus resolved assumed difficulties in Mendelian laws. It follows in particular that under conditions of random mating the frequencies of the three genotypes must stand in the ratios $p^2:2pq:q^2$. This can in turn be used to check the assumption of random mating.

Hardy also pointed out that emphasis must be put on the word "approximately." Even with a stationary distribution we must expect small changes from generation to generation, which leads us to the following picture. Starting from any parent population, random mating tends to establish the stationary distribution (5.3) within *one* generation. For a stationary distribution there is no tendency toward a systematic change of any kind. However, chance fluctuations will change

---

[3] Without this our probability model would be void of operational meaning. The statement is made precise by the law of large numbers and the central limit theorem, which permits us to estimate the effect of chance fluctuations.

[4] G. H. Hardy, Mendelian proportions in a mixed population, Letter to the Editor, *Science*, N.S., vol. 28 (1908), pp. 49–50. Anticipating the language of chapters IX and XV, we can describe the situation as follows. The frequencies of the three genotypes in the nth generation are three random variables whose expected values are given by (5.2) and do not depend on n. Their actual values will vary from generation to generation and form a stochastic process of the Markov type.

the gene frequencies p and q from generation to generation, and the genetic composition will slowly drift. There are no restoring forces seeking to re-establish original frequencies. On the contrary, our simplified model leads to the conclusion [cf. example $XV(2.k)$] that, for a population bounded in size, one gene should ultimately die out, so that the population would eventually belong to one of the pure types, AA or aa. In nature this does not necessarily occur because of the creation of new genes by mutations, selections, and many other effects, which can be studied by more refined mathematical tools (Markov chains, diffusion theory).

Hardy's theorem is frequently interpreted to imply a strict stability for all times. It is a common fallacy to believe that the law of large numbers acts as a force endowed with memory seeking a return to the original state, and many wrong conclusions have been drawn from this assumption. (The biological processes here considered are typical of the important class of Markov processes which will be studied in detail in chapter XV.) Note that Hardy's law does not apply to the distribution of two pairs of genes (e.g., eye color and left-handedness) with the nine genotypes $AABB$, $AABb$, $\ldots$, $aabb$. There is still a tendency toward a stationary distribution, but equilibrium is not reached in the first generation (cf. problem 31).

* 6. SEX-LINKED CHARACTERS

In the introduction to the preceding section it was mentioned that genes lie on chromosomes. These appear in pairs and are transmitted as units, so that all genes on a chromosome stick together.[5] Our scheme for the inheritance of genes therefore applies also to chromosomes as units. Sex is determined by two chromosomes; females are XX, males XY. The mother necessarily transmits an X-chromosome, and the sex of offspring depends on the chromosome transmitted by the father. Accordingly, male and female gametes are produced in equal numbers. The difference in birth rate for boys and girls is explained by variations in prenatal survival chances.

It has been said that both genes and chromosomes appear in pairs. There is an exception inasmuch as the genes situated on the X-chromosome have no corresponding gene on Y. Females have two X-chromosomes, and hence two of such X-linked genes; however, in males the X-genes appear as singles. Typical are two sex-linked genes causing

---

* This section treats a special topic and may be omitted.

[5] This picture is somewhat complicated by occasional breakings and recombinations of chromosomes [cf., problem $II(10.12)$].

colorblindness and haemophilia. With respect to each of them, females can still be classified into the three genotypes, AA, Aa, aa, but, having only *one* gene, males have only the two genotypes A and a. Note that a son always has the father's Y-chromosome so that a sex-linked character cannot be inherited from father to son. However, it can pass from father to daughter and from her to a grandson.

We now proceed to generalize the analysis of the preceding section. Assume again random mating and let the frequencies of the genotypes AA, Aa, aa in the *female* population be u, $2v$, w, respectively. As before put $p = u + v$, $q = v + w$. The frequencies of the two *male* genotypes A and a will be denoted by p' and q' ($p' + q' = 1$). Then p and p' are the frequencies of the A-gene in the female and male populations, respectively. The probability for a female descendant to be of genotype AA, Aa, aa will be denoted by u_1, $2v_1$, w_1; the analogous probabilities for the male types A and a are p'_1, q'_1. Now a male offspring receives his X-chromosome from the female parent, and hence

$$(6.1) \qquad\qquad p'_1 = p, \qquad q'_1 = q.$$

For the three female genotypes we find, as in section 5,

$$(6.2) \qquad u_1 = pp', \qquad 2v_1 = pq' + qp', \qquad w_1 = qq'.$$

Hence

$$(6.3) \quad p_1 = u_1 + v_1 = \tfrac{1}{2}(p + p'), \qquad q_1 = v_1 + w_1 = \tfrac{1}{2}(q + q').$$

We can interpret these formulas as follows. Among the male descendants the genes A and a appear approximately with the frequencies p, q of the maternal population; the gene frequencies among female descendants are approximately p_1 and q_1, or halfway between those of the paternal and maternal populations. We discern a tendency toward equalization of the gene frequencies. In fact, from (6.1) and (6.3) we get

$$(6.4) \qquad p'_1 - p_1 = \tfrac{1}{2}(p - p'), \qquad q'_1 - q_1 = \tfrac{1}{2}(q - q').$$

This means that random mating will in one generation reduce approximately by one-half the differences between gene frequencies among males and females. However, it will not eliminate the differences, and a tendency toward further reduction will subsist. In contrast to Hardy's law, we have here no stationary situation after one generation. We can pursue the systematic component of the changes from generation to generation by neglecting chance fluctuations and identifying the theoretical probabilities (6.2) and (6.3) with corresponding actual frequencies in the first filial generation.[6] For the second generation we obtain by the same process

(6.5) $p_2 = \frac{1}{2}(p_1 + p'_1) = \frac{3}{4}p + \frac{1}{4}p'$, $q_2 = \frac{1}{2}(q_1 + q'_1) = \frac{3}{4}q + \frac{1}{4}q'$

and, of course, $p'_2 = p_1$, $q'_2 = q_1$. A few more trials will lead to the general expression for the probabilities p_n and q_n among females of the nth descendant generation. Put

(6.6) $\alpha = \frac{1}{3}(2p + p')$, $\beta = \frac{1}{3}(2q + q')$.

(Note that $\alpha + \beta = 1$.)   Then

(6.7)

$$p_n = \frac{p_{n-1} + p'_{n-1}}{2} = \alpha + (-1)^n \frac{p - p'}{3 \cdot 2^n},$$

$$q_n = \frac{q_{n-1} + q'_{n-1}}{2} = \beta + (-1)^n \frac{q - q'}{3 \cdot 2^n},$$

and $p'_n = p_{n-1}$, $q'_n = q_{n-1}$. Hence

(6.8) $p_n \to \alpha$, $p'_n \to \alpha$, $q_n \to \beta$, $q'_n \to \beta$.

The genotype frequencies in the female population, as given by (6.2), are

(6.9) $u_n = p_{n-1}p'_{n-1}$, $2v_n = p_{n-1}q'_{n-1} + q_{n-1}p'_{n-1}$,

$$w_n = q_{n-1}q'_{n-1}.$$

Hence

(6.10) $u_n \to \alpha^2$, $2v_n \to 2\alpha\beta$, $w_n \to \beta^2$.

These formulas show that there is a strong systematic tendency, from generation to generation, toward a state where the genotypes A and a appear among males with frequencies α and β, and the female genotypes AA, Aa, aa have probabilities α^2, $2\alpha\beta$, β^2, respectively. The convergence is very fast, as indicated by (6.7). In practice, equilibrium will be reached after three or four generations. To be sure, small chance fluctuations will be superimposed on the described changes, but the latter represent the prevailing systematic tendency.

Our main conclusion is that under random mating we can expect the sex-linked genotypes A and a among males, and AA, Aa, aa among

---

[6] In the terminology introduced in footnote 4 we can interpret p_n and q_n as the expected values of the gene frequencies in the nth female generation. With this interpretation the formulas for p_n and q_n are no longer approximations but exact.

females to occur approximately with the frequencies α, β, α^2, $2\alpha\beta$, β^2, respectively, where $\alpha + \beta = 1$.

Application. Many sex-linked genes, like colorblindness, are *recessive* and cause defects. Let a be such a gene. Then all a-males and all aa-females show the defect. Females of Aa-type may transmit the defect to their offspring but are not themselves affected. Hence we expect that a *recessive sex-linked defect which occurs among males with frequency α occurs among females with frequency α^2*. If one man in 100 is colorblind, one woman in 10,000 should be affected.

* 7. SELECTION

As a typical example of the influence of selection we shall investigate the case where aa-individuals cannot multiply. This happens when the a-gene is recessive and lethal, so that aa-individuals are born but cannot survive. Another case occurs when artificial interference by breeding or laws prohibits mating of aa-individuals.

Assume random mating among AA- and Aa-individuals but no mating of aa-types. Let the frequencies with which the genotypes AA, Aa, aa appear in the *total* population be u, $2v$, w. The corresponding frequencies for *parents* are then

$$(7.1) \qquad u^* = \frac{u}{1-w}, \qquad 2v^* = \frac{2v}{1-w}, \qquad w^* = 0.$$

We can proceed as in section 5, but we must use the quantities (7.1) instead of u, $2v$, w. Hence, (5.1) is to be replaced by

$$(7.2) \qquad p = \frac{u+v}{1-w}, \qquad q = \frac{v}{1-w}.$$

The probabilities of the three genotypes in the first filial generation are again given by (5.2) or $u_1 = p^2$, $2v_1 = 2pq$, $w_1 = q^2$.

As before, in order to investigate the systematic changes from generation to generation, we have to replace u, v, w by u_1, v_1, w_1 and thus obtain probabilities u_2, v_2, w_2 for the second descendant generation, etc. In general we get from (7.2)

$$(7.3) \qquad p_n = \frac{u_n + v_n}{1-w_n}, \qquad q_n = \frac{v_n}{1-w_n}$$

and

$$(7.4) \qquad u_{n+1} = p_n^2, \qquad 2v_{n+1} = 2p_n q_n, \qquad w_{n+1} = q_n^2.$$

---

* This section treats a special subject and may be omitted.

A comparison of (7.3) and (7.4) shows that

$$(7.5) \qquad p_{n+1} = \frac{u_{n+1} + v_{n+1}}{1 - w_{n+1}} = \frac{p_n}{1 - q_n^2} = \frac{1}{1 + q_n}$$

and similarly

$$(7.6) \qquad q_{n+1} = \frac{v_{n+1}}{1 - w_{n+1}} = \frac{q_n}{1 + q_n}.$$

From (7.6) we can calculate q_n explicitly. In fact

$$(7.7) \qquad \frac{1}{q_{n+1}} = 1 + \frac{1}{q_n}$$

whence successively

$$(7.8) \qquad \frac{1}{q_1} = 1 + \frac{1}{q}, \quad \frac{1}{q_2} = 2 + \frac{1}{q}, \quad \frac{1}{q_3} = 3 + \frac{1}{q}, \quad \dots \quad \frac{1}{q_n} = n + \frac{1}{q}$$

or

$$(7.9) \qquad q_n = \frac{q}{1 + nq}, \qquad w_{n+1} = \left(\frac{q}{1 + qn}\right)^2.$$

We see that the unproductive (or undesirable) genotype gradually drops out, but the process is extremely slow. For $q = 0.1$ it takes ten generations to reduce the frequency of a-genes by one-half; this reduces the frequency of the aa-type approximately from 1 to $\frac{1}{4}$ per cent. (If a is sex-linked, the elimination proceeds much faster as shown in problem 29; for a generalized selection scheme see problem 30.)[7]

8. PROBLEMS FOR SOLUTION

1. Three dice are rolled. If no two show the same face, what is the probability that one is an ace?

2. Given that a throw with ten dice produced at least one ace, what is the probability p of two or more aces?

3. *Bridge.* In a bridge party West has no ace. What probability should be attributed to the event of his partner having (a) no ace, (b) two or more aces? Verify the result by a direct argument.

4. *Bridge.* North and South have ten trumps between them (trumps being cards of a specified suit). (a) Find the probability that all three remaining trumps are in the same hand (either East or West has no trumps). (b) If it is known that the king of trumps is included among the three, what is the probability that he is "unguarded" (that is, one player has the king, the other the remaining two trumps)?

---

[7] For a further analysis of various eugenic effects (which are frequently different from the ideas of enthusiastic proponents of sterilization laws) see G. Dahlberg, *Mathematical methods for population genetics*, New York and Basel, 1948.

5. Discuss the key problem in example II(7.*b*) in terms of conditional probabilities following the pattern of example (2.*b*).

6. In a bolt factory machines A, B, C manufacture, respectively, 25, 35, and 40 per cent of the total. Of their output 5, 4, and 2 per cent are defective bolts. A bolt is drawn at random from the produce and is found defective. What are the probabilities that it was manufactured by machines A, B, C?

7. Suppose that 5 men out of 100 and 25 women out of 10,000 are colorblind. A colorblind person is chosen at random. What is the probability of his being male? (Assume males and females to be in equal numbers.)

8. Seven balls are distributed randomly in seven cells; the probabilities of the various arrangements are tabulated in table 1 of chapter II, section 5. Using this table, verify that the probability of a cell's being triply occupied, given that exactly two cells are empty, is $\frac{1}{4}$ to five decimals. Show that $\frac{1}{4}$ is the correct answer.

9. A die is thrown as long as necessary for an ace to turn up. Assuming that the ace does not turn up at the first throw, what is the probability that more than three throws will be necessary?

10. *Continuation.* Suppose that the number, n, of throws is even. What is the probability that $n = 2$?

11. Let [8] the probability p_n that a family has exactly n children be αp^n when $n \geq 1$, and $p_0 = 1 - \alpha p(1 + p + p^2 + \ldots)$. Suppose that all sex distributions of n children have the same probability. Show that for $k \geq 1$ the probability that a family contains exactly k boys is $2\alpha p^k/(2 - p)^{k+1}$.

12. *Continuation.* Given that a family includes at least one boy, what is the probability that there are two or more?

13. Die A has four red and two white faces, whereas die B has two red and four white faces. A coin is flipped *once*. If it falls heads, the game continues by throwing die A alone; if it falls tails, die B is to be used. (*a*) Show that the probability of red at any throw is $\frac{1}{2}$. (*b*) If the first two throws resulted in red, what is the probability of red at the third throw? (*c*) If red turns up at the first n throws, what is the probability that die A is being used? (*d*) To which urn model is this game equivalent?

14. In example (2.*a*) let x_n be the conditional probability that the winner of the nth trial wins the entire game given that the game does not terminate at the nth trial; let y_n and z_n be the corresponding probabilities of victory for the losing and the pausing player, respectively, of the nth trial. (*a*) Show that

$$(*) \qquad x_n = \tfrac{1}{2} + \tfrac{1}{2}y_{n+1}, \qquad y_n = \tfrac{1}{2}z_{n+1}, \qquad z_n = \tfrac{1}{2}x_{n+1}.$$

(*b*) Show by a direct simple argument that in reality $x_n = x$, $y_n = y$, $z_n = z$ are independent of n. (*c*) Conclude that the probability that player a wins the game is $\frac{5}{14}$ (in agreement with problem I, 5). (*d*) Show that $x_n = \frac{4}{7}$, $y_n = \frac{1}{7}$, $z_n = \frac{2}{7}$ is the only bounded solution of $(*)$.

15. Let the events A_1, A_2, $\ldots$, A_n be independent and $\mathbf{P}\{A_k\} = p_k$. Find the probability p that none of the events occurs.

---

[8] According to A. J. Lotka, American family statistics satisfies our hypothesis with $p = 0.7358$. See Théorie analytique des associations biologiques II, *Actualités scientifiques et industrielles*, no. 780 Paris, 1939.

16. *Continuation.* Show that always $p < e^{-\Sigma p_k}$.

17. *Continuation.* From Bonferroni's inequality IV(5.7) deduce that the probability of k or more of the events $A_1, \ldots, A_n$ occurring simultaneously is less than $(p_1 + \ldots + p_n)^k/k!$.

18. *To Polya's urn scheme, example (2.c).* Given that the second ball was black, what is the probability that the first was black?

19. *To Polya's urn scheme, example (2.c).* Show by induction that the probability of a black ball at any trial is $b/(b + r)$.

20. *Continuation.* Prove by induction: for any $m < n$ the probabilities that the mth and the nth drawings produce black, black or black, red are

$$\frac{b(b + c)}{(b + r)(b + r + c)}, \qquad \frac{br}{(b + r)(b + r + c)},$$

respectively. Generalize to more than two drawings.

21. *Time symmetry of Polya's scheme.* Let A and B stand for either black or red (so that AB can be any of the four combinations). Show that the probability of A at the nth drawing, given that the mth drawing yields B, is the same as the probability of A at the mth drawing when the nth drawing yields B.

22. In the Polya scheme let $p_k(n)$ be the probability of k black balls in the first n drawings. Prove the recurrence relation

$$p_k(n + 1) = p_k(n)\frac{r + (n - k)c}{b + r + nc} + p_{k-1}(n)\frac{b + (k - 1)c}{b + r + nc}$$

where $p_{-1}(n)$ is to be interpreted as 0. Use this relation for a new proof of (2.3).

23. *The Polya distribution.* In (2.4) set

(8.1)
$$\frac{b}{b + r} = p, \qquad \frac{r}{b + r} = q, \qquad \frac{c}{b + r} = \gamma.$$

Show that

(8.2)
$$p_{n_1,n} = \frac{\left(-\dfrac{p}{\gamma}\right)_{n_1} \left(-\dfrac{q}{\gamma}\right)_{n_2}}{\left(-\dfrac{1}{\gamma}\right)_n}, \qquad n = n_1 + n_2,$$

remains meaningful for arbitrary (not necessarily rational) constants $p > 0$, $q > 0$, $\gamma > -1$ such that $p + q = 1$. Verify that $p_{n_1,n} > 0$ and

$$\sum_{\nu=0}^{n} p_{\nu,n} = 1.$$

Thus equation (8.2) defines a probability distribution on the integers $0, 1, \ldots, n$, the Polya distribution.

24. *Limiting form of the Polya distribution.* If $n \to \infty$, $p \to 0$, $\gamma \to 0$ so that $np \to \lambda$, $n\gamma \to \rho^{-1}$, then

$$p_{n_1,n} \to \binom{\lambda\rho + n_1 - 1}{n_1} \left(\frac{\rho}{1 + \rho}\right)^{\lambda\rho} \left(\frac{1}{1 + \rho}\right)^{n_1}.$$

Verify this and show that for fixed λ, ρ the terms on the right add to unity. (The right side represents the so-called *negative binomial distribution;* cf. chapter VI, section 8, and problem VI, 37.)

25. Interpret equation II(11.8) in terms of conditional probabilities.

Applications in Biology

26. Under random mating less than half the population belongs to genotype Aa.

27. Generalize the results of section 5 to the case where each gene can have any of the forms $A_1, A_2, \ldots, A_k$, so that there are $\binom{k+1}{2}$ genotypes instead of three (multiple alleles).

28. *Brother-sister mating.* Two parents are selected at random from a population in which the genotypes AA, Aa, aa occur with frequencies u, $2v$, w. This process is repeated in their progeny. Find the probabilities that both parents of the first, second, third filial generation belong to AA [cf. examples XV(2.l) and XVI(4.b)].

29. *Selection.* Let a be a recessive sex-linked gene, and suppose that a selection process makes mating of a-males impossible. If the genotypes AA, Aa, aa appear among females with frequencies u, $2v$, w, show that for female descendants of the first generation $u_1 = u + v$, $2v_1 = v + w$, $w_1 = 0$ and hence $p_1 = p + \frac{1}{2}q$, $q_1 = \frac{1}{2}q$. That is to say, the frequency of the a-gene among females is reduced to one-half.

30. The selection problem of section 7 can be generalized by assuming that only the fraction $\lambda(0 < \lambda \leq 1)$ of the aa-class is eliminated. Show that

$$p = \frac{u+v}{1-\lambda w}, \qquad q = \frac{v+(1-\lambda)w}{1-\lambda w}.$$

More generally, (7.3) is to be replaced by

$$p_{n+1} = \frac{p_n}{1-\lambda q_n{}^2}, \qquad q_{n+1} = q_n \frac{1-\lambda q_n}{1-\lambda q_n{}^2}.$$

(The general solution of these equations appears to be unknown.)

31. Consider simultaneously two pairs of genes with possible forms (A, a) and (B, b), respectively. Any person transmits to each descendant one gene of each pair, and we shall suppose that each of the four possible combinations has probability $\frac{1}{4}$. (This is the case if the genes are on separate chromosomes; otherwise there is strong dependence.) There exist nine genotypes, and we assume that their frequencies in the parent population are U_{AABB}, U_{aaBB}, U_{AAbb}, U_{aabb}, $2U_{AaBB}$, $2U_{Aabb}$, $2U_{AABb}$, $2U_{aaBb}$, $4U_{AaBb}$. Put $p_{AB} = U_{AABB} +$ $+ U_{AABb} + U_{AaBB} + U_{AaBb}$, $p_{Ab} = U_{AAbb} + U_{Aabb} + U_{AABb} + U_{AaBb}$, $p_{aB} = U_{aaBB} + U_{aaBb} + U_{AaBB} + U_{AaBb}$, $p_{ab} = U_{aabb} + U_{Aabb} + U_{aaBb} +$ $+ U_{AaBb}$. Compute the corresponding quantities for the first descendant generation. Show that for it $p_{AB}^{(1)} = p_{AB} - \delta$, $p_{Ab}^{(1)} = p_{Ab} + \delta$, $p_{aB}^{(1)} = p_{aB} + \delta$, $p_{ab}^{(1)} = p_{ab} - \delta$ with $2\delta = p_{AB}p_{ab} - p_{Ab}p_{aB}$. The stationary distribution is given by $p_{AB} - 2\delta = p_{Ab} + 2\delta$, etc. (Notice that Hardy's law does *not* apply; the composition changes from generation to generation.)

32. Assume that the genotype frequencies in a population are $u = p^2$, $2v = 2pq$, $w = q^2$. Given that a man is of genotype Aa, the probability that his brother is of the same genotype is $(1 + pq)/2$.

Note: [9] *The following problems are on family relations and give a meaning to the notion of degree of relationship. Each problem is a continuation of the preceding one. Random mating and the notations of section 5 are assumed. We are here concerned with a special case of Markov chains (cf. chapter* XV). *Matrix algebra simplifies the writing.*

33. Number the genotypes AA, Aa, aa by 1, 2, 3, respectively, and let $p_{ik}(i, k = 1, 2, 3)$ be the conditional probability that an offspring is of genotype k if it is known that the male (or female) parent is of genotype i. Compute the nine probabilities p_{ik}, assuming that the probabilities for the other parent to be of genotype 1, 2, 3 are p^2, $2pq$, q^2, respectively.

34. Show that p_{ik} is also the conditional probability that the parent is of genotype k if it is known that a specified offspring is of genotype i.

35. Prove that the conditional probability of a grandson (grandfather) to be of genotype k if it is known that the grandfather (grandson) is of genotype i is given by

$$p_{ik}^{(2)} = p_{i1}p_{1k} + p_{i2}p_{2k} + p_{i3}p_{3k}.$$

[The matrix $(p_{ik}^{(2)})$ is the square of the matrix (p_{ik}).]

36. Show that $p_{ik}^{(2)}$ is also the conditional probability that a man is of genotype k if it is known that a specified half-brother is of genotype i.

37. Show that the conditional probability of a man to be of genotype k when it is known that a specified great-grandfather (or great-grandson) is of genotype i is given by

$$p_{ik}^{(3)} = p_{i1}^{(2)}p_{1k} + p_{i2}^{(2)}p_{2k} + p_{i3}^{(2)}p_{3k} = p_{i1}p_{1k}^{(2)} + p_{i2}p_{2k}^{(2)} + p_{i3}p_{3k}^{(2)}.$$

(The matrix $(p_{ik}^{(3)})$ is the third power of the matrix (p_{ik}). This procedure gives a precise meaning to the notion of the degree of family relationship.)

38. More generally, define probabilities $p_{ik}^{(n)}$ that a descendant of nth generation is of genotype k if a specified ancestor was of genotype i. Prove by induction that the $p_{ik}^{(n)}$ are given by the elements of the following matrix

$$\begin{pmatrix} p^2 + pq/2^{n-1} & 2pq + q(q-p)/2^{n-1} & q^2 - q^2/2^{n-1} \\ p^2 + p(q-p)/2^n & 2pq + (1 - 4pq)/2^n & q^2 + q(p-q)/2^n \\ p^2 - p^2/2^{n-1} & 2pq + p(p-q)/2^{n-1} & q^2 + pq/2^{n-1} \end{pmatrix}.$$

(This shows that the influence of an ancestor decreases from generation to generation by the factor $\frac{1}{2}$.)

---

[9] The first edition contained an error since the word brother (two common parents) was used where a *half*-brother was meant. This error is pointed out and the correct formulas are given in C. C. Li and Louis Sacks, The derivation of the joint distribution and correlation between relatives by the use of stochastic matrices, *Biometrika*, vol. 40 (1954), pp. 347–360.

39. Consider the problem 36 for a *full* brother instead of a half-brother. Show that the corresponding matrix is

$$\begin{pmatrix} \frac{1}{4}(1+p)^2 & \frac{1}{2}q(1+p) & \frac{1}{4}q^2 \\ \frac{1}{4}p(1+p) & \frac{1}{2}(1+pq) & \frac{1}{4}q(1+q) \\ \frac{1}{4}p^2 & \frac{1}{2}p(1+q) & \frac{1}{4}(1+q)^2 \end{pmatrix}.$$

40. Show that the degree of relationship between uncle and nephew is the same as between grandfather and grandson.

CHAPTER VI

The Binomial
and the Poisson Distributions

1. BERNOULLI TRIALS [1]

Repeated independent trials are called Bernoulli trials if there are only two possible outcomes for each trial and their probabilities remain the same throughout the trials. It is usual to denote the two probabilities by p and q, and to refer to the outcome with probability p as "*success*," S, and to the other as "*failure*," F. Clearly, p and q must be non-negative, and

$$(1.1) \qquad\qquad p + q = 1.$$

The sample space of each individual trial is formed by the two points S and F. The sample space of n Bernoulli trials contains 2^n points or successions of n symbols S and F, each point representing one possible outcome of the compound experiment. Since the trials are independent, the probabilities multiply. In other words, *the probability of any specified sequence is the product obtained on replacing the symbols S and F by p and q, respectively.* Thus $\mathbf{P}\{(SSFSF \ldots FFS)\} = ppqpq \cdots qqp$.

Examples. The most familiar example of Bernoulli trials is provided by successive tosses of a true or symmetric coin; here $p = q = \frac{1}{2}$. If the coin is unbalanced, we still assume that the successive tosses are independent so that we have a model of Bernoulli trials in which the probability p for success can have an arbitrary value. Repeated random drawings from an urn containing at each drawing r red and b black balls represent Bernoulli trials with $p = r/(r + b)$. Often we have no interest in distinguishing among several outcomes and prefer to describe any result simply as A or non-A. Thus with good dice the distinction between ace (S) and non-ace (F) leads to Bernoulli trials with

---

[1] James Bernoulli (1654–1705). His main work, the *Ars conjectandi*, was published in 1713.

$p = \frac{1}{6}$, whereas distinguishing between even or odd leads to Bernoulli trials with $p = \frac{1}{2}$. If the die is unbalanced, the successive throws still form Bernoulli trials, but the corresponding probabilities p are different. Royal flush in poker or double ace in rolling dice may represent success; calling all other outcomes failure, we have Bernoulli trials with $p = 1/649,740$ and $p = \frac{1}{36}$, respectively. Reductions of this type are usual in statistical applications. For example, washers produced in mass production may vary in thickness, but, on inspection, they are classified as conforming (S) or defective (F) according as their thickness is, or is not, within prescribed limits.

The Bernoulli scheme of trials is a theoretical model, and only experience can show whether it is suitable for the description of specified experiments. Our knowledge that successive tossings of a coin conform to the Bernoulli scheme is derived from experimental evidence. The man in the street, and also the philosopher K. Marbe,[2] believes that after a run of seventeen heads tail becomes more probable. This argument has nothing to do with imperfections of physical coins; it endows nature with memory, or, in our terminology, it denies the stochastic independence of successive trials. Marbe's theory cannot be refuted by logic but is rejected because of lack of empirical support.

In sampling practice, industrial quality control, etc., the scheme of Bernoulli trials provides an ideal standard even though it can never be fully attained. Thus, in the example above of the production of washers, there are many reasons why the output cannot conform to the Bernoulli scheme. The machines are subject to changes, and hence the probabilities do not remain constant; there is a persistence in the action of machines, and therefore long runs of deviations of like kind are more probable than they would be if the trials were truly independent. From the point of view of quality control, however, it is desirable that the process conform to the Bernoulli scheme, and it is an important discovery that, within certain limits, production can be made to behave in this way. The purpose of continuous control is then to discover at an early stage flagrant departures from the ideal scheme and to use them as an indication of impending trouble.

2. THE BINOMIAL DISTRIBUTION

Frequently we are interested only in the total number of successes produced in a succession of n Bernoulli trials but not in their order.

---

[2] *Die Gleichförmigkeit in der Welt*, Munich, 1916. There exists a huge critical literature on Marbe's theory.

The number of successes can be 0, 1, ..., n, and our first problem is to determine the corresponding probabilities. Now the event "n trials result in k successes and $n - k$ failures" can happen in as many ways as k letters S can be distributed among n places. In other words, our event contains $\binom{n}{k}$ points, and, by definition, each point has the probability $p^k q^{n-k}$. This proves the

Theorem. *Let $b(k; n, p)$ be the probability that n Bernoulli trials with probabilities p for success and $q = 1 - p$ for failure result in k successes and $n - k$ failures $(0 \leq k \leq n)$. Then*

$$(2.1) \qquad b(k; n, p) = \binom{n}{k} p^k q^{n-k}.$$

In particular, the probability of no success is q^n, and the probability of at least one success is $1 - q^n$.

We shall treat p as a constant and denote the number of successes in n trials by $\mathbf{S}_n$; then $b(k; n, p) = \mathbf{P}\{\mathbf{S}_n = k\}$. In the general terminology $\mathbf{S}_n$ is a *random variable*, and the function (2.1) is the "distribution" of this random variable; we shall refer to it as the *binomial distribution*. The attribute "binomial" refers to the fact that (2.1) represents the kth term of the binomial expansion of $(q + p)^n$. This remark shows also that $b(0; n, p) + b(1; n, p) + \ldots + b(n; n, p) = (q + p)^n = 1$, as is required by the notion of probability. The binomial distribution has been tabulated.[3]

Examples. (a) *Weldon's dice data.* Let an experiment consist in throwing twelve dice and let us count fives and sixes as "success." If the dice are perfect, the probability of success is $p = \frac{1}{3}$ and the number of successes should follow the binomial distribution $b(k; 12, \frac{1}{3})$. Table 1 gives these probabilities, together with the corresponding observed average frequencies in 26,306 actual experiments. The agreement looks good, but for such extensive data it is really very bad. Statisticians usually judge closeness of fit by the chi-square criterion. According to it, deviations as large as those observed would happen with true dice only once in 10,000 times. It is, therefore, reasonable to assume that

---

[3] For $n \leq 50$, see National Bureau of Standards, *Tables of the binomial probability distribution*, Applied Mathematics Series, vol. 6 (1950). For $50 \leq n \leq 100$, see H. C. Romig, *50–100 Binomial tables*, John Wiley and Sons, 1953. For a wider range see *Tables of the cumulative binomial probability distribution*, by the Harvard Computation Laboratory, 1955, and *Tables of the cumulative binomial probabilities*, by the Ordnance Corps, ORDP 20-11 (1952).

the dice were biased. A bias with probability of success $p = 0.3377$ would fit the observations.[4]

TABLE 1

WELDON'S DICE DATA

k	$b(k; 12, \frac{1}{3})$	Observed Frequency	$b(k; 12, 0.3377)$
0	0.007 707	0.007 033	0.007 123
1	.046 244	.043 678	.043 584
2	.127 171	.124 116	.122 225
3	.211 952	.208 127	.207 736
4	.238 446	.232 418	.238 324
5	.190 757	.197 445	.194 429
6	.111 275	.116 589	.115 660
7	.047 689	.050 597	.050 549
8	.014 903	.015 320	.016 109
9	.003 312	.003 991	.003 650
10	.000 497	.000 532	.000 558
11	.000 045	.000 152	.000 052
12	.000 002	.000 000	.000 002

(b) In chapter IV, section 4, we have encountered the binomial distribution in connection with a card-guessing problem, and the columns b_m of table 3 exhibit the terms of the distribution for $n = 3, 4, 5, 6, 10$ and $p = 1/n$. In the occupancy problem II(4.c) we found formula II(4.5), which is another special case of the binomial distribution.

(c) If the probability of success is 0.01, how many trials are necessary in order for the probability of at least one success to be $\frac{1}{2}$ or more? Here we seek the smallest integer n for which $1 - (0.99)^n \geq \frac{1}{2}$, or $-n \log (0.99) \geq \log 2$; therefore $n \geq 70$.

(d) A power supply problem. Suppose that $n = 10$ workers are to use intermittently electric power, and we are interested in estimating the total load to be expected. For a crude approximation imagine that at any given time each worker has the same probability p of requiring a unit of power. If they work independently, the probability of exactly k workers requiring power at the same time should be $b(k; n, p)$. If, on the average, a worker uses power for 12 minutes per hour, we would put $p = \frac{1}{5}$. The probability of seven or more workers requiring cur-

---

[4] R. A. Fisher, *Statistical methods for research workers*, Edinburgh-London, 1932, p. 66, or T. C. Fry, *Probability and its engineering uses*, New York, 1928, pp. 303ff.

rent at the same time is then $b(7; 10, 0.2) + \ldots + b(10; 10, 0.2) =$
$= 0.0008643584$. In other words, if the supply is adjusted to six power
units, an overload has probability $0.00086 \ldots$ and should be expected
for about one minute in 1157, that is, about one minute in twenty
hours. The probability of eight or more workers requiring current
at the same time is only 0.0000779264 or about eleven times less.

(e) *Testing sera or vaccines.*[5] Suppose that the normal rate of infection of a certain disease in cattle is 25 per cent. To test a newly discovered serum n healthy animals are injected with it. How are we to
evaluate the result of the experiment? If the serum is absolutely
worthless, the probability that exactly k of the n test animals remain
free from infection may be equated to $b(k; n, 0.75)$. For $k = n = 10$
this probability is about 0.056, and for $k = n = 12$ only 0.032. Thus,
if out of ten or twelve test animals none catches infection, this may be
taken as an indication that the serum has had an effect, although it is
not a conclusive proof. Note that, without serum, the probability that
out of seventeen animals at most one catches infection is about 0.0501.
It is therefore *stronger evidence* in favor of the serum if out of seventeen
test animals only one gets infected than if out of ten all remain healthy.
For $n = 23$ the probability of at most two animals catching infection
is about 0.0492, and thus two failures out of twenty-three is again
better evidence for the serum than one out of seventeen or none out
of ten.

(f) *Another statistical test.* Suppose n people have their blood pressure measured with and without a certain drug. Let the observations
be $x_1, \ldots, x_n$ and $x'_1, \ldots, x'_n$. We say that the ith trial resulted in
success if $x_i < x'_i$, and in failure if $x_i > x'_i$. (For simplicity we may
assume that no two measurements lead to *exactly* the same result.) If
the drug has no effect, then our observation should correspond to n
Bernoulli trials with $p = \frac{1}{2}$, and an excessive number of successes is
to be taken as evidence that the drug has an effect.

3. THE CENTRAL TERM AND THE TAILS

From (2.1) we see that

$$(3.1) \qquad \frac{b(k; n, p)}{b(k - 1; n, p)} = \frac{(n - k + 1)p}{kq} = 1 + \frac{(n + 1)p - k}{kq}.$$

Accordingly, the term $b(k; n, p)$ is greater than the preceding one for

---

[5] P. V. Sukhatme and V. G. Panse, Size of experiments for testing sera or vaccines, *Indian Journal of Veterinary Science and Animal Husbandry*, vol. 13 (1943),
pp. 75–82.

$k < (n + 1)p$ and is smaller for $k > (n + 1)p$. If $(n + 1)p = m$ happens to be an integer, then $b(m; n, p) = b(m-1; n, p)$. There exists exactly one integer m such that

$$(3.2) \qquad (n + 1)p - 1 < m \leq (n + 1)p,$$

and we have the

Theorem 1. *As k goes from 0 to n, the terms $b(k; n, p)$ first increase monotonically, then decrease monotonically, reaching their greatest value when $k = m$, except that $b(m-1; n, p) = b(m; n, p)$ when $m = (n + 1)p$.*

We shall call $b(m; n, p)$ the *central* term. Often m is called "the most probable number of successes," but it must be understood that for large values of n all terms $b(k; n, p)$ are small. In 100 tossings of a true coin the most probable number of heads is 50, but its probability is less than 0.08. In the next chapter we shall find that $b(m; n, p)$ is approximately $(2\pi npq)^{-\frac{1}{2}}$.

It is obvious that the ratio in formula (3.1) decreases monotonically as k increases; thus, when $k \geq r + 1$

$$(3.3) \qquad \frac{b(k; n, p)}{b(k - 1; n, p)} \leq \frac{(n - r)p}{(r + 1)q}.$$

Set herein $k = r+1, \ldots, r+\nu$ and multiply the ν inequalities to obtain

$$(3.4) \qquad \frac{b(r + \nu; n, p)}{b(r; n, p)} \leq \left\{ \frac{(n - r)p}{(r + 1)q} \right\}^{\nu}.$$

For $r \geq np$ the fraction within braces is less than unity, and summation over ν leads to a finite geometric series with ratio $(n - r)p/(r + 1)q$. We conclude that for $r \geq np$

$$(3.5) \qquad \sum_{\nu=0}^{n-r} b(r + \nu; n, p) \leq b(r; n, p) \frac{(r + 1)q}{r + 1 - (n + 1)p}.$$

On the left we have the right "tail" of the binomial distribution, namely the probability of at least r successes. The same calculation applied to the left tail shows that for $s \leq np$

$$(3.6) \qquad \sum_{\rho=0}^{s} b(\rho; n, p) \leq b(s; n, p) \frac{(n - s + 1)p}{(n + 1)p - s}.$$

We have proved

Theorem 2. *If $r \geq np$, the probability of at least r successes satisfies the inequality* (3.5); *if $s \leq np$, the probability of at most s successes satisfies the inequality* (3.6).

[For an alternative proof see problem 39(a).]

4. THE LAW OF LARGE NUMBERS

On several occasions we have mentioned that our *intuitive notion of probability* is based on the following assumption. If in n identical trials A occurs ν times, and if n is very large, then ν/n should be near the probability p of A. Clearly, a formal mathematical theory can never refer directly to real life, but it should at least provide theoretical counterparts to the phenomena which it tries to explain. Accordingly, we require that the vague introductory remark be made precise in the form of a theorem. For this purpose we translate "identical trials" as "Bernoulli trials" with probability p for success. If S_n is the number of successes in n trials, then S_n/n is the average number of successes and should be near p. It is now easy to give a precise meaning to this. Consider, for example, the probability that S_n/n exceeds $p + \epsilon$, where $\epsilon > 0$ is arbitrarily small but fixed. This probability is the same as $P\{S_n > n(p + \epsilon)\}$ and equals the left side of (3.5) when r is the smallest integer exceeding $n(p + \epsilon)$. Then (3.5) implies

$$(4.1) \qquad P\{S_n > n(p + \epsilon)\} < b(r; n, p)\, \frac{n(p + \epsilon) + q}{n\epsilon + q}.$$

With increasing n the fraction on the right remains bounded, whereas $b(r; n, p) \to 0$ since $b(r; n, p) < b(k; n, p)$ for each k such that $(n + 1)p \leq k < r$, and there are about $n\epsilon$ such terms $b(k; n, p)$. It follows that as n increases, $P\{S_n > n(p + \epsilon)\} \to 0$. Using formula (3.6), we see in the same way that $P\{S_n < n(p - \epsilon)\} \to 0$, and we have thus

$$(4.2) \qquad P\left\{ \left| \frac{S_n}{n} - p \right| < \epsilon \right\} \to 1.$$

In words: As n increases, the probability that the average number of successes deviates from p by more than any preassigned ϵ tends to zero. This is one form of the *law of large numbers* and serves as a basis for the intuitive notion of probability as a measure of relative frequencies. For practical applications it must be supplemented by a more precise estimate of the probability on the left side in (4.2); such an estimate is provided by the normal approximation to the binomial distribution [cf. the typical example VII(3.*g*)]. Actually formula (4.2) is a simple consequence of the latter (problem VII, 18).

The assertion (4.2) is the classical law of large numbers. It is of very limited interest and should be replaced by the more precise and more useful *strong law of large numbers* (see chapter VIII, section 4).

Warning. It is usual to read into the law of large numbers things which it definitely does not imply. If Peter and Paul toss a perfect coin 10,000 times, it is customary to expect that Peter will be in the lead roughly half the time. *This is not true.* The arc sine law (chapter III, section 5) states that such an equalization is least probable. The probability *that Peter leads in less than* 20 *trials is very much larger than the probability that the number of trials in which he leads lies between* 4990 *and* 5010. There does not exist any tendency for the periods of lead to equalize. The law of large numbers asserts *only* that in a large number of *different* coin-tossing games the frequency of those in which heads lead is, at any given moment, close to $\frac{1}{2}$. Nothing is said about the fluctuations of the lead within a *fixed* game.

5. THE POISSON APPROXIMATION [6]

In many applications we deal with Bernoulli trials where, comparatively speaking, n is large and p is small, whereas the product

$$(5.1) \qquad \lambda = np$$

is of moderate magnitude. In such cases it is convenient to use an approximation formula to $b(k; n, p)$ which is due to Poisson and which we proceed to derive. We have $b(0; n, p) = (1 - p)^n$ or, substituting from (5.1),

$$(5.2) \qquad b(0; n, p) = \left(1 - \frac{\lambda}{n}\right)^n .$$

Passing to logarithms and using the Taylor expansion II(8.10), we find

$$(5.3) \qquad \log b(0; n, p) = n \log\left(1 - \frac{\lambda}{n}\right) = -\lambda - \frac{\lambda^2}{2n} - \ldots$$

so that for large n

$$(5.4) \qquad b(0; n, p) \approx e^{-\lambda},$$

where the sign $\approx$ is used to indicate approximate equality (in the present case up to terms of order of magnitude n^{-1}). Furthermore, from (3.1) it is seen that for any fixed k and sufficiently large n we have

---

[6] Siméon D. Poisson (1781–1840). His book, *Recherches sur la probabilité des jugements en matière criminelle et en matière civile, précédées des règles générales du calcul des probabilités*, appeared in 1837.

$$(5.5) \qquad \frac{b(k; n, p)}{b(k-1; n, p)} = \frac{\lambda - (k - 1)p}{kq} \approx \frac{\lambda}{k}.$$

For $k = 1$ we get from this and (5.4) $b(1; n, p) \approx \lambda e^{-\lambda}$. For $k = 2$ we get $b(2; n, p) \approx \lambda^2 e^{-\lambda}/2$. Generally we see by induction that

$$(5.6) \qquad b(k; n, p) \approx \frac{\lambda^k}{k!} e^{-\lambda}.$$

This is the famous *Poisson approximation to the binomial distribution*. (See problems 30–34 for an estimate of the error and a proof that the approximation in (5.6) is uniform when $n \to \infty$ and $p \to 0$ in such a way that $\lambda = np$ remains bounded.) It is convenient to have a symbol for the right-hand member in (5.6), and we shall put

$$(5.7) \qquad p(k; \lambda) = e^{-\lambda} \frac{\lambda^k}{k!}.$$

With this notation $p(k; \lambda)$ should be an approximation to $b(k; n, \lambda/n)$ when n is sufficiently large.

Examples. (a) The entries p_m of the last column of table 3 in chapter IV give the values $p(m; 1)$. In the preceding columns b_m stands for $b(m; N, 1/N)$. The table enables us to compare the Poisson distribution $p(m; 1)$ with the binomial distributions with $p = 1/n$ and $n = 3, 4, 5, 6, 10$. It will be seen that the agreement is surprisingly good despite the small values of n.

(b) Table 2 compares $p(k; 1)$ to the binomial distribution with

TABLE 2

AN EXAMPLE OF THE POISSON APPROXIMATION

k	$b(k; 100, \frac{1}{100})$	$p(k; 1)$	N_k
0	0.366 032	0.367 879	41
1	.369 730	.367 879	34
2	.184 865	.183 940	16
3	.060 999	.061 313	8
4	.014 942	.015 328	0
5	.002 898	.003 066	1
6	.000 463	.000 511	0
7	.000 063	.000 073	0
8	.000 007	.000 009	0
9	.000 001	.000 001	0

The first columns illustrate the Poisson approximation to the binomial distribution. The last column records the number of batches of 100 pairs of random digits each in which the combination (7, 7) appears exactly k times.

$n = 100$, $p = \frac{1}{100}$. It shows the approximation to be satisfactory for many purposes. As an example take the occurrence of the combination $(7, 7)$ among 100 pairs of random digits, which should have the binomial distribution $b(k; 100, \frac{1}{100})$. The last column of table 2 [7] gives the actual counts in 100 batches of 100 random digits each. To obtain relative frequencies all entries of the last column should be divided by 100. These frequencies agree reasonably with the theoretical probabilities. (As judged by the χ^2-criterion, chance fluctuations should, in about 75 out of 100 similar cases, produce larger deviations of observed frequencies from the theoretical probabilities.)

(c) *Birthdays.* What is the probability, p_k, that in a company of 500 people exactly k will have birthdays on New Year's Day? If the 500 people are chosen at random, we may apply the scheme of 500 Bernoulli trials with probability of success $p = \frac{1}{365}$. Then $p_0 = (\frac{364}{365})^{500} = 0.2537\ldots$. For the Poisson approximation we put $\lambda = \frac{500}{365} = 1.3699\ldots$. Then $p(0; \lambda) = 0.2541$, which involves an error only in the fourth decimal place. For $k = 1, 2, \ldots$ the correct values of p_k as calculated from the binomial formula are $p_1 = 0.3484\ldots$, $p_2 = 0.2388\ldots$, $p_3 = 0.1089\ldots$, $p_4 = 0.0372\ldots$, $p_5 = 0.0101\ldots$, $p_6 = 0.0023\ldots$. The corresponding Poisson approximations are $p(1; \lambda) = 0.3481\ldots$, $p(2; \lambda) = 0.2385\ldots$, $p(3; \lambda) = 0.1089\ldots$, $p(4; \lambda) = 0.0373\ldots$, $p(5; \lambda) = 0.0102\ldots$, $p(6; \lambda) = 0.0023\ldots$. All errors are in the fourth decimal place.

(d) *Defective items.* Suppose that screws are produced under statistical quality control so that it is legitimate to apply the Bernoulli scheme of trials. If the probability of a screw's being defective is $p = 0.015$, then the probability that a box of 100 screws does not contain a defective one is $(0.985)^{100} = 0.22061$. The corresponding Poisson approximation is $e^{-1.5} = 0.22313\ldots$, which should be close enough for most practical purposes. We now ask: How many screws should a box contain in order that the probability of finding at least 100 conforming screws be 0.8 or better? If $100 + x$ is the required number, then x is a small integer. To apply the Poisson approximation for $n = 100 + x$ trials we should put $\lambda = np$, but np is approximately $100p = 1.5$. We then require the smallest integer x for which

$$(5.8) \qquad e^{-1.5}\left\{1 + \frac{1.5}{1} + \ldots + \frac{(1.5)^x}{x!}\right\} \geq 0.8.$$

---

[7] M. G. Kendall and Babington Smith, *Tables of random sampling numbers,* Tracts for Computers No. 24, Cambridge, 1940.

In tables [8] we find that for $x = 1$ the left side is approximately 0.56, and for $x = 2$ it is 0.809. Thus the Poisson approximation would lead to the conclusion that 102 screws are required. Since 0.809 is dangerously near the given threshold of 0.8, the number 103 is safer. Actually the probability of finding at least 100 conforming screws in a box of 102 is

$$(0.985)^{102} + \binom{102}{1} (0.985)^{101}(0.015) +$$

$$+ \binom{102}{2} (0.985)^{100}(0.015)^2 = 0.8022\ldots.$$

(e) *Centenarians.* At birth any particular person has a small chance of living 100 years, and in a large community the number of yearly births is large. Owing to wars, epidemics, etc., different lives are not stochastically independent, but as a first approximation we may compare n births to n Bernoulli trials with death after 100 years as success. In a stable community, where neither size nor mortality rate changes appreciably, it is reasonable to expect that the frequency of years in which exactly k centenarians die is approximately $p(k; \lambda)$, with λ depending on the size and health of the community. Records of Switzerland confirm this conclusion.[9]

(f) *Misprints, raisins, etc.* If in printing a book there is a constant probability of any letter's being misprinted, and if the conditions of printing remain unchanged, then we have as many Bernoulli trials as there are letters. The frequency of pages containing exactly k misprints will then be approximately $p(k; \lambda)$, where λ is a characteristic of the printer. Occasional fatigue of the printer, difficult passages, etc., will increase the chances of errors and may produce clusters of misprints. Thus the Poisson formula may be used to discover radical departures from uniformity or from the state of statistical control. A similar argument applies in many cases. For example, if many raisins are distributed in the dough, we should expect that thorough mixing will result in the frequency of loaves with exactly k raisins to be approximately $p(k; \lambda)$ with λ a measure of the density of raisins in the dough.

---

[8] E. C. Molina, *Poisson's exponential binomial limit*, New York, 1942. (These are tables giving $p(k; \lambda)$ and $p(k; \lambda) + p(k+1; \lambda) + \ldots$ for k ranging from 0 to 100.)

[9] E. J. Gumbel, *Les centenaires*, Aktuárske Vedy, Prague, vol. 7 (1937), pp. 1–8.

6. THE POISSON DISTRIBUTION

In the preceding section we have used the Poisson expression (5.7) merely as a convenient approximation to the binomial distribution in the case of large n and small p. In connection with the matching and occupancy problems of chapter IV we have studied different probability distributions, which have also led to the Poisson expressions $p(k; \lambda)$ as a limiting form. We have here a special case of the remarkable fact that there exist a few distributions of great universality which occur in a surprisingly great variety of problems. The three principal distributions, with ramifications throughout probability theory, are the binomial distribution, the normal distribution (to be introduced in the following chapter), and the *Poisson distribution*

$$(6.1) \qquad p(k; \lambda) = e^{-\lambda} \frac{\lambda^k}{k!},$$

which we shall now consider on its own merits.

We note first that on adding the equations (6.1) for $k = 0, 1, 2, \ldots$ we get on the right side $e^{-\lambda}$ times the Taylor series for e^{λ}. Hence for any fixed λ the quantities $p(k; \lambda)$ add to unity, and therefore it is possible to conceive of an ideal experiment in which $p(k; \lambda)$ is the probability of exactly k successes. We shall now indicate why many physical experiments and statistical observations actually lead to such an interpretation of (6.1). The examples of the next section will illustrate the wide range and the importance of various applications of (6.1). The true nature of the Poisson distribution will become apparent only in connection with the theory of stochastic processes (cf. chapter XVII, where a new approach to the Poisson distribution is given).

Consider a sequence of random events occurring in time, such as radioactive disintegrations or incoming calls at a telephone exchange. Each event is represented by a point on the time axis, and we are concerned with chance distributions of points. There exist many different types of such distributions, but their study belongs to the domain of continuous probabilities which we have postponed to the second volume. Here we shall be content to show that the simplest physical assumptions lead to $p(k; \lambda)$ as the probability of finding exactly k points (events) within a fixed interval of specified length. Our methods are necessarily crude, and we shall return to the same problem with more adequate methods in chapter XVII.

The physical assumptions which we want to express mathematically are that the conditions of the experiment remain constant in time, and that non-overlapping time intervals are stochastically independent in the sense that information concerning the number of events in one interval reveals nothing about the other. The theory of probabilities in a continuum makes it possible to express these statements directly, but being restricted to discrete probabilities, we have to use an approximate finite model and pass to the limit.

Imagine the unit time interval divided into a great number n of intervals, each of length $1/n$. Either a particular subinterval is empty, or it contains at least one of our random points (or events), and we agree to call the two possibilities failure and success, respectively. The probability p_n of success must be the same for all n subintervals, since they have the same length. The assumed independence of non-overlapping intervals then implies that we have n Bernoulli trials, and the probability of exactly k successes is given by $b(k; n, p_n)$. Now the number of successes is not necessarily the same as the number of random points, since a subinterval may contain several random points. However, it is natural to introduce the additional assumption that the probability of two or more random points during a very short time interval is in the limit negligible.[10] In this case the probability of finding exactly k random points in the unit time interval is given by the limit of $b(k; n, p_n)$ as $n \to \infty$. When we divide each subinterval into two parts of equal length, we find that $p_n = 2p_{2n} - p_{2n}^2$; this equation states that success in an interval of length $1/n$ means either success in the left half, or success in the right half, or in both. It follows that $p_n < 2p_{2n}$, and this suggests that np_n increases monotonically (which can be proved rigorously). If $np_n \to \lambda$, then $b(k; n, p_n) \sim b(k; n, \lambda/n) \to \to p(k; \lambda)$, and we find (6.1) as the probability that there is a total of k random points contained in our unit interval. The assumption $np_n \to \infty$ leads to no sensible result, as it would imply infinitely many random points even in the smallest interval.

If, instead of the unit interval, we take an arbitrary interval of length t and again use a subdivision into intervals of length $1/n$, then we have Bernoulli trials with the same probability p_n of success, but the number of trials is the integer nearest to nt rather than n. The passage to the limit is the same, but we get λt instead of λ. This leads

---

[10] This assumption is implicit in the intuitive picture of isolated random points. However, it is necessary to exclude the possibility of our events appearing in doublets. For example, if the events are automobile accidents, then the probability of two events within a short time is negligible in comparison with the probability of one event. On the other hand, an accident is likely to involve two cars, and if the events mean "a car smashed" then they are likely to appear in pairs and our assumption does not apply.

us to consider

$$(6.2) \qquad p(k; \lambda t) = e^{-\lambda t} \frac{(\lambda t)^k}{k!}$$

as the probability of finding exactly k points in a fixed interval of length t. In particular, the probability of no point in an interval of length t is

$$(6.3) \qquad p(0; \lambda t) = e^{-\lambda t},$$

and the probability of one or more points is therefore $1 - e^{-\lambda t}$.

The parameter λ is a physical constant which determines the density of points on the t-axis. The larger λ is, the smaller is the probability (6.3) of finding no point. Suppose that a physical experiment is repeated a great number N of times, and that each time we count the number of events in an interval of fixed length t. Let N_k be the number of times that exactly k events are observed. Then

$$(6.4) \qquad N_0 + N_1 + N_2 + \ldots = N.$$

The total number of points observed in the N experiments is

$$(6.5) \qquad N_1 + 2N_2 + 3N_3 + \ldots = T,$$

and T/N is the average. If N is large, we expect that

$$(6.6) \qquad N_k \approx Np(k; \lambda t)$$

(this lies at the root of all applications of probability and will be justified and made more precise by the law of large numbers in chapter X). Substituting from (6.6) into (6.5), we find

$$(6.7) \quad T \approx N\{p(1; \lambda t) + 2p(2; \lambda t) + 3p(3; \lambda t) + \ldots\} =$$

$$= Ne^{-\lambda t}\lambda t \left\{ 1 + \frac{\lambda t}{1} + \frac{(\lambda t)^2}{2!} + \ldots \right\} = N\lambda t$$

and hence

$$(6.8) \qquad \lambda t \approx \frac{T}{N}.$$

This relation gives us a means of estimating λ from observations and of comparing theory with experiments.   The examples of the next section will illustrate this point.

Spatial Distributions

We have considered the distribution of random events or points along the t-axis, but the same argument applies to the distribution of points in plane or space.   Instead of intervals of length t we have domains of area or volume t, and the fundamental assumption is that the probability of finding k points in any specified domain depends only on the area or volume of the domain but not on its shape.   Otherwise we have the same assumptions as before: (1) if t is small, the probability of finding more than one point in a domain of volume t is small as compared to t; (2) non-overlapping domains are mutually independent. To find the probability that a domain of volume t contains exactly k random points, we subdivide it into n subdomains and approximate the required probability by the probability of k successes in n trials. This means neglecting the possibility of finding more than one point in the same subdomain, but our assumption (1) implies that the error tends to zero as $n \rightarrow \infty$.   In the limit we get again the Poisson distribution (6.2).   Stars in space, raisins in cake, weed seeds among grass seeds, flaws in materials, animal litters in fields are distributed in accordance with the Poisson law.   See examples (7.b) and (7.e).

7. OBSERVATIONS FITTING THE POISSON DISTRIBUTION [11]

(a) *Radioactive disintegrations.*   A radioactive substance emits α-particles; the number of particles reaching a given portion of space during time t is the best-known example of random events obeying the Poisson law.   Of course, the substance continues to decay, and in the long run the density of α-particles will decline.   However, with radium it takes years before a decrease of matter can be detected; for relatively short periods the conditions may be considered constant, and we have an ideal realization of the hypotheses which led to the Poisson distribution.

In a famous experiment [12] a radioactive substance was observed during $N = 2608$ time intervals of 7.5 seconds each; the number of par-

---

[11] The Poisson distribution has become known as the law of small numbers or of rare events.   These are misnomers which proved detrimental to the realization of the fundamental role of the Poisson distribution.   The following examples will show how misleading the two names are.

[12] Rutherford, Chadwick, and Ellis, *Radiations from radioactive substances*, Cambridge, 1920, p. 172.   Table 3 and the χ^2-estimate of the text are taken from H. Cramér, *Mathematical methods of statistics*, Uppsala and Princeton, 1945, p. 436.

TABLE 3

EXAMPLE (a): RADIOACTIVE DISINTEGRATIONS

k	N_k	$Np(k; 3.870)$
0	57	54.399
1	203	210.523
2	383	407.361
3	525	525.496
4	532	508.418
5	408	393.515
6	273	253.817
7	139	140.325
8	45	67.882
9	27	29.189
$k \geq 10$	16	17.075
Total	2608	2608.000

ticles reaching a counter was obtained for each period. Table 3 records
the number N_k of periods with exactly k particles. The total number
of particles is $T = \Sigma k N_k = 10,094$, the average $T/N = 3.870$. The
theoretical values $Np(k; 3.870)$ are seen to be rather close to the observed numbers N_k. To judge the closeness of fit, an estimate of the
probable magnitude of chance fluctuations is required. Statisticians
judge the closeness of fit by the χ^2-criterion. Measuring by this standard, we should expect that under ideal conditions about 17 out of 100
comparable cases would show worse agreement than exhibited in table 3.

(b) *Flying-bomb hits on London.* As an example of a spatial distribution of random points consider the statistics of flying-bomb hits in

TABLE 4

EXAMPLE (b): FLYING-BOMB HITS ON LONDON

k	0	1	2	3	4	5 and over
N_k	229	211	93	35	7	1
$Np(k; 0.9323)$	226.74	211.39	98.54	30.62	7.14	1.57

the south of London during World War II. The entire area is divided
into $N = 576$ small areas of $t = \frac{1}{4}$ square kilometers each, and table 4
records the number N_k of areas with exactly k hits.[13] The total number

---

[13] The figures are taken from R. D. Clarke, An application of the Poisson distribution, *Journal of the Institute of Actuaries*, vol. 72 (1946), p. 48.

TABLE 5

EXAMPLE (c): CHROMOSOME INTERCHANGES INDUCED BY X-RAY IRRADIATION

Experiment Number		Cells with k Interchanges				Total N	χ^2-Level in Per Cent
		0	1	2	≥ 3		
1	Observed N_k	753	266	49	5	1073	95
	$Np(k; 0.35508)$	752.3	267.1	47.4	6.2		
2	Observed N_k	434	195	44	9	682	85
	$Np(k; 0.45601)$	432.3	197.1	44.9	7.7		
3	Observed N_k	280	75	12	1	368	65
	$Np(k; 0.27717)$	278.9	77.3	10.7	1.1		
4	Observed N_k	2278	273	15	0	2566	65
	$Np(k; 0.11808)$	2280.2	269.2	15.9	0.7		
5	Observed N_k	593	143	20	3	759	45
	$Np(k; 0.25296)$	589.4	149.1	18.8	1.7		
6	Observed N_k	639	141	13	0	793	45
	$Np(k; 0.21059)$	642.4	135.3	14.2	1.1		
7	Observed N_k	359	109	13	1	482	40
	$Np(k; 0.28631)$	362.0	103.6	14.9	1.5		
8	Observed N_k	493	176	26	2	697	35
	$Np(k; 0.33572)$	498.2	167.3	28.1	3.4		
9	Observed N_k	793	339	62	5	1199	20
	$Np(k; 0.39867)$	804.8	320.8	64.0	9.4		
10	Observed N_k	579	254	47	3	883	20
	$Np(k; 0.40544)$	588.7	238.7	48.4	7.2		
11	Observed N_k	444	252	59	1	756	5
	$Np(k; 0.49339)$	461.6	227.7	56.2	10.5		

of hits is $T = \Sigma k N_k = 537$, the average $\lambda t = T/N = 0.9323\ldots$. The fit of the Poisson distribution is surprisingly good; as judged by the χ^2-criterion, under ideal conditions some 88 per cent of comparable observations should show a worse agreement. It is interesting to note that most people believed in a tendency of the points of impact to cluster. If this were true, there would be a higher frequency of areas with either many hits or no hit and a deficiency in the intermediate classes. Table 4 indicates perfect randomness and homogeneity of the area; we have here an instructive illustration of the established fact that to the untrained eye randomness appears as regularity or tendency to cluster.

(c) *Chromosome interchanges in cells.* Irradiation by X-rays produces certain processes in organic cells which we call chromosome interchanges. As long as radiation continues, the probability of such interchanges remains constant, and, according to theory, the numbers N_k of cells with exactly k interchanges should follow a Poisson distribution. The theory is also able to predict the dependence of the parameter λ on the intensity of radiation, the temperature, etc., but we shall not enter into these details. Table 5 records the result of eleven different series of experiments.[14] These are arranged according to goodness of fit. The last column indicates the approximate percentage of ideal cases in which chance fluctuations would produce a worse agreement (as judged by the χ^2-standard). The agreement between theory and observation is striking.

(d) *Connections to wrong number.* Table 6 shows statistics of telephone connections to a wrong number.[15] A total of $N = 267$ numbers was observed; N_k indicates how many numbers had exactly k wrong connections. The Poisson distribution $p(k; 8.74)$ shows again an excellent fit. (As judged by the χ^2-criterion the deviations are near the median value.) In Thorndike's paper the reader will find other telephone statistics following the Poisson law. Sometimes (as with party lines, calls from groups of coin boxes, etc.) there is an obvious interdependence among the events, and the Poisson distribution no longer fits.

---

[14] D. G. Catcheside, D. E. Lea, and J. M. Thoday, Types of chromosome structural change induced by the irradiation of *Tradescantia* microspores, *Journal of Genetics*, vol. 47 (1945–46), pp. 113–136. Our table is table IX of this paper, except that the χ^2-levels were recomputed, using a single degree of freedom.

[15] The observations are taken from F. Thorndike, Applications of Poisson's probability summation, *The Bell System Technical Journal*, vol. 5 (1926), pp. 604–624. This paper contains a graphical analysis of 32 different statistics.

TABLE 6

EXAMPLE (d): CONNECTIONS TO WRONG NUMBER

k	N_k	$Np(k; 8.74)$
0–2	1	2.05
3	5	4.76
4	11	10.39
5	14	18.16
6	22	26.45
7	43	33.03
8	31	36.09
9	40	35.04
10	35	30.63
11	20	24.34
12	18	17.72
13	12	11.92
14	7	7.44
15	6	4.33
≥ 16	2	4.65
	267	267.00

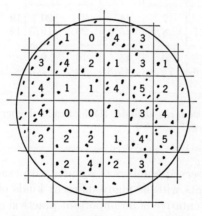

FIGURE 1.   Bacteria on a Petri plate.

(e) *Bacteria and blood counts.* Figure 1 reproduces a photograph of a Petri plate with bacterial colonies, which are visible under the microscope as dark spots. The plate is divided into small squares. Table 7

Table 7

Example (e): Counts of Bacteria

k	0	1	2	3	4	5	6	7	χ^2-Level
Observed N_k	5	19	26	26	21	13	8		97
Poisson theor.	6.1	18.0	26.7	26.4	19.6	11.7	9.5		
Observed N_k	26	40	38	17	7				66
Poisson theor.	27.5	42.2	32.5	16.7	9.1				
Observed N_k	59	86	49	30	20				26
Poisson theor.	55.6	82.2	60.8	30.0	15.4				
Observed N_k	83	134	135	101	40	16	7		63
Poisson theor.	75.0	144.5	139.4	89.7	43.3	16.7	7.4		
Observed N_k	8	16	18	15	9	7			97
Poisson theor.	6.8	16.2	19.2	15.1	9.0	6.7			
Observed N_k	7	11	11	11	7	8			53
Poisson theor.	3.9	10.4	13.7	12.0	7.9	7.1			
Observed N_k	3	7	14	21	20	19	7	9	85
Poisson theor.	2.1	8.2	15.8	20.2	19.5	15	9.6	9.6	
Observed N_k	60	80	45	16	9				78
Poisson theor.	62.6	75.8	45.8	18.5	7.3				

The last entry in each row includes the figures for higher classes and should be labeled "k or more."

reproduces the observed numbers of squares with exactly k dark spots in eight experiments with as many different kinds of bacteria.[16] We have here a representative of an important practical application of the Poisson distribution to spatial distributions of random points.

[16] The table is taken from J. Neyman, *Lectures and conferences on mathematical statistics* (mimeographed), Dept. of Agriculture, Washington, 1938. The original (by T. Matuszewsky, J. Supinska, and J. Neyman) appeared, together with related material, in *Zentralblatt für Bakteriologie, Parasitenkunde und Infektionskrankheiten*, II Abt., vol. 95 (1936).

8. WAITING TIMES. THE NEGATIVE BINOMIAL DISTRIBUTION

Consider a succession of n Bernoulli trials and let us inquire how long it will take for the rth success to turn up. Here r is a fixed positive integer. The total number of successes in n trials may, of course, fall short of r, but the probability that the rth success occurs at the trial number $\nu \leq n$ is clearly independent of n and depends only on ν, r, and p. Since necessarily $\nu \geq r$, it is preferable to write $\nu = k + r$. *The probability that the rth success occurs at the trial number $r + k$ (where $k = 0, 1, \ldots$) will be denoted by $f(k; r, p)$.* It equals *the probability that exactly k failures precede the rth success.* This event occurs if, and only if, among the $r + k - 1$ trials there are exactly k failures and the following, or $(r+k)$th, trial results in success; the corresponding probabilities are $\binom{r + k - 1}{k} \cdot p^{r-1}q^k$ and p, so that

$$(8.1) \qquad f(k; r, p) = \binom{r + k - 1}{k} \cdot p^r q^k.$$

Rewriting the binomial coefficient in accordance with formula II(12.4), we find the alternative form

$$(8.2) \qquad f(k; r, p) = \binom{-r}{k} p^r (-q)^k, \qquad k = 0, 1, 2, \ldots.$$

Suppose now that *Bernoulli trials are continued as long as necessary for r successes to turn up.* A typical sample point is represented by a sequence containing an arbitrary number, k, of letters F and exactly r letters S, the sequence terminating by an S; the probability of such a point is, by definition, $p^r q^k$. We must ask, however, whether it is possible that the trials *never* end, that is, whether an infinite sequence of trials may produce fewer than r successes. Now $\sum_{k=0}^{\infty} f(k; r, p)$ is the probability that the rth success occurs after finitely many trials; accordingly, the possibility of an infinite sequence with fewer than r successes can be discounted if, and only if,

$$(8.3) \qquad \sum_{k=0}^{\infty} f(k; r, p) = 1.$$

To prove that (8.3) holds it suffices to note that by the binomial theorem

$$(8.4) \qquad \sum_{k=0}^{\infty} \binom{-r}{k} (-q)^k = (1 - q)^{-r} = p^{-r}.$$

Multiplying (8.4) by p^r we get (8.3).

In our waiting time problem r is necessarily a positive integer, but the quantity defined by either (8.1) or (8.2) is non-negative and (8.3) holds for any positive r. *For arbitrary fixed real $r > 0$ and $0 < p < 1$ the sequence $\{f(k; r, p)\}$ is called a negative binomial distribution.* It occurs in many applications (and we have encountered it in problem V, 24 as the limiting form of the Polya distribution). When r is a positive integer, $\{f(k; r, p)\}$ may be interpreted as the *probability distribution for the waiting time to the rth success;* as such it is also called the *Pascal* distribution. For $r = 1$ it reduces to the *geometric distribution* $\{pq^k\}$.

TABLE 8

PROBABILITIES (8.5)

r	u_r	U_r	r	u_r	U_r
0	0.079 589	0.079 589	15	0.023 171	0.917 941
1	.079 589	.159 178	16	.019 081	.937 022
2	.078 785	.237 963	17	.015 447	.952 469
3	.077 177	.315 140	18	.012 283	.964 752
4	.074 790	.389 931	19	.009 587	.974 338
5	.071 674	.461 605	20	.007 338	.981 676
6	.067 902	.529 506	21	.005 504	.987 180
7	.063 568	.593 073	22	.004 041	.991 220
8	.058 783	.651 855	23	.002 901	.994 121
9	.053 671	.705 527	24	.002 034	.996 155
10	.048 363	.753 890	25	.001 392	.997 547
11	.042 989	.796 879	26	.000 928	.998 475
12	.037 676	.834 555	27	.000 602	.999 077
13	.032 538	.867 094	28	.000 379	.999 456
14	.027 676	.894 770	29	.000 232	.999 688

u_r is the probability that, at the moment the first match box is found empty, the second contains exactly r matches, assuming that initially each box contained 50 matches. $U_r = u_0 + u_1 + \ldots + u_r$ is the corresponding probability of having not more than r matches.

Example. *Banach's match box problem.*[17] A certain mathematician always carries one match box in his right pocket and one in his left. When he wants a match, he selects a pocket at random, the successive choices thus constituting Bernoulli trials with $p = \frac{1}{2}$. Suppose that initially each box contained exactly N matches and consider the moment when, for the first time, our mathematician *discovers* that a box is empty. At that moment the other box may contain $0, 1, 2, \ldots, N$ matches, and we denote the corresponding probabilities by u_r. Let us identify "success" with choice of the left pocket. The left pocket will be found empty at a moment when the right pocket contains exactly r matches if, and only if, exactly $N - r$ failures precede the $(N+1)$st success. The probability of this event is $f(N-r; N+1, \frac{1}{2})$. The same argument applies to the right pocket and therefore the required probability is

$$(8.5) \qquad u_r = 2f(N-r; N+1, \tfrac{1}{2}) = \binom{2N-r}{N} 2^{-2N+r}.$$

Numerical values for the case $N = 50$ are given in table 8. [Cf. problems 21–23 and example IX(3.f).]

9. THE MULTINOMIAL DISTRIBUTION

The binomial distribution can easily be generalized to the case of n repeated independent trials where each trial can have one of several outcomes. Denote the possible outcomes of each trial by $E_1, \ldots, E_r$, and suppose that the probability of the realization of E_i in each trial is p_i $(i = 1, \ldots, r)$. For $r = 2$ we have Bernoulli trials; in general, the numbers p_i are subject only to the condition

$$(9.1) \qquad\qquad p_1 + \ldots + p_r = 1, \qquad\qquad p_i \geq 0.$$

The result of n trials is a succession like $E_3 E_1 E_2 \ldots$. *The probability that in n trials E_1 occurs k_1 times, E_2 occurs k_2 times, etc., is*

$$(9.2) \qquad\qquad \frac{n!}{k_1! k_2! \cdots k_r!} p_1^{k_1} p_2^{k_2} p_3^{k_3} \cdots p_r^{k_r};$$

here the k_i are arbitrary non-negative integers subject to the obvious condition

$$(9.3) \qquad\qquad k_1 + k_1 + \ldots + k_r = n.$$

If $r = 2$, then (9.2) reduces to the binomial distribution with $p_1 = p$,

---

[17] Communicated by H. Steinhaus.

$p_2 = q$, $k_1 = k$, $k_2 = n - k$. The proof in the general case proceeds along the same lines, starting with formula II(4.7).

Formula (9.2) is called the *multinomial distribution* because the right-hand member is the general term of the *multinomial* expansion of $(p_1 + \ldots + p_r)^n$. Its main application is to *sampling with replacement* when the individuals are classified into more than two categories (e.g., according to professions).

Examples. (a) In rolling twelve dice, what is the probability of getting each face twice? Here $E_1, \ldots, E_6$ represent the six faces, all k_i equal 2, and all p_i equal $\frac{1}{6}$. Therefore, the answer is $(12!)(2)^{-6}(6)^{-12} =$
$= 0.0034\ldots$

(b) *Sampling.* Let a population of N elements be divided into sub-classes $E_1, \ldots, E_r$ of sizes $Np_1, \ldots, Np_r$. The multinomial distribution gives the probabilities of the several possible compositions of a random sample with replacement of size n taken from this population.

(c) *Multiple Bernoulli trials.* Two sequences of Bernoulli trials with probabilities of success and failure p_1, q_1, and p_2, q_2, respectively, may be considered one compound experiment with four possible outcomes in each trial, namely, the combinations (S, S), (S, F), (F, S), (F, F). The assumption that the two original sequences are independent is translated into the statement that the probabilities of the four outcomes are p_1p_2, p_1q_2, q_1p_2, q_1q_2, respectively. If k_1, k_2, k_3, k_4 are four integers adding to n, the probability that in n trials SS will appear k_1 times, SF k_2 times, etc., is

$$(9.4) \qquad \frac{n!}{k_1!\,k_2!\,k_3!\,k_4!}\, p_1^{k_1+k_2} q_1^{k_3+k_4} p_2^{k_1+k_3} q_2^{k_2+k_4}.$$

A special case occurs in *sampling inspection*. An item is conforming or defective with probabilities p and q. It may or may not be inspected with corresponding probabilities p' and q'. The decision of whether an item is inspected is made without knowledge of its quality, so that we have independent trials. (Cf. problems 25, 26, and IX, 12.)

10. PROBLEMS FOR SOLUTION

1. Assuming all sex distributions to be equally probable, what proportion of families with exactly six children should be expected to have three boys and three girls?

2. A bridge player had no ace in three consecutive hands. Did he have reason to complain of ill luck?

3. How long has a series of random digits to be in order for the probability of the digit 7 appearing to be at least $\frac{9}{10}$?

4. How many independent bridge dealings are required in order for the probability of a preassigned player having four aces at least once to be $\frac{1}{2}$ or better? Solve again for some player instead of a given one.

5. If the probability of hitting a target is $\frac{1}{5}$ and ten shots are fired independently, what is the probability of the target's being hit at least twice?

6. In problem 5, find the conditional probability of the target's being hit at least twice, assuming that at least one hit is scored.

7. Find the probability that a hand of thirteen bridge cards selected at random contains exactly two red cards. Compare it with the corresponding probability in Bernoulli trials with $p = \frac{1}{2}$. (For a definition of bridge see footnote 1, chapter I.)

8. What is the probability that the birthdays of six people fall in two calendar months leaving exactly ten months free? (Assume independence and equal probabilities for all months.)

9. In rolling six true dice, find the probability of obtaining (a) at least one, (b) exactly one, (c) exactly two, aces. Compare with the Poisson approximations.

10. If there are on the average 1 per cent left-handers, estimate the chances of having at least four left-handers among 200 people.

11. A book of 500 pages contains 500 misprints. Estimate the chances that a given page contains at least three misprints.

12. Colorblindness appears in 1 per cent of the people in a certain population. How large must a random sample (with replacements) be if the probability of its containing a colorblind person is to be 0.95 or more?

13. In the preceding exercise, what is the probability that a sample of 100 will contain (a) no, (b) two or more, colorblind people?

14. Estimate the number of raisins which a cookie should contain on the average if it is desired that the probability of a cookie to contain at least one raisin be 0.99 or more.

15. The probability of a royal flush in poker is $p = 1/649,740$. How large has n to be to render the probability of no royal flush in n hands smaller than $1/e \approx \frac{1}{3}$? (*Note:* No calculations are necessary for the solution.)

16. A book of n pages contains on the average λ misprints per page. Estimate the probability that at least one page will contain more than k misprints.

17. Suppose that there exist two kinds of stars (or raisins in a cake, or flaws in a material). The probability that a given volume contains j stars of the first kind is $p(j; a)$, and the probability that it contains k stars of the second kind is $p(k; b)$; the two events are assumed to be independent. Prove that the probability that the volume contains a total of n stars is $p(n; a + b)$. (Interpret the assertion and the assumptions abstractly.)

18. *A traffic problem.* The flow of traffic at a certain street crossing is described by saying that the probability of a car's passing during any given second is a constant p; and that there is no interaction between the passing of cars at different seconds. Treating seconds as indivisible time units, the model of Bernoulli trials applies. Suppose that a pedestrian can cross the street only if no car is to pass during the next three seconds. Find the probability that the pedestrian has to wait for exactly $k = 0, 1, 2, 3, 4$ seconds.

(The corresponding general formulas are not obvious and will be derived in connection with the theory of success runs in chapter XIII, section 7.)

19. Two people toss a true coin n times each. Find the probability that they will score the same number of heads.

20. In a sequence of Bernoulli trials with probability p for success, find the probability that a successes will occur before b failures. (*Note:* The issue is decided after at most $a + b - 1$ trials. This problem played a role in the classical theory of games in connection with the question of how to divide the pot when the game is interrupted at a moment when one player lacks a points to victory, the other b points.)

21. In *Banach's match box problem* (section 8) find the probability that at the moment when the first box is emptied (not found empty) the other contains exactly r matches (where $r = 1, 2, \ldots, N$).

22. *Continuation.* Using the preceding result, find the probability x that the box first emptied is not the one first found to be empty. Show that the expression thus obtained reduces to $x = \binom{2N}{N} 2^{-2N-1}$ or $\frac{1}{2}(N\pi)^{-\frac{1}{2}}$, approximately.

23. Proofs of a certain book were read independently by two proofreaders who found, respectively, k_1 and k_2 misprints; k_{12} misprints were found by both. Give a reasonable estimate of the unknown number, n, of misprints in the proofs. (Assume that proofreading corresponds to Bernoulli trials in which the two proofreaders have, respectively, probabilities p_1 and p_2 of catching a misprint. Use the law of large numbers.)

Note: The problem describes in simple terms an experimental setup used by Rutherford for the count of scintillations.

24. To estimate the size of an animal population by trapping,[18] traps are set r times in succession. Assuming that each animal has the same probability q of being trapped; that originally there were n animals in all; and that the only changes in the situation between the successive settings of traps are that animals have been trapped (and thus removed); find the probability that the r trappings yield, respectively, $n_1, n_2, \ldots, n_r$ animals.

25. *Multiple Bernoulli trials.* In example (9.c) find the conditional probabilities p and q of (S, F) and (F, S), respectively, assuming that one of these combinations has occurred. Show that $p > \frac{1}{2}$ or $p < \frac{1}{2}$, according as $p_1 > p_2$ or $p_2 > p_1$.

26. *Continuation.*[19] If in n pairs of trials exactly m resulted in one of the combinations (S, F) or (F, S), show that the probability that (S, F) has occurred exactly k times is $b(k; m, p)$.

27. *Combination of the binomial and Poisson distributions.* Suppose that the

---

[18] P. A. P. Moran, A mathematical theory of animal trapping, *Biometrika*, vol. 38 (1951), pp. 307–311.

[19] A. Wald, Sequential tests of statistical hypotheses, *Annals of Mathematical Statistics*, vol. 16 (1945), p. 166. Wald uses the results given above to devise a practical method of comparing two empirically given sequences of trials (say, the output of two machines), with a view of selecting the one with the greater probability of success. He reduces this problem to the simpler one of finding whether in a sequence of Bernoulli trials the frequency of success differs significantly from $\frac{1}{2}$.

probability of an insect's laying r eggs is $p(r; \lambda)$ and that the probability of an egg's developing is p. Assuming mutual independence of the eggs, show that the probability of a total of k survivors is given by the Poisson distribution with parameter λp.

Note: Another example for the same situation: the probability of k chromosome breakages is $p(k; \lambda)$, and the probability of a breakage healing is p. (For additional examples of a similar nature see IX(1.d) and chapter XII, section 1.)

---

28. Prove the *theorem:* [20] The maximal term of the multinomial distribution (9.2) satisfies the inequalities

(10.1) $$np_i - 1 < k_i \leq (n + r - 1)p_i, \qquad i = 1, 2, \ldots, r.$$

(*Hint:* Prove first that the term is maximal if, and only if, $p_i k_j \leq p_j(k_i + 1)$ for each pair (i, j). Add these inequalities for all j, and also for all $i \neq j$.)

29. The terms $p(k; \lambda)$ of the Poisson distribution reach their maximum when k is the largest integer not exceeding λ.

Note: *Problems 30–34 refer to the Poisson approximation of the binomial distribution. It is understood that $\lambda = np$, and m is the largest integer not exceeding $(n + 1)p$ (that is, m is the index of the central term of the binomial distribution).*

30. Show that as k goes from 0 to ∞ the ratios $a_k = b(k; n, p)/p(k; \lambda)$ first increase, then decrease, reaching their maximum for $k = m$.

31. As k increases, the terms $b(k; n, p)$ are first smaller, then larger, and then again smaller than $p(k; \lambda)$.

32. If $n \to \infty$ and $p \to 0$ so that $np = \lambda$ remains constant, then

$$b(k; n, p) \to p(k; \lambda)$$

uniformly for all k.

33. Show that

(10.2) $$\frac{\lambda^k}{k!}\left(1 - \frac{\lambda}{n}\right)^{n-k} \geq b(k; n, p) \geq \frac{\lambda^k}{k!}\left(1 - \frac{k}{n}\right)^k \left(1 - \frac{\lambda}{n}\right)^n.$$

34. Conclude from (10.2), using the inequalities II(8.12), that

(10.3) $$p(k; \lambda)e^{k\lambda/n} > b(k; n, p) > p(k; \lambda)e^{-k^2/(n-k) - \lambda^2/(n-\lambda)}.$$

Note: Although (10.2) is very crude, the inequalities (10.3) provide excellent error estimates. It is easy to improve on (10.3) by calculations similar to those used in chapter II, section 9. Incidentally, using the result of problem 30, it is obvious that the exponent on the left in (10.3) may be replaced by $m\lambda/n$ which is $\leq (p + n^{-1})\lambda$.

Further Limit Theorems

35. *Binomial approximation to the hypergeometric distribution.* A population of N elements is divided into red and black elements in the proportion $p:q$

---

[20] In the first edition it was only asserted that $|k_i - np_i| \leq r$. The present improvement and its elegant proof are due to P. A. P. Moran.

(where $p + q = 1$). A sample of size n is taken without replacement. The probability that it contains exactly k red elements is given by the hypergeometric distribution of chapter II, section 6. Show that as $N \to \infty$ this probability approaches $b(k; n, p)$.

36. In the preceding problem let p be small, n large, and $\lambda = np$ of moderate magnitude. The hypergeometric distribution can then be approximated by the Poisson distribution $p(k; \lambda)$. Verify this directly without using the binomial approximation.

37. In the *negative binomial distribution* $\{f(k; r, p)\}$ of section 8 let $q \to 0$ and $r \to \infty$ in such a way that $rq = \lambda$ remains fixed. Show that

$$f(k; r, p) \to p(k; \lambda).$$

(*Note:* This provides a limit theorem for the *Polya distribution;* cf. problem V, 24.)

38. *Multiple Poisson distribution.* When n is large and $np_j = \lambda_j$ is moderate, the multinomial distribution (9.2) can be approximated by

$$e^{-(\lambda_1 + \cdots + \lambda_r)} \frac{\lambda_1^{k_1} \lambda_2^{k_2} \cdots \lambda_r^{k_r}}{k_1! k_2! \cdots k_r!}.$$

Prove also that the terms of this distribution add to unity. (Note that problem 17 refers to a double Poisson distribution.)

---

39. (*a*) Derive (3.6) directly from (3.5) using the obvious relation

$$b(k; n, p) = b(n-k; n, q).$$

(*b*) Deduce the binomial distribution both by induction and from the general summation formula IV(3.1).

40. Prove $\Sigma k b(k; n, p) = np$, and $\Sigma k^2 b(k; n, p) = n^2 p^2 + npq$.

41. Prove $\Sigma k^2 p(k; \lambda) = \lambda^2 + \lambda$.

42. Verify the identity

$$(10.4) \qquad \sum_{\nu=0}^{k} b(\nu; n_1, p) b(k - \nu; n_2, p) = b(k; n_1 + n_2, p)$$

and interpret it probabilistically. *Hint:* Use II(6.4).

Note: Equation (10.4) is a special case of *convolutions*, to be introduced in chapter XI; (10.5) is another example.

43. Verify the identity

$$(10.5) \qquad \sum_{\nu=0}^{k} p(\nu; \lambda_1) p(k - \nu; \lambda_2) = p(k; \lambda_1 + \lambda_2)$$

44. Let

$$(10.6) \qquad B(k; n, p) = \sum_{\nu=0}^{k} b(\nu; n, p)$$

be the probability of at most k successes in n trials. Then

(10.7) $B(k; n + 1, p) = B(k; n, p) - pb(k; n, p),$

$$B(k+1; n+1, p) = B(k; n, p) + qb(k+1; n, p).$$

Verify this (a) from the definition, (b) analytically.

45. With the same notation

(10.8) $B(k; n, p) = (n - k) \binom{n}{k} \int_0^q t^{n-k-1}(1 - t)^k \, dt$

and

(10.9) $1 - B(k; n, p) = n \binom{n-1}{k} \int_0^p t^k(1 - t)^{n-k-1} \, dt.$

Hint: Integrate by parts or differentiate both sides with respect to p. Deduce one formula from the other.

Note: The integral in (10.9) is the *incomplete beta function.* Tables of $1 - B(k; n, p)$ to 7 decimals for k and n up to 50 and $p = 0.01, 0.02, 0.03, \ldots$ are given in K. Pearson, *Tables of the incomplete beta function,* London (Biometrika Office), 1934.

46. Prove

(10.10) $p(0; \lambda) + \ldots + p(n; \lambda) = \dfrac{1}{n!} \displaystyle\int_\lambda^\infty e^{-x} x^n \, dx.$

Note: *In the following problems we give an upper bound for all the terms of the binomial distribution. The calculations are quite simple and the method can be improved to give the simplest derivation of the DeMoivre-Laplace limit theorem (cf. problems VII, 19–21). Put for abbreviation*

(10.11) $\xi_k = \dfrac{k - (n + 1)p + \frac{1}{2}}{\{(n + 1)pq\}^{\frac{1}{2}}}$

and let m be the index of the central term; that is, m is the integer satisfying (3.2).

47. Prove that for $r \geq (n + 1)p$

(10.12) $b(r; n, p) \leq b(m; n, p) \cdot e^{-\frac{1}{2}p\xi_r^2 + \delta^2}$

where $\delta = m - (n + 1)p + \frac{1}{2}$ whence $|\delta| < \frac{1}{2}.$
Hint: Rewrite (3.1) in the form

(10.13) $\dfrac{b(k; n, p)}{b(k - 1; n, p)} = \dfrac{(n + 1)pq - \{k - (n + 1)p\}p}{(n + 1)pq + \{k - (n + 1)p\}q}.$

Conclude that for $k \geq (n + 1)p$

(10.14) $\log \dfrac{b(k; n, p)}{b(k - 1; n, p)} < \log \left\{ 1 - \dfrac{k - (n + 1)p}{(n + 1)pq} p \right\} < - \dfrac{k - (n + 1)p}{(n + 1)pq} p$

whence the assertion follows by summation.

48. For $r \leq (n + 1)p$ the inequality (10.12) holds with the factor p in the exponent replaced by q. Hence, if p is replaced by pq, the inequality holds for all r.

CHAPTER VII

The Normal Approximation to the Binomial Distribution

1. THE NORMAL DISTRIBUTION

In order to avoid later interruptions we pause here to introduce two functions of great importance.

Definition. *The function defined by*

(1.1) $$\phi(x) = \frac{1}{(2\pi)^{\frac{1}{2}}} e^{-\frac{1}{2}x^2}$$

is called the normal density function; its integral

(1.2) $$\Phi(x) = \frac{1}{(2\pi)^{\frac{1}{2}}} \int_{-\infty}^{x} e^{-\frac{1}{2}y^2}\, dy$$

is the normal distribution function.

The graph of $\phi(x)$ is the symmetric, bell-shaped curve shown in figure 1. Note that different units are used along the two axes: The maximum of $\phi(x)$ is $(2\pi)^{-\frac{1}{2}} = 0.399$, approximately, so that in an ordinary Cartesian system the curve $y = \phi(x)$ would be much flatter.

Lemma 1. *The domain bounded by the graph of $\phi(x)$ and the x-axis has unit area, that is,*

(1.3) $$\int_{-\infty}^{+\infty} \phi(x)\, dx = 1.$$

Proof. We have

(1.4) $$\left\{ \int_{-\infty}^{+\infty} \phi(x)\, dx \right\}^2 = \int_{-\infty}^{+\infty} \int_{-\infty}^{+\infty} \phi(x)\phi(y)\, dx\, dy =$$

$$= \frac{1}{2\pi} \int_{-\infty}^{+\infty} \int_{-\infty}^{+\infty} e^{-\frac{1}{2}(x^2+y^2)}\, dx\, dy.$$

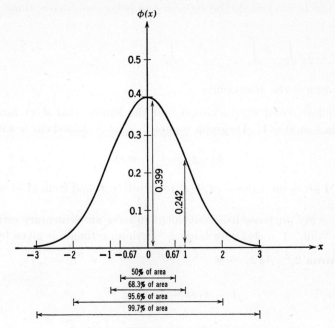

FIGURE 1.   The normal density function.

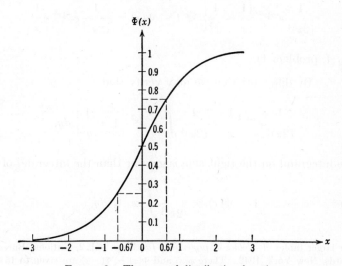

FIGURE 2.   The normal distribution function.

This double integral can be expressed in polar coordinates thus:

$$(1.5) \qquad \frac{1}{2\pi} \int_0^{2\pi} d\theta \int_0^\infty e^{-\frac{1}{2}r^2} r\, dr = \int_0^\infty e^{-\frac{1}{2}r^2} r\, dr = -e^{-\frac{1}{2}r^2} \Big|_0^\infty = 1$$

which proves the assertion.

It follows from the definition and the lemma that $\Phi(x)$ *increases steadily from 0 to 1*. Its graph (figure 2) is an S-shaped curve with

$$(1.6) \qquad \Phi(-x) = 1 - \Phi(x).$$

Table 1 gives the values [1] of $\Phi(x)$ for positive x, and from (1.6) we get $\Phi(-x)$.

For many purposes it is convenient to have an elementary estimate of the "tail," $1 - \Phi(x)$, for large x. Such an estimate is given by

Lemma 2.[2] *As $x \to \infty$*

$$(1.7) \qquad 1 - \Phi(x) \sim \frac{1}{(2\pi)^{\frac{1}{2}} x} e^{-\frac{1}{2}x^2};$$

more precisely, for every $x > 0$ the double inequality

$$(1.8) \qquad \frac{1}{(2\pi)^{\frac{1}{2}}} e^{-\frac{1}{2}x^2} \left\{ \frac{1}{x} - \frac{1}{x^3} \right\} < 1 - \Phi(x) < \frac{1}{(2\pi)^{\frac{1}{2}}} e^{-\frac{1}{2}x^2} \cdot \frac{1}{x}$$

holds (cf. problem 1).

Proof. By differentiation we may verify that

$$(1.9) \qquad \frac{1}{(2\pi)^{\frac{1}{2}}} e^{-\frac{1}{2}x^2} \frac{1}{x} = \frac{1}{(2\pi)^{\frac{1}{2}}} \int_x^\infty e^{-\frac{1}{2}y^2} \left\{ 1 + \frac{1}{y^2} \right\} dy.$$

The integrand on the right side is greater than the integrand of

$$(1.10) \qquad 1 - \Phi(x) = \frac{1}{(2\pi)^{\frac{1}{2}}} \int_x^\infty e^{-\frac{1}{2}y^2}\, dy,$$

---

[1] For larger tables cf. *Tables of probability functions*, vol. 2, National Bureau of Standards, New York, 1942. There $\phi(x)$ and $\Phi(x) - \Phi(-x)$ are given to 15 decimals for x from 0 to 1 in steps of 0.0001 and for $x > 1$ in steps of 0.001.

[2] Here and in the sequel the sign $\sim$ is used to indicate that the *ratio* of the two sides tends to one.

TABLE 1

THE NORMAL DISTRIBUTION

t	$\phi(t)$	$\Phi(t)$
0.0	0.398 942	0.500 000
0.1	.396 952	.539 828
0.2	.391 043	.579 260
0.3	.381 388	.617 911
0.4	.368 270	.655 422
0.5	.352 065	.691 462
0.6	.333 225	.725 747
0.7	.312 254	.758 036
0.8	.289 692	.788 145
0.9	.266 085	.815 940
1.0	.241 971	.841 345
1.1	.217 852	.864 334
1.2	.194 186	.884 930
1.3	.171 369	.903 200
1.4	.149 727	.919 243
1.5	.129 518	.933 193
1.6	.110 921	.945 201
1.7	.094 049	.955 435
1.8	.078 950	.964 070
1.9	.065 616	.971 283
2.0	.053 991	.977 250
2.1	.043 984	.982 136
2.2	.035 475	.986 097
2.3	.028 327	.989 276
2.4	.022 395	.991 802
2.5	.017 528	.993 790
2.6	.013 583	.995 339
2.7	.010 421	.996 533
2.8	.007 915	.997 445
2.9	.005 953	.998 134
3.0	.004 432	.998 650
3.1	.003 267	.999 032
3.2	.002 384	.999 313
3.3	.001 723	.999 517
3.4	.001 232	.999 663
3.5	.000 873	.999 767
3.6	.000 612	.999 841
3.7	.000 425	.999 892
3.8	.000 292	.999 928
3.9	.000 199	.999 952
4.0	.000 134	.999 968
4.1	.000 089	.999 979
4.2	.000 059	.999 987
4.3	.000 039	.999 991
4.4	.000 025	.999 995
4.5	.000 016	.999 997

which proves the second inequality in (1.8). The first inequality follows in the same way, using as new integrand $e^{-\frac{1}{2}y^2}\{1 - 3/y^4\}$ which is smaller than $e^{-\frac{1}{2}y^2}$.

Note on Terminology. The term *distribution function* is used in the mathematical literature for never-decreasing functions of x which tend to 0 as $x \to -\infty$, and to 1 as $x \to \infty$. Statisticians currently prefer the term *cumulative distribution function*, but the adjective "cumulative" is redundant. A *density function* is a non-negative function $f(x)$ whose integral, extended over the entire x-axis, is unity. The integral from $-\infty$ to x of any density function is a distribution function. The older term *frequency function* is a synonym for density function.

The normal distribution function is often called the *Gaussian distribution*, but it was used in probability theory earlier by DeMoivre and Laplace. If the origin and the unit of measurement are changed, then $\Phi(x)$ is transformed into $\Phi((x - a)/b)$; this function is called the normal distribution function with mean a and variance b^2 (or standard deviation $|b|$). The function $2\Phi(x2^{\frac{1}{2}}) - 1$ is often called *error function*.

2. THE DeMOIVRE-LAPLACE LIMIT THEOREM

Let $\mathbf{S}_n$ stand for the number of successes in n Bernoulli trials with probability p for success. Then $b(k; n, p)$ is the probability of the event that $\mathbf{S}_n = k$. In practice we are usually interested in *the probability of the event that the number of successes lies between preassigned limits α and β*. If α and β are integers and $\alpha < \beta$, then this event is defined by the inequality $\alpha \leq \mathbf{S}_n \leq \beta$, and its probability is

$$(2.1) \quad \mathbf{P}\{\alpha \leq \mathbf{S}_n \leq \beta\} = b(\alpha; n, p) + b(\alpha+1; n, p) + \ldots + b(\beta; n, p).$$

This sum may involve many terms, and a direct evaluation is usually impractical. Fortunately, whenever n is large, the normal distribution function can be used to derive simple approximations to the probability (2.1). This discovery is due to DeMoivre [3] and Laplace.[4] We shall see that its importance goes far beyond the domain of numerical calculations.

Our first aim is to derive an asymptotic formula for the individual terms

$$(2.2) \qquad b(k; n, p) = \frac{n!}{k!(n - k)!} p^k q^{n-k}.$$

The probability p will be kept fixed, but we shall let $n \to \infty$. According to the law of large numbers [VI(4.2)], the probability that $|\mathbf{S}_n - np| > n\epsilon$ tends to zero for each $\epsilon > 0$, and therefore only values

---

[3] Abraham DeMoivre (1667–1754). His *The doctrine of chance* appeared in 1718.
[4] Pierre S. Laplace (1749–1827). His *Théorie analytique des probabilités* appeared in 1812.

of k such that $|k - np|n^{-1} \to 0$ present a problem. It is now convenient to introduce the new variable $\delta_k = k - np$. Then

$$(2.3) \qquad k = np + \delta_k, \qquad n - k = nq - \delta_k,$$

and we are interested only in combinations n, k such that $n \to \infty$ and $\delta_k/n \to 0$.

Expressing the factorials in (2.2) by means of Stirling's formula II(9.1), we get [5]

$$(2.4) \quad b(k; n, p) \sim \left\{\frac{n}{2\pi k(n-k)}\right\}^{\frac{1}{2}} \left(\frac{np}{k}\right)^k \left(\frac{nq}{n-k}\right)^{n-k} =$$

$$= \left\{\frac{n}{2\pi(np+\delta_k)(nq-\delta_k)}\right\}^{\frac{1}{2}} \frac{1}{(1+\delta_k/np)^{np+\delta_k}(1-\delta_k/nq)^{nq-\delta_k}}$$

where the sign $\sim$ indicates that the ratio of the two sides tends to unity.

To evaluate the last fraction we pass to logarithms. In the interval $|\delta_k| \leq npq$ we may use Taylor's expansion II(8.9) and find for the logarithm of the denominator

$$(2.5) \quad (np + \delta_k) \log (1 + \delta_k/np) + (nq - \delta_k) \log (1 - \delta_k/nq) =$$

$$= (np + \delta_k)\left(\frac{\delta_k}{np} - \frac{\delta_k^2}{2n^2p^2} + \frac{\delta_k^3}{3n^3p^3} - + \ldots\right) -$$

$$- (nq - \delta_k)\left(\frac{\delta_k}{nq} + \frac{\delta_k^2}{2n^2q^2} + \frac{\delta_k^3}{3n^3q^3} + \ldots\right).$$

Reordering the terms according to powers of δ_k, we get

$$(2.6) \quad \frac{\delta_k^2}{2n}\left(\frac{1}{p} + \frac{1}{q}\right) - \frac{\delta_k^3}{6n^2}\left(\frac{1}{p^2} - \frac{1}{q^2}\right) + \ldots =$$

$$= \frac{\delta_k^2}{2npq}\left\{1 + \frac{p-q}{3pq} \cdot \frac{\delta_k}{n} + \ldots\right\}.$$

Here the term of $\delta_k^2/2npq$ is dominant, since $\delta_k/n \to 0$. If we suppose that $\delta_k^3/n^2 \to 0$, then all terms in (2.6) except the first tend to

---

[5] It will be recalled that in chapter II we did not complete the proof of Stirling's formula but showed only that $r! \sim Cr^{r+\frac{1}{2}}e^{-r}$, where C is a positive constant. In the text it is assumed that $C = (2\pi)^{\frac{1}{2}}$. If we want to *prove* this fact, then the factor $(2\pi)^{\frac{1}{2}}$ in equations (2.4), (2.7), and (2.8) must be replaced by C. In this case a factor $C \cdot (2\pi)^{-\frac{1}{2}}$ must be inserted on the right sides in (2.11), (2.14), and (2.18). To show that this factor really equals 1 it suffices to choose x_β and $-x_\alpha$ very large. The right side in the modified equation (2.18) is then arbitrarily near to $C \cdot (2\pi)^{-\frac{1}{2}}$, and the left side is near 1 by the estimates of chapter VI, section 3.

zero, and (2.4) takes on the simpler form

$$(2.7) \qquad b(k; n, p) \sim \left\{ \frac{n}{2\pi(np + \delta_k)(nq - \delta_k)} \right\}^{\frac{1}{2}} e^{-\delta_k^2/2npq}.$$

However, $np + \delta_k \sim np$ and $nq - \delta_k \sim nq$, and so (2.7) may be further simplified to

$$(2.8) \qquad b(k; n, p) \sim \frac{1}{\{2\pi npq\}^{\frac{1}{2}}} e^{-\delta_k^2/2npq} = \frac{1}{(npq)^{\frac{1}{2}}} \phi\left(\frac{\delta_k}{(npq)^{\frac{1}{2}}} \right).$$

This is the desired asymptotic formula. We simplify it by the use of a more convenient notation. Put

$$(2.9) \qquad\qquad h = \frac{1}{(npq)^{\frac{1}{2}}}$$

and define a function x_k of the variable k by

$$(2.10) \qquad\qquad x_k = (k - np)h = \frac{\delta_k}{(npq)^{\frac{1}{2}}}.$$

In terms of these quantities we can rewrite (2.8) in the form

$$(2.11) \qquad\qquad b(k; n, p) \sim h\phi(x_k).$$

To derive this formula we had to suppose that $n \rightarrow \infty$ and $k \rightarrow \infty$ in such a way that $\delta_k n^{-1} \rightarrow 0$ and also $\delta_k^3 n^{-2} \rightarrow 0$. The last condition obviously implies the first and is the same as $x_k^3 n^{-\frac{1}{2}} \rightarrow 0$. We have thus

Theorem 1. *If $n \rightarrow \infty$ and $k \rightarrow \infty$ in such a way that $x_k^3 n^{-\frac{1}{2}} \rightarrow 0$, then* (2.11) *holds.* More precisely, we have shown that there exist two constants A and B such that

$$(2.12) \qquad \left| \frac{b(k; n, p)}{h\phi(x_k)} - 1 \right| < \frac{A}{n} + \frac{B|x_{k+1}^3|}{n^{\frac{1}{2}}}.$$

(For an alternative for (2.11) see problems 19 and 21.)

Figure 3 illustrates the theorem in the case $n = 10$, $p = 0.2$ where npq is only 1.6. It is seen that even in this extremely unfavorable case the approximation is surprisingly good.[6]

---

[6] The values of $b(k; 10, 0.2)$ for $k = 0, 1, \ldots, 6$ are 0.1074, 0.2684, 0.3020, 0.2013, 0.0880, 0.0264, 0.0055. The corresponding approximations $h\phi(x_k)$ are 0.0904, 0.2307, 0.3154, 0.2307, 0.0904, 0.0189, 0.0021.

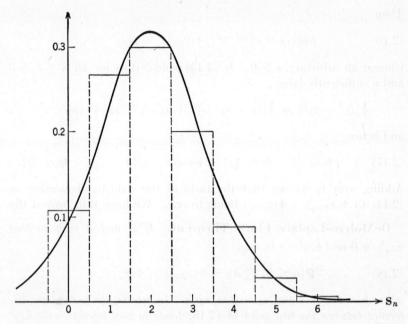

FIGURE 3. The normal approximation to the binomial distribution. The step function gives the probabilities $b(k; 10, \frac{1}{5})$ of k successes in ten Bernoulli trials with $p = \frac{1}{5}$. The continuous curve gives for each integer k the corresponding normal approximation.

Our theorem leads directly to simple approximations for the sum (2.1). If

$$(2.13) \qquad hx_\alpha{}^3 \to 0 \qquad \text{and} \qquad hx_\beta{}^3 \to 0,$$

then (2.11) holds uniformly for all terms in (2.1), and therefore

$$(2.14) \quad \mathbf{P}\{\alpha \leq \mathbf{S}_n \leq \beta\} \sim h\{\phi(x_\alpha) + \phi(x_{\alpha+1}) + \ldots + \phi(x_\beta)\}.$$

The right side is a Riemann sum approximating an integral [7] and we proceed to investigate the goodness of this approximation.

By the mean value theorem there exists a value ξ_k such that

$$(2.15) \qquad \Phi(x_{k+\frac{1}{2}}) - \Phi(x_{k-\frac{1}{2}}) = h\phi(\xi_k), \qquad x_k - \tfrac{1}{2}h < \xi_k < x_k + \tfrac{1}{2}h.$$

---

[7] It is clear that $\Phi(x_{k+\frac{1}{2}}) - \Phi(x_{k-\frac{1}{2}})$ represents the area of the trapezoid with basis $x_k - \tfrac{1}{2}h < x < x_k + \tfrac{1}{2}h$ and bounded above by the tangent to the curve $y = \phi(x)$ at $x = x_k$ and $h\phi(x_k)$ represents the area of a rectangle with the same basis.

Then

$$(2.16) \qquad h\phi(x_k) = e^{\frac{1}{2}(\xi_k^2 - x_k^2)}\{\Phi(x_{k+\frac{1}{2}}) - \Phi(x_{k-\frac{1}{2}})\}.$$

Choose an arbitrary $\epsilon > 0$. If (2.13) holds, then for all $\alpha \le k \le \beta$ and n sufficiently large

$$\tfrac{1}{2}|\xi_k^2 - x_k^2| = \tfrac{1}{2}|\xi_k - x_k| \cdot |\xi_k + x_k| < h[|x_k| + \tfrac{1}{4}h] < \epsilon$$

and hence

$$(2.17) \quad e^{-\epsilon}\{\Phi(x_{k+\frac{1}{2}}) - \Phi(x_{k-\frac{1}{2}})\} < h\phi(x_k) < e^{\epsilon}\{\Phi(x_{k+\frac{1}{2}}) - \Phi(x_{k-\frac{1}{2}})\}.$$

Adding over k, we see that the ratio of the right-hand member in (2.14) to $\Phi(x_{\beta+\frac{1}{2}}) - \Phi(x_{\alpha-\frac{1}{2}})$ tends to one. We have thus proved the

DeMoivre-Laplace Limit Theorem. *If α and β vary so that $hx_\alpha^3 \to 0$ and $hx_\beta^3 \to 0$, then*

$$(2.18) \qquad \mathbf{P}\{\alpha \le \mathbf{S}_n \le \beta\} \sim \Phi(x_{\beta+\frac{1}{2}}) - \Phi(x_{\alpha-\frac{1}{2}}),$$

where $h = (npq)^{-\frac{1}{2}}$ and $x_t = (t - np)h$. In words, the percentage difference between the two sides in (2.18) tends to zero together with hx_β^3 and hx_α^3.

In particular, (2.18) holds if α and β are restricted to values for which x_α and x_β remain within a fixed interval. (The case where α and β are so large that the condition (2.13) is not satisfied will be discussed in section 5 and in problem 14.)

In statistical applications (2.18) is usually used in a range in which $|x_\alpha|$ and $|x_\beta|$ do not exceed 3 or 4. In theoretical applications it is often necessary to use (2.18) for intervals (α, β) which are far off the central part of the binomial distribution and for which both x_α and x_β are large. In such cases both sides of (2.18) are small, and it becomes important to know that their *ratio* is near unity as well as that their difference tends to zero.

The limit theorem (2.18) takes on a simpler form if, instead of $\mathbf{S}_n$, we introduce the *reduced number of successes* defined by

$$(2.19) \qquad \mathbf{S}_n^* = \frac{\mathbf{S}_n - np}{(npq)^{\frac{1}{2}}}.$$

This amounts to measuring the deviations of $\mathbf{S}_n$ from np in units of $(npq)^{\frac{1}{2}}$. The quantity np *is called the mean, and* $(npq)^{\frac{1}{2}}$ *the standard deviation of* $\mathbf{S}_n$; this terminology is suggested by the theory of random variables (cf. chapter IX). The inequality $\alpha \le \mathbf{S}_n \le \beta$ is the same as

$x_\alpha \leq \mathbf{S}_n^* \leq x_\beta$, and (2.18) states that for arbitrary fixed $x_\alpha < x_\beta$

$$(2.20) \qquad \mathbf{P}\{x_\alpha \leq \mathbf{S}_n^* \leq x_\beta\} \sim \Phi\left(x_\beta + \frac{h}{2}\right) - \Phi\left(x_\alpha - \frac{h}{2}\right),$$

where $h = (npq)^{-\frac{1}{2}}$. Now $h \to 0$ as $n \to \infty$, and therefore the right side tends to $\Phi(x_\beta) - \Phi(x_\alpha)$. Thus we have the following

Corollary to the Limit Theorem. *For every fixed* $a < b$

$$(2.21) \qquad\qquad \mathbf{P}\{a \leq \mathbf{S}_n^* \leq b\} \to \Phi(b) - \Phi(a).$$

This is a weakened version of (2.18) but represents the traditional form of Laplace's limit theorem. The dropping of $h/2$ in (2.20) introduces an error which tends to zero as $n \to \infty$ but has a considerable influence when npq is of moderate magnitude [as is the case in the three examples 3(a)–(c)].

The main fact revealed by (2.21) is that for large n the probability on the left is practically independent of p. This permits us to compare fluctuations in different series of Bernoulli trials simply by referring to our standard units.

Theorem (2.21) is historically the first limit theorem of probability. From a modern point of view it is only an exceedingly special case of the *central limit theorem*, to which we shall return in chapter X but whose general derivation must be postponed to the second volume. Statisticians use (2.21) as an approximation even where npq is relatively small, and in such cases an estimate of the error is desired. It turns out that in most cases the error in (2.11) is small as compared to the error committed by replacing the sum in (2.14) by the integral. (Fortunately this error can be avoided by the use of the Euler-MacLaurin summation formula.) Serge Bernstein devoted a series of papers to the investigation of the error term in the general case and discussed how the definition of x_t should be modified in order to improve the convergence in (2.18). His papers are written in Russian and are difficult to obtain. A simplified derivation with an improvement of his results is, however, available in English.[8]

Note on Optional Stopping

It is essential to note that our limit and *approximation theorems are valid only if the number n of trials is fixed in advance independently of the outcome of the trials.* If a gambler has the privilege of stopping at a moment favorable to him, his ultimate gain cannot be judged from the normal approximation, for now the duration of the game depends on chance. For *every fixed* n it is very improbable that $\mathbf{S}_n^*$ is large. However, in the long run, even the most improbable thing is bound to

---

[8] W. Feller, On the normal approximation to the binomial distribution, *Annals of Mathematical Statistics*, vol. 16 (1945), pp. 319–329.

happen, and we shall see that in a continued game $S_n{}^*$ is practically certain to have a sequence of maxima of the order of magnitude $(\log \log n)^{\frac{1}{2}}$ (this is the law of the iterated logarithm of chapter VIII, section 5).

3. EXAMPLES

(a) Let $p = \frac{1}{2}, n = 200, \alpha = 95, \beta = 105$. Here $\mathbf{P}\{95 \leq S_n \leq 105\}$ may be interpreted as the probability that in 200 tossings of a coin the number of heads deviates from 100 by at most 5. We have $h = (50)^{-\frac{1}{2}} = 0.141421\ldots$ and $-x_{\alpha-\frac{1}{2}} = x_{\beta+\frac{1}{2}} = (5.5)h = 0.7778\ldots$ From tables we get $\Phi(x_{\beta+\frac{1}{2}}) - \Phi(x_{\alpha-\frac{1}{2}}) = 0.56331\ldots$ The true value (again obtainable from tables) is $0.56325\ldots$ The error is ridiculously small, but only because of the accident that in the interval in question the integral overestimates the sum in (2.14) and the approximation (2.11) underestimates each term.

(b) Let $p = \frac{1}{10}$, $n = 500$, $\alpha = 50$, $\beta = 55$. The correct value is $\mathbf{P}\{50 \leq S_n \leq 55\} = 0.317573\ldots$ Now $h = (45)^{-\frac{1}{2}} = 0.1490712\ldots$, and we get the approximation $\Phi(5.5h) - \Phi(-0.5h) = 0.3235\ldots$ The error is about 2 per cent.

(c) Let $n = 100$, $p = 0.3$. Table 2 shows in a typical example (for relatively small n) how the normal approximation deteriorates as the interval (α, β) moves away from the central term.

TABLE 2

COMPARISON OF THE BINOMIAL DISTRIBUTION FOR $n = 100$, $p = 0.3$
AND THE NORMAL APPROXIMATION

Number of Successes	Probability	Normal Approximation	Percentage Error
$9 \leq S_n \leq 11$	0.000 006	0.000 03	+400
$12 \leq S_n \leq 14$	.000 15	.000 33	+100
$15 \leq S_n \leq 17$	.002 01	.002 83	+40
$18 \leq S_n \leq 20$	.014 30	.015 99	+12
$21 \leq S_n \leq 23$	.059 07	.058 95	0
$24 \leq S_n \leq 26$	.148 87	.144 47	−3
$27 \leq S_n \leq 29$	.237 94	.234 05	−2
$31 \leq S_n \leq 33$	.230 13	.234 05	+2
$34 \leq S_n \leq 36$	.140 86	.144 47	+3
$37 \leq S_n \leq 39$	.058 89	.058 95	0
$40 \leq S_n \leq 42$	.017 02	.015 99	−6
$43 \leq S_n \leq 45$	.003 43	.002 83	−18
$46 \leq S_n \leq 48$	.000 49	.000 33	−33
$49 \leq S_n \leq 51$	.000 05	.000 03	−40

(d) Let us find a number a such that, for large n, the inequality $|S_n{}^*| > a$ has a probability near $\frac{1}{2}$. For this it is necessary that $\Phi(a) - \Phi(-a) = \frac{1}{2}$ or $\Phi(a) = \frac{3}{4}$. From tables of the normal distribution we find that $a = 0.6745$, and hence the two inequalities

$$(3.1) \quad |S_n - np| < 0.6745(npq)^{\frac{1}{2}} \quad \text{and} \quad |S_n - np| > 0.6745(npq)^{\frac{1}{2}}$$

are about equally probable. In particular, the probability is about $\frac{1}{2}$ that in n tossings of a coin the number of heads lies within the limits $n/2 \pm 0.337n^{\frac{1}{2}}$, and, similarly, that in n throws of a die the number of aces lies within the interval $n/6 \pm 0.251n^{\frac{1}{2}}$. The probability of S_n lying within the limits $np \pm 2(npq)^{\frac{1}{2}}$ is about $\Phi(2) - \Phi(-2) = 0.9545\ldots$, and for $np \pm 3(npq)^{\frac{1}{2}}$ the probability is $0.9973\ldots$.

(e) *A competition problem.* This example illustrates practical applications of formula (2.21). Two competing railroads operate one train each between Chicago and Los Angeles; the two trains leave and arrive simultaneously and have comparable equipment. We suppose that n passengers select trains independently and at random so that the number of passengers in each train is the outcome of n Bernoulli trials with $p = \frac{1}{2}$. If a train carries $s < n$ seats, then there is a positive probability $f(s)$ that more than s passengers will turn up, in which case not all patrons can be accommodated. Using the approximation (2.21), we find

$$(3.2) \qquad\qquad f(s) \approx 1 - \Phi\!\left(\frac{2s - n}{n^{\frac{1}{2}}}\right).$$

If s is so large that $f(s) < 0.01$, then the number of seats will be sufficient in 99 out of 100 cases. More generally, the company may decide on an arbitrary risk level α and determine s so that $f(s) < \alpha$. For that purpose it suffices to put

$$(3.3) \qquad\qquad s \geq \tfrac{1}{2}(n + t_\alpha n^{\frac{1}{2}}),$$

where t_α is the root of the equation $\alpha = 1 - \Phi(t_\alpha)$, which can be found from tables. For example, if $n = 1000$ and $\alpha = 0.01$, then $t_\alpha \approx 2.33$ and $s = 537$ seats should suffice. If both railroads accept the risk level $\alpha = 0.01$, the two trains will carry a total of 1074 seats of which 74 will be empty. The loss from competition (or chance fluctuations) is remarkably small. In the same way, 514 seats should suffice in about 80 per cent of all cases, and 549 seats in 999 out of 1000 cases.

Similar considerations apply in other competitive supply problems. For example, if m movies compete for the same n patrons, each movie will put for its probability of success $p = 1/m$, and (3.3) is to be replaced by $s \geq (1/m)[n + t_\alpha n^{\frac{1}{2}}(m - 1)^{\frac{1}{2}}]$. The total number of empty seats under this system is $ms - n \approx t_\alpha n^{\frac{1}{2}}(m - 1)^{\frac{1}{2}}$. For $\alpha = 0.01$, $n = 1000$, and $m = 2, 3, 4$, this number is about 74, 126, and 147, respectively. The loss of efficiency because of competition is again small.

(f) *Random digits.* In example II(3.b), we considered an event with $p = 0.3024$. In $n = 1200$ trials this event had an average frequency of 0.3142. The deviation from p is $\epsilon = 0.0118$. In this case $(pq)^{\frac{1}{2}} = 0.4593$ and $\epsilon(n/pq)^{\frac{1}{2}} \approx 0.890 \ldots$ Hence the probability of $\left| \dfrac{S_n}{n} - p \right| > \epsilon$ is in this case about $0.37 \ldots$ This indicates that in about 37 per cent of all cases the average number of successes should deviate from p by more than it does in our material.

(g) *Sampling.* A fraction p of a certain population are smokers. Suppose that p is unknown and that random sampling with replacement is to be used to determine p. It is desired to find p with an error not exceeding 0.005. How large should the sample size n be? If p' is the fraction of smokers in the sample, we desire that $|p' - p| < 0.005$. However, no sample size can give absolute assurance that $|p' - p| < 0.005$; it is conceivable that the sample contains only smokers. Since absolute certainty is unattainable, we settle for an arbitrary *confidence level* α, say, $\alpha = 0.95$, and require that $|p' - p| < 0.005$ with probability 0.95 or better. Note that np' is the number of successes in n trials, and hence

$$\mathbf{P}\{|p' - p| < 0.005\} = \mathbf{P}\left\{ \left| \frac{S_n}{n} - p \right| < 0.005 \right\}.$$

We seek an n large enough to make this quantity greater than 0.95. For the present purposes the normal approximation is sufficient. The root x of $\Phi(x) - \Phi(-x) = 0.95$ is $x = 1.96\ldots$, and hence we should have $0.005(n/pq)^{\frac{1}{2}} \geq 1.96$. Thus we are led to the inequality $n \geq 392^2 pq$ or $n \geq 160{,}000pq$, approximately. It involves the unknown p, but pq never exceeds $\frac{1}{4}$, and hence the sample size $n = 40{,}000$ would be safe under all circumstances; with it the odds are about 20 to 1 that $|p' - p| < 0.005$.

4. RELATION TO THE POISSON APPROXIMATION

The error of the normal approximation will be small if npq is large. On the other hand, if n is large and p small, the terms $b(k; n, p)$ will be found to be near the Poisson probabilities $p(k; \lambda)$ with $\lambda = np$. If λ is small, then only the Poisson approximation can be used. However, if λ is large, we can use either the normal or the Poisson approximation. This implies that for large values of λ it must be possible to approximate the Poisson distribution by the normal distribution, and in example X(1.c) we shall see that this is indeed so (cf. also problem 9). Here we shall be content to illustrate the point by a numerical and a practical example.

Examples. (a) Consider the Poisson distribution $p(k; 100)$ as an approximation, say, to the binomial distribution with $n = 100,000,000$ and $p = 1/1,000,000$. Then $npq \approx 100$; this quantity, even though not large, suffices for the normal distribution to give reasonable approximations at least for the central sector of the binomial distribution. The Poisson distribution $p(k; 100)$ agrees with $b(k; 10^8, 10^{-6})$ to many decimals, and we can compare it with the normal approximation to the latter. Put, for brevity, $P(a, b) = p(a; 100) + p(a+1; 100) + \ldots + p(b; 100)$, so that $P(a, b)$ stands for $\mathbf{P}\{a \leq S_n \leq b\}$ and should be approximated by $\Phi\left(\dfrac{b - 99.5}{10}\right) - \Phi\left(\dfrac{a - 100.5}{10}\right)$. The following sample gives an idea of the degree of approximation.

	Correct Values	Normal Approximation
$P(85, 90)$	0.113 84	0.110 49
$P(90, 95)$	.184 85	.179 50
$P(95, 105)$	.417 63	.417 68
$P(90, 110)$	.706 52	.706 28
$P(110, 115)$	.107 38	.110 49
$P(115, 120)$	.053 23	.053 35

(b) *A telephone trunking problem.* The following problem is, with some simplifications, taken from actual practice.[9] A telephone exchange A is to serve 2000 subscribers in a nearby exchange B. It would be too expensive and extravagant to install 2000 trunklines from A to B. It will suffice to make the number N of lines so large that, under ordinary conditions, only one out of every hundred calls will fail to find an idle trunkline immediately at its disposal. Suppose that during the busy hour of the day each subscriber requires a trunkline to B for an average of 2 minutes. At a fixed moment of the busy hour we compare the situation to a set of 2000 trials with a probability $p = \frac{1}{30}$ in each that a line will be required. Under ordinary conditions these trials can be assumed to be independent (although this is not true when events like unexpected showers or earthquakes cause

---

[9] E. C. Molina, Probability in engineering, *Electrical Engineering*, vol. 54 (1935), pp. 423–427, or *Bell Telephone System Technical Publications Monograph* B-854. There the problem is treated by the Poisson method given in the text, which is preferable from the engineer's point of view.

many people to call for taxicabs or the local newspaper; the theory no longer applies, and the trunks will be "jammed"). . We have, then, 2000 Bernoulli trials with $p = \frac{1}{30}$, and the smallest number N is required such that the probability of more than N "successes" will be smaller than 0.01; in symbols $\mathbf{P}\{S_{2000} \geq N\} < 0.01$.

For the *Poisson approximation* we should take $\lambda = \frac{200}{3} \approx 66.67$. From the tables we find that the probability of 87 or more successes is about 0.0097, whereas the probability of 86 or more successes is about 0.013. This would indicate that 87 *trunklines should suffice*. For the *normal approximation* we first find from tables the root x of $1 - \Phi(x) = 0.01$, which is $x = 2.327$. Then it is required that $(N - \frac{1}{2} - np)/(npq)^{\frac{1}{2}} \geq 2.327$. Since $n = 2000$, $p = \frac{1}{30}$, this means $N \geq 67.17 + (2.327)(8.027) \approx 85.8$. Hence the normal approximation would indicate that 86 *trunklines should suffice*.

For practical purposes the two solutions agree. They yield further practical results. Conceivably, the installation might be cheaper if the 2000 subscribers were divided into two groups of 1000 each, and two separate groups of trunklines from A to B were installed. Using the method above, we find that actually some ten additional trunklines would be required so that the first arrangement is preferable.

5. LARGE DEVIATIONS [10]

Frequently we desire an estimate of the probability that the reduced number of successes $\mathbf{S}_n*$ [cf. (2.19)] exceeds a given number x. Hence the upper limit of the interval is infinity, and it requires a special argument to show that our limit theorem (2.18) still applies.

Theorem. *If* $n \to \infty$ *and* x *varies as a function of* n *in such a way that* $x \to \infty$ *but* $x^3 h \to 0$, *then*

$$(5.1) \qquad \mathbf{P}\{\mathbf{S}_n* > x\} \sim 1 - \Phi(x).$$

In view of (1.7) *this is equivalent to*

$$(5.2) \qquad \mathbf{P}\{\mathbf{S}_n* > x\} \sim \frac{1}{(2\pi)^{\frac{1}{2}}x} e^{-\frac{1}{2}x^2}.$$

Proof. Choose in (2.18) the integers α and β so that x lies between x_α and $x_{\alpha+1}$, and that $x_\beta \approx x + \log x$. Then $x_\beta^3 h \to 0$ and (2.18) holds. Hence

$$(5.3) \qquad \mathbf{P}\{\alpha < \mathbf{S}_n < \beta\} \sim \{1 - \Phi(x_\alpha)\} - \{1 - \Phi(x_\beta)\}.$$

---

[10] The theorem is of general interest but will be used in this book only for the proof of the law of the iterated logarithm, chapter VIII, section 5.

However, from (1.7) and the fact that $x_\beta \approx x_\alpha + \log x_\alpha$ it is readily seen that $1 - \Phi(x_\beta)$ is of smaller order of magnitude than $1 - \Phi(x_\alpha)$, while $1 - \Phi(x_\alpha) \sim 1 - \Phi(x)$.   Hence

$$(5.4) \qquad \mathbf{P}\{\alpha < \mathbf{S}_n < \beta\} \sim 1 - \Phi(x).$$

On the other hand, from (2.11) and VI(3.5) we have

$$(5.5) \qquad \mathbf{P}\{\mathbf{S}_n \geq \beta\} \leq \frac{n}{\beta - np}\, b(\beta; n, p) \sim \frac{nh^2}{x_\beta}\, \phi(x_\beta).$$

Now $nh^2 = 1/pq$ is a constant, and

$$(5.6) \qquad \frac{1}{x_\beta}\, \phi(x_\beta) \sim 1 - \Phi(x_\beta).$$

We saw that the right side tends to zero faster than $1 - \Phi(x)$, which means that $\mathbf{P}\{\mathbf{S}_n \geq \beta\}$ is of smaller order of magnitude than $1 - \Phi(x)$. Combining this result with (5.4), we see then that

$$(5.7) \qquad \mathbf{P}\{\mathbf{S}_n > \alpha\} \sim 1 - \Phi(x),$$

and this is our theorem. (Further limit theorems for large deviations are given in problems 12–17.)

6. PROBLEMS FOR SOLUTION

1. Generalizing (1.8), prove that

$$(6.1) \quad 1 - \Phi(x) \sim \frac{1}{(2\pi)^{\frac{1}{2}}}\, e^{-\frac{1}{2}x^2} \left\{ \frac{1}{x} - \frac{1}{x^3} + \frac{1\cdot 3}{x^5} - \frac{1\cdot 3\cdot 5}{x^7} + - \cdots + \right.$$
$$\left. + (-1)^k \frac{1\cdot 3 \cdots (2k-1)}{x^{2k+1}} \right\}$$

and that for $x > 0$ the right side *overestimates* $1 - \Phi(x)$ if k is even, and *underestimates* if k is odd.

2. For every constant $a > 0$

$$(6.2) \qquad \left\{ 1 - \Phi\left(x + \frac{a}{x} \right) \right\} \div \{1 - \Phi(x)\} \to e^{-a}$$

as $x \to \infty$.

3. Find the probability that among 10,000 random digits the digit 7 appears not more than 968 times.

4. Find an approximation to the probability that the number of aces obtained in 12,000 rollings of a die is between 1900 and 2150.

5. Find a number k such that the probability is about 0.5 that the number of heads obtained in 1000 tossings of a coin will be between 440 and k.

6. A sample is taken in order to find the fraction f of females in a population. Find a sample size such that the probability of a sampling error less than 0.005 will be 0.99 or greater.

7. In 10,000 tossings, a coin fell heads 5400 times. Is it reasonable to assume that the coin is skew?

---

8. Find an approximation to the maximal term of the trinomial distribution

$$\frac{n!}{k!r!(n-k-r)!}\, p_1{}^k p_2{}^r (1-p_1-p_2)^{n-k-r}.$$

9. *Normal approximation to the Poisson distribution.* Using Stirling's formula, show that, if $\lambda \to \infty$, then for every fixed $\alpha < \beta$

(6.3) $$\sum_{\lambda+\alpha\lambda^{\frac{1}{2}}<k<\lambda+\beta\lambda^{\frac{1}{2}}} p(k;\lambda) \to \Phi(\beta) - \Phi(\alpha).$$

10. *Normal approximation to the hypergeometric distribution.* Let n, m, k be positive integers and suppose that

(6.4) $$\frac{r}{n+m} \to t, \quad \frac{n}{n+m} \to p, \quad \frac{m}{n+m} \to q, \quad h\{k-rp\} \to x$$

where $1/h = \{(n+m)pqt(1-t)\}^{\frac{1}{2}}$. Prove that

(6.5 $$\frac{\binom{n}{k}\binom{m}{r-k}}{\binom{n+m}{r}} \sim h\phi(x).$$

Hint: Use the normal approximation to the binomial distribution rather than Stirling's formula.

11. *Normal distribution and combinatorial runs.*[11] In II(11.19) we found that in an arrangement of n alphas and m betas the probability of having exactly k runs of alphas is

(6.6) $$\pi_k = \binom{n-1}{k-1}\binom{m+1}{k} \div \binom{n+m}{n}.$$

Let $n \to \infty$, $m \to \infty$ so that (6.4) holds. For fixed $\alpha < \beta$ the probability that the number of alpha runs lies between $npq + \alpha(pqn)^{\frac{1}{2}}$ and $npq + \beta(pqn)^{\frac{1}{2}}$ tends to $\Phi(\beta) - \Phi(\alpha)$.

Note: *In the following problems $h^2 = npq$ and $\mathbf{S}_n{}^*$ is the reduced number of successes defined in (2.19). Finally*

(6.7) $$F_n(x) = \mathbf{P}\{\mathbf{S}_n{}^* > x\}.$$

12. If x varies as a function of n so that $x^{3+a}h \to 0$ but $x \to \infty$, then [12]

---

[11] A. Wald and J. Wolfowitz, On a test whether two samples are from the same population, *Annals of Mathematical Statistics*, vol. 11 (1940), pp. 147–162. For more general results, see A. M. Mood, The distribution theory of runs, *ibid.*, pp. 367–392.

[12] N. Smirnov, Über Wahrscheinlichkeiten grosser Abweichungen (in Russian, German summary), *Recueil Mathématique* [*Sbornik*] *Moscou*, vol. 40 (1933), pp. 443–454.

(6.8)
$$\frac{F_n(x)}{1 - \Phi(x)} = 1 + o(x^a),$$

where $o(x^a)$ stands for terms that are of smaller order of magnitude than x^a.

13. If $x^3 h \to 0$, $x \to \infty$, then [13] for any constant $a > 0$

(6.9)
$$\frac{F_n(x) - F_n(x + a/x)}{F_n(x)} \to 1 - e^{-a}.$$

In words, the conditional probability of $x < S_n{}^* < x + a/x$, given that $S_n{}^* > x$, tends to $1 - e^{-a}$. [Hint: Use (5.2).]

14. *Probabilities of large deviations.* Starting with (2.4), prove the following theorem. If $n \to \infty$, and k varies so that $(k - np)/n \to 0$, then

(6.10)
$$b(k; n, p) \sim \frac{h}{(2\pi)^{\frac{1}{2}}} e^{-\frac{1}{2}x^2 - f(x)}$$

where $x = (k - np)h$ and

(6.11)
$$f(x) = \sum_{\nu=3}^{\infty} \frac{p^{\nu-1} - (-q)^{\nu-1}}{\nu(\nu - 1)} h^{\nu-2} x^{\nu}.$$

Note: If $x^3 h \to 0$, then $f(x) \to 0$, and (6.10) reduces to (2.11). If x is of the order of magnitude of $h^{-\frac{1}{3}}$ but negligible as compared to $h^{-\frac{1}{2}}$, then

(6.12)
$$f(x) \approx \frac{p - q}{6} x^3 h.$$

If x is of the order of magnitude of $h^{-\frac{1}{2}}$, then

(6.13)
$$f(x) \approx \frac{p - q}{6} x^3 h + \frac{p^3 + q^3}{12} x^4 h^2,$$

etc.

15. *Continuation.* Prove that if $x \to \infty$, $xh \to 0$,

(6.14)
$$f\left(x + \frac{a}{x}\right) - f(x) \to 0$$

and hence

(6.15)
$$F_n(x) \sim e^{f(x)}\{1 - \Phi(x)\}.$$

16. Deduce (6.9) from (6.15), assuming only $xh \to 0$.

17. If $p > q$, then for large x

(6.16)
$$P\{S_n > x\} < P\{S_n < -x\}.$$

(*Hint:* Use problem 14.)

18. *A new derivation of the law of large numbers.* Show that the law of large numbers is a consequence of the DeMoivre-Laplace limit theorem.

---

[13] A. Khintchine, Über einen neuen Grenzwertsatz der Wahrscheinlichkeitsrechnung, *Mathematische Annalen*, vol. 101 (1929), pp. 745–752. See also problem 16.

19. *A new derivation of the normal approximation.*[14] Starting from VI(10.11)–(10.13), prove that when $n \to \infty$ and $k \to \infty$ in such a way that $\xi_k^3 n^{-\frac{1}{2}} \to 0$, we have

$$(6.17) \qquad\qquad b(k; n, p) \sim b(m; n, p)e^{-\frac{1}{2}\xi_k^2}.$$

20. If $np \le m \le (n+1)p$, show that

$$(6.18) \qquad b\left(m; n, \frac{m+1}{n+1}\right) \le b(m; n, p) \le b\left(m; n, \frac{m}{n}\right).$$

If $(n+1)p - 1 < m \le np$, the same inequality holds with $(m+1)/(n+1)$ in the extreme left member replaced by $m/(n+1)$.

21. Conclude that $b(m; n, p) \sim \{2\pi(n+1)pq\}^{-\frac{1}{2}}$ and give upper and lower bounds.

──────────

[14] Problems 19 and 20 together imply that $b(k; n, p) \sim \{(n+1)pq\}^{-\frac{1}{2}}\phi(\xi_k)$. This is the same as the basic approximation formula (2.11) with x_k replaced by ξ_k and $h = \{npq\}^{-\frac{1}{2}}$ replaced by $h' = \{(n+1)pq\}^{-\frac{1}{2}}$. Since $x_k \sim \xi_k$ and $h \sim h'$, the two formulas are asymptotically equivalent. Actually the new formula involves a smaller error term (in its derivation the error committed in passing from (2.7) to (2.8) is avoided). It should also be noted that the calculations required for problems 19 and 20 are simpler and more intuitive than those used in the text; they involve only the standard estimates for logarithms as used in chapter II, section 8, and chapter VI, section 3. In short, the new formula and its derivation are superior to those of the text, but they do not conform to the time-honored use of np instead of $(n+1)p$.

CHAPTER VIII*

Unlimited Sequences
of Bernoulli Trials

This chapter discusses certain properties of randomness and the important law of the iterated logarithm for Bernoulli trials. A different aspect of the fluctuation theory of Bernoulli trials (at least for $p = \frac{1}{2}$) is covered in chapter III.

1. INFINITE SEQUENCES OF TRIALS

In the preceding chapter we have dealt with probabilities connected with n Bernoulli trials and have studied their asymptotic behavior as $n \to \infty$. We turn now to a more general type of problem where the events themselves cannot be defined in a finite sample space.

Example. *A problem in runs.* Let α and β be positive integers, and consider a potentially unlimited sequence of Bernoulli trials, such as tossing a coin or throwing dice. Suppose that Paul bets Peter that a run of α consecutive successes will occur before a run of β consecutive failures. It has an intuitive meaning to speak of the event that Paul wins, but it must be remembered that in the mathematical theory the term event stands for "aggregate of sample points" and is meaningless unless an appropriate sample space has been defined. The model of a finite number of trials is insufficient for our present purpose, but the difficulty is solved by a simple passage to the limit. In n trials Peter wins or loses, or the game remains undecided. Let the corresponding probabilities be x_n, y_n, z_n $(x_n + y_n + z_n = 1)$. As the number n of trials increases, the probability z_n of a tie can only decrease, and both x_n and y_n necessarily increase. Hence $x = \lim x_n$, $y = \lim y_n$, and $z = \lim z_n$ exist. Nobody would hesitate to call them the probabilities of Peter's ultimate gain or loss or of a tie. However, the corresponding

---

* This chapter is not directly connected with the material covered in subsequent chapters and may be omitted at first reading.

three events are defined only in the sample space of infinite sequences of trials, and this space is not discrete.

The example was introduced for illustration only, and the numerical values of x_n, y_n, z_n are not our immediate concern. We shall return to their calculation in example XIII(8.b). The limits x, y, z may be obtained by a simpler method which is applicable to more general cases. We indicate it here because of its importance and intrinsic interest.

Let A be the event that *a run of α consecutive successes occurs before a run of β consecutive failures*. Then A means Paul's winning and $x = \mathbf{P}\{A\}$. If u and v are the conditional probabilities of A under the hypotheses, respectively, that the first trial results in success or failure, then $x = pu + qv$ [see V(1.8)]. Suppose first that the first trial results in success. In this case the event A can occur in α mutually exclusive ways: (1) The following $\alpha - 1$ trials result in successes; the probability for this is $p^{\alpha-1}$. (2) The first failure occurs at the νth trial where $2 \leq \nu \leq \alpha$. Let this event be H_ν. Then $\mathbf{P}\{H_\nu\} = p^{\nu-2}q$, and $\mathbf{P}\{A \mid H_\nu\} = v$. Hence (using once more the formula for compound probabilities)

$$(1.1) \qquad u = p^{\alpha-1} + qv(1 + p + \ldots p^{\alpha-2}) = p^{\alpha-1} + v(1 - p^{\alpha-1}).$$

If the first trial results in failure, a similar argument leads to

$$(1.2) \qquad v = pu(1 + q + \ldots + q^{\beta-2}) = u(1 - q^{\beta-1}).$$

We have thus two equations for the two unknowns u and v and find for $x = pu + qv$

$$(1.3) \qquad x = p^{\alpha-1} \frac{1 - q^\beta}{p^{\alpha-1} + q^{\beta-1} - p^{\alpha-1}q^{\beta-1}}.$$

To obtain y we have only to interchange p and q, and α and β. Thus

$$(1.4) \qquad y = q^{\beta-1} \frac{1 - p^\alpha}{p^{\alpha-1} + q^{\beta-1} - p^{\alpha-1}q^{\beta-1}}.$$

Since $x + y = 1$, we have $z = 0$; *the probability of a tie is zero.*

For example, in tossing a coin ($p = \frac{1}{2}$) the probability that a run of two heads appears before a run of three tails is 0.7; for two consecutive heads before four consecutive tails the probability is $\frac{5}{6}$, for three consecutive heads before four consecutive tails $\frac{15}{22}$. In rolling dice there is probability 0.1753 that two consecutive aces will appear before five consecutive non-aces, etc.

In the present volume we are confined to the theory of discrete sample spaces, and this means a considerable loss of mathematical elegance. The general theory considers n Bernoulli trials only as the beginning of an infinite sequence of trials. A sample point is then represented by an infinite sequence of letters S and F, and the sample space is the aggregate of all such sequences. A finite sequence, like $SSFS$, stands for the aggregate of all points with this beginning, that is, for the compound event that in an infinite sequence of trials the first four result in S, S, F, S, respectively. In the infinite sample space the game of our example can be interpreted without a limiting process.

Take any point, that is, a sequence $SSFSFF \ldots$ In it a run of α consecutive S's may or may not occur. If it does, it may or may not be preceded by a run of β consecutive F's. In this way we get a classification of all sample points into three classes, representing the events "Peter wins," "Peter loses," "no decision." Their probabilities are the numbers x, y, z, computed above. The only trouble with this sample space is that it is not discrete, and we have not yet defined probabilities in general sample spaces.

Note that we are discussing a question of terminology rather than a genuine difficulty. In our example there was no question about the proper definition or interpretation of the number x. The trouble is only that for consistency we must either decide to refer to the number x as "the limit of the probability x_n that Peter wins in n trials" or else talk of the event "that Peter wins," which means referring to a nondiscrete sample space. We propose to do both. For simplicity of language we shall refer to events even when they are defined in the infinite sample space; for precision, the theorems will also be formulated in terms of finite sample spaces and passages to the limit. The events to be studied in this chapter share the following salient feature of our example. The event "Peter wins," although defined in an infinite space, is the union of the events "Peter wins at the nth trial" $(n = 1, 2, \ldots)$, each of which depends only on a finite number of trials. The required probability x is the limit of a monotonic sequence of probabilities x_n which depend only on finitely many trials. We require no theory going beyond the model of n Bernoulli trials; we merely take the liberty of simplifying clumsy expressions [1] by calling certain numbers probabilities instead of using the term "limits of probabilities."

2. SYSTEMS OF GAMBLING

The painful experience of many gamblers has taught us the lesson that no system of betting is successful in improving the gambler's chances. If the theory of probability is true to life, this experience must correspond to a provable statement.

For orientation let us consider a potentially unlimited sequence of Bernoulli trials and suppose that at each trial the bettor has the free choice of whether or not to bet. A "system" consists in fixed rules

---

[1] For the reader familiar with general measure theory the situation may be described as follows. We consider only events which either depend on a finite number of trials or are limits of *monotonic* sequences of such events. We calculate the obvious limits of probabilities and clearly require no measure theory for that purpose. However, only general measure theory shows that our limits are independent of the particular passage to the limit and are completely additive.

selecting those trials on which the player is to bet. For example, the bettor may make up his mind to bet at every seventh trial or to wait as long as necessary for seven heads to occur between two bets. He may bet only following a head run of length 13, or bet for the first time after the first head, for the second time after the first run of two consecutive heads, and generally, for the kth time, just after k heads have appeared in succession. In the latter case he would bet less and less frequently. We need not consider the stakes at the individual trials; we want to show that no "system" changes the bettor's situation and that he can achieve the same result by betting every time. It goes without saying that this statement can be proved only for systems in the ordinary meaning where the bettor does not know the future (the existence or non-existence of genuine prescience is not our concern). It must also be admitted that the rule "go home after losing three times" does change the situation, but we shall rule out such uninteresting systems.

We define a system as a set of fixed rules which for every trial uniquely determines whether or not the bettor is to bet; at the kth trial the decision may depend on the outcomes of the first $k - 1$ trials, but not on the outcome of trials number k, $k+1$, $k+2$, $\ldots$; finally the rules must be such as to ensure an indefinite continuation of the game. Since the set of rules is fixed, the event "in n trials the bettor bets more than r times" is well defined and its probability calculable. The last condition requires that for every r, as $n \to \infty$, this probability tends to 1.

We now formulate our fundamental theorem to the effect that *under any system the successive bets form a sequence of Bernoulli trials with unchanged probability for success.* With an appropriate change of phrasing this theorem holds for all kinds of independent trials; the successive bets form in each case an exact replica of the original trials, so that no system can affect the bettor's fortunes. The importance of this statement was first recognized by von Mises, who introduced the impossibility of a successful gambling system as a fundamental axiom. The present formulation and proof follow Doob.[2] For simplicity we assume that $p = \frac{1}{2}$.

Let A_k be the event "first bet occurs at the kth trial." Our definition of system requires that as $n \to \infty$ the probability tends to one that the first bet has occurred before the nth trial. This means that $\mathbf{P}\{A_1\} + \mathbf{P}\{A_2\} + \ldots + \mathbf{P}\{A_n\} \to 1$, or

$$(2.1) \qquad\qquad \Sigma\mathbf{P}\{A_k\} = 1.$$

---

[2] J. L. Doob, Note on probability, *Annals of Mathematics*, vol. 37 (1936), pp. 363–367.

Next, let B_k be the event "head at kth trial." Then the event B "when first bet is made the trial results in heads" is the union of the events A_1B_1, A_2B_2, A_3B_3, ... which are mutually exclusive. Now A_k depends only on the outcome of the first $k - 1$ trials, and B_k only on the trial number k. Hence A_k and B_k are independent and $\mathbf{P}\{A_kB_k\} = \mathbf{P}\{A_k\}\mathbf{P}\{B_k\} = \frac{1}{2}\mathbf{P}\{A_k\}$. Thus $\mathbf{P}\{B\} = \Sigma\mathbf{P}\{A_kB_k\} = \frac{1}{2}\Sigma\mathbf{P}\{A_k\} = \frac{1}{2}$. This shows that under this system the probability of heads at the first bet is $\frac{1}{2}$, and the same statement holds for all subsequent bets.

It remains to show that the bets are stochastically independent. This means that the probability that the coin falls heads at both the first and the second bet should be $\frac{1}{4}$ (and similarly for all other combinations and for the subsequent trials). To verify this statement let A_k^* be the event that the second bet occurs at the kth trial. Let E represent the event "heads at the first two bets"; it is the union of all events $A_jB_jA_k^*B_k$ where $j < k$ (if $j \geq k$, then A_j and A_k^* are mutually exclusive and $A_jA_k^* = 0$). Therefore

$$(2.2) \qquad \mathbf{P}\{E\} = \sum_{j=1}^{\infty} \sum_{k=j+1}^{\infty} \mathbf{P}\{A_jB_jA_k^*B_k\}.$$

As before, we see that for fixed j and $k > j$, the event B_k (heads at kth trial) is independent of the event $A_jB_jA_k^*$ (which depends only on the outcomes of the first $k - 1$ trials). Hence

$$(2.3) \qquad \mathbf{P}\{E\} = \frac{1}{2} \sum_{j=1}^{\infty} \sum_{k=j+1}^{\infty} \mathbf{P}\{A_jB_jA_k^*\} =$$

$$= \frac{1}{2} \sum_{j=1}^{\infty} \mathbf{P}\{A_jB_j\} \sum_{k=j+1}^{\infty} \mathbf{P}\{A_k^* | A_jB_j\}$$

[cf. V(1.8)]. Now, whenever the first bet occurs and whatever its outcome, the game is sure to continue, that is, the second bet occurs sooner or later. This means that for given A_jB_j with $\mathbf{P}\{A_jB_j\} > 0$ the conditional probabilities that the second bet occurs at the kth trial must add to unity. The second series in (2.3) is therefore unity, and we have already seen that $\Sigma\mathbf{P}\{A_jB_j\} = \frac{1}{2}$. Hence $\mathbf{P}\{E\} = \frac{1}{4}$ as contended. A similar argument holds for any combination of trials.

Note that the situation is different when the player is permitted to vary arbitrarily the amounts which he puts down. With systems depending on the accumulated gain, there exist advantageous strategies, and the game depends on the strategy. We shall return to this point in chapter XIV, section 2.

3. THE BOREL-CANTELLI LEMMAS

Two simple lemmas concerning infinite sequences of trials are used so frequently that they deserve special attention. We formulate them for Bernoulli trials, but they apply to more general cases.

We refer again to an infinite sequence of Bernoulli trials. Let A_1, A_2, ... be an infinite sequence of events each of which depends only on a finite number of trials; in other words, we suppose that there exists an integer n_k such that A_k is an event in the sample space of the first n_k Bernoulli trials. Put

$$(3.1) \qquad a_k = \mathbf{P}\{A_k\}.$$

(For example, A_k may be the event that the $2k$th trial concludes a run of at least k consecutive successes. Then $n_k = 2k$ and $a_k = p^k$.)

For every infinite sequence of letters S and F it is possible to establish whether it belongs to 0, 1, 2, ... or infinitely many among the $\{A_k\}$. This means that we can speak of the event U_r, that an unending sequence of trials produces more than r among the events $\{A_k\}$, and also of the event U_∞, that infinitely many among the $\{A_k\}$ occur. The event U_r is defined only in the infinite sample space, and its probability is the limit of $\mathbf{P}\{U_{n,r}\}$, the probability that n trials produce more than r among the events $\{A_k\}$. Finally, $\mathbf{P}\{U_\infty\} = \lim \mathbf{P}\{U_r\}$; this limit exists since $\mathbf{P}\{U_r\}$ decreases as r increases.

Lemma 1. *If Σa_k converges, then with probability one only finitely many events A_k occur.* More precisely, it is claimed that for r sufficiently large, $\mathbf{P}\{U_r\} < \epsilon$ or: *to every $\epsilon > 0$ it is possible to find an integer r such that the probability that n trials produce one or more among the events A_{r+1}, A_{r+2}, ... is less than ϵ for all n.*

Proof. Determine r so that $a_{r+1} + a_{r+2} + \ldots < \epsilon$; this is possible since Σa_k converges. Without loss of generality we may suppose that the A_k are ordered in such a way that $n_1 \leq n_2 \leq n_3 \leq \ldots$. Let N be the last subscript for which $n_N \leq n$. Then $A_1, \ldots, A_N$ are defined in the space of n trials, and the lemma asserts that the probability that one or more among the events $A_{r+1}, A_{r+2}, \ldots, A_N$ occur is less than ϵ. This is true, since by the fundamental inequality I(7.6) we have

$$(3.2) \qquad \mathbf{P}\{A_{r+1} \cup A_{r+2} \cup \ldots \cup A_N\} \leq a_{r+1} + a_{r+2} + \ldots + a_N \leq \epsilon,$$

as contended.

A satisfactory converse to the lemma is known only for the special case of mutually independent A_k. This situation occurs when the trials are divided into non-overlapping blocks and A_k depends only on the trials in the kth block (for example, A_k may be the event that the kth thousand of trials produces more than 600 successes).

Lemma 2. *If the events A_k are mutually independent, and if Σa_k diverges, then with probability one infinitely many A_k occur.* In other words, it is claimed that for every r the probability that n trials produce more than r among the events $\{A_k\}$ tends to 1 as $n \to \infty$.

Proof. As in the proof of lemma 1 let A_1, A_2, ..., A_N be the events defined in the sample space of n trials. The probability that none of them occurs is, because of the assumed independence, $(1 - a_1)(1 - a_2) \cdots (1 - a_N)$. Now $1 - x < e^{-x}$ for $0 < x < 1$, and hence $(1 - a_1)(1 - a_2) \cdots (1 - a_N) < e^{-(a_1+a_2+\cdots+a_N)}$; with increasing N the last quantity tends to zero. We have thus proved that with probability one at least one among the $\{A_k\}$ occurs.

Next, divide the sequence $\{A_k\}$ into two subsequences $\{A_k{}^*\}$ and $\{A_k{}^{**}\}$ so that both series $\Sigma \mathbf{P}\{A_k{}^*\}$ and $\Sigma \mathbf{P}\{A_k{}^{**}\}$ diverge. Applying our result to these subsequences we find that, with probability one, at least one $A_k{}^*$ and one $A_k{}^{**}$ occur. Therefore there is probability one that at least two among the $\{A_k\}$ occur. Applying, in turn, this statement to the sequences $\{A_k{}^*\}$ and $\{A_k{}^{**}\}$ we find that at least four among the $\{A_k\}$ are bound to occur, etc.

Example. What is the probability that in a sequence of Bernoulli trials the pattern *SFS* appears infinitely often? Let A_k be the event that the trials number k, $k + 1$, and $k + 2$ produce the sequence *SFS*. The events A_k are obviously not mutually independent, but the sequence A_1, A_4, A_7, A_{10}, ... contains only mutually independent events (since no two depend on the outcome of the same trials). Since $a_k = p^2 q$ is independent of k, the series $a_1 + a_4 + a_7 + \ldots$ diverges, and hence with probability one the pattern *SFS* occurs infinitely often. A similar argument obviously applies for arbitrary patterns. (For further examples see problems 4 and 5.)

4. THE STRONG LAW OF LARGE NUMBERS

The intuitive notion of probability is based on the expectation that the following is true: If the number of successes in the first n trials of a sequence of Bernoulli trials is $\mathbf{S}_n$, then

(4.1)
$$\frac{\mathbf{S}_n}{n} \to p.$$

In the abstract theory this cannot be true for *every* sequence of trials; in fact, our sample space contains a point representing the conceptual possibility of an infinite sequence of uninterrupted successes, and for it $S_n/n = 1$. However, it is demonstrable that (4.1) holds with probability one, so that the cases where (4.1) does not hold form a negligible exception.

Note that we deal with a statement much stronger than the weak law of large numbers [VI(4.2)]. The latter says that for every sufficiently large *fixed* n the average S_n/n is likely to be near p, but it does not say that S_n/n is bound to stay near p if the number of trials is increased. It leaves open the possibility that in n additional trials at least one of the events $S_{n+1}/(n+1) < p - \epsilon$, or $S_{n+2}/(n+2) < p - \epsilon$, ..., or $S_{2n}/2n < p - \epsilon$, occurs; the probability of this is the sum of a large number of probabilities of which we know only that they are individually small. We shall now prove that with probability one $S_n/n - p$ becomes *and remains* small.

Strong Law of Large Numbers. *For every $\epsilon > 0$ we have probability one that only finitely many of the events*

$$(4.2) \qquad \left| \frac{S_n}{n} - p \right| > \epsilon$$

occur. This implies that (4.1) holds with probability one. In terms of finite sample spaces, it is asserted that to every $\epsilon > 0$, $\delta > 0$ there corresponds an r such that for all ν the probability of the simultaneous realization of the ν inequalities

$$(4.3) \qquad \left| \frac{S_{r+k}}{r+k} - p \right| < \epsilon, \qquad k = 1, 2, \ldots, \nu$$

is greater than $1 - \delta$.

Proof. We shall prove a much stronger statement. Let A_k be the event

$$(4.4) \qquad |S_k^*| = \left| \frac{S_k - kp}{(kpq)^{\frac{1}{2}}} \right| \geq (2a \log k)^{\frac{1}{2}},$$

where $a > 1$. It is then obvious from VII(5.2) that, at least for all k sufficiently large,

$$(4.5) \qquad \mathbf{P}\{A_k\} < e^{-a \log k} = \frac{1}{k^a}.$$

Hence $\Sigma \mathbf{P}\{A_k\}$ converges, and lemma 1 of the preceding section ensures that *with probability one only finitely many inequalities* (4.4) *hold.* On the other hand, if (4.2) holds, then

(4.6)
$$\left| \frac{S_n - np}{(npq)^{\frac{1}{2}}} \right| > \frac{\epsilon}{(pq)^{\frac{1}{2}}} \cdot n^{\frac{1}{2}}$$

and for large n the right side is larger than $(2a \log n)^{\frac{1}{2}}$. Hence, the realization of infinitely many inequalities (4.2) implies the realization of infinitely many A_k and has therefore probability zero.

The strong law of large numbers was first formulated by Cantelli (1917), after Borel and Hausdorff had discussed certain special cases. Like the weak law, it is only a very special case of a general theorem on random variables. Taken in conjunction with our theorem on the impossibility of gambling systems, the law of large numbers implies the existence of the limit (4.1) not only for the original sequence of trials but also for all subsequences obtained in accordance with the rules of section 2. *Thus the two theorems together describe the fundamental properties of randomness which are inherent in the intuitive notion of probability and whose importance was stressed with special emphasis by von Mises.*

5. THE LAW OF THE ITERATED LOGARITHM

As in chapter VII let us again introduce the reduced number of successes in n trials

(5.1)
$$S_n^* = \frac{S_n - np}{(npq)^{\frac{1}{2}}}.$$

The Laplace limit theorem asserts that $P\{S_n^* > x\} \sim 1 - \Phi(x)$. Thus, for every particular value of n it is improbable to have a large S_n^*, but it is intuitively clear that in a prolonged sequence of trials S_n^* will sooner or later take on arbitrarily large values. Moderate values of S_n^* are most probable, but the maxima will slowly increase. How fast? In the course of the proof of the strong law of large numbers we have concluded from (4.5) that with probability one the inequality $S_n^* < (2a \log n)^{\frac{1}{2}}$ holds for each $a > 1$ and all sufficiently large n. This provides us with an upper bound for the fluctuations of S_n^*, but this bound is bad. To see this, let us apply the same argument to the subsequence $S_2^*, S_4^*, S_8^*, S_{16}^*, \ldots$; that is, let us define the event A_k by $S_{2^k}^* \geq (2a \log k)^{\frac{1}{2}}$. The inequality (4.5) now implies that $S_{2^k}^* < (2a \log k)^{\frac{1}{2}}$ for $a > 1$ and all sufficiently large k. But for $n = 2^k$ we have $\log k \sim \log \log n$, and we conclude that for each $a > 1$ and all n of the form $n = 2^k$ the inequality

(5.2)
$$S_n^* < (2a \log \log n)^{\frac{1}{2}}$$

will hold from some k onward. It is now a fair guess that in reality (5.2) holds for *all* n sufficiently large and, in fact, this is one part of the law of the iterated logarithm. This remarkable theorem [3] asserts that $(2 \log \log n)^{\frac{1}{2}}$ is the *precise* upper bound in the sense that for each $a < 1$ the reverse of the inequality (5.2) will hold for infinitely many n.

Theorem. *With probability one we have*

$$(5.3) \qquad \limsup_{n \to \infty} \frac{S_n{}^*}{(2 \log \log n)^{\frac{1}{2}}} = 1.$$

This means: For $\lambda > 1$ with probability one only finitely many of the events

$$(5.4) \qquad S_n > np + \lambda(2npq \log \log n)^{\frac{1}{2}}$$

occur; for $\lambda < 1$ with probability one (5.4) holds for infinitely many n.

For reasons of symmetry equation (5.3) implies that

$$(5.3a) \qquad \liminf_{n \to \infty} \frac{S_n{}^*}{(2 \log \log n)^{\frac{1}{2}}} = -1.$$

Proof. We start with two preliminary remarks.

(1) There exists a constant $c > 0$ which depends on p, but not on n, such that

$$(5.5) \qquad P\{S_n > np\} > c$$

for all n. In fact, an inspection of the binomial distribution shows that the left side in (5.5) is never zero, and the Laplace limit theorem shows that it tends to $\frac{1}{2}$ as $n \to \infty$. Accordingly, the left side is bounded away from zero, as asserted.

(2) We require the following *lemma:* Let x be fixed, and let A be the event that for at least one k with $k \leq n$

$$(5.6) \qquad S_k - kp > x.$$

Then

$$(5.7) \qquad P\{A\} \leq \frac{1}{c} P\{S_n - np > x\}.$$

---

[3] A. Khintchine, Über einen Satz der Wahrscheinlichkeitsrechnung, *Fundamenta Mathematicae*, vol. 6 (1924), pp. 9–20. The discovery was preceded by partial results due to other authors. The present proof is arranged so as to permit straightforward generalization to more general random variables.

For a proof of the lemma let A_ν be the event that (5.6) holds for $k = \nu$ but not for $k = 1, 2, \ldots, \nu-1$ (here $1 \leq \nu \leq n$). The events $A_1, A_2, \ldots, A_n$ are mutually exclusive, and A is their union. Hence

$$(5.8) \qquad \mathbf{P}\{A\} = \mathbf{P}\{A_1\} + \ldots + \mathbf{P}\{A_n\}.$$

Next, for $\nu < n$ let U_ν be the event that the total number of successes in the trials number $\nu+1, \nu+2, \ldots, n$ exceeds $(n - \nu)p$. If both A_ν and U_ν occur, then $\mathbf{S}_n > \mathbf{S}_\nu + (n - \nu)p > np + x$, and since the $A_\nu U_\nu$ are mutually exclusive, this implies

$$(5.9) \quad \mathbf{P}\{\mathbf{S}_n - np > x\} \geq \mathbf{P}\{A_1 U_1\} + \mathbf{P}\{A_2 U_2\} + \ldots +$$
$$+ \mathbf{P}\{A_{n-1} U_{n-1}\} + \mathbf{P}\{A_n\}.$$

Now A_ν depends only on the first ν trials and U_ν only on the following $n - \nu$ trials. Hence A_ν and U_ν are independent, and $\mathbf{P}\{A_\nu U_\nu\} = \mathbf{P}\{A_\nu\}\mathbf{P}\{U_\nu\}$. From the preliminary remark (5.5) we know that $\mathbf{P}\{U_\nu\} > c$, and since $c < 1$, we get from (5.9) and (5.8)

$$(5.10) \qquad \mathbf{P}\{\mathbf{S}_n - np > x\} \geq c \, \Sigma \mathbf{P}\{A_\nu\} = c \, \mathbf{P}\{A\}.$$

This proves (5.7).

(3) We now prove the part of the theorem relating to (5.4) with $\lambda > 1$. Let γ be a number such that

$$(5.11) \qquad 1 < \gamma < \lambda^{\frac{1}{2}},$$

and let n_r be the integer nearest to γ^r ($r = 1, 2, \ldots$). Let B_r be the event that the inequality

$$(5.12) \qquad \mathbf{S}_n - np > \lambda(2 n_r pq \log \log n_r)^{\frac{1}{2}}$$

holds for at least one n with $n_r \leq n < n_{r+1}$. Obviously (5.4) can hold for infinitely many n only if infinitely many B_r occur. Using the first Borel-Cantelli lemma, we see therefore that it suffices to prove that

$$(5.13) \qquad \Sigma \mathbf{P}\{B_r\} \text{ converges.}$$

By the inequality (5.7)

$$(5.14) \quad \mathbf{P}\{B_r\} \leq c^{-1} \, \mathbf{P}\{\mathbf{S}_{n_{r+1}} - n_{r+1}p > \lambda(2 n_r pq \log \log n_r)^{\frac{1}{2}}\} =$$
$$= c^{-1} \, \mathbf{P}\left\{\mathbf{S}^*_{n_{r+1}} > \lambda\left(2\frac{n_r}{n_{r+1}} \log \log n_r\right)^{\frac{1}{2}}\right\}.$$

Now $n_r/n_{r+1} \sim \gamma^{-1} > \lambda^{-\frac{1}{2}}$, and hence for sufficiently large r

$$(5.15) \qquad \mathbf{P}\{B_r\} \leq c^{-1} \, \mathbf{P}\{\mathbf{S}^*_{n_{r+1}} > (2\lambda \log \log n_r)^{\frac{1}{2}}\}.$$

From formula VII(5.2) we get, therefore, for large r,

$$(5.16) \qquad \mathbf{P}\{B_r\} \leq c^{-1}e^{-\lambda \log \log n_r} = \frac{1}{c(\log n_r)^\lambda} \sim \frac{1}{c(r \log \gamma)^\lambda}.$$

Since $\lambda > 1$, the assertion (5.13) is proved.

(4) Finally, we prove the assertion concerning (5.4) with $\lambda < 1$. This time we choose for γ an integer so large that

$$(5.17) \qquad \frac{\gamma - 1}{\gamma} > \eta > \lambda$$

where η is a constant to be determined later, and put $n_r = \gamma^r$. The second Borel-Cantelli lemma applies only to independent events, and for this reason we introduce

$$(5.18) \qquad \mathbf{D}_r = \mathbf{S}_{n_r} - \mathbf{S}_{n_{r-1}};$$

$\mathbf{D}_r$ is the total number of successes following trial number n_{r-1} and up to and including trial n_r; for it we have the binomial distribution $b(k; n, p)$ with $n = n_r - n_{r-1}$. Let A_r be the event

$$(5.19) \qquad \mathbf{D}_r - (n_r - n_{r-1})p > \eta(2pqn_r \log \log n_r)^{\frac{1}{2}}.$$

We claim that *with probability one infinitely many A_r occur*. Since the various A_r depend on non-overlapping blocks of trials (namely, $n_{r-1} < n \leq n_r$), they are mutually independent, and, according to the second Borel-Cantelli lemma, it suffices to prove that $\Sigma \mathbf{P}\{A_r\}$ diverges. Now

$$(5.20) \quad \mathbf{P}\{A_r\} =$$

$$= \mathbf{P}\left\{ \frac{\mathbf{D}_r - (n_r - n_{r-1})p}{\{(n_r - n_{r-1})pq\}^{\frac{1}{2}}} > \eta \left(2 \frac{n_r}{n_r - n_{r-1}} \log \log n_r \right)^{\frac{1}{2}} \right\}.$$

Here $n_r/(n_r - n_{r-1}) = \gamma/(\gamma - 1) < \eta^{-1}$, by (5.17). Hence

$$(5.21) \quad \mathbf{P}\{A_r\} \geq \mathbf{P}\left\{ \frac{\mathbf{D}_r - (n_r - n_{r-1})p}{\{(n_r - n_{r-1})pq\}^{\frac{1}{2}}} > (2\eta \log \log n_r)^{\frac{1}{2}} \right\}.$$

Using again the estimate (5.2) of chapter VII, we find for large r

$$(5.22) \quad \mathbf{P}\{A_r\} > \frac{1}{2\eta \log \log n_r} e^{-\eta \log \log n_r} = \frac{1}{2\eta(\log \log n_r)(\log n_r)^\eta}.$$

Since $n_r = \gamma^r$ and $\eta < 1$, we find that for large r we have $\mathbf{P}\{A_r\} > 1/r$, which proves the divergence of $\Sigma \mathbf{P}\{A_r\}$.

The last step of the proof consists in showing that $\mathbf{S}_{n_{r-1}}$ in (5.18) can be neglected. From the first part of the theorem, which has already been proved, we know that to every $\epsilon > 0$ we can find an N so that, with probability $1 - \epsilon$ or better, for all $r > N$,

$$(5.23) \qquad |\mathbf{S}_{n_{r-1}} - n_{r-1}p| < 2(2pqn_{r-1} \log \log n_{r-1})^{\frac{1}{2}}.$$

Now suppose that η is chosen so close to 1 that

$$(5.24) \qquad 1 - \eta < \left(\frac{\eta - \lambda}{2}\right)^2.$$

Then from (5.17)

$$(5.25) \qquad 4n_{r-1} = 4\frac{n_r}{\gamma} < n_r(\eta - \lambda)^2$$

and hence (5.23) implies

$$(5.26) \qquad \mathbf{S}_{n_{r-1}} - n_{r-1}p > -(\eta - \lambda)(2pqn_r \log \log n_r)^{\frac{1}{2}}.$$

Adding (5.26) to (5.19), we obtain (5.4) with $n = n_r$. It follows that, with probability $1 - \epsilon$ or better, this inequality holds for infinitely many r, and this accomplishes the proof.

The law of the iterated logarithm for Bernoulli trials is a special case of a more general theorem first formulated by Kolmogorov.[4] At present it is possible to formulate stronger theorems (cf. problems 7 and 8).

6. INTERPRETATION IN NUMBER THEORY LANGUAGE

Let x be a real number in the interval $0 \le x < 1$, and let

$$(6.1) \qquad x = .a_1a_2a_3 \ldots$$

be its decimal expansion (so that each a_j stands for one of the digits $0, 1, \ldots, 9$). This expansion is unique except for numbers of the form $a/10^n$ (where a is an integer), which can be written either by means of an expansion containing infinitely many zeros or by means of an expansion containing infinitely many nines. To avoid ambiguities we now agree not to use the latter form.

The decimal expansions are connected with Bernoulli trials with $p = \frac{1}{10}$, the digit 0 representing success and all other digits failure. If we replace in (6.1) all zeros by the letter S and all other digits by F, then (6.1) represents a possible outcome of an infinite sequence of

---

[4] A. Kolmogoroff, Das Gesetz des iterierten Logarithmus, *Mathematische Annalen*, vol. 101 (1929), pp. 126–135.

Bernoulli trials with $p = \frac{1}{10}$. Conversely, an arbitrary sequence of letters S and F can be obtained in the described manner from the expansion of certain numbers x. In this way every event in the sample space of Bernoulli trials is represented by a certain aggregate of numbers x. For example, the event "success at the nth trial" is represented by all those x whose nth decimal is zero. This is an aggregate of 10^{n-1} intervals each of length 10^{-n}, and the total length of these intervals equals $\frac{1}{10}$, which is the probability of our event. Every particular finite sample sequence of length n corresponds to an aggregate of certain intervals; for example, the sequence SFS is represented by the nine intervals $0.01 \le x < 0.011$, $0.02 \le x < 0.021$, $\ldots$, $0.09 \le x < 0.091$. The probability of each such sample sequence equals the total length of the corresponding intervals on the x-axis. Probabilities of more complicated events are always expressed in terms of probabilities of finite sample sequences, and the calculation proceeds according to the same addition rule that is valid for the familiar Lebesgue measure on the x-axis. Accordingly, our probabilities will always coincide with the measure of the corresponding aggregate of points on the x-axis. We have thus a means of translating all limit theorems for Bernoulli trials with $p = \frac{1}{10}$ into theorems concerning decimal expansions. The phrase "with probability one" is equivalent to "for almost all x" or "almost everywhere."

We have considered the random variable $\mathbf{S}_n$ which gives the number of successes in n trials. Here it is more convenient to emphasize the fact that $\mathbf{S}_n$ is a function of the sample point, and we write $\mathbf{S}_n(x)$ *for the number of zeros among the first n decimals of x.* Obviously the graph of $\mathbf{S}_n(x)$ is a step polygon whose discontinuities are necessarily points of the form $a/10^n$, where a is an integer. The ratio $\mathbf{S}_n(x)/n$ is called the *frequency of zeros* among the first n decimals of x.

In the language of ordinary measure theory the weak law of large numbers asserts that $\mathbf{S}_n(x)/n \to \frac{1}{10}$ in measure, whereas the strong law states that $\mathbf{S}_n(x)/n \to \frac{1}{10}$ almost everywhere. Khintchine's law of the iterated logarithm shows that

$$(6.2) \qquad \limsup \frac{\mathbf{S}_n(x) - n/10}{(n \log \log n)^{\frac{1}{2}}} = (0.3)2^{\frac{1}{2}}$$

for almost all x. It gives an answer to a problem treated in a series of papers initiated by Hausdorff [5] (1913) and Hardy and Littlewood [6]

---

[5] F. Hausdorff, *Grundzüge der Mengenlehre*, Leipzig, 1913.

[6] Hardy and Littlewood, Some problems of Diophantine approximation, *Acta Mathematica*, vol. 37 (1914), pp. 155–239.

(1914). For a further improvement of this result see problems 7 and 8.

Instead of the digit zero we may consider any other digit and can formulate the strong law of large numbers to the effect that the frequency of each of the ten digits tends to $\frac{1}{10}$ for almost all x. A similar theorem holds if the base 10 of the decimal system is replaced by any other base. This fact was discovered by Borel (1909) and is usually expressed by saying that almost all numbers are "normal."

7. PROBLEMS FOR SOLUTION

1. Find an integer β such that in rolling dice there are about even chances that a run of three consecutive aces appears before a non-ace run of length β.

2. Consider repeated independent trials with three possible outcomes A, B, C and corresponding probabilities p, q, r $(p + q + r = 1)$. Find the probability that a run of α consecutive A's will occur before a B-run of length β.

3. *Continuation.* Find the probability that an A-run of length α will occur before either a B-run of length β or a C-run of length γ.

4. In a sequence of Bernoulli trials let A_n be the event that a run of n consecutive successes occurs between the 2^nth and the 2^{n+1}st trial. If $p \geq \frac{1}{2}$, there is probability one that infinitely many A_n occur; if $p < \frac{1}{2}$, then with probability one only finitely many A_n occur.

5.[7] Denote by $\mathbf{N}_n$ the length of the success run beginning at the nth trial (i.e., $\mathbf{N}_n = 0$ if the nth trial results in F, etc.). Prove that with probability one

(7.1) $$\limsup \frac{\mathbf{N}_n}{\text{Log } n} = 1$$

where Log denotes the logarithm to the basis $1/p$.

Hint: Consider the event A_n that the nth trial is followed by a run of more than a Log n successes. For $a > 1$ the calculation is straightforward. For $a < 1$ consider the subsequence of trials number $a_1, a_2, \ldots$ where a_n is an integer very close to n Log n.

6. From the law of the iterated logarithm conclude: With probability one it will happen for infinitely many n that all $\mathbf{S}_k$ with $n < k < 17n$ are positive. (*Note:* Considerably stronger statements can be proved using the results of chapter III.)

7. Let $\phi(t)$ be a positive monotonically increasing function, and let n_r be the nearest integer to $e^{r/\log r}$. If

(7.2) $$\sum \frac{1}{\phi(n_r)} e^{-\frac{1}{2}\phi^2(n_r)}$$

converges, then with probability one, the inequality

(7.3) $$\mathbf{S}_n > np + (npq)^{\frac{1}{2}}\phi(n)$$

takes place only for finitely many n. Note that without loss of generality we

---

[7] Suggested by a communication from D. J. Newman.

may suppose that $\phi(n) < 10(\log \log n)^{\frac{1}{2}}$; the law of the iterated logarithm takes care of the larger $\phi(n)$.

8. Prove [8] that the series (7.2) converges if, and only if,

$$(7.4) \qquad\qquad \sum \frac{\phi(n)}{n} e^{-\frac{1}{2}\phi^2(n)}$$

converges. (*Hint:* Collect the terms for which $n_{r-1} < n < n_r$ and note that $n_r - n_{r-1} \sim n_r(1 - 1/\log r)$; furthermore, (7.4) can converge only if $\phi^2(n) > 2 \log \log n$.)

---

[8] Problems 7 and 8 together show that in case of convergence of (7.4) the inequality (7.3) holds with probability one only for finitely many n. Conversely, if (7.4) diverges, the inequality (7.3) holds with probability one for infinitely many n. This converse is much more difficult to prove; cf. W. Feller, The general form of the so-called law of the iterated logarithm, *Transactions of the American Mathematical Society*, vol. 54 (1943), pp. 373–402, where more general theorems are proved for arbitrary random variables. For the special case of Bernoulli trials with $p = \frac{1}{2}$ cf. P. Erdös, On the law of the iterated logarithm, *Annals of Mathematics* (2), vol. 43 (1942), pp. 419–436. The law of the iterated logarithm follows from the particular case $\phi(t) = \lambda(2 \log \log t)$.

CHAPTER IX

Random Variables; Expectation

1. RANDOM VARIABLES

According to the definition given in calculus textbooks, the quantity y is called a *function* of the real number x if to every x there corresponds a value y. This definition can be extended to cases where the independent variable is not a real number. Thus we call the distance a function of a pair of points; the perimeter of a triangle is a function defined on the set of triangles; a sequence a_n is a function defined for all positive integers; the binomial coefficient $\binom{x}{k}$ is a function defined for pairs of numbers (x, k) of which the second is a non-negative integer. In the same sense we can say that the number S_n of successes in n Bernoulli trials is a function defined on the sample space; to each of the 2^n points in this space there corresponds a number S_n.

A function defined on a sample space is called a random variable. Throughout the preceding chapters we have been concerned with random variables without using this term. Typical random variables are the number of aces in a hand at bridge, of multiple birthdays in a company of n people, of success runs in n Bernoulli trials. In each case there is a unique rule which associates a number X with any sample point. The classical theory of probability was devoted mainly to a study of the gambler's gain, which is again a random variable; in fact, every random variable can be interpreted as the gain of a real or imaginary gambler in a suitable game. The position of a particle under diffusion, the energy, temperature, etc., of physical systems are random variables; but they are defined in non-discrete sample spaces, and their study is therefore deferred. In the case of a discrete sample space we can actually tabulate any random variable X by enumerating in some order all points of the space and associating with each the corresponding value of X.

199

The term random variable is somewhat confusing; random function would be more appropriate (the independent variable being a point in sample space, that is, outcome of an experiment).

Let $\mathbf{X}$ be a random variable and let x_1, x_2, ... be the values which it assumes;[1] in most of what follows the x_j will be integers. The aggregate of all sample points on which $\mathbf{X}$ assumes the fixed value x_j forms the event that $\mathbf{X} = x_j$; its probability is denoted by $\mathbf{P}\{\mathbf{X} = x_j\}$. *The function*

$$(1.1) \qquad \mathbf{P}\{\mathbf{X} = x_j\} = f(x_j) \qquad (j = 1, 2, \ldots)$$

is called the (probability) distribution [2] *of the random variable* $\mathbf{X}$. Clearly

$$(1.2) \qquad f(x_j) \geq 0, \qquad \Sigma f(x_j) = 1.$$

With this terminology we can say that in Bernoulli trials the number of successes $\mathbf{S}_n$ is a random variable with probability distribution $\{b(k; n, p)\}$, whereas the number of trials up to and including the first success is a random variable with the distribution $\{q^{k-1}p\}$.

Consider now two random variables $\mathbf{X}$ and $\mathbf{Y}$ defined on the same sample space, and denote the values which they assume, respectively, by x_1, x_2, ..., and y_1, y_2, ...; let the corresponding probability distributions be $\{f(x_j)\}$ and $\{g(y_k)\}$. The aggregate of points in which the two conditions $\mathbf{X} = x_j$ and $\mathbf{Y} = y_k$ are satisfied forms an event whose probability will be denoted by $\mathbf{P}\{\mathbf{X} = x_j, \mathbf{Y} = y_k\}$. *The function*

$$(1.3) \qquad \mathbf{P}\{\mathbf{X} = x_j, \mathbf{Y} = y_k\} = p(x_j, y_k) \qquad (j, k = 1, 2, \ldots)$$

is called the joint probability distribution of $\mathbf{X}$ *and* $\mathbf{Y}$. It is best exhibited

---

[1] In the standard mathematical terminology the set of points x_1, x_2, ... should be called *the range of* $\mathbf{X}$. Unfortunately the statistical literature uses the term range for the difference between the maximum and the minimum of $\mathbf{X}$.

[2] For a discrete variable $\mathbf{X}$ the probability distribution is the function $f(x_j)$ defined on the aggregate of values x_j assumed by $\mathbf{X}$. This term must be distinguished from the term "distribution function," which applies to non-decreasing functions which tend to 0 as $x \to -\infty$ and to 1 as $x \to \infty$. The distribution function $F(x)$ of $\mathbf{X}$ is defined by

$$F(x) = \mathbf{P}\{\mathbf{X} \leq x\} = \sum_{x_j \leq x} f(x_j),$$

the last sum extending over all those x_j which do not exceed x. Thus the distribution function of a variable can be calculated from its probability distribution and vice versa. In this volume we shall not be concerned with distribution functions in general.

in the form of a double-entry table as exemplified in tables 1 and 2. Clearly

$$(1.4) \qquad p(x_j, y_k) \geq 0, \qquad \sum_{j,k} p(x_j, y_k) = 1.$$

Moreover, for every fixed j

$$(1.5) \quad p(x_j, y_1) + p(x_j, y_2) + p(x_j, y_3) + \ldots = \mathbf{P}\{\mathbf{X} = x_j\} = f(x_j)$$

and for every fixed k

$$(1.6) \quad p(x_1, y_k) + p(x_2, y_k) + p(x_3, y_k) + \ldots = \mathbf{P}\{\mathbf{Y} = y_k\} = g(y_k).$$

In other words, by adding the probabilities in individual rows and columns, we obtain the probability distributions of $\mathbf{X}$ and $\mathbf{Y}$. They may be exhibited as shown in tables 1 and 2 and are then called *marginal distributions*. The adjective "marginal" refers to the outer appearance in the double-entry table and is also used for stylistic clarity when the joint distribution of two variables and also their individual (marginal) distributions appear in the same context. Strictly speaking, the adjective "marginal" is redundant.

The notion of joint distribution carries over to *systems of more than two random variables.*

Examples. (*a*) *Random placements of 3 balls into 3 cells.* We refer to the sample space of 27 points defined formally in table 1 accompanying example I(2.*a*); to each point we attach probability $\frac{1}{27}$. Let $\mathbf{N}$ denote the number of occupied cells, and for $i = 1, 2, 3$ let $\mathbf{X}_i$ denote the number of balls in the cell number i. These are picturesque descriptions. Formally $\mathbf{N}$ is the function assuming the value 1 on the sample points number 1–3; the value 2 on the points number 4–21; and the value 3 on the points number 22–27. Accordingly, the probability distribution of $\mathbf{N}$ is defined by $\mathbf{P}\{\mathbf{N} = 1\} = \frac{1}{9}$, $\mathbf{P}\{\mathbf{N} = 2\} = \frac{2}{3}$, $\mathbf{P}\{\mathbf{N} = 3\} = \frac{2}{9}$. The joint distributions of $(\mathbf{N}, \mathbf{X}_1)$ and of $(\mathbf{X}_1, \mathbf{X}_2)$ are given in tables 1 and 2.

(*b*) *Dice.* In n throws of an ideal die let $\mathbf{X}_1, \mathbf{X}_2, \mathbf{X}_3$, respectively, denote the number of ones, twos, and threes. The probability $p(k_1, k_2, k_3)$ that the n throws result in k_1 ones, k_2 twos, k_3 threes, and $n - k_1 - k_2 - k_3$ other faces is given by the multinomial distribution VI(9.2) with $p_1 = p_2 = p_3 = \frac{1}{6}$, $p_4 = \frac{1}{2}$, that is, by

$$(1.7) \quad p(k_1, k_2, k_3) = \frac{n!}{k_1!k_2!k_3!(n - k_1 - k_2 - k_3)!} \cdot 3^{n-k_1-k_2-k_3} 6^{-n}.$$

This is the joint distribution of $\mathbf{X}_1, \mathbf{X}_2, \mathbf{X}_3$. Keeping k_1, k_2 fixed and

TABLE 1

JOINT DISTRIBUTION OF $(\mathbf{N}, \mathbf{X}_1)$ IN EXAMPLE (a)

	$\mathbf{X}_1$				
	0	1	2	3	Distribution of $\mathbf{N}$
1	$2q$	0	0	q	$3q = \frac{1}{9}$
$\mathbf{N}$　2	$6q$	$6q$	$6q$	0	$18q = \frac{2}{3}$
3	0	$6q$	0	0	$6q = \frac{2}{9}$
Distribution of $\mathbf{X}_1$	$8q$	$12q$	$6q$	q	

$$E(\mathbf{N}) = \tfrac{19}{9}, \qquad E(\mathbf{N}^2) = \tfrac{129}{27}, \qquad \operatorname{Var}(\mathbf{N}) = \tfrac{26}{81}$$
$$E(\mathbf{X}_1) = 1, \qquad E(\mathbf{X}_1^2) = \tfrac{45}{27}, \qquad \operatorname{Var}(\mathbf{X}_1) = \tfrac{2}{3}$$
$$E(\mathbf{NX}_1) = \tfrac{19}{9}, \qquad\qquad\qquad \operatorname{Cov}(\mathbf{N}, \mathbf{X}_1) = 0.$$

$\mathbf{N}$ is the number of occupied cells, $\mathbf{X}_1$ the number of balls in the first cell when 3 balls are distributed randomly in 3 cells. For abbreviation $q = \tfrac{1}{27}$.

TABLE 2

JOINT DISTRIBUTION OF $(\mathbf{X}_1, \mathbf{X}_2)$ IN EXAMPLE (a)

	$\mathbf{X}_1$				
	0	1	2	3	Distribution of $\mathbf{X}_2$
0	q	$3q$	$3q$	q	$8q$
1	$3q$	$6q$	$3q$	0	$12q$
$\mathbf{X}_2$　2	$3q$	$3q$	0	0	$6q$
3	q	0	0	0	q
Distribution of $\mathbf{X}_1$	$8q$	$12q$	$6q$	q	

$$E(\mathbf{X}_i) = 1, \qquad E(\mathbf{X}_i^2) = \tfrac{45}{27}, \qquad \operatorname{Var}(\mathbf{X}_i) = \tfrac{2}{3}$$
$$E(\mathbf{X}_1, \mathbf{X}_2) = \tfrac{2}{3}, \qquad\qquad\qquad \operatorname{Cov}(\mathbf{X}_1, \mathbf{X}_2) = -\tfrac{1}{3}.$$

$\mathbf{X}_i$ is the number of balls in the ith cell when 3 balls are distributed randomly in 3 cells. For abbreviation $q = \tfrac{1}{27}$.

summing (1.7) over the possible values $k_3 = 0, 1, \ldots, n-k_1-k_2$, we get, using the binomial theorem,

$$(1.8) \qquad p(k_1, k_2) = \frac{n!}{k_1!k_2!(n-k_1-k_2)!} \cdot 4^{n-k_1-k_2}6^{-n}.$$

This is the joint distribution of $(\mathbf{X}_1, \mathbf{X}_2)$, which now appears as marginal distribution for the triple distribution of $\mathbf{X}_1, \mathbf{X}_2, \mathbf{X}_3$. Needless to say that (1.8) could have been obtained directly from the multinomial distribution. Summing (1.8) once more over all $k_2 = 0, 1, \ldots, n-k_1$ we obtain the distribution of $\mathbf{X}_1$, namely the binomial distribution with $p = \frac{1}{6}$.

(c) *Sampling.* Let a population of n elements be divided into three classes of respective sizes $n_1 = np_1$, $n_2 = np_2$, and $n_3 = np_3$ (where $p_1 + p_2 + p_3 = 1$). Suppose that a random sample of size r is drawn, and denote by $\mathbf{X}_1$ and $\mathbf{X}_2$ the numbers of representatives of the first and second class in the sample. If the sample is *with replacement*, $\mathbf{P}\{\mathbf{X}_1 = k_1, \mathbf{X}_2 = k_2\}$ is given by the multinomial distribution

$$(1.9) \qquad f(k_1, k_2) = \frac{r!}{k_1!k_2!(r-k_1-k_2)!} p_1^{k_1}p_2^{k_2}p_3^{r-k_1-k_2}.$$

[See formula VI(9.2).] The variable $\mathbf{X}_i$ has the binomial distribution $\{b(k; r, p_i)\}$. If the sampling is *without replacement*, then $\mathbf{P}\{\mathbf{X}_1 = k_1, \mathbf{X}_2 = k_2\}$ is given by the double hypergeometric distribution II(6.5) and $\mathbf{X}_1$ has the simple hypergeometric distribution II(6.1).

(d) *Randomized sampling.* Consider once more the preceding example but suppose that the sample size r, instead of being fixed in advance, depends on the outcome of a random experiment. More precisely, suppose that the size of the sample depends on a Poisson distribution: The probability that the sample size is r is $p(r; \lambda) = e^{-\lambda}\lambda^r/r!$ and, given the sample size r, the (conditional) probability that $\mathbf{X}_1 = k_1$ and $\mathbf{X}_2 = k_2$ is $f(k_1, k_2)$ of (1.9). For the joint probability distribution of $(\mathbf{X}_1, \mathbf{X}_2)$ we have then

$$(1.10) \qquad \mathbf{P}\{\mathbf{X}_1 = k_1, \mathbf{X}_2 = k_2\} = e^{-\lambda} \sum_{r=k_1+k_2}^{\infty} \lambda^r f(k_1, k_2)/r! =$$

$$= e^{-\lambda} \cdot \frac{(\lambda p_1)^{k_1}(\lambda p_2)^{k_2}}{k_1!k_2!} \sum_{k_3=0}^{\infty} \frac{(\lambda p_3)^{k_3}}{k_3!} = e^{-\lambda(1-p_3)} \frac{(\lambda p_1)^{k_1}(\lambda p_2)^{k_2}}{k_1!k_2!}$$

or

$$(1.11) \qquad \mathbf{P}\{\mathbf{X}_1 = k_1, \mathbf{X}_2 = k_2\} = p(k_1; \lambda p_1)p(k_2; \lambda p_2).$$

Summing over k_2 we find that $\mathbf{X}_1$ has the Poisson distribution $p(k; \lambda p_1)$.

(Problem VI, 27 paraphrases the same statement.) The joint distribution of $(\mathbf{X}_1, \mathbf{X}_2)$ takes on the form of a multiplication table of the two marginal distributions $\{p(k; \lambda p_1)\}$ and $\{p(k; \lambda p_2)\}$. We shall express this by saying that $\mathbf{X}_1$ and $\mathbf{X}_2$ are *independent*.

With the notation (1.3) the conditional probability of the event $\mathbf{Y} = y_k$, given that $\mathbf{X} = x_j$ (with $f(x_j) > 0$), becomes

$$(1.12) \qquad \mathbf{P}\{\mathbf{Y} = y_k \,|\, \mathbf{X} = x_j\} = \frac{p(x_j, y_k)}{f(x_j)}.$$

It is convenient to abbreviate (1.12) to $\mathbf{P}\{\mathbf{Y} = y_k \,|\, \mathbf{X}\}$; this defines the (*conditional*) *distribution of* $\mathbf{Y}$ *for given* $\mathbf{X}$. A glance at tables 1 and 2 shows that the conditional probability (1.12) is in general different from $g(y_k)$. This indicates that inference can be drawn from the values of $\mathbf{X}$ to those of $\mathbf{Y}$ and vice versa; the two variables are (stochastically) *dependent*. The strongest degree of dependence exists when $\mathbf{Y}$ is a function of $\mathbf{X}$, that is, when the value of $\mathbf{X}$ uniquely determines $\mathbf{Y}$. For example, if a coin is tossed n times and $\mathbf{X}$ and $\mathbf{Y}$ are the numbers of heads and tails, then $\mathbf{Y} = n - \mathbf{X}$. Similarly, when $\mathbf{Y} = \mathbf{X}^2$, we can compute $\mathbf{Y}$ from $\mathbf{X}$. In the joint distribution this means that in each row all entries but one are zero. If, on the other hand, $p(x_j, y_k) = = f(x_j)g(y_k)$ for all combinations of x_j, y_k, then the events $\mathbf{X} = x_j$ and $\mathbf{Y} = y_k$ are independent; the joint distribution assumes the form of a multiplication table. In this case we speak of *independent* random variables. They occur in particular in connection with independent trials; for example, the numbers scored in two throws of a die are independent. An example of a different nature is found in example (*d*).

Note that the joint distribution of $\mathbf{X}$ and $\mathbf{Y}$ determines the distributions of $\mathbf{X}$ and $\mathbf{Y}$, but that we cannot calculate the joint distribution of $\mathbf{X}$ and $\mathbf{Y}$ from their marginal distributions. If two variables $\mathbf{X}$ and $\mathbf{Y}$ have the same distribution, they may or may not be independent. For example, the two variables $\mathbf{X}_1$ and $\mathbf{X}_2$ in table 2 have the same distribution and are dependent.

All our notions apply also to the case of more than two variables. We recapitulate in the formal

Definition. *A random variable* $\mathbf{X}$ *is a function defined on a given sample space, that is, an assignment of a real number to each sample point. The probability distribution of* $\mathbf{X}$ *is the function defined in (1.1). If two random variables* $\mathbf{X}$ *and* $\mathbf{Y}$ *are defined on the same sample space, their joint distribution is given by (1.3) and assigns probabilities to all combinations* (x_j, y_k) *of values assumed by* $\mathbf{X}$ *and* $\mathbf{Y}$. *This notion carries*

over, *in an obvious manner, to any finite set of variables* **X, Y, ..., W**
defined on the same sample space. *These variables are called mutually
independent if, for any combination of values,* $(x, y, \ldots, w)$ *assumed by
them,*

(1.13) $\mathbf{P}\{\mathbf{X} = x, \mathbf{Y} = y, \ldots, \mathbf{W} = w\} =$

$$= \mathbf{P}\{\mathbf{X} = x\}\,\mathbf{P}\{\mathbf{Y} = y\}\, \cdots \mathbf{P}\{\mathbf{W} = w\}.$$

In chapter V, section 4, we have defined the sample space corresponding to n mutually independent trials. Comparing this definition
to (1.13), we see that *if* $\mathbf{X}_k$ *depends only on the outcome of the kth trial,
then the variables* $\mathbf{X}_1, \ldots, \mathbf{X}_n$ *are mutually independent.* More generally,
if a random variable **U** depends only on the outcomes of the first k
trials, and another variable **V** depends only on the outcomes of the
last $n-k$ trials, then **U** and **V** are independent (cf. problem 39).

We may conceive of a random variable as a labeling of the points
of the sample space. This procedure is familiar from dice, where the
faces are numbered, and we speak of numbers as the possible outcomes
of individual trials. In conventional mathematical terminology we
could say that a random variable **X** is a mapping of the original sample
space onto a new space whose points are $x_1, x_2, \ldots$. Therefore:

Whenever $\{f(x_j)\}$ *satisfies the obvious conditions* (1.2) *it is legitimate to talk of a random variable* **X**, *assuming the values* $x_1, x_2, \ldots$
with probabilities $f(x_1), f(x_2), \ldots$ *without further reference to the old
sample space; a new one is formed by the sample points* $x_1, x_2, \ldots$.
*Specifying a probability distribution is equivalent to specifying a sample
space whose points are real numbers.* *Speaking of two independent ran-
dom variables* **X** *and* **Y** *with distributions* $\{f(x_j)\}$ *and* $\{g(y_k)\}$ *is equivalent to referring to a sample space whose points are pairs of numbers*
(x_j, y_k) *to which probabilities are assigned by the rule* $\mathbf{P}\{(x_j, y_k)\} =$
$= f(x_j)g(y_k)$. *Similarly, for the sample space corresponding to a set of
n random variables* $(\mathbf{X}, \mathbf{Y}, \ldots, \mathbf{W})$ *we can take an aggregate of points*
$(x, y, \ldots, w)$ *in the n-dimensional space to which probabilities are
assigned by the joint distribution.* *The variables are mutually independent
if their joint distribution is given by* (1.13).

Example. (*e*) *Bernoulli trials with variable probabilities.* Consider
n *independent* trials, each of which has only two possible outcomes,
S and F. The probability of S at the kth trial is p_k, that of F is
$q_k = 1 - p_k$. If $p_k = p$, this scheme reduces to Bernoulli trials. The
simplest way of describing it is to attribute the values 1 and 0 to S
and F. The model is then completely described by saying that we
have n mutually independent random variables $\mathbf{X}_k$ with distributions

$\mathbf{P}\{\mathbf{X}_k = 1\} = p_k$, $\mathbf{P}\{\mathbf{X}_k = 0\} = q_k$. This scheme is known under the confusing name of *"Poisson trials."* [See examples (5.b) and XI(6.b).]

It is clear that the same distribution can occur in conjunction with different sample spaces. If we say that the random variable $\mathbf{X}$ assumes the values 0 and 1 with probabilities $\frac{1}{2}$, then we refer tacitly to a sample space consisting of the two points 0 and 1. However, the variable $\mathbf{X}$ might have been defined by stipulating that it equals 0 or 1 according as the tenth tossing of a coin produces heads or tails; in this case $\mathbf{X}$ is defined in a sample space of sequences $(HHT\ldots)$, and this sample space has 2^{10} points.

In principle, it is possible to restrict the theory of probability to sample spaces defined in terms of probability distributions of random variables. This procedure avoids references to abstract sample spaces and also to terms like "trials" and "outcomes of experiments." The reduction of probability theory to random variables is a short cut to the use of analysis and simplifies the theory in many ways. However, it also has the drawback of obscuring the probability background. The notion of random variable easily remains vague as "something that takes on different values with different probabilities." But random variables are ordinary functions, and this notion is by no means peculiar to probability theory.

Example. (*f*) Let $\mathbf{X}$ be a random variable with possible values $x_1, x_2, \ldots$ and corresponding probabilities $f(x_1), f(x_2), \ldots$. If it helps the reader's imagination, he may always construct a conceptual experiment leading to $\mathbf{X}$. For example, subdivide a roulette wheel into arcs $l_1, l_2, \ldots$ whose lengths are as $f(x_1):f(x_2):\ldots$. Imagine a gambler receiving the (positive or negative) amount x_j if the roulette comes to rest at a point of l_j. Then $\mathbf{X}$ is the gambler's gain. In n trials, the gains are assumed to be n independent variables with the common distribution $\{f(x_j)\}$. To obtain two variables with a given joint distribution $\{p(x_j, y_k)\}$ let an arc correspond to each combination (x_j, y_k) and think of two gamblers receiving the amounts x_j and y_k, respectively.

If $\mathbf{X}, \mathbf{Y}, \mathbf{Z}, \ldots$ are random variables defined on the same sample space, then any function $F(\mathbf{X}, \mathbf{Y}, \mathbf{Z}, \ldots)$ is again a random variable. Its distribution can be obtained from the joint distribution of $\mathbf{X}, \mathbf{Y}, \mathbf{Z}, \ldots$ simply by collecting the terms which correspond to combinations of $(\mathbf{X}, \mathbf{Y}, \mathbf{Z}, \ldots)$ giving the same value of $F(\mathbf{X}, \mathbf{Y}, \mathbf{Z}, \ldots)$.

Example. (*g*) In the example illustrated by table 2 the sum $\mathbf{X}_1 + \mathbf{X}_2$ is a random variable assuming the values 0, 1, 2, 3 with probabilities q, $6q$, $12q$, $8q$ (where $q = \frac{1}{27}$). The product $\mathbf{X_1X_2}$ assumes the values 0, 1, 2 with probabilities $15q$, $6q$, $6q$.

2. EXPECTATIONS

To achieve reasonable simplicity it is often necessary to describe probability distributions rather summarily by a few "typical values." An example is provided by the median which was used above in connection with waiting times. The *median x_m of the distribution* (1.1) is that value assumed by $\mathbf{X}$ for which $\mathbf{P}\{\mathbf{X} \leq x_m\} \leq \frac{1}{2}$ and also $\mathbf{P}\{\mathbf{X} \geq x_m\} \leq \frac{1}{2}$. In other words, x_m is chosen so that the probabilities of $\mathbf{X}$ exceeding or falling short of x_m are as close to $\frac{1}{2}$ as possible.

However, among the typical values the expectation or mean is by far the most important. It lends itself best to analytical manipulations, and it is preferred by statisticians because of a property known as sampling stability. Its definition follows the customary notion of an average. If in a certain population n_k families have exactly k children, the total number of families is $n = n_0 + n_1 + n_2 + \ldots$ and the total number of children $m = n_1 + 2n_2 + 3n_3 + \ldots$. The average number of children per family is m/n. The analogy between probabilities and frequencies suggests the following

Definition. *Let $\mathbf{X}$ be a random variable assuming the values x_1, x_2, $\ldots$ with corresponding probabilities $f(x_1)$, $f(x_2)$, $\ldots$. The mean or expected value of $\mathbf{X}$ is defined by*

$$(2.1) \qquad\qquad \mathbf{E}(\mathbf{X}) = \Sigma x_k f(x_k)$$

provided that the series converges absolutely. In this case we say that $\mathbf{X}$ has a finite expectation. If $\Sigma |x_k| f(x_k)$ diverges, then we say that $\mathbf{X}$ has no finite expectation.

It goes without saying that the most common random variables have finite expectations; otherwise the concept would be impractical. However, variables without finite expectations occur in connection with important recurrence problems in physics. The terms *mean, average,* and *mathematical expectation are synonymous.* We also speak of the *mean of a distribution* instead of referring to a corresponding random variable. The notation $\mathbf{E}(\mathbf{X})$ is generally accepted in mathematics and statistics. In physics $\overline{\mathbf{X}}$, $<\mathbf{X}>$, $<\mathbf{X}>_{\mathrm{Av}}$ are common substitutes for $\mathbf{E}(\mathbf{X})$.

We wish to calculate expectations of functions such as $\mathbf{X}^2$. This function is a new random variable assuming the values $x_k{}^2$; in general, the probability of $\mathbf{X}^2 = x_k{}^2$ is not $f(x_k)$ but $f(x_k) + f(-x_k)$ and $\mathbf{E}(\mathbf{X}^2)$

is defined as the sum of $x_k{}^2\{f(x_k) + f(-x_k)\}$ for all k such that $x_k \geq 0$. Obviously

$$(2.2) \qquad \mathbf{E}(\mathbf{X}^2) = \Sigma x_k{}^2 f(x_k)$$

provided the series converges. The same procedure of collecting terms leads to the general

Theorem 1. *Any function* $\phi(x)$ *defines a new random variable* $\phi(\mathbf{X})$. *If* $\phi(\mathbf{X})$ *has finite expectation, then*

$$(2.3) \qquad \mathbf{E}(\phi(\mathbf{X})) = \Sigma\phi(x_k)f(x_k);$$

the series converges absolutely if, and only if, $\mathbf{E}(\phi(\mathbf{X}))$ *exists. For any constant* a *we have* $\mathbf{E}(a\mathbf{X}) = a\mathbf{E}(\mathbf{X})$.

If several random variables $\mathbf{X}_1, \ldots, \mathbf{X}_n$ are defined on the same sample space, then their sum $\mathbf{X}_1 + \ldots + \mathbf{X}_n$ is a new random variable. Its possible values and the corresponding probabilities can be readily found from the joint distribution of the $\mathbf{X}_\nu$ and thus $\mathbf{E}(\mathbf{X}_1 + \ldots + \mathbf{X}_n)$ can be calculated. A simpler procedure is furnished by the following important

Theorem 2. *If* $\mathbf{X}_1, \mathbf{X}_2, \ldots, \mathbf{X}_n$ *are random variables with expectations, then the expectation of their sum exists and is the sum of their expectations:*

$$(2.4) \qquad \mathbf{E}(\mathbf{X}_1 + \ldots + \mathbf{X}_n) = \mathbf{E}(\mathbf{X}_1) + \ldots + \mathbf{E}(\mathbf{X}_n).$$

Proof. It suffices to prove (2.4) for two variables $\mathbf{X}$ and $\mathbf{Y}$. Using the notation (1.3), we can write

$$(2.5) \qquad \mathbf{E}(\mathbf{X}) + \mathbf{E}(\mathbf{Y}) = \sum_{j,k} x_j p(x_j, y_k) + \sum_{j,k} y_k p(x_j, y_k),$$

the summation extending over all possible values x_j, y_k (which need not be all different). The two series converge; their sum can therefore be rearranged to give $\Sigma_{jk}(x_j + y_k)p(x_j, y_k)$, which is by definition the expectation of $\mathbf{X} + \mathbf{Y}$. This accomplishes the proof.

Clearly, no corresponding general theorem holds for products; for example, $\mathbf{E}(\mathbf{X}^2)$ is generally different from $(\mathbf{E}(\mathbf{X}))^2$. Thus, if $\mathbf{X}$ is the number scored with a balanced die, $\mathbf{E}(\mathbf{X}) = \frac{7}{2}$, but $\mathbf{E}(\mathbf{X}^2) = (1 + 4 + 9 + 16 + 25 + 36)/6 = \frac{91}{6}$. However, the simple multiplication rule holds for mutually independent variables.

Theorem 3. *If* $\mathbf{X}$ *and* $\mathbf{Y}$ *are mutually independent random variables with finite expectations, then their product is a random variable with finite* *expectation and*

(2.6) $$\mathbf{E(XY) = E(X)E(Y)}.$$

Proof. To calculate $\mathbf{E(XY)}$ we should multiply each possible value $x_j y_k$ with the corresponding probability. We have already remarked that the values x_k in the definition (2.1) need not be different. Hence

(2.7) $$\mathbf{E(XY)} = \sum_{j,k} x_j y_k f(x_j) g(y_k) = \left\{ \sum_j x_j f(x_j) \right\} \left\{ \sum_k y_k g(y_k) \right\},$$

the rearrangement being justified since the series converge absolutely. This proves the theorem. By induction the same multiplication rule holds for any number of *mutually independent random variables.*

It is convenient to have a notation also for the expectation of a conditional probability distribution. If $\mathbf{X}$ and $\mathbf{Y}$ are two random variables with the joint distribution (1.3), the *conditional expectation* $\mathbf{E(Y\,|\,X)}$ *of* $\mathbf{Y}$ *for given* $\mathbf{X}$ *is the function*

(2.8) $$\sum_k y_k \mathbf{P}\{\mathbf{Y} = y_k \,|\, \mathbf{X} = x_j\} = \frac{\sum_k y_k p(x_j, y_k)}{f(x_j)},$$

provided the series converges absolutely and $f(x_j) > 0$ for all j.

3. EXAMPLES AND APPLICATIONS

(a) *Binomial distribution.* Let $\mathbf{S}_n$ be the number of successes in n Bernoulli trials with probability p for success. We know that $\mathbf{S}_n$ has the binomial distribution $\{b(k; n, p)\}$, whence $\mathbf{E(S}_n) = \Sigma k b(k; n, p) = np\Sigma b(k-1; n-1, p)$. The last sum includes all terms of the binomial distribution for $n - 1$ and hence equals 1. Therefore *the mean of the binomial distribution* is

(3.1) $$\mathbf{E(S}_n) = np.$$

The same result could have been obtained without calculation by a method which is often expedient. Let $\mathbf{X}_k$ be the number of successes scored at the kth trial. This random variable assumes only the values 0 and 1 with corresponding probabilities q and p. Hence $\mathbf{E(X}_k) = 0 \cdot q + 1 \cdot p = p$, and since

(3.2) $$\mathbf{S}_n = \mathbf{X}_1 + \mathbf{X}_2 + \ldots + \mathbf{X}_n,$$

we get (3.1) directly from (2.4).

(b) *Poisson distribution.* If $\mathbf{X}$ has the Poisson distribution $p(k; \lambda) = e^{-\lambda}\lambda^k/k!$ (where $k = 0, 1, \ldots$) then

$$\mathbf{E(X)} = \Sigma k p(k; \lambda) = \lambda \Sigma p(k-1; \lambda).$$

The last series contains all terms of the distribution and therefore adds to unity. Accordingly, *the Poisson distribution* $\{e^{-\lambda}\lambda^k/k!\}$ *has the mean* λ.

(c) *Negative binomial distribution.* Let $\mathbf{X}$ be a variable with the *geometric distribution* $\mathbf{P}\{\mathbf{X} = k\} = q^k p$ where $k = 0, 1, 2, \ldots$. Then $\mathbf{E}(\mathbf{X}) = qp(1 + 2q + 3q^2 + \ldots)$. On the right we have the derivative of a geometric series so that $\mathbf{E}(\mathbf{X}) = qp(1 - q)^{-2} = q/p$. We have seen in chapter VI, section 8, that $\mathbf{X}$ may be interpreted as the number of failures preceding the first success in a sequence of Bernoulli trials. More generally, we have studied the sample space corresponding to Bernoulli trials which are continued until the nth success. For $r < n$, let $\mathbf{X}_1 = \mathbf{X}$, and let $\mathbf{X}_r$ be the number of failures following the $(r-1)$st success and preceding the rth success. Then each $\mathbf{X}_\nu$ has the geometric distribution $\{q^k p\}$, and $\mathbf{E}(\mathbf{X}_\nu) = q/p$. The sum $\mathbf{Y}_r = \mathbf{X}_1 + + \ldots + \mathbf{X}_r$ is the number of failures preceding the rth success. In other words, $\mathbf{Y}_r$ is a random variable whose distribution is the negative binomial defined by either of the two equivalent formulas VI(8.1) or VI(8.2). It follows that *the mean of this negative binomial is* rq/p. This can be verified by direct computation. From VI(8.2) it is clear that $kf(k; r, p) = rp^{-1}qf(k-1; r+1, p)$, and the terms of the distribution $\{f(k-1; r+1, p)\}$ add to unity. This direct calculation has the advantage that it applies also to *non-integral* r. On the other hand, the first argument leads to the result without requiring knowledge of the explicit form of the distribution of $\mathbf{X}_1 + \ldots + \mathbf{X}_r$.

(d) *Waiting times in sampling.* A population of N distinct elements is sampled with replacement. Because of repetitions a random sample of size r will in general contain fewer than r distinct elements. As the sample size increases, new elements will enter the sample more and more rarely. We are interested in the sample size $\mathbf{S}_r$ necessary for the acquisition of r distinct elements. (As a special case, consider the population of $N = 365$ possible birthdays; here $\mathbf{S}_r$ represents the number of people sampled up to the moment where the sample contains r different birthdays. A similar interpretation is possible with random placements of balls into cells. Our problem is of particular interest to collectors of coupons and other items where the acquisition can be compared to random sampling.[3])

---

[3] G. Polya, Eine Wahrscheinlichkeitsaufgabe zur Kundenwerbung, *Zeitschrift für Angewandte Mathematik und Mechanik*, vol. 10 (1930), pp. 96–97. Polya treats a slightly more general problem with different methods. There exists a huge literature treating variants of the coupon collector's problem. [Cf. problems 24, 25, XI, 12–14, and II(11.12).]

The first element enters the sample at the first drawing. The number of drawings from the second up to and including the drawing at which a new element enters the sample is a random variable $\mathbf{X}_1$; generally, let $\mathbf{X}_r$ be the number of drawings following the selection of the rth element up to and including the selection of the next new element. Then $\mathbf{S}_r = 1 + \mathbf{X}_1 + \ldots + \mathbf{X}_{r-1}$ is the sample size at the moment that the rth element enters the sample. Once the sample contains k different elements the probability of drawing a new one is at each drawing $p = (N - k)/N$. The number, $\mathbf{X}_k$, of drawings up to and including the drawing of a new element equals one plus the number of failures preceding the first success in Bernoulli trials with $p = (N - k)/N$. Therefore $\mathbf{E}(\mathbf{X}_k) = 1 + q/p = N/(N - k)$ and, from the addition theorem (2.4),

$$(3.3) \quad \mathbf{E}(\mathbf{S}_r) = N \left\{ \frac{1}{N} + \frac{1}{N - 1} + \frac{1}{N - 2} + \ldots + \frac{1}{N - r + 1} \right\}.$$

For $r = N$ we get the expected number of drawings necessary to exhaust the entire population. For $N = 10$ we have $\mathbf{E}(\mathbf{S}_{10}) = 29.29\ldots$, and $\mathbf{E}(\mathbf{S}_5) = 6.46\ldots$. This means that we can expect to cover half the population in about six to seven drawings, whereas the second half requires some 23 more drawings. A reasonable approximation to (3.3) for large N is

$$(3.4) \qquad\qquad \mathbf{E}(\mathbf{S}_r) \approx N \log \frac{N}{N - r + 1}.$$

In particular, for any fraction $\alpha < 1$ *the expected number of drawings required to obtain a sample containing about the fraction α of the entire population is, for large N, approximately $N \log [1/(1 - \alpha)]$; the expected number of drawings necessary to have all N elements included in the sample is, approximately, $N \log N$.* Note that our results are again obtained without use of the distribution.

(e) *An estimation problem.* An urn contains balls numbered 1 to N. Let $\mathbf{X}$ be *the largest number drawn* in n drawings when random sampling with replacement is used. The event $\mathbf{X} \leq k$ means that each of n numbers drawn is less than or equal to k and therefore $\mathbf{P}\{\mathbf{X} \leq k\} = (k/N)^n$. Hence the probability distribution of $\mathbf{X}$ is given by

$$(3.5) \qquad p_k = \mathbf{P}\{\mathbf{X} = k\} = \mathbf{P}\{\mathbf{X} \leq k\} - \mathbf{P}\{\mathbf{X} \leq k - 1\} =$$

$$= \{k^n - (k - 1)^n\}N^{-n}.$$

It follows that

$$(3.6) \quad \mathbf{E}(X) = \sum_{k=1}^{N} kp_k = N^{-n} \sum_{k=1}^{N} \{k^{n+1} - (k-1)^{n+1} - (k-1)^n\} =$$

$$= N^{-n} \{N^{n+1} - \sum_{k=1}^{N} (k-1)^n\}.$$

For large N the last sum is approximately the area under the curve $y = x^n$ from $x = 0$ to $x = N$, that is, $N^{n+1}/(n+1)$. It follows that for large N

$$(3.7) \qquad\qquad \mathbf{E}(X) \approx \frac{n}{n+1} N.$$

If a town has $N = 1000$ cars and a sample of $n = 10$ is observed, the expected number of the highest observed license plate (assuming randomness) is about 910. (The median is 934.) The practical statistician uses the observed maximum in a sample to estimate the unknown true number N. This method was used during the last war to estimate enemy production (cf. problems 8–11).

(*f*) *Banach's match box problem.* In chapter VI, section 8, we found the distribution

$$(3.8) \qquad\qquad u_r = \binom{2N-r}{N} \frac{1}{2^{2N-r}}$$

for the number X of matches left at the moment when the first box is found empty. We are unable to calculate the expectation $\mathbf{E}(X) = \mu$ in a direct way, but the following indirect way is applicable in many similar cases. Using the fact that the u_r add to unity (which is not easily verified), we find

$$(3.9) \quad N - \mu = \sum_{r=0}^{N-1} (N-r)u_r = \sum_{r=0}^{N-1} (N-r) \binom{2N-r}{N-r} \frac{1}{2^{2N-r}}.$$

By a simple operation on the binomial coefficients the last sum is transformed into

$$(3.10) \quad \sum_{r=0}^{N-1} (2N-r) \binom{2N-r-1}{N-r-1} \frac{1}{2^{2N-r}} =$$

$$= \frac{2N+1}{2} \sum_{r=0}^{N-1} u_{r+1} - \frac{1}{2} \sum_{r=0}^{N-1} (r+1)u_{r+1}.$$

The last sum is identical with the sum defining $\mu = \mathbf{E}(X)$. In the first sum all u_r except u_0 occur, and hence the terms add to $1 - u_0$. Thus from (3.9) and (3.10)

$$(3.11) \qquad N - \mu = \frac{2N + 1}{2} (1 - u_0) - \frac{\mu}{2}$$

or

$$(3.12) \qquad \mu = (2N + 1)u_0 - 1 = \frac{2N + 1}{2^{2N}} \binom{2N}{N} - 1.$$

Using Stirling's formula, we find

$$(3.13) \qquad \mu \approx 2(N/\pi)^{\frac{1}{2}} - 1.$$

In particular, in the distribution of chapter VI, table 8, we had $N = 50$. For it $\mu = 7.04\ldots$ and the median is 6.

4. THE VARIANCE

Let $\mathbf{X}$ be a random variable with distribution $\{f(x_j)\}$, and let $r \geq 0$ be an integer. *If the expectation of the random variable $\mathbf{X}^r$, that is,*

$$(4.1) \qquad \mathbf{E}(\mathbf{X}^r) = \Sigma x_j^r \, f(x_j),$$

exists, then it is called the rth moment of $\mathbf{X}$ about the origin. If the series does not converge absolutely, we say that the rth moment does not exist. Since $|\mathbf{X}|^{r-1} \leq |\mathbf{X}|^r + 1$, it follows that *whenever the rth moment exists so does the $(r-1)$st, and hence all preceding moments.*

Moments play an important role in the general theory, but in the present volume we shall use only the second moment. If it exists, so does the mean

$$(4.2) \qquad \mu = \mathbf{E}(\mathbf{X}).$$

It is then natural to introduce instead of the random variable its *deviation from the mean*, $\mathbf{X} - \mu$. Since $(x - \mu)^2 \leq 2(x^2 + \mu^2)$ we see that the second moment of $\mathbf{X} - \mu$ exists whenever $\mathbf{E}(\mathbf{X}^2)$ exists. We find

$$(4.3) \qquad \mathbf{E}((\mathbf{X} - \mu)^2) = \sum_j (x_j^2 - 2\mu x_j + \mu^2) f(x_j).$$

Splitting the right side into three individual sums, we find it equal to $\mathbf{E}(\mathbf{X}^2) - 2\mu\mathbf{E}(\mathbf{X}) + \mu^2 = \mathbf{E}(\mathbf{X}^2) - \mu^2$.

Definition. *Let $\mathbf{X}$ be a random variable with second moment $\mathbf{E}(\mathbf{X}^2)$ and let $\mu = \mathbf{E}(\mathbf{X})$ be its mean. We define a number called the variance of $\mathbf{X}$ by*

$$(4.4) \qquad \mathrm{Var}(\mathbf{X}) = \mathbf{E}((\mathbf{X} - \mu)^2) = \mathbf{E}(\mathbf{X}^2) - \mu^2.$$

Its positive square root (or zero) is called the standard deviation of $\mathbf{X}$.

For simplicity we often speak of the variance of a distribution without mentioning the random variable. "Dispersion" is a synonym for the now generally accepted term "variance."

Examples. (a) If $\mathbf{X}$ assumes the values $\pm c$, each with probability $\frac{1}{2}$, then $\mathrm{Var}(\mathbf{X}) = c^2$.

(b) If $\mathbf{X}$ is the number of points scored with a symmetric die, then $\mathrm{Var}(\mathbf{X}) = \frac{1}{6}(1^2 + 2^2 + \ldots + 6^2) - (\frac{7}{2})^2 = \frac{35}{12}$.

(c) For the *Poisson distribution* $p(k; \lambda)$ the mean is λ [cf. example (3.b)] and hence the variance $\Sigma k^2 p(k; \lambda) - \lambda^2 = \lambda \Sigma k p(k-1; \lambda) - \lambda^2 = \lambda \Sigma (k-1)p(k-1; \lambda) + \lambda \Sigma p(k-1; \lambda) - \lambda^2 = \lambda^2 + \lambda - \lambda^2 = \lambda$. In this case mean and variance are equal.

(d) For the *binomial distribution* [cf. example (3.a)] a similar computation shows that the variance is

$$\Sigma k^2 b(k; n, p) - (np)^2 = np \Sigma k b(k-1; n-1, p) - (np)^2 =$$

$$= np\{(n-1)p + 1\} - (np)^2 = npq.$$

The usefulness of the notion of variance will appear only gradually, in particular, in connection with limit theorems of chapter X. Here we observe that the variance is a rough *measure of spread*. In fact, if $\mathrm{Var}(\mathbf{X}) = \Sigma(x_j - \mu)^2 f(x_j)$ is small, then each term in the sum is small. A value x_j for which $|x_j - \mu|$ is large must therefore have a small probability $f(x_j)$. In other words, in case of small variance large deviations of $\mathbf{X}$ from the mean μ are improbable. Conversely, a large variance indicates that not all values assumed by $\mathbf{X}$ lie near the mean.

Some readers may be helped by the following interpretation in mechanics. Suppose that a unit mass is distributed on the x-axis so that the mass $f(x_j)$ is concentrated at the point x_j. Then the mean μ is the abscissa of the *center of gravity*, and the variance is the *moment of inertia*. Clearly different mass distributions may have the same center of gravity and the same moment of inertia, but it is well known that the most important mechanical properties can be described in terms of these two quantities.

If $\mathbf{X}$ represents a measurable quantity like length or temperature, then its numerical values depend on the origin and the unit of measurement. A change of the latter means passing from $\mathbf{X}$ to a new variable $a\mathbf{X} + b$, where a and b are constants. Clearly $\mathrm{Var}(\mathbf{X} + b) = \mathrm{Var}(\mathbf{X})$, and hence

$$(4.5) \qquad \mathrm{Var}(a\mathbf{X} + b) = a^2 \mathrm{Var}(\mathbf{X}).$$

The choice of the origin and unit of measurement is to a large degree arbitrary, and often it is most convenient to take the mean as origin and the standard deviation as unit. We have done so in chapter VII,

when we introduced the normalized number of successes $\mathbf{S}_n{}^* =$
$= (\mathbf{S}_n - np)/(npq)^{\frac{1}{2}}$. In general, if $\mathbf{X}$ has mean μ and variance
$\sigma^2 (\sigma > 0)$, then $\mathbf{X} - \mu$ has mean zero and variance σ^2, and hence *the
variable*

$$(4.6) \qquad\qquad \mathbf{X}^* = \frac{\mathbf{X} - \mu}{\sigma}$$

has mean 0 *and variance* 1. *It is called the normalized variable corresponding to* $\mathbf{X}$. In the physicist's language, the passage from $\mathbf{X}$ to $\mathbf{X}^*$
would be interpreted as the introduction of dimensionless quantities.

5. COVARIANCE; VARIANCE OF A SUM

Let $\mathbf{X}$ and $\mathbf{Y}$ be two random variables on the same sample space.
Then $\mathbf{X} + \mathbf{Y}$ and $\mathbf{XY}$ are again random variables, and their distributions can be obtained by a simple rearrangement of the joint distribu-
tion of $\mathbf{X}$ and $\mathbf{Y}$. Our aim now is to calculate $\mathrm{Var}(\mathbf{X} + \mathbf{Y})$. For that
purpose we introduce the notion of covariance, which will be analyzed
in greater detail in section 8. If the joint distribution of $\mathbf{X}$ and $\mathbf{Y}$ is
$\{p(x_j, y_k)\}$, then the expectation of $\mathbf{XY}$ is given by

$$(5.1) \qquad\qquad \mathbf{E}(\mathbf{XY}) = \Sigma x_j y_k p(x_j, y_k),$$

provided, of course, that the series converges absolutely. Now
$|x_j y_k| \leq (x_j{}^2 + y_k{}^2)/2$ and therefore $\mathbf{E}(\mathbf{XY})$ certainly exists if $\mathbf{E}(\mathbf{X}^2)$
and $\mathbf{E}(\mathbf{Y}^2)$ exist. In this case there exist also the expectations

$$(5.2) \qquad\qquad \mu_x = \mathbf{E}(\mathbf{X}), \qquad \mu_y = \mathbf{E}(\mathbf{Y}),$$

and the variables $\mathbf{X} - \mu_x$ and $\mathbf{Y} - \mu_y$ have means zero. For their
product we have from the addition rule of section 2

$$(5.3) \quad \mathbf{E}((\mathbf{X} - \mu_x)(\mathbf{Y} - \mu_y)) = \mathbf{E}(\mathbf{XY}) - \mu_x\mathbf{E}(\mathbf{Y}) - \mu_y\mathbf{E}(\mathbf{X}) + \mu_x\mu_y =$$

$$= \mathbf{E}(\mathbf{XY}) - \mu_x\mu_y.$$

Definition. *The covariance of* $\mathbf{X}$ *and* $\mathbf{Y}$ *is defined by*

$$(5.4) \qquad \mathrm{Cov}(\mathbf{X}, \mathbf{Y}) = \mathbf{E}((\mathbf{X} - \mu_x)(\mathbf{Y} - \mu_y)) = \mathbf{E}(\mathbf{XY}) - \mu_x\mu_y.$$

This definition is meaningful whenever $\mathbf{X}$ *and* $\mathbf{Y}$ *have finite variances.*

We know from section 2 that for independent variables $\mathbf{E}(\mathbf{XY}) =$
$= \mathbf{E}(\mathbf{X})\mathbf{E}(\mathbf{Y})$. Hence from (5.4) we have

Theorem 1. *If* $\mathbf{X}$ *and* $\mathbf{Y}$ *are independent, then* $\mathrm{Cov}(\mathbf{X}, \mathbf{Y}) = 0$.

Note that *the converse is not true.* For example, a glance at table 1
shows that the two variables are dependent, but their covariance van-

ishes nevertheless. We shall return to this point in section 8. The next theorem is important, and the addition rule (5.6) for independent variables is constantly applied.

Theorem 2. *If* $X_1, \ldots, X_n$ *are random variables with finite variances* $\sigma_1{}^2, \ldots, \sigma_n{}^2$, *and* $S_n = X_1 + \ldots + X_n$, *then*

$$(5.5) \qquad \mathrm{Var}(S_n) = \sum_{k=1}^{n} \sigma_k{}^2 + 2 \sum_{j,k} \mathrm{Cov}(X_j, X_k)$$

the last sum extending over each of the $\binom{n}{2}$ *pairs* (X_j, X_k) *with* $j < k$.

In particular, if the X_j *are mutually independent, then the addition rule*

$$(5.6) \qquad \mathrm{Var}(S_n) = \sigma_1{}^2 + \sigma_2{}^2 + \ldots + \sigma_n{}^2$$

holds.

Proof. Put $\mu_k = \mathbf{E}(X_k)$ and $m_n = \mu_1 + \ldots + \mu_n = \mathbf{E}(S_n)$. Then $S_n - m_n = \Sigma(X_k - \mu_k)$ and

$$(5.7) \quad (S_n - m_n)^2 = \sum (X_k - \mu_k)^2 + 2\sum (X_j - \mu_j)(X_k - \mu_k).$$

Taking expectations and applying the addition rule, we get (5.5). Equation (5.6) follows from the preceding theorem.

Examples. (*a*) *Binomial distribution* $\{b(k; n, p)\}$. In example (3.*a*), the variables X_k are mutually independent. We have $\mathbf{E}(X_k{}^2) = 0 \cdot {}^2 q + {} + 1 \cdot {}^2 p = p$, and $\mathbf{E}(X_k) = p$. Hence $\sigma_k{}^2 = p - p^2 = pq$, and from (5.6) we see that *the variance of the binomial distribution* is npq. The same result was derived by direct computation in example (4.*d*).

(*b*) *Bernoulli trials with variable probabilities.* Let $X_1, \ldots, X_n$ be mutually independent random variables such that X_k assumes the values 1 and zero with probabilities p_k and $q_k = 1 - p_k$ respectively. Then $\mathbf{E}(X_k) = p_k$ and $\mathrm{Var}(X_k) = p_k - p_k{}^2 = p_k q_k$. Putting again $S_n = X_1 + \ldots + X_n$ we have from (5.6)

$$(5.8) \qquad \mathrm{Var}(S_n) = \sum_{k=1}^{n} p_k q_k.$$

As in example (1.*e*) the variable S_n may be interpreted as the total number of successes in n independent trials, each of which results in success or failure. Then $p = (p_1 + \ldots + p_n)/n$ is the average probability of success, and it seems natural to compare the present situation to Bernoulli trials with the constant probability of success p. Such a comparison leads to a striking result. We may rewrite (5.8) in the form $\mathrm{Var}(\mathbf{S}_n) = np - \Sigma p_k^2$. Next, it is easily seen (by elementary calculus or simple induction) that among all combinations $\{p_k\}$ such that $\Sigma p_k = np$ the sum Σp_k^2 assumes its minimum value when all p_k are equal. It follows that, if the average probability of success p is kept constant, $\mathrm{Var}(\mathbf{S}_n)$ *assumes its maximum value when* $p_1 = \ldots = p_n = p$. We have thus the surprising result that the *variability of* p_k, *or lack of uniformity, decreases the magnitude of chance fluctuations* as measured by the variance.[4] For example, the number of annual fires in a community may be treated as a random variable; for a given average number, the variability is *maximal* if all households have the *same* probability of fire. Given a certain average quality p of n machines, the *output will be least uniform if all machines are equal.* (An application to modern education is obvious but hopeless.)

(c) *Card matching.* A deck of n numbered cards is put into random order so that all $n!$ arrangements have equal probabilities. The number of matches (cards in their natural place) is a random variable $\mathbf{S}_n$ which assumes the values $0, 1, \ldots, n$. Its probability distribution was derived in chapter IV, section 4. From it the mean and variance could be obtained, but the following way is simpler and more instructive.

Define a random variable $\mathbf{X}_k$ which is either 1 or 0, according as card number k is or is not at the kth place. Then $\mathbf{S}_n = \mathbf{X}_1 + \ldots + \mathbf{X}_n$. Now each card has probability $1/n$ to appear at the kth place. Hence $\mathbf{P}\{\mathbf{X}_k = 1\} = 1/n$ and $\mathbf{P}\{\mathbf{X}_k = 0\} = (n-1)/n$. Therefore $\mathbf{E}(\mathbf{X}_k) = 1/n$, and it follows that $\mathbf{E}(\mathbf{S}_n) = 1$: the average is one match per deck. To find $\mathrm{Var}(\mathbf{S}_n)$ we first calculate the variance σ_k^2 of $\mathbf{X}_k$:

$$(5.9) \qquad \sigma_k^2 = \frac{1}{n} - \left(\frac{1}{n}\right)^2 = \frac{n-1}{n^2}.$$

Next we calculate $\mathbf{E}(\mathbf{X}_j\mathbf{X}_k)$. The product $\mathbf{X}_j\mathbf{X}_k$ is 0 or 1; the latter is true if both card number j and card number k are at their proper places, and the probability for that is $1/n(n-1)$. Hence

$$(5.10) \qquad \mathbf{E}(\mathbf{X}_j\mathbf{X}_k) = \frac{1}{n(n-1)},$$

$$\mathrm{Cov}(\mathbf{X}_j, \mathbf{X}_k) = \frac{1}{n(n-1)} - \frac{1}{n^2} = \frac{1}{n^2(n-1)}.$$

---

[4] For stronger results in the same direction see W. Hoeffding, On the distribution of the number of successes in independent trials, *Annals of Mathematical Statistics*, vol. 27 (1956), pp. 713–721.

Thus finally

$$(5.11) \qquad \mathrm{Var}(\mathbf{S}_n) = n\,\frac{n-1}{n^2} + 2\binom{n}{2}\frac{1}{n^2(n-1)} = 1.$$

We see that both mean and variance to the number of matches are equal to one. This result may be applied to the problem of *card guessing* discussed in chapter IV, section 4. There we considered three methods of guessing, one of which corresponds to card matching. The second can be described as a sequence of n Bernoulli trials with probability $p = 1/n$, in which case the expected number of correct guesses is $np = 1$ and the variance $npq = (n-1)/n$. The expected numbers are the same in both cases, but the larger variance with the first method indicates greater chance fluctuations about the mean and thus promises a slightly more exciting game. (With more complicated decks of cards the difference between the two variances is somewhat larger but never really big.) With the last mode of guessing the subject keeps calling the same card; the number of correct guesses is necessarily one, and chance fluctuations are completely eliminated (variance 0). We see that the strategy of calling cannot influence the expected number of correct guesses but has some influence on the magnitude of chance fluctuations.

(*d*) *Sampling without replacement.* Suppose that a population consists of b black and g green elements, and that a random sample of size r is taken (without possible repetitions). The number $\mathbf{S}_k$ of black elements in the sample is a random variable with the *hypergeometric distribution* (chapter II, section 6) from which the mean and the variance can be obtained by direct computation. However, the following method is preferable. Define the random variable $\mathbf{X}_k$ to assume the values 1 or 0 according as the kth element in the sample is or is not black ($k \leq r$). For reasons of symmetry the probability that $\mathbf{X}_k = 1$ is $b/(b+g)$, and hence

$$(5.12) \qquad \mathbf{E}(\mathbf{X}_k) = \frac{b}{b+g}, \qquad \mathrm{Var}(\mathbf{X}_k) = \frac{bg}{(b+g)^2}.$$

Next, if $j \neq k$, then $\mathbf{X}_j\mathbf{X}_k = 1$ if the jth and kth elements of the sample are black, and otherwise $\mathbf{X}_j\mathbf{X}_k = 0$. The probability of $\mathbf{X}_j\mathbf{X}_k = 1$ is $b(b-1)/(b+g)(b+g-1)$, and therefore

$$(5.13) \qquad \mathbf{E}(\mathbf{X}_j\mathbf{X}_k) = \frac{b(b-1)}{(b+g)(b+g-1)},$$

$$\mathrm{Cov}(\mathbf{X}_j\mathbf{X}_k) = \frac{-bg}{(b+g)^2(b+g-1)}.$$

Thus,

$$(5.14) \quad \mathbf{E}(\mathbf{S}_r) = \frac{rb}{b+g}, \qquad \mathrm{Var}(\mathbf{S}_r) = \frac{rbg}{(b+g)^2} \left\{ 1 - \frac{r-1}{b+g-1} \right\}.$$

In sampling with replacement we would have the same mean, but the variance would be slightly larger, namely, $rbg/(b+g)^2$.

6. CHEBYSHEV'S INEQUALITY [5]

It has been pointed out that a small variance indicates that large deviations from the mean are improbable. This statement is made more precise by Chebyshev's inequality, which is an exceedingly useful and handy tool.

Theorem. *Let* $\mathbf{X}$ *be a random variable with mean* $\mu = \mathbf{E}(\mathbf{X})$ *and variance* $\sigma^2 = \mathrm{Var}(\mathbf{X})$. *Then for any* $t > 0$

$$(6.1) \qquad \qquad \mathbf{P}\{|\mathbf{X} - \mu| \geq t\} \leq \frac{\sigma^2}{t^2}.$$

Proof. The variance is defined in (4.3) by a series with positive terms. Delete all terms for which $|x_j - \mu| < t$; this cannot increase the value of the series, and hence

$$(6.2) \qquad \qquad \sigma^2 \geq \Sigma^*(x_j - \mu)^2 f(x_j)$$

where the star indicates that the summation extends only over those j for which $|x_j - \mu| \geq t$. It is then clear that

$$(6.3) \qquad \Sigma^*(x_j - \mu)^2 f(x_j) \geq t^2 \Sigma^* f(x_j) = t^2 \mathbf{P}\{|\mathbf{X} - \mu| \geq t\}$$

which proves the theorem.

Chebyshev's inequality must be regarded as a theoretical tool rather than a practical method of estimation. Its importance is due to its universality, but no statement of great generality can be expected to yield sharp results in individual cases.

Examples. (*a*) If $\mathbf{X}$ is the number scored in a throw of a true die, then [cf. example (4.*b*)], $\mu = \frac{7}{2}$, $\sigma^2 = \frac{35}{12}$. The maximum deviation of $\mathbf{X}$ from μ is $2.5 \approx 3\sigma/2$. The probability of greater deviations is zero, whereas Chebyshev's inequality only asserts that this probability is smaller than 0.47.

(*b*) For the binomial distribution $\{b(k; n, p)\}$ we have [cf. example (5.*a*)] $\mu = np$, $\sigma^2 = npq$. For large n we know that

$$(6.4) \qquad \mathbf{P}\{|\mathbf{S}_n - np| > x(npq)^{\frac{1}{2}}\} \approx 1 - \Phi(x) + \Phi(-x).$$

---

[5] P. L. Chebyshev (1821–1894).

Chebyshev's inequality states only that the left side is less than $1/x^2$; this is obviously a much poorer estimate than (6.4).

*7. KOLMOGOROV'S INEQUALITY [6]

As an example of more refined methods we prove:

Let $\mathbf{X}_1, \ldots, \mathbf{X}_n$ *be mutually independent variables with expectations* $\mu_k = \mathbf{E}(\mathbf{X}_k)$ *and variances* $\sigma_k{}^2$. *Put*

$$(7.1) \qquad\qquad \mathbf{S}_k = \mathbf{X}_1 + \ldots + \mathbf{X}_k$$

and

$$(7.2) \qquad\qquad m_k = \mathbf{E}(\mathbf{S}_k) = \mu_1 + \ldots + \mu_k,$$

$$s_k{}^2 = \mathrm{Var}(\mathbf{S}_k) = \sigma_1{}^2 + \ldots + \sigma_k{}^2.$$

For every $t > 0$ *the probability of the simultaneous realization of the* n *inequalities*

$$(7.3) \qquad\qquad |\mathbf{S}_k - m_k| < ts_n, \qquad k = 1, 2, \ldots, n$$

is at least $1 - t^{-2}$.

For $n = 1$ this theorem reduces to Chebyshev's inequality. For $n > 1$ Chebyshev's inequality gives the same bound for the probability of the single relation $|\mathbf{S}_n - m_n| < ts_n$, so that Kolmogorov's inequality is considerably stronger.

Proof. We want to estimate the probability x that at least one of the inequalities (7.3) does not hold. The theorem asserts that $x \leq t^{-2}$.

Define n random variables $\mathbf{Y}_k$ as follows: $\mathbf{Y}_\nu = 1$ if

$$(7.4) \qquad\qquad |\mathbf{S}_\nu - m_\nu| \geq ts_n$$

but

$$(7.5) \qquad |\mathbf{S}_k - m_k| < ts_n \quad \text{for} \quad k = 1, 2, \ldots, \nu-1;$$

$\mathbf{Y}_\nu = 0$ for all other sample points. In words, $\mathbf{Y}_\nu$ equals 1 at those points in which the νth of the inequalities (7.3) is the *first* to be violated. Then at any particular sample point at most one among the $\mathbf{Y}_k$ is 1, and the sum $\mathbf{Y}_1 + \mathbf{Y}_2 + \ldots + \mathbf{Y}_n$ can assume only the values 0 or 1;

---

* This section treats a special topic and should be omitted at first reading.

[6] Über die Summen zufälliger Grössen, *Mathematische Annalen*, vol. 99 (1928), pp. 309–319, and vol. 102 (1929), pp. 484–488.

it is 1 if, and only if, at least one of the inequalities (7.3) is violated, and therefore

$$(7.6) \qquad x = \mathbf{P}\{\mathbf{Y}_1 + \ldots + \mathbf{Y}_n = 1\}.$$

Since $\mathbf{Y}_1 + \ldots + \mathbf{Y}_n$ is 0 or 1, we have $\Sigma \mathbf{Y}_k \leq 1$. Multiplying by $(\mathbf{S}_n - m_n)^2$ and taking expectations, we get

$$(7.7) \qquad \sum_{k=1}^{n} \mathbf{E}(\mathbf{Y}_k(\mathbf{S}_n - m_n)^2) \leq s_n{}^2.$$

For an evaluation of the terms on the left we put

$$(7.8) \qquad \mathbf{U}_k = (\mathbf{S}_n - m_n) - (\mathbf{S}_k - m_k) = \sum_{\nu=k+1}^{n} (\mathbf{X}_\nu - \mu_\nu).$$

Then

$$(7.9) \quad \mathbf{E}(\mathbf{Y}_k(\mathbf{S}_n - m_n)^2) = \mathbf{E}(\mathbf{Y}_k(\mathbf{S}_k - m_k)^2) +$$
$$+ 2\mathbf{E}(\mathbf{Y}_k\mathbf{U}_k(\mathbf{S}_k - m_k)) + \mathbf{E}(\mathbf{Y}_k\mathbf{U}_k{}^2).$$

However, $\mathbf{U}_k$ depends only on $\mathbf{X}_{k+1}, \ldots, \mathbf{X}_n$ while $\mathbf{Y}_k$ and $\mathbf{S}_k$ depend only on $\mathbf{X}_1, \ldots, \mathbf{X}_k$. Hence $\mathbf{U}_k$ is independent of $\mathbf{Y}_k(\mathbf{S}_k - m_k)$ and therefore $\mathbf{E}(\mathbf{Y}_k\mathbf{U}_k(\mathbf{S}_k - m_k)) = \mathbf{E}(\mathbf{Y}_k(\mathbf{S}_k - m_k))\mathbf{E}(\mathbf{U}_k) = 0$, since $\mathbf{E}(\mathbf{U}_k) = 0$. Thus from (7.9)

$$(7.10) \qquad \mathbf{E}(\mathbf{Y}_k(\mathbf{S}_n - m_n)^2) \geq \mathbf{E}(\mathbf{Y}_k(\mathbf{S}_k - m_k)^2).$$

But $\mathbf{Y}_k \neq 0$ only if $|\mathbf{S}_k - m_k| \geq ts_n$, so that $\mathbf{Y}_k(\mathbf{S}_k - m_k)^2 \geq t^2 s_n{}^2 \mathbf{Y}_k$. Hence, combining (7.7) and (7.10), we get

$$(7.11) \qquad s_n{}^2 \geq t^2 s_n{}^2 \mathbf{E}(\mathbf{Y}_1 + \ldots + \mathbf{Y}_n).$$

Since $\mathbf{Y}_1 + \ldots + \mathbf{Y}_n$ equals either 0 or 1, the expectation to the right equals the probability x defined in (7.6). Thus $xt^2 \leq 1$ as asserted.

* 8. THE CORRELATION COEFFICIENT

Let $\mathbf{X}$ and $\mathbf{Y}$ be any two random variables with means μ_x and μ_y and positive variances $\sigma_x{}^2$ and $\sigma_y{}^2$. We introduce the corresponding normalized variables $\mathbf{X}^*$ and $\mathbf{Y}^*$ defined by (4.6). Their covariance is called *the correlation coefficient of* $\mathbf{X}$, $\mathbf{Y}$ *and is denoted by* $\rho(\mathbf{X}, \mathbf{Y})$. Thus, using (5.4),

$$(8.1) \qquad \rho(\mathbf{X}, \mathbf{Y}) = \mathrm{Cov}(\mathbf{X}^*, \mathbf{Y}^*) = \frac{\mathrm{Cov}(\mathbf{X}, \mathbf{Y})}{\sigma_x \sigma_y}.$$

---

* This section treats a special topic and may be omitted at first reading.

Clearly this correlation coefficient is independent of the origins and units of measurements, that is, for any constants a_1, a_2, b_1, b_2, with $a_1 > 0$, $a_2 > 0$, we have $\rho(a_1\mathbf{X} + b_1, a_2\mathbf{Y} + b_2) = \rho(\mathbf{X}, \mathbf{Y})$.

The use of the correlation coefficient amounts to a fancy way of writing the covariance.[7] Unfortunately, the term correlation is suggestive of implications which are not inherent in it. We know from section 5 that $\rho(\mathbf{X}, \mathbf{Y}) = 0$ whenever $\mathbf{X}$ and $\mathbf{Y}$ are independent. It is important to realize that the converse is not true. In fact, *the correlation coefficient $\rho(\mathbf{X}, \mathbf{Y})$ can vanish even if $\mathbf{Y}$ is a function of $\mathbf{X}$.*

Examples. (a) Let $\mathbf{X}$ assume the values ± 1, ± 2 each with probability $\frac{1}{4}$. Let $\mathbf{Y} = \mathbf{X}^2$. The joint distribution is given by $p(-1, 1) = = p(1, 1) = p(2, 4) = p(-2, 4) = \frac{1}{4}$. For reasons of symmetry $\rho(\mathbf{X}, \mathbf{Y}) = 0$ even though we have a direct functional dependence of $\mathbf{Y}$ on $\mathbf{X}$.

(b) Let $\mathbf{U}$ and $\mathbf{V}$ be *independent* variables with the same distribution, and let $\mathbf{X} = \mathbf{U} + \mathbf{V}$, $\mathbf{Y} = \mathbf{U} - \mathbf{V}$. Then $\mathbf{E}(\mathbf{XY}) = \mathbf{E}(\mathbf{U}^2) - \mathbf{E}(\mathbf{V}^2) = 0$ and $\mathbf{E}(\mathbf{Y}) = 0$. Hence $\text{Cov}(\mathbf{X}, \mathbf{Y}) = 0$ and therefore also $\rho(\mathbf{X}, \mathbf{Y}) = 0$. For example, $\mathbf{X}$ and $\mathbf{Y}$ may be the sum and difference of points on two dice. Then $\mathbf{X}$ and $\mathbf{Y}$ are either both odd or both even and therefore dependent.

It follows that the correlation coefficient is by no means a general measure of dependence between $\mathbf{X}$ and $\mathbf{Y}$. However, $\rho(\mathbf{X}, \mathbf{Y})$ is connected with the *linear* dependence of $\mathbf{X}$ and $\mathbf{Y}$.

Theorem. *We have always $|\rho(\mathbf{X}, \mathbf{Y})| \leq 1$; furthermore, $\rho(\mathbf{X}, \mathbf{Y}) = = \pm 1$ only if there exist constants a and b such that $\mathbf{Y} = a\mathbf{X} + b$, except, perhaps, for values of $\mathbf{X}$ with zero probability.*

Proof. Let $\mathbf{X}^*$ and $\mathbf{Y}^*$ be the normalized variables. Then

$$(8.2) \quad \text{Var}(\mathbf{X}^* \pm \mathbf{Y}^*) = \text{Var}(\mathbf{X}^*) \pm 2\,\text{Cov}(\mathbf{X}^*, \mathbf{Y}^*) + \text{Var}(\mathbf{Y}^*) =$$
$$= 2(1 \pm \rho(\mathbf{X}, \mathbf{Y})).$$

The left side cannot be negative; hence $|\rho(\mathbf{X}, \mathbf{Y})| \leq 1$. For $\rho(\mathbf{X}, \mathbf{Y}) = 1$ it is necessary that $\text{Var}(\mathbf{X}^* - \mathbf{Y}^*) = 0$ which means that with unit probability the variable $\mathbf{X}^* - \mathbf{Y}^*$ assumes only one value. In this case $\mathbf{X}^* - \mathbf{Y}^* = \text{const.}$, and hence $\mathbf{Y} = a\mathbf{X} + \text{const.}$ with $a = \sigma_y/\sigma_x$. A similar argument applies to the case $\rho(\mathbf{X}, \mathbf{Y}) = -1$.

---

[7] The physicist would define the correlation coefficient as "dimensionless covariance."

9. PROBLEMS FOR SOLUTION

1. Seven balls are distributed randomly in seven cells. Let X_i be the number of cells containing exactly i balls. Using the probabilities tabulated in chapter II, section 5, write down the joint distribution of (X_2, X_3).

2. Two ideal dice are thrown. Let X be the score on the first die and Y be the larger of two scores. (*a*) Write down the joint distribution of X and Y. (*b*) Find the means, the variances, and the covariance.

3. In five tosses of a coin let X, Y, Z be, respectively, the number of heads, the number of head runs, the length of the largest head run. Tabulate the 32 sample points together with the corresponding values of X, Y, and Z. By simple counting derive the joint distributions of the pairs $(X, Y), (X, Z), (Y, Z)$ and the distributions of $X + Y$ and XY. Find the means, variances, covariances of the variables.

4. The random variables X_1 and X_2 are independent and have the same *geometric distribution* $\{q^k p\}$, where $k = 0, 1, \ldots$. Let Z be defined as the larger of X_1 and X_2 [in symbols, $Z = \max(X_1, X_2)$]. Derive the joint distribution of Z and X_1, and the distribution of Z.

5. Let X_1 and X_2 be independent random variables with Poisson distributions $\{p(k; \lambda_1)\}$ and $\{p(k; \lambda_2)\}$. Prove that $X_1 + X_2$ has the Poisson distribution $\{p(k; \lambda_1 + \lambda_2)\}$.

6. *Continuation.* Show that the *conditional distribution of* X_1 *given* $X_1 + X_2$ *is binomial*, namely

$$(9.1) \qquad \mathbf{P}\{X_1 = k \mid X_1 + X_2 = n\} = b\left(k; n, \frac{\lambda_1}{\lambda_1 + \lambda_2}\right).$$

7. Let X_1 and X_2 be independent and have the common geometric distribution $\{q^k p\}$ (as in problem 4). Show without calculations that the *conditional distribution of* X_1 *given* $X_1 + X_2$ *is uniform*, that is,

$$(9.2) \qquad \mathbf{P}\{X_1 = k \mid X_1 + X_2 = n\} = \frac{1}{n+1}, \qquad k = 0, \ldots, n.$$

8. Let $X_1, \ldots, X_n$ be mutually independent random variables, each having the *uniform distribution* $\mathbf{P}\{X_i = k\} = 1/N$ for $k = 1, 2, \ldots, N$. Let U_n be the smallest among the $X_1, \ldots, X_n$ and V_n the largest. Find the distributions of U_n and V_n. What is the connection with the *estimation problem* (3.*e*)?

9. In the estimation problem (3.*e*) find the joint distribution of the largest and the smallest observation. Specialize to $n = 2$. (*Hint:* Calculate first $\mathbf{P}\{X \leq r, Y \geq s\}$.)

10. *Continuation.* Find the conditional probability that the first two observations are j and k, given that $X = r$.

11. *Continuation.* Find $\mathbf{E}(X^2)$ and hence an asymptotic expression for $\mathrm{Var}(X)$ as $N \to \infty$ (with n fixed).

12. *Sampling inspection.* Suppose that items with a probability p of being acceptable are subjected to inspection in such a way that the probability of an item being inspected is p'. We have four classes, namely, "acceptable and inspected," "acceptable but not inspected," etc. with corresponding probabilities $pp', pq', p'q, qq'$ where $q = 1 - p, q' = 1 - p'$. We are concerned with

double Bernoulli trials [see example VI(9.c)]. Let **N** be the number of items passing the inspection desk (both inspected and uninspected) before the first defective is found, and let **K** be the (undiscovered) number of defectives among them. Find the joint distributions of **N** and **K** and the marginal distributions.

13. *Continuation.* Find $\mathbf{E}\left(\dfrac{\mathbf{K}}{\mathbf{N}+1}\right)$ and $\mathrm{Cov}(\mathbf{K}, \mathbf{N})$. [In industrial practice the discovered defective item is replaced by an acceptable one so that $\mathbf{K}/(\mathbf{N}+1)$ is the fraction of defectives and measures the quality of the lot. Note that $\mathbf{E}\left(\dfrac{\mathbf{K}}{\mathbf{N}+1}\right)$ is not $\mathbf{E}(\mathbf{K})/\mathbf{E}(\mathbf{N}+1)$.]

14. In a sequence of Bernoulli trials let **X** be the length of the run (of either successes or failures) started by the first trial. Find the distribution of **X**, $\mathbf{E}(\mathbf{X})$, $\mathrm{Var}(\mathbf{X})$.

15. *Continuation.* Let **Y** be the length of the *second* run. Find the distribution of **Y**, $\mathbf{E}(\mathbf{Y})$, $\mathrm{Var}(\mathbf{Y})$, and the joint distribution of **X**, **Y**.

16. If two random variables **X** and **Y** assume only two values each, and if $\mathrm{Cov}(\mathbf{X}, \mathbf{Y}) = 0$, then **X** and **Y** are independent.

---

17. *Birthdays.* For a group of n people find the expected number of days of the year which are birthdays of exactly k people. (Assume 365 days and that all arrangements are equally probable.)

18. *Continuation.* Find the expected number of multiple birthdays. How large should n be to make this expectation exceed 1?

19. A man with n keys wants to open his door and tries the keys independently and at random. Find the mean and variance of the number of trials (a) if unsuccessful keys are not eliminated from further selections; (b) if they are. (Assume that only one key fits the door. The exact distributions are given in chapter II, section 7, but are not required for the present problem.)

20. Let $(\mathbf{X}, \mathbf{Y})$ be random variables whose joint distribution is the trinomial defined by (1.9). Find $\mathbf{E}(\mathbf{X})$, $\mathrm{Var}(\mathbf{X})$, and $\mathrm{Cov}(\mathbf{X}, \mathbf{Y})$ (a) by direct computation, (b) by representing **X** and **Y** as sums of n variables each and using the methods of section 5.

21. Find the covariance of the number of ones and sixes in n throws of a die.

22. In the animal trapping problem VI, 24 prove that the expected number of animals trapped at the νth trapping is $nqp^{\nu-1}$.

23. If **X** has the *geometric* distribution $\mathbf{P}\{\mathbf{X} = k\} = q^k p$ (where $k = 0, 1, \ldots$), show that $\mathrm{Var}(\mathbf{X}) = qp^{-2}$. Conclude that the *negative* binomial distribution $\{f(k; r, p)\}$ has variance rqp^{-2} provided r is a positive integer. Prove by direct calculation that the statement remains true for all $r > 0$.

24. In the *waiting time problem* (3.d) prove that

$$\mathrm{Var}(\mathbf{S}_r) = N\left\{\frac{1}{(N-1)^2} + \frac{2}{(N-2)^2} + \cdots + \frac{r-1}{(N-r+1)^2}\right\}.$$

Hint. Use the variance of the geometric distribution obtained in problem 23. Incidentally, as $N \to \infty$ we find $N^{-2}\,\mathrm{Var}(\mathbf{S}_n) = \pi^2/6$.

25. *Continuation.* Let $\mathbf{Y}_r$ be the number of drawings required to include r preassigned elements (instead of any r different elements as in the text).

Find $E(Y_r)$ and $Var(Y_r)$. (*Note:* The exact distribution of Y_r was found in problem II(11.12) but is not required for the present purpose.)

26.[8] A large number, N, of people are subject to a blood test. This can be administered in two ways. (i) Each person can be tested separately. In this case N tests are required. (ii) The blood samples of k people can be pooled and analyzed together. If the test is *negative*, this *one* test suffices for the k people. If the test is *positive*, each of the k persons must be tested separately, and in all $k + 1$ tests are required for the k people.

Assume the probability p that the test is positive is the same for all people and that people are stochastically independent.

(*a*) What is the probability that the test for a pooled sample of k people will be positive?

(*b*) What is the expected value of the number, X, of tests necessary under plan (ii)?

(*c*) Which k will minimize the expected number of tests under plan (ii)? Do not try numerical evaluations, since the problem leads to a rather cumbersome equation for k.

27. *Sample structure.* A population consists of r classes whose sizes are in the proportion $p_1 : p_2 : \ldots : p_r$. A random sample of size n is taken with replacement. Find the expected number of classes *not* represented in the sample.

28. Let X be the number of α runs in a random arrangement of r_1 alphas and r_2 betas. The distribution of X is given in problem II(11.23). Find $E(X)$ and $Var(X)$.

29. In *Polya's urn scheme* [V(2.c)] let X_n be one or zero according as the nth trial results in black or red. Prove $\rho(X_n, X_m) = c/(b + r + c)$ for $n \neq m$.

30. *Continuation.* Let S_n be the total number of black balls extracted in the first n drawings (that is, $S_n = X_1 + \ldots + X_n$). Find $E(S_n)$ and $Var(S_n)$. (Use problems V, 19 and V, 20; verify the result by means of the recursion formula of problem V, 22.)

31. *Stratified sampling.* A city has n blocks of which n_j have x_j inhabitants each ($n_1 + n_2 + \ldots = n$). Let $m = \Sigma n_j x_j / n$ be the mean number of inhabitants per block and put $a^2 = \Sigma n_j x_j^2 / n - m^2$. In sampling without replacement r blocks are selected at random, and in each the inhabitants are counted. Let $X_1, \ldots, X_r$ be the respective number of inhabitants. Show that

$$E(X_1 + \ldots + X_r) = mr \qquad Var(X_1 + \ldots + X_r) = \frac{a^2 r(n - r)}{n - 1}.$$

(In sampling with replacement the variance would be larger, namely, $a^2 r$.)

32. *Length of random chains.*[9] A chain in the x, y-plane consists of n links, each of unit length. The angle between two consecutive links is $\pm \alpha$ where α is a positive constant; each possibility has probability $\frac{1}{2}$, and the successive

---

[8] This problem is based on a new technique developed during World War II. See R. Dorfman, The detection of defective members of large populations, *Annals of Mathematical Statistics*, vol. 14 (1943), pp. 436–440. In army practice, plan (ii) introduced up to 80 per cent savings.

[9] This is the two-dimensional analogue to the problem of length of *long polymer molecules* in chemistry. The problem illustrates applications to random variables which are not expressible as sums of simple variables.

angles are mutually independent. The distance $\mathbf{L}_n$ from the beginning to the end of the chain is a random variable, and we wish to prove that

$$(9.3) \qquad \mathbf{E}(\mathbf{L}_n{}^2) = n \frac{1 + \cos \alpha}{1 - \cos \alpha} - 2 \cos \alpha \frac{1 - \cos^n \alpha}{(1 - \cos \alpha)^2}.$$

Without loss of generality the first link may be assumed to lie in the direction of the positive x-axis. The angle between the kth link and the positive x-axis is a random variable $\mathbf{S}_{k-1}$ where $\mathbf{S}_0 = 0$, $\mathbf{S}_k = \mathbf{S}_{k-1} + \mathbf{X}_k \alpha$ and the $\mathbf{X}_k$ are mutually independent variables, assuming the values ± 1 with probability $\frac{1}{2}$. The projections on the two axes of the kth link are $\cos \mathbf{S}_{k-1}$ and $\sin \mathbf{S}_{k-1}$. Hence for $n \geq 1$

$$(9.4) \qquad \mathbf{L}_n{}^2 = \left(\sum_{k=0}^{n-1} \cos \mathbf{S}_k \right)^2 + \left(\sum_{k=0}^{n-1} \sin \mathbf{S}_k \right)^2.$$

Prove by induction successively for $m < n$

$$(9.5) \qquad \mathbf{E}(\cos \mathbf{S}_n) = \cos^n \alpha, \qquad \mathbf{E}(\sin \mathbf{S}_n) = 0;$$

$$(9.6) \qquad \mathbf{E}((\cos \mathbf{S}_m) \cdot (\cos \mathbf{S}_n)) = \cos^{n-m} \alpha \cdot \mathbf{E}(\cos^2 \mathbf{S}_m)$$

$$(9.7) \qquad \mathbf{E}((\sin \mathbf{S}_m) \cdot (\sin \mathbf{S}_n)) = \cos^{n-m} \alpha \cdot \mathbf{E}(\sin^2 \mathbf{S}_m)$$

$$(9.8) \qquad \mathbf{E}(\mathbf{L}_n{}^2) - \mathbf{E}(\mathbf{L}_{n-1}^2) = 1 + 2 \cos \alpha \cdot \frac{1 - \cos^{n-1} \alpha}{1 - \cos \alpha}$$

(with $\mathbf{L}_0 = 0$) and hence finally (9.3).

---

33. A sequence of Bernoulli trials is continued as long as necessary to obtain r successes, where r is a fixed integer. Let $\mathbf{X}$ be the number of trials required. Find [10] $\mathbf{E}(r/\mathbf{X})$. (The definition leads to infinite series for which a finite expression can be obtained.)

34. In a random placement of r balls into n cells the probability of finding exactly m cells empty satisfies the recursion formula II(11.8). Let m_r be the expected number of empty cells. *From the recursion formula* prove that

$$m_{r+1} = (1 - n^{-1})m_r, \quad \text{and conclude} \quad m_r = n \left(1 - \frac{1}{n} \right)^r.$$

35. Let $\mathbf{S}_n$ be the number of successes in n Bernoulli trials. Prove

$$\mathbf{E}(|\mathbf{S}_n - np|) = 2\nu q b(\nu; n, p)$$

where ν is the integer such that $np < \nu \leq np + 1$.

36. Let $\{\mathbf{X}_k\}$ be a sequence of mutually independent random variables with a common distribution. Suppose that the $\mathbf{X}_k$ assume only positive values and

---

[10] This example illustrates the effect of *optional stopping*. If the number n of trials is fixed, the ratio of the number N of successes to the number n of trials is a random variable whose expectation is p. It is often erroneously assumed that the same is true in our example where the number r of successes is fixed and the number of trials depends on chance. If $p = \frac{1}{2}$ and $r = 2$, then $\mathbf{E}(2/\mathbf{X}) = 0.614$ instead of 0.5; for $r = 3$ we find $\mathbf{E}(3/\mathbf{X}) = 0.579$.

that $\mathbf{E}(\mathbf{X}_k) = a$ and $\mathbf{E}(\mathbf{X}_k{}^{-1}) = b$ exist. Let $\mathbf{S}_n = \mathbf{X}_1 + \ldots + \mathbf{X}_n$. Prove that $\mathbf{E}(\mathbf{S}_n{}^{-1})$ is finite and that $\mathbf{E}(\mathbf{X}_k/\mathbf{S}_n) = 1/n$ for $k = 1, 2, \ldots, n$.

37. *Continuation.*[11]   Prove that

$$\mathbf{E}\left(\frac{\mathbf{S}_m}{\mathbf{S}_n}\right) = \frac{m}{n}, \qquad \text{if } m \leq n$$

$$\mathbf{E}\left(\frac{\mathbf{S}_m}{\mathbf{S}_n}\right) = 1 + (m - n)a\mathbf{E}(\mathbf{S}_n{}^{-1}), \qquad \text{if } m \geq n.$$

38. Let $\mathbf{X}_1, \ldots, \mathbf{X}_n$ be mutually independent random variables with a common distribution; let its mean be m, its variance σ^2. Let $\overline{\mathbf{X}} = (\mathbf{X}_1 + \ldots + \mathbf{X}_n)/n$. Prove that [12]

$$\frac{1}{n-1}\mathbf{E}\left(\sum_{k=1}^{n}(\mathbf{X}_k - \overline{\mathbf{X}})^2\right) = \sigma^2.$$

39. Let $\mathbf{X}_1, \ldots, \mathbf{X}_n$ be mutually independent random variables. Let $\mathbf{U}$ be a function of $\mathbf{X}_1, \ldots, \mathbf{X}_k$ and $\mathbf{V}$ a function of $\mathbf{X}_{k+1}, \ldots, \mathbf{X}_n$ $(k < n)$. Prove that $\mathbf{U}$ and $\mathbf{V}$ are mutually independent random variables.

---

40. *Generalized Chebyshev inequality.* Let $\phi(x) > 0$ for $x > 0$ be monotonically increasing and suppose that $\mathbf{E}(\phi(|\mathbf{X}|)) = M$ exists. Prove that

$$\mathbf{P}\{|\mathbf{X}| \geq t\} \leq \frac{M}{\phi(t)}.$$

41. *Schwarz inequality.* For any two random variables with finite variances one has $\mathbf{E}^2(\mathbf{XY}) \leq \mathbf{E}(\mathbf{X}^2)\mathbf{E}(\mathbf{Y}^2)$. Prove this from the fact that the quadratic polynomial $\mathbf{E}((t\mathbf{X} + \mathbf{Y})^2)$ is non-negative.

---

[11] The observation that 37 can be proved by introducing 36 is due to K. L. Chung.
[12] This can be expressed by saying that $\Sigma(\mathbf{X}_k - \overline{\mathbf{X}})^2/(n-1)$ is an *unbiased estimator* of σ^2.

CHAPTER X

Laws of Large Numbers

1. IDENTICALLY DISTRIBUTED VARIABLES

The limit theorems for Bernoulli trials derived in chapters VII and VIII are special cases of general limit theorems which cannot be treated in this volume. However, we shall here discuss at least some cases of the law of large numbers in order to reveal a new aspect of the expectation of a random variable.

The connection between Bernoulli trials and the theory of random variables becomes clearer when we consider the dependence of the number S_n of successes on the number n of trials. With each trial S_n increases by 1 or 0, and we can write

$$(1.1) \qquad S_n = X_1 + \ldots + X_n,$$

where the random variable X_k equals 1 if the kth trial results in success and zero otherwise. Thus S_n is a sum of n mutually independent random variables, each of which assumes the values 1 and 0 with probabilities p and q. From this it is only one step to consider sums of the form (1.1) where the X_k are mutually independent variables with an arbitrary distribution. The (weak) law of large numbers of chapter VI, section 4, states that for large n the average proportion of successes S_n/n is likely to lie near p. This is a special case of the following

Law of Large Numbers. *Let* $\{X_k\}$ *be a sequence of mutually independent random variables with a common distribution. If the expectation* $\mu = \mathbf{E}(X_k)$ *exists, then for every* $\epsilon > 0$ *as* $n \to \infty$

$$(1.2) \qquad \mathbf{P}\left\{\left|\frac{X_1 + \ldots + X_n}{n} - \mu\right| > \epsilon\right\} \to 0;$$

in words, the probability that the average S_n/n will differ from the expectation by less than an arbitrarily prescribed ϵ tends to one.

In this generality the theorem was first proved by Khintchine.[1] Older proofs had to introduce the unnecessary restriction that the variance $\text{Var}(\mathbf{X}_k)$ should also be finite.[2] For this case, however, there exists a much more precise result which generalizes the DeMoivre-Laplace limit theorem for Bernoulli trials, namely the

Central Limit Theorem. *Let $\{\mathbf{X}_k\}$ be a sequence of mutually independent random variables with a common distribution. Suppose that $\mu = \mathbf{E}(\mathbf{X}_k)$ and $\sigma^2 = \text{Var}(\mathbf{X}_k)$ exist and let $\mathbf{S}_n = \mathbf{X}_1 + \ldots + \mathbf{X}_n$. Then for every fixed β*

$$(1.3) \qquad \mathbf{P}\left\{\frac{\mathbf{S}_n - n\mu}{\sigma n^{\frac{1}{2}}} < \beta\right\} \to \Phi(\beta)$$

where $\Phi(x)$ is the normal distribution introduced in chapter VII, section 1. This theorem is due to Lindeberg;[3] Ljapunov and other authors had previously proved it under more restrictive conditions. It must be understood that this theorem is only a special case of a much more general theorem whose formulation and proof are deferred to the second volume. Here we note that (1.3) is stronger than (1.2), since it gives an estimate for the probability that the discrepancy $\left|\dfrac{1}{n}\mathbf{S}_n - \mu\right|$ is larger than $\sigma/n^{\frac{1}{2}}$. On the other hand, the law of large numbers (1.2) holds even when the random variables $\mathbf{X}_k$ have no finite variance so that it is more general than the central limit theorem. For this reason we shall give an independent proof of the law of large numbers, but first we illustrate the two limit theorems.

Examples. (a) In a sequence of independent throws of a symmetric die let $\mathbf{X}_k$ be the number scored at the kth throw. Then $\mathbf{E}(\mathbf{X}_k) = (1 + 2 + 3 + 4 + 5 + 6)/6 = 3.5$, and $\text{Var}(\mathbf{X}_k) = (1^2 + 2^2 + 3^2 + 4^2 + 5^2 + 6^2)/6 - (3.5)^2 = \frac{35}{12}$. The law of large numbers states that for large n the average score $\mathbf{S}_n/n$ is likely to be near 3.5. The central limit theorem states that the probability of $|\mathbf{S}_n - 3.5n| < \alpha \cdot (35n/12)^{\frac{1}{2}}$ is about $\Phi(\alpha) - \Phi(-\alpha)$. For $n = 1000$ and $\alpha = 1$ we find that there is roughly probability 0.68 that $3450 < \mathbf{S}_n < 3550$. Choosing for α the median value $\alpha = 0.6744$, we find that there are

---

[1] A. Khintchine, Sur la loi des grands nombres, *Comptes rendus de l'Académie des Sciences*, vol. 189 (1929), pp. 477–479. Incidentally, the reader should observe the warning given in connection with the law of large numbers for Bernoulli trials at the end of chapter VI, section 4.

[2] A. Markov showed that the existence of $\mathbf{E}(|\mathbf{X}_k|^{1+a})$ for some $a > 0$ suffices.

[3] J. W. Lindeberg, Eine neue Herleitung des Exponentialgesetzes in der Wahrscheinlichkeitsrechnung, *Mathematische Zeitschrift*, vol. 15 (1922), pp. 211–225.

roughly equal chances that $\mathbf{S}_n$ lies within or without the interval 3500 ± 36.

(b) *Sampling.* Suppose that in a population of N families there are N_k families with exactly k children ($k = 0, 1, \ldots;$ $\Sigma N_k = N$). For a family chosen at random, the number of children is a random variable which assumes the value ν with probability $p_\nu = N_\nu/N$. A sample of size n with replacement represents n independent random variables or "observations" $\mathbf{X}_1, \ldots, \mathbf{X}_n$, each with the same distribution; $\mathbf{S}_n/n$ is the *sample average.* The law of large numbers tells us that for sufficiently large random samples the sample average is likely to be near $\mu = \Sigma \nu p_\nu = \Sigma \nu N_\nu/N$, namely the population average. The central limit theorem permits us to estimate the probable magnitude of the discrepancy and to determine the sample size necessary for reliable estimates. In practice both μ and σ^2 are unknown. However, it is usually easy to obtain a preliminary estimate of σ^2, and it is always possible to keep to the safe side. If it is desired that there be probability 0.99 or better that the sample average $\mathbf{S}_n/n$ differ from the unknown population mean μ by less than $\frac{1}{10}$, then the sample size should be such that

$$(1.4) \qquad \mathbf{P}\left\{\left|\frac{\mathbf{S}_n - n\mu}{n}\right| < \frac{1}{10}\right\} \geq 0.99.$$

The root of $\Phi(x) - \Phi(-x) = 0.99$ is $x = 2.57\ldots$, and hence n should satisfy $n^{\frac{1}{2}}/10\sigma \geq 2.57$ or $n \geq 660\sigma^2$. A cautious preliminary estimate of σ^2 gives us an idea of the required sample size. Similar situations occur frequently. Thus when the experimenter takes the mean of n measurements he, too, relies on the law of large numbers and uses a sample mean as an estimate for an unknown theoretical expectation. The reliability of this estimate can be judged only in terms of σ^2, and usually we are compelled to use rather crude estimates for σ^2.

(c) *The Poisson distribution.* In chapter VII, section 4, we found that for large λ the Poisson distribution $\{p(k; \lambda)\}$ can be approximated by the normal distribution. This is really a direct consequence of the central limit theorem. Suppose that the variables $\mathbf{X}_k$ have a Poisson distribution $\{p(k; \gamma)\}$. Then $\mathbf{S}_n$ has a Poisson distribution $\{p(k; n\gamma)\}$ with mean and variance equal to $n\gamma$. Writing λ for $n\gamma$, we conclude that as $n \to \infty$

$$(1.5) \qquad \sum_{k < \lambda + \beta\lambda^{\frac{1}{2}}} e^{-\lambda}\lambda^k/k! \to \Phi(\beta)$$

the summation extending over all k up to $\lambda + \beta\lambda^{\frac{1}{2}}$. It is now obvious that (1.5) holds also when λ approaches ∞ in an arbitrary manner.

This theorem is used in the theory of summability of divergent series and is of general interest; estimates of the difference of the two sides in (1.5) are available from the general theory.

Note on Variables without Expectation

Both the law of large numbers and the central limit theorem become meaningless if the expectation μ does not exist, but they can be replaced by more general theorems supplying the same sort of information. In the modern theory variables without expectation play an important role and many *waiting and recurrence times* in physics turn out to be of this type. This is true even of the simple coin-tossing game.

Suppose that n coins are tossed one by one. For the kth coin let $\mathbf{X}_k$ be the waiting time up to the first equalization of the accumulated numbers of heads and tails. The $\mathbf{X}_k$ are mutually independent random variables with a common distribution: each $\mathbf{X}_k$ assumes only even positive values and $\mathbf{P}\{\mathbf{X}_k = 2r\} = f_{2r}$ with the probability distribution $\{f_{2r}\}$ defined in III(4.2). According to theorem 3 of chapter III, section 4, the distribution of the sum $\mathbf{S}_n = \mathbf{X}_1 + \ldots + \mathbf{X}_n$ is given by

$$(1.6) \qquad \mathbf{P}\{\mathbf{S}_n = 2r\} = f_{2r}^{(n)}$$

with $f_{2r}^{(n)}$ defined in III(4.11). In chapter III, section 8(c), it was shown that as $n \to \infty$

$$(1.7) \qquad \mathbf{P}\{\mathbf{S}_n < n^2 x\} \to 2[1 - \Phi(x^{-\frac{1}{2}})].$$

We have here a *limit theorem of the same character as the central limit theorem with the remarkable difference that this time the variable* $\mathbf{S}_n/n^2$, *rather than* $\mathbf{S}_n/n$, *possesses a limiting distribution.*

In physical language the $\mathbf{X}_k$ represent independent measurements on the same quantity, and the limit theorem asserts that, in probability, the average $\mathbf{S}_n/n$ increases linearly with n. The surprising consequences of this behavior were discussed in chapter III.[4]

* 2. PROOF OF THE LAW OF LARGE NUMBERS

We proceed in two steps. First assume that $\sigma^2 = \text{Var}(\mathbf{X}_k)$ exists and note that here $\text{Var}(\mathbf{S}_n) = n\sigma^2$, by the addition rule IX(5.6). According to the Chebyshev inequality IX(6.1), we have for every $t > 0$

$$(2.1) \qquad \mathbf{P}\{|\mathbf{S}_n - n\mu| > t\} \leq \frac{n\sigma^2}{t^2}.$$

---

[4] For an analogue to the law of large numbers in a case of variables without finite expectation see section 4 and problem 13.

* This section treats a special topic and may be omitted at first reading.

For $t > \epsilon n$ the left side is less than $\sigma^2/\epsilon^2 n$, which tends to zero. This accomplishes the proof.

Next we drop the restriction that $\mathrm{Var}(\mathbf{X}_k)$ exists. This case is reduced to the preceding one by the *method of truncation* which is an important standard tool. Define two new collections of random variables depending on the $\mathbf{X}_k$ as follows:

$$
\begin{aligned}
(2.2) \quad && \mathbf{U}_k = \mathbf{X}_k, \quad && \mathbf{V}_k = 0 && \text{if} \quad |\mathbf{X}_k| \leq \epsilon n; \\
&& \mathbf{U}_k = 0, \quad && \mathbf{V}_k = \mathbf{X}_k && \text{if} \quad |\mathbf{X}_k| > \epsilon n.
\end{aligned}
$$

Here $k = 1, \ldots, n$ and $\epsilon > 0$ is fixed. Then identically

$$
(2.3) \qquad\qquad \mathbf{X}_k = \mathbf{U}_k + \mathbf{V}_k.
$$

If $\{f(x_j)\}$ is the common probability distribution of the variables $\mathbf{X}_k$, the sum

$$
(2.4) \qquad\qquad \Sigma\, |x_j| f(x_j) = A
$$

is finite since $\mu = \mathbf{E}(\mathbf{X}_k)$ was assumed to exist. Now

$$
(2.5) \qquad\qquad \mu'_n = \mathbf{E}(\mathbf{U}_k) = \sum_{|x_j| \leq \epsilon n} x_j f(x_j),
$$

the summation extending over those j for which $|x_j| \leq \epsilon n$. Clearly $\mu'_n \to \mu$ as $n \to \infty$, and hence for all n sufficiently large and for arbitrary $\delta > 0$

$$
(2.6) \qquad\qquad |\mu'_n - \mu| < \delta.
$$

Furthermore, from (2.5) and (2.4),

$$
(2.7) \qquad \mathrm{Var}(\mathbf{U}_k) \leq \mathbf{E}(\mathbf{U}_k{}^2) \leq \epsilon n \sum_{|x_j| \leq \epsilon n} |x_j| f(x_j) \leq \epsilon A n.
$$

The $\mathbf{U}_k$ are mutually independent, and their sum $\mathbf{U}_1 + \mathbf{U}_2 + \ldots + \mathbf{U}_n$ can be treated exactly as the $\mathbf{X}_k$ in the case of finite variances; applying the Chebyshev inequality, we get the following analogue to (2.1)

$$
(2.8) \qquad \mathbf{P}\left\{ \left| \frac{\mathbf{U}_1 + \ldots + \mathbf{U}_n}{n} - \mu'_n \right| > \delta \right\} < \frac{\mathrm{Var}(\mathbf{U}_k)}{n\delta^2} < \frac{\epsilon A}{\delta^2}.
$$

In view of (2.6) this implies

$$
(2.9) \qquad \mathbf{P}\left\{ \left| \frac{\mathbf{U}_1 + \ldots + \mathbf{U}_n}{n} - \mu \right| > 2\delta \right\} < \frac{\epsilon A}{\delta^2}.
$$

Note that there is a large probability that $\mathbf{V}_k = 0$.   In fact

$$(2.10) \qquad \mathbf{P}\{\mathbf{V}_k \neq 0\} = \sum_{|x_j| > \epsilon n} f(x_j) \leq \frac{1}{\epsilon n} \sum_{|x_j| > \epsilon n} |x_j| f(x_j),$$

and the last sum tends to 0 with increasing n.   Therefore for n sufficiently large

$$(2.11) \qquad\qquad\qquad \mathbf{P}\{\mathbf{V}_k \neq 0\} \leq \frac{\epsilon}{n}$$

and hence by the basic inequality I(7.6)

$$(2.12) \qquad\qquad \mathbf{P}\{\mathbf{V}_1 + \ldots + \mathbf{V}_n \neq 0\} \leq \epsilon.$$

Now $\mathbf{S}_n = (\mathbf{U}_1 + \ldots + \mathbf{U}_n) + (\mathbf{V}_1 + \ldots + \mathbf{V}_n)$, and therefore from (2.9) and (2.12)

$$(2.13) \quad \mathbf{P}\left\{\left|\frac{\mathbf{S}_n}{n} - \mu\right| > 2\delta\right\} \leq \mathbf{P}\left\{\left|\frac{\mathbf{U}_1 + \ldots + \mathbf{U}_n}{n} - \mu\right| > 2\delta\right\} +$$

$$+ \mathbf{P}\{\mathbf{V}_1 + \ldots + \mathbf{V}_n \neq 0\} \leq \frac{\epsilon A}{\delta^2} + \epsilon.$$

Since ϵ and δ are arbitrary, the right side can be made arbitrarily small, and this proves the assertion.

3. THE THEORY OF "FAIR" GAMES

For a further analysis of the implications of the law of large numbers we shall use the time-honored terminology of gamblers, but our discussion bears equally on less frivolous applications, and our two basic assumptions are more realistic in statistics and physics than in gambling halls.   First, we shall assume that our gambler possesses an *unlimited capital* so that no loss can force a termination of the game.   (Dropping this assumption leads to the problem of the gambler's *ruin*, which from the very beginning has intrigued students of probability.   It is of importance in Wald's sequential analysis and in the theory of stochastic processes, and will be taken up in chapter XIV.)   Second, we shall assume that the gambler *does not have the privilege of optional stopping; the number n of trials must be fixed in advance* independently of the development of the game.   In reality a player blessed with an unlimited capital would wait for a run of good luck and quit at an opportune moment.   He is not interested in the probable state at a prescribed moment, but only in the maximal fluctuations in the long run. Light is shed on this problem by the law of the iterated logarithm rather than by the law of large numbers (cf. chapter VIII, section 5).

The random variable $\mathbf{X}_k$ will be interpreted as the (positive or negative) gain at the kth trial of a player who keeps playing the same type of game of chance. The sum $\mathbf{S}_n = \mathbf{X}_1 + \ldots + \mathbf{X}_n$ is the accumulated gain in n independent trials. If the player pays for each trial an entrance fee μ' (not necessarily positive), then $n\mu'$ represents the accumulated entrance fees, and $\mathbf{S}_n - n\mu'$ the *accumulated net gain*. The law of large numbers applies when $\mu = \mathbf{E}(\mathbf{X}_k)$ exists. It says roughly that for sufficiently large n the difference $\mathbf{S}_n - n\mu$ is likely to be small in comparison to n. Therefore, if the entrance fee μ' is smaller than μ, then, for large n, the player is likely to have a positive gain of the order of magnitude $n(\mu - \mu')$. For the same reason an entrance fee $\mu' > \mu$ is practically sure to lead to a loss. In short, the case $\mu' < \mu$ is *favorable* to the player, while $\mu' > \mu$ is *unfavorable*.

Note that nothing is said about the case $\mu' = \mu$. The *only* possible conclusion in this case is that, for n sufficiently large, *the accumulated gain or loss* $\mathbf{S}_n - n\mu$ *will with overwhelming probability be small in comparison with* n. It is not stated whether $\mathbf{S}_n - n\mu$ is likely to be positive or negative, that is, whether the game is favorable or unfavorable. This was overlooked in the classical theory which called $\mu' = \mu$ a "fair" price and a game with $\mu' = \mu$ *"fair."* Much harm was done by the misleading suggestive power of this name. It must be understood that a "fair" game may be distinctly favorable or unfavorable to the player.

It is clear that "normally" not only $\mathbf{E}(\mathbf{X}_k)$ but also $\mathrm{Var}(\mathbf{X}_k)$ exists. In this case the law of large numbers is supplemented by the central limit theorem, and the latter tells us that, with a "fair" game, the long-run net gain $\mathbf{S}_n - n\mu$ is likely to be of the order of magnitude $n^{\frac{1}{2}}$ and that for large n there are about equal odds for this net gain to be positive or negative. Thus, when the central limit theorem applies, the term "fair" appears justified, but even in this case we deal with a limit theorem with emphasis on the words "long run."

For illustration, consider a slot machine where the player has a probability of 10^{-6} to win $10^6 - 1$ dollars, and the alternative of losing the entrance fee $\mu' = 1$. Here we have Bernoulli trials, and the game is "fair." In a million trials the player pays as many dollars in entrance fees. He may hit the jackpot $0, 1, 2, \ldots$ times. We know from the Poisson approximation to the binomial distribution that, with an accuracy to several decimal places, the probability of hitting the jackpot exactly k times is $e^{-1}/k!$. Thus the player has probability $0.368\ldots$ to lose a million, and the same probability of barely recovering his expenses; he has probability $0.184\ldots$ to gain exactly one million, etc. Here 10^6 trials are equivalent to one single trial in a game with the gain distributed according to a Poisson distribution (which could be realized by matching two large decks of cards; cf. chapter IV, section 4). Obviously the law of large numbers is operationally meaningless in such situations. Now all fire, automobile, and similar insurance is of the described type; the risk involves a huge sum, but the corresponding probability is very small. Moreover, the insured plays ordinarily only one trial per year, so that the number n of trials never grows large. For him the game is necessarily "unfair," and yet it is usually economically advantageous; the law of large numbers is of no relevance to him. As for the company, it plays a large number of games, but because of the large variance the chance fluctuations are pronounced. The premiums must be fixed so as to preclude a huge loss in any specific year, and hence the company is concerned with the ruin problem rather than the law of large numbers.

When the variance is infinite, the term "fair game" becomes an absolute misnomer; there is no reason to believe that the accumulated net gain $S_n - n\mu'$ fluctuates around zero. In fact, there exist examples of "fair" games [5] where the probability tends to one that the player will have sustained a net loss. The law of large numbers asserts that this net loss is likely to be of smaller order of magnitude than n. However, nothing more can be asserted. If a_n is an arbitrary sequence such that $a_n/n \to 0$, it is possible to construct a "fair" game where the probability tends to one that at the nth trial the accumulated net loss exceeds a_n. Problem 15 contains an example where the player has a practical assurance that his loss will exceed $n/\log n$. This game is "fair," and the entrance fee is unity. It is difficult to imagine that a player will find it "fair" if he is practically sure to sustain a steadily increasing loss.

* 4. THE PETERSBURG GAME

In the classical theory the notion of expectation was not clearly disassociated from the definition of probability, and no mathematical formalism existed to handle it. Random variables with infinite expectations therefore produced insurmountable difficulties, and even quite recent discussions appear strange to the student of modern probability. The importance of variables without expectation has been stressed at the conclusion of section 1, and it seems appropriate here to give an example for the analogue of the law of large numbers in the case of

---

[5] W. Feller, Note on the law of large numbers and "fair" games, *Annals of Mathematical Statistics*, vol. 16 (1945), pp. 301–304.

* Starred sections treat special topics and may be omitted at first reading.

such variables. For that purpose we use the time-honored so-called Petersburg paradox.[6]

A single trial in the Petersburg game consists in tossing a true coin until it falls heads; if this occurs at the rth throw the player receives 2^r dollars. In other words, the gain at each trial is a random variable assuming the values 2^1, 2^2, 2^3, ... with corresponding probabilities 2^{-1}, 2^{-2}, 2^{-3}, ... The expectation is formally defined by $\Sigma x_r f(x_r)$ with $x_r = 2^r$ and $f(x_r) = 2^{-r}$, so that each term of the series equals 1. Thus the gain has no finite expectation, and the law of large numbers is inapplicable. Now the game becomes less favorable to the player when amended by the rule that he receives nothing if a trial takes more than N tosses (i.e., if the coin falls tails N times in succession). In this amended game the gain has the finite expectation N, and the law of large numbers applies. It follows that after n trials the accumulated gain is likely to exceed nN for every N. The player can therefore expect to have a net profit even if he pays an arbitrary fixed entrance fee μ' for each trial. This is true for every μ', but the larger μ', the larger must n be in order that a positive gain be probable. The classical theory concluded that $\mu' = \infty$ is a "fair" entrance fee, but the modern student will hardly understand the mysterious discussions of this "paradox."

It is perfectly possible to determine entrance fees with which the Petersburg game will have all properties of a "fair" game in the classical sense, except that these entrance fees will depend on the number of trials instead of remaining constant. Variable entrance fees are undesirable in gambling halls, but there the Petersburg game is impossible anyway because of limited resources. In the case of a finite expectation $\mu = \mathbf{E}(\mathbf{X}_k) > 0$, a game is called "fair" if for large n the ratio of the accumulated gain $\mathbf{S}_n$ to the accumulated entrance fees $e_n = n\mu'$ is likely to be near 1 (that is, if the difference $\mathbf{S}_n - e_n$ is likely to be of smaller order of magnitude than $e_n = n\mu'$). If $\mathbf{E}(\mathbf{X}_k)$ does not exist, we cannot put $e_n = n\mu'$ but must determine e_n in another way. We shall say that *a game with accumulated entrance fees e_n is fair in the classical sense if for every $\epsilon > 0$*

$$(4.1) \qquad \mathbf{P}\left\{\left|\frac{\mathbf{S}_n}{e_n} - 1\right| > \epsilon\right\} \to 0.$$

This is the complete analogue of the law of large numbers where $e_n = n\mu'$. The latter is interpreted by the physicist to the effect that

---

[6] This paradox was discussed by Daniel Bernoulli (1700–1782). Note that Bernoulli trials are named after James Bernoulli.

the average of n independent measurements is bound to be near μ. In the present instance the average of n measurements is bound to be near e_n/n. Our limit theorem (4.1), when it applies, has a mathematical and operational meaning which does not differ from the law of large numbers.

We shall now show [7] that the *Petersburg game becomes "fair" in the classical sense if we put* $e_n = n \operatorname{Log} n$, where $\operatorname{Log} n$ is the logarithm to the base 2, that is, $2^{\operatorname{Log} n} = n$.

Proof. We use the method of truncation of section 2, this time defining the variables $\mathbf{U}_k$ and $\mathbf{V}_k$ $(k = 1, 2, \ldots, n)$ by

$$
\begin{aligned}
&\mathbf{U}_k = \mathbf{X}_k, \qquad \mathbf{V}_k = 0 \qquad \text{if} \quad \mathbf{X}_k \leq n \operatorname{Log} n; \\
&\mathbf{U}_k = 0, \qquad \mathbf{V}_k = \mathbf{X}_k \qquad \text{if} \quad \mathbf{X}_k > n \operatorname{Log} n.
\end{aligned}
$$
(4.2)

Again $\mathbf{X}_k = \mathbf{U}_k + \mathbf{V}_k$, and the $\mathbf{U}_k$ are mutually independent. For every t we have $\mathbf{P}\{\mathbf{X}_k > t\} \leq 2/t$ and hence $\mathbf{P}\{\mathbf{V}_k \neq 0\} < 2/(n \operatorname{Log} n)$, or

$$
\mathbf{P}\{\mathbf{V}_1 + \mathbf{V}_2 + \ldots + \mathbf{V}_n > 0\} < \frac{2}{\operatorname{Log} n} \to 0.
$$
(4.3)

To verify (4.1) it suffices therefore to prove that

$$
\mathbf{P}\{|\mathbf{U}_1 + \ldots + \mathbf{U}_n - n \operatorname{Log} n| > \epsilon n \operatorname{Log} n\} \to 0.
$$
(4.4)

Put $\mu_n = \mathbf{E}(\mathbf{U}_k)$ and $\sigma_n^2 = \operatorname{Var}(\mathbf{U}_k)$; these quantities depend on n, but are common to $\mathbf{U}_1, \mathbf{U}_2, \ldots, \mathbf{U}_n$. If r is the largest integer such that $2^r \leq n \operatorname{Log} n$, then $\mu_n = r$ and hence for sufficiently large n

$$
\operatorname{Log} n < \mu_n \leq \operatorname{Log} n + \operatorname{Log} \operatorname{Log} n.
$$
(4.5)

Similarly

$$
\sigma_n^2 < \mathbf{E}(\mathbf{U}_k^2) = 2 + 2^2 + \ldots + 2^r < 2^{r+1} \leq 2n \operatorname{Log} n.
$$
(4.6)

Since the sum $\mathbf{U}_1 + \ldots + \mathbf{U}_n$ has mean $n\mu_n$ and variance $n\sigma_n^2$, we have by Chebyshev's inequality

$$
\mathbf{P}\{|\mathbf{U}_1 + \ldots + \mathbf{U}_n - n\mu_n| > \epsilon n \mu_n\} \leq \frac{n\sigma_n^2}{\epsilon^2 n^2 \mu_n^2} < \frac{2}{\epsilon^2 \operatorname{Log} n} \to 0.
$$
(4.7)

Now by (4.5) $\mu_n \sim \operatorname{Log} n$, and hence (4.7) is equivalent to (4.4).

---

[7] This is a special case of a generalized law of large numbers from which necessary and sufficient conditions for (4.1) can easily be derived; cf. W. Feller, *Acta Scientiarum Litterarum Univ. Szeged*, vol. 8 (1937), pp. 191–201.

5. VARIABLE DISTRIBUTIONS

Up to now we have considered only the case where the variables $\mathbf{X}_k$ have the same distribution. This situation corresponds to a repetition of the same game of chance, but it is more interesting to see what happens if the type of game changes at each step. It is not necessary to think of gambling places; the statistician who applies statistical tests is engaged in a dignified sort of gambling, and in his case the distribution of the random variables changes from occasion to occasion.

To fix ideas we shall imagine that an infinite sequence of probability distributions is given so that for each n we have n mutually independent variables $\mathbf{X}_1, \ldots, \mathbf{X}_n$ with the prescribed distributions. We shall assume that the means and variances exist and put

$$(5.1) \qquad \mu_k = \mathbf{E}(\mathbf{X}_k), \qquad \sigma_k^2 = \mathrm{Var}(\mathbf{X}_k).$$

The sum $\mathbf{S}_n = \mathbf{X}_1 + \ldots + \mathbf{X}_n$ has also finite mean and variance

$$(5.2) \qquad m_n = \mathbf{E}(\mathbf{S}_n), \qquad s_n^2 = \mathrm{Var}(\mathbf{S}_n)$$

given by

$$(5.3) \qquad m_n = \mu_1 + \ldots + \mu_n, \qquad s_n^2 = \sigma_1^2 + \ldots + \sigma_n^2$$

[cf. formulas IX(2.4) and IX(5.6)]. In the special case of identical distributions we had $m_n = n\mu$, $s_n^2 = n\sigma^2$.

The (weak) law of large numbers is said to hold for the sequence $\{\mathbf{X}_k\}$ *if for every* $\epsilon > 0$

$$(5.4) \qquad \mathbf{P}\left\{ \frac{|\mathbf{S}_n - m_n|}{n} > \epsilon \right\} \to 0.$$

The sequence $\{\mathbf{X}_k\}$ *is said to obey the central limit theorem if for every fixed* $\alpha < \beta$

$$(5.5) \qquad \mathbf{P}\left\{ \alpha < \frac{\mathbf{S}_n - m_n}{s_n} < \beta \right\} \to \Phi(\beta) - \Phi(\alpha).$$

It is one of the salient features of probability theory that both the law of large numbers and the central limit theorem hold for a surprisingly large class of sequences $\{\mathbf{X}_k\}$. In particular, *the law of large numbers holds whenever the* $\mathbf{X}_k$ *are uniformly bounded*, that is, whenever there exists a constant A such that $|\mathbf{X}_k| < A$ for all k. More generally, *a sufficient condition for the law of large numbers to hold is that*

$$(5.6) \qquad \frac{s_n}{n} \to 0.$$

This is a direct consequence of the Chebyshev inequality, and the proof given in the opening passage of section 2 applies. Note, however, that the condition (5.6) is not necessary (cf. problem 14).

Various sufficient conditions for the central limit theorem have been discovered, but all were superseded by the *Lindeberg* [8] *theorem according to which the central limit theorem holds whenever for every* $\epsilon > 0$ *the truncated variables* $\mathbf{U}_k$ *defined by*

(5.7)
$$\mathbf{U}_k = \mathbf{X}_k - \mu_k \qquad \text{if} \quad |\mathbf{X}_k - \mu_k| \leq \epsilon s_n,$$
$$\mathbf{U}_k = 0 \qquad \text{if} \quad |\mathbf{X}_k - \mu_k| > \epsilon s_n,$$

satisfy the conditions $s_n \to \infty$ *and*

(5.8)
$$\frac{1}{s_n^2} \sum_{k=1}^{n} \mathbf{E}(\mathbf{U}_k^2) \to 1.$$

If the $\mathbf{X}_k$ are uniformly bounded, that is, if $|\mathbf{X}_k| < A$, then $\mathbf{U}_k = \mathbf{X}_k - \mu_k$ for all n which are so large that $s_n > 2A\epsilon^{-1}$. The left side in (5.8) then equals 1. Therefore the Lindeberg theorem implies that *every uniformly bounded sequence* $\{\mathbf{X}_k\}$ *of mutually independent random variables obeys the central limit theorem*, provided, of course, that $s_n \to \infty$. It was found that the Lindeberg conditions are also necessary for (5.5) to hold.[9] The proof is deferred to the second volume, where we shall also give estimates for the difference between the two sides in (5.5).

In the case where the variables $\mathbf{X}_k$ have a common distribution we found the central limit theorem to be stronger than the law of large numbers. This is not so in general, and we shall see that the central limit theorem may apply to sequences which do not obey the law of large numbers.

Examples. (a) Let $\lambda > 0$ be fixed, and let $\mathbf{X}_k = \pm k^\lambda$, each with probability $\frac{1}{2}$ (e.g., a coin is tossed, and at the kth throw the stakes are $\pm k^\lambda$). Here $\mu_k = 0$, $\sigma_k^2 = k^{2\lambda}$, and

(5.9)
$$s_n^2 = 1^{2\lambda} + 2^{2\lambda} + 3^{2\lambda} + \ldots + n^{2\lambda} \sim \frac{n^{2\lambda+1}}{2\lambda + 1}.$$

---

[8] J. W. Lindeberg, *loc. cit.* (footnote 3).

[9] W. Feller, Über den zentralen Grenzwertsatz der Wahrscheinlichkeitsrechnung, *Mathematische Zeitschrift*, vol. 40 (1935), pp. 521–559. There also a generalized central limit theorem is derived which may apply to variables without expectations. Note that we are here considering only independent variables; for dependent variables the Lindeberg condition is neither necessary nor sufficient.

The condition (5.6) is satisfied if $\lambda < \frac{1}{2}$. Therefore the law of large numbers holds if $\lambda < \frac{1}{2}$; we proceed to show that it does not hold if $\lambda \geq \frac{1}{2}$.

For $k = 1, 2, \ldots, n$ we have $|\mathbf{X}_k| = k^\lambda \leq n^\lambda$, so that for $n > (2\lambda + 1)\epsilon^{-2}$ the truncated variables $\mathbf{U}_k$ are identical with the $\mathbf{X}_k$. Hence the Lindeberg condition applies for $\lambda > 0$, and

$$(5.10) \qquad \mathbf{P}\left\{ \alpha < \left(\frac{2\lambda + 1}{n^{2\lambda+1}}\right)^{\frac{1}{2}} \mathbf{S}_n < \beta \right\} \to \Phi(\beta) - \Phi(\alpha).$$

It follows that $\mathbf{S}_n$ is likely to be of the order of magnitude $n^{\lambda+\frac{1}{2}}$, so that the law of large numbers cannot apply for $\lambda \geq \frac{1}{2}$. We see that in this example *the central limit theorem applies for all $\lambda > 0$, but the law of large numbers only if $\lambda < \frac{1}{2}$.*

(b) Consider two independent sequences of 1000 tossings of a coin (or emptying two bags of 1000 coins each), and let us examine the *difference* $\mathbf{D}$ of the number of heads. Let the tossings of the two sequences be numbered from 1 to 1000 and from 1001 to 2000, respectively and define 2000 random variables $\mathbf{X}_k$ as follows: If the kth coin falls tails, then $\mathbf{X}_k = 0$. If it falls heads, we put $\mathbf{X}_k = 1$ for $k \leq 1000$ and $\mathbf{X}_k = -1$, for $k > 1000$. Then $\mathbf{D} = \mathbf{X}_1 + \mathbf{X}_2 + \ldots + + \mathbf{X}_{2000}$. Moreover, $\mu_k = \pm\frac{1}{2}$, depending on the sequence to which the coin belongs, $\sigma_k{}^2 = \frac{1}{4}$, $m_{2000} = 0$, $s_{2000}{}^2 = 500$. Therefore the probability that the difference $\mathbf{D}$ will lie within the limits $\pm(500)^{\frac{1}{2}}\alpha$ is $\Phi(\alpha) - \Phi(-\alpha)$, approximately, and $\mathbf{D}$ is comparable to the deviation $\mathbf{S}_{2000} - 1000$ of the number of heads in 2000 tossings from its expected number 1000.

(c) An application to the *theory of inheritance* will illustrate the great variety of conclusions based on the central limit theorem. In chapter V, section 5, we have studied traits which depend essentially only on one pair of genes (alleles). We conceive of other characters (like height) as the cumulative effect of many pairs of genes. For simplicity, suppose that for each particular pair of genes there exist three genotypes AA, Aa, or aa. Let x_1, x_2, and x_3 be the corresponding contributions. The genotype of an individual is a random event, and the contribution of a particular pair of genes to the height is a random variable $\mathbf{X}$, assuming the three values x_1, x_2, x_3 with certain probabilities. The height is the cumulative effect of many such random variables $\mathbf{X}_1$, $\mathbf{X}_2$, $\ldots$, $\mathbf{X}_n$, and since the contribution of each is small, we may in first approximation assume that the height is the *sum* $\mathbf{X}_1 + \ldots + \mathbf{X}_n$. It is true that not *all* the $\mathbf{X}_k$ are mutually independent. However, the central limit theorem holds also for large classes of dependent variables, and, besides, it is plausible that the great majority of the $\mathbf{X}_k$ can be treated as independent. These considerations can be rendered more precise; here they serve only as indication of how the central limit theorem explains why many biometric characters, like height, exhibit an empirical distribution close to the normal distribution. This theory permits also the prediction of properties of inheritance, e.g., the dependence of the mean height of children on the height of their parents. Such biometric investigations were initiated by F. Galton and Karl Pearson.

* 6. APPLICATIONS TO COMBINATORIAL ANALYSIS

We shall give two examples of applications of the central limit theorem to problems not directly connected with probability theory. Both relate to the $n!$ permutations of the n elements $a_1, a_2, \ldots, a_n$, to each of which we attribute probability $1/n!$.

(a) Inversions

In a given permutation the element a_k is said to induce r inversions if it precedes exactly r elements with smaller index (i.e., elements which precede a_k in the natural order). For example, in $(a_3 a_6 a_1 a_5 a_2 a_4)$ the elements a_1 and a_2 induce no inversion, a_3 induces two, a_4 none, a_5 two, and a_6 four. In $(a_6 a_5 a_4 a_3 a_2 a_1)$ the element a_k induces $k-1$ inversions and there are fifteen inversions in all. The number $\mathbf{X}_k$ of inversions induced by a_k is a random variable, and $\mathbf{S}_n = \mathbf{X}_1 + \ldots + \mathbf{X}_n$ is the total number of inversions. Here $\mathbf{X}_k$ assumes the values $0, 1, \ldots, k-1$, each with probability $1/k$, and therefore

$$\mu_k = \frac{k-1}{2},$$

(6.1)

$$\sigma_k{}^2 = \frac{1 + 2^2 + \ldots + (k-1)^2}{k} - \left(\frac{k-1}{2}\right)^2 = \frac{k^2 - 1}{12}.$$

The number of inversions produced by a_k does not depend on the relative order of $a_1, a_2, \ldots, a_{k-1}$, and the $\mathbf{X}_k$ are mutually independent. From (6.1) we get

(6.2) $$m_n = \frac{1 + 2 + \ldots + (n-1)}{2} = \frac{n(n-1)}{4} \sim \frac{n^2}{4}$$

and

(6.3) $$s_n{}^2 = \frac{1}{12} \sum_{k=1}^{n} (k^2 - 1) = \frac{2n^3 + 3n^2 - 5n}{72} \sim \frac{n^3}{36}.$$

---

* This section treats a special topic and may be omitted.

For large n we have $\epsilon s_n > n \geq \mathbf{U}_k$, and hence the variables $\mathbf{U}_k$ of the Lindeberg condition are identical with $\mathbf{X}_k$. Therefore the central limit theorem applies, and we conclude that the *number $\mathbf{N}_n$ of permutations for which the number of inversions lies between the limits* $\dfrac{n^2}{4} \pm \dfrac{\alpha}{6} n^{\frac{3}{2}}$ *is, asymptotically, given by* $n!\{\Phi(\alpha) - \Phi(-\alpha)\}$. In particular, for about one-half of all permutations the number of inversions lies between the limits $(n^2/4) \pm (0.11)n^{\frac{3}{2}}$.

(b) Cycles

Every permutation can be broken down into cycles, that is, groups of elements permuted among themselves. Thus in $(a_3 a_6 a_1 a_5 a_2 a_4)$ we find that a_1 and a_3 are interchanged, and that the remaining four elements are permuted among themselves; this permutation contains two cycles. If an element is in its natural place, it forms a cycle so that the identical permutation $(a_1, a_2, \ldots, a_n)$ contains as many cycles as elements. On the other hand, the cyclical permutations $(a_2, a_3, \ldots, a_n, a_1)$, $(a_3, a_4, \ldots, a_n, a_1, a_2)$ etc. contain a single cycle each. For the study of cycles it is convenient to describe the permutation by means of arrows indicating the places occupied by the several elements. For example, $1 \rightarrow 3 \rightarrow 4 \rightarrow 1$ indicates that a_1 is at the third place, a_3 at the fourth, and a_4 at the first, the third step thus completing the cycle. This description continues with a_2, which is the next element in the natural order. In this notation the permutation $(a_4, a_8, a_1, a_3, a_2, a_5, a_7, a_6)$ is described by: $1 \rightarrow 3 \rightarrow 4 \rightarrow 1$; $2 \rightarrow 5 \rightarrow 6 \rightarrow 8 \rightarrow 2$; $7 \rightarrow 7$.

Let $\mathbf{X}_k$ equal 1 if a cycle is completed at the kth step in this build-up; otherwise let $\mathbf{X}_k = 0$. (In the last example $\mathbf{X}_3 = \mathbf{X}_7 = \mathbf{X}_8 = 1$ and $\mathbf{X}_1 = \mathbf{X}_2 = \mathbf{X}_4 = \mathbf{X}_5 = \mathbf{X}_6 = 0$.) Clearly $\mathbf{X}_1 = 1$ if, and only if, a_1 is at the first place. At the step number $1, 2, \ldots, n$ we have $n, n-1, \ldots, 0$ choices, respectively, and among them just one leads to the completion of a cycle. Therefore [10] $\mathbf{X}_k = 1$ with probability $1/(n - k + 1)$ and $\mathbf{X}_k = 0$ with probability $(n - k)/(n - k + 1)$. The variables $\mathbf{X}_k$ are mutually independent with means and variances

$$(6.4) \qquad \mu_k = \frac{1}{n - k + 1}, \qquad \sigma_k{}^2 = \frac{n - k}{(n - k + 1)^2}$$

whence

$$(6.5) \qquad m_n = 1 + \frac{1}{2} + \frac{1}{3} + \ldots + \frac{1}{n} \sim \log n$$

---

[10] Formally, the distribution of $\mathbf{X}_k$ depends not only on k but also on n. It suffices to reorder the $\mathbf{X}_k$, starting from $k = n$ down to $k = 1$, to have the distribution depend only on the subscript.

and

$$(6.6) \qquad s_n{}^2 = \sum_{k=1}^{n} \frac{n - k}{(n - k + 1)^2} \sim \log n.$$

$\mathbf{S}_n = \mathbf{X}_1 + \ldots + \mathbf{X}_n$ is the total number of cycles. *The average is m_n; the number of permutations with cycles between $\log n + \alpha(\log n)^{\frac{1}{2}}$ and $\log n + \beta(\log n)^{\frac{1}{2}}$ is given by $n!\{\Phi(\beta) - \Phi(\alpha)\}$, approximately.* The refined forms of the central limit theorem give more precise estimates.[11]

* 7. THE STRONG LAW OF LARGE NUMBERS

The (weak) law of large numbers (5.4) asserts that for every particular sufficiently large n the deviation $|\mathbf{S}_n - m_n|$ is likely to be small in comparison to n. It has been pointed out in connection with Bernoulli trials (chapter VIII) that this does not imply that $|\mathbf{S}_n - m_n|/n$ remains small for all large n; it can happen that the law of large numbers applies but that $|\mathbf{S}_n - m_n|/n$ continues to fluctuate between finite or infinite limits. The law of large numbers permits only the conclusion that large values of $|\mathbf{S}_n - m_n|/n$ occur at infrequent moments.

We say that the sequence $\mathbf{X}_k$ obeys the strong law of large numbers if to every pair $\epsilon > 0$, $\delta > 0$, there corresponds an N such that there is probability $1 - \delta$ or better that for every $r > 0$ all $r + 1$ inequalities

$$(7.1) \qquad \frac{|\mathbf{S}_n - m_n|}{n} < \epsilon, \quad n = N, N+1, \ldots, N+r$$

will be satisfied.

We can interpret (7.1) roughly by saying that with an overwhelming probability $|\mathbf{S}_n - m_n|/n$ *remains small* [12] for all $n > N$.

The Kolmogorov Criterion. *The convergence of the series*

$$(7.2) \qquad \sum \frac{\sigma_k{}^2}{k^2}$$

---

[11] A great variety of asymptotic estimates in combinatorial analysis were derived by other methods by V. Gončarov, Du domaine d'analyse combinatoire, *Bulletin de l'Académie Sciences URSS, Sér. Math.* (in Russian, French summary), vol. 8 (1944), pp. 3–48. The present method is simpler but more restricted in scope; cf. W. Feller, The fundamental limit theorems in probability, *Bulletin of the American Mathematical Society,* vol. 51 (1945), pp. 800–832.

* This section treats a special topic and may be omitted.

[12] The general theory introduces a sample space corresponding to the infinite sequence $\{\mathbf{X}_k\}$. The strong law then states that with probability one $|\mathbf{S}_n - m_n|/n$ tends to zero. In real variable terminology the strong law asserts convergence almost everywhere, and the weak law is equivalent to convergence in measure.

is a sufficient condition for the strong law of large numbers to apply to the sequence of mutually independent random variables $\mathbf{X}_k$ with variances σ_k^2.

Proof. Let A_ν be the event that for at least one n with $2^{\nu-1} < n \leq 2^\nu$ the inequality (7.1) does *not* hold. Obviously it suffices to prove that for all ν sufficiently large ($\nu > \log N$) and all r

$$\mathbf{P}\{A_\nu\} + \mathbf{P}\{A_{\nu+1}\} + \ldots + \mathbf{P}\{A_{\nu+r}\} < \delta,$$

that is, that the series $\Sigma \mathbf{P}\{A_\nu\}$ converges. Now the event A_ν implies that for some n with $2^{\nu-1} < n \leq 2^\nu$

$$(7.3) \qquad |\mathbf{S}_n - m_n| \geq \frac{\epsilon}{2} \cdot 2^\nu$$

and by Kolmogorov's inequality (chapter IX, section 7)

$$(7.4) \qquad \mathbf{P}\{A_\nu\} \leq 4\epsilon^{-2} \cdot s_{2^\nu}^2 \cdot 2^{-2\nu}.$$

Hence

$$(7.5) \quad \sum_{\nu=1}^{\infty} \mathbf{P}\{A_\nu\} \leq 4\epsilon^{-2} \sum_{\nu=1}^{\infty} 2^{-2\nu} \sum_{k=1}^{2^\nu} \sigma_k^2 = 4\epsilon^{-2} \sum_{k=1}^{\infty} \sigma_k^2 \sum_{2^\nu \geq k} 2^{-2\nu} \leq$$

$$\leq 8\epsilon^{-2} \sum_{k=1}^{\infty} \frac{\sigma_k^2}{k^2}$$

which accomplishes the proof.

As a typical application we prove the

Theorem. *If the mutually independent random variables $\mathbf{X}_k$ have a common distribution $\{f(x_j)\}$ and if $\mu = \mathbf{E}(\mathbf{X}_k)$ exists, then the strong law of large numbers applies to the sequence $\{\mathbf{X}_k\}$.*

This theorem is, of course, stronger than the weak law of section 1. The two theorems are treated independently because of the methodological interest of the proofs. For a converse cf. problem 17.

Proof. We again use the method of truncation. Two new sequences of random variables are introduced by

$$(7.6) \qquad \begin{aligned} \mathbf{U}_k = \mathbf{X}_k, \quad & \mathbf{V}_k = 0 \qquad && \text{if} \quad |\mathbf{X}_k| < k, \\ \mathbf{U}_k = 0, \quad & \mathbf{V}_k = \mathbf{X}_k \qquad && \text{if} \quad |\mathbf{X}_k| \geq k. \end{aligned}$$

The $\mathbf{U}_k$ are mutually independent, and we shall show that they satisfy Kolmogorov's criterion. Clearly

$$(7.7) \qquad \sigma_k^2 \leq \mathbf{E}(\mathbf{U}_k^2) = \sum_{|x_i| < k} x_j^2 f(x_j).$$

Put for abbreviation

$$(7.8) \qquad a_\nu = \sum_{\nu-1 \leq |x_j| < \nu} |x_j| f(x_j).$$

Then the series Σa_ν converges since $\mathbf{E}(\mathbf{X}_k)$ exists. Moreover, from (7.7),

$$(7.9) \qquad \sigma_k^2 \leq a_1 + 2a_2 + 3a_3 + \ldots + ka_k$$

and

$$(7.10) \quad \sum_{k=1}^{\infty} \frac{\sigma_k^2}{k^2} \leq \sum_{k=1}^{\infty} \frac{1}{k^2} \sum_{\nu=1}^{k} \nu a_\nu = \sum_{\nu=1}^{\infty} \nu a_\nu \sum_{k=\nu}^{\infty} \frac{1}{k^2} < 2 \sum_{\nu=1}^{\infty} a_\nu < \infty.$$

Finally

$$(7.11) \qquad \mathbf{E}(\mathbf{U}_k) = \mu_k = \sum_{|x_j| < k} x_j f(x_j)$$

so that $\mu_k \to \mu$ and hence $(\mu_1 + \mu_2 + \ldots + \mu_n)/n \to \mu$. Applying the strong law of large numbers to $\{\mathbf{U}_k\}$, we conclude that with probability $1 - \delta$ or better

$$(7.12) \qquad \left| n^{-1} \sum_{k=1}^{n} \mathbf{U}_k - \mu \right| < \epsilon$$

for all $n \geq N$. It suffices now to prove that the $\mathbf{V}_n$ can be neglected, that is, that the probability of one or more $\mathbf{V}_n$ with $n > N$ being different from zero tends to 0 with $N \to \infty$. The first Borel-Cantelli lemma (chapter VIII, section 3) applies with obvious verbal changes, and it suffices to prove that $\Sigma \mathbf{P}\{\mathbf{V}_n \neq 0\}$ converges. Now

$$(7.13) \quad \mathbf{P}\{\mathbf{V}_n \neq 0\} = \sum_{|x_j| \geq n} f(x_j) \leq \frac{a_{n+1}}{n} + \frac{a_{n+2}}{n+1} + \frac{a_{n+3}}{n+2} + \ldots$$

and hence

$$(7.14) \quad \Sigma \mathbf{P}\{\mathbf{V}_n \neq 0\} \leq \sum_{n=1}^{\infty} \sum_{\nu=n}^{\infty} \frac{a_{\nu+1}}{\nu} = \sum_{\nu=1}^{\infty} \frac{a_{\nu+1}}{\nu} \sum_{n=1}^{\nu} 1 = \sum_{\nu} a_{\nu+1} < \infty,$$

as asserted.

8. PROBLEMS FOR SOLUTION

1. Prove that the law of large numbers applies in example (5.a) also when $\lambda \leq 0$. The central limit theorem holds if $\lambda \geq -\frac{1}{2}$.

2. Decide whether the law of large numbers and the central limit theorem hold for the sequences of mutually independent variables $\mathbf{X}_k$ with distributions defined as follows ($k \geq 1$):

(a) $\mathbf{P}\{\mathbf{X}_k = \pm 2^k\} = \frac{1}{2}$;

(b) $\mathbf{P}\{\mathbf{X}_k = \pm 2^k\} = 2^{-(2k+1)}$, $\qquad \mathbf{P}\{\mathbf{X}_k = 0\} = 1 - 2^{-2k}$;

(c) $\mathbf{P}\{\mathbf{X}_k = \pm k\} = \frac{1}{2}k^{-\frac{1}{2}}$, $\qquad \mathbf{P}\{\mathbf{X}_k = 0\} = 1 - k^{-\frac{1}{2}}$.

3. *Ljapunov's condition* (1901). Suppose that for some fixed $\delta > 0$ we have $\mathbf{E}(|\mathbf{X}_k|^{2+\delta}) = \lambda_k$ where $\lambda_k/s_k^2 < $ const. Show that Lindeberg's conditions are satisfied if $s_n \to \infty$.

4. Find sufficient conditions on $\{L_n\}$ for the weak law of large numbers and/or the central limit theorem to hold for the mutually independent variables $\{\mathbf{X}_n\}$, where $\{\mathbf{X}_k\}$ assumes the values

$$0, \quad \pm \frac{1}{2k+1} L_k, \quad \pm \frac{2}{2k+1} L_k, \quad \ldots, \quad \pm \frac{k}{2k+1} L_k,$$

each with probability $1/(2k+1)$.

5. Do the same problem if $\mathbf{X}_k$ assumes the values a_k, $-a_k$, and 0 with probabilities p_k, p_k and $1 - 2p_k$.

Note: *The following seven problems treat the weak law of large numbers for dependent variables.*

6. In problem V, 13 let $\mathbf{X}_k = 1$ if the kth throw results in red, and $\mathbf{X}_k = 0$ otherwise. Show that the law of large numbers does not apply.

7. Let the $\{\mathbf{X}_k\}$ be mutually independent and have a common distribution with mean μ and finite variance. If $\mathbf{S}_n = \mathbf{X}_1 + \ldots + \mathbf{X}_n$, prove that the law of large numbers does not hold for the sequence $\{\mathbf{S}_n\}$ but holds for $a_n\mathbf{S}_n$ if $na_n \to 0$.

8. Let $\{\mathbf{X}_k\}$ be a sequence of random variables such that $\mathbf{X}_k$ may depend on $\mathbf{X}_{k-1}$ and $\mathbf{X}_{k+1}$ but is independent of all other $\mathbf{X}_j$. Show that the law of large numbers holds, provided the $\mathbf{X}_k$ have bounded variances.

9. If the joint distribution of $(\mathbf{X}_1, \ldots, \mathbf{X}_n)$ is defined for every n so that the variances are bounded and all covariances are negative, the law of large numbers applies.

10. *Continuation.* Replace the condition $\mathrm{Cov}(\mathbf{X}_j, \mathbf{X}_k) \leq 0$ by the assumption that $\mathrm{Cov}(\mathbf{X}_j, \mathbf{X}_k) \to 0$ uniformly as $|j - k| \to \infty$. Prove that the law of large numbers holds.

11. If $|\mathbf{S}_n| < cn$ and $\mathrm{Var}(\mathbf{S}_n) > \alpha n^2$, then the law of large numbers does not apply to $\{\mathbf{X}_k\}$.

12. In the Polya urn scheme [example V(2.c)] let $\mathbf{X}_k$ equal 1 or 0 according to whether the kth ball drawn is black or red. Then $\mathbf{S}_n$ is the number of black balls in n drawings. Prove that the law of large numbers does not apply to $\{\mathbf{X}_k\}$. (*Hint:* Use problems 11 and IX, 30.)

---

13. The mutually independent random variables $\mathbf{X}_k$ assume the values $r = 2, 3, 4, \ldots$ with probability $p_r = c/(r^2 \log r)$ where c is a constant such that $\Sigma p_r = 1$. Show that the generalized law of large numbers (4.1) holds if we put $e_n = c \cdot n \log \log n$.

14. Let $\{\mathbf{X}_n\}$ be a sequence of mutually independent random variables such that $\mathbf{X}_n = \pm 1$ with probability $(1 - 2^{-n})/2$ and $\mathbf{X}_n = \pm 2^n$ with probability 2^{-n-1}. Prove that both the weak and the strong law of large numbers apply to $\{\mathbf{X}_k\}$. (*Note:* This shows that the condition (5.6) is not necessary.)

15. *Example of an unfavorable "fair" game.* Let the possible values of the gain at each trial be $0, 2, 2^2, 2^3, \ldots$; the probability of the gain being 2^k is

(8.1)
$$p_k = \frac{1}{2^k k(k+1)},$$

and the probability of 0 is $p_0 = 1 - (p_1 + p_2 + \ldots)$. The expected gain is

(8.2) $\mu = \Sigma 2^k p_k = (1 - \frac{1}{2}) + (\frac{1}{2} - \frac{1}{3}) + (\frac{1}{3} - \frac{1}{4}) + \ldots = 1.$

Assume that at each trial the player pays a unit amount as entrance fee, so that after n trials his net gain (or loss) is $S_n - n$. Show that for every $\epsilon > 0$ *the probability approaches unity that in n trials the player will have sustained a loss greater than* $(1 - \epsilon)n/\text{Log}_2\, n$, where $\text{Log}_2\, n$ denotes the logarithm to the base 2. In symbols, prove that

(8.3)
$$\mathbf{P}\left\{ S_n - n < -\frac{(1 - \epsilon)n}{\text{Log}_2\, n} \right\} \to 1,$$

Hint: Use the truncation method of section 4, but replace the bound $n\, \text{Log}\, n$ of (4.2) by $n/\text{Log}_2\, n$. Show that the probability that $\mathbf{U}_k = \mathbf{X}_k$ for all $k \leq n$ tends to 1 and prove that

(8.4)
$$\mathbf{P}\left\{ |\mathbf{U}_1 + \ldots + \mathbf{U}_n - n\mathbf{E}(\mathbf{U}_1)| < \frac{\epsilon n}{\text{Log}_2\, n} \right\} \to 1.$$

(8.5)
$$1 - \frac{1}{\text{Log}_2\, n} \geq \mathbf{E}(\mathbf{U}_1) \geq 1 - \frac{1 + \epsilon}{\text{Log}_2\, n}.$$

For details see the paper cited in footnote 5.

16. Let $\{\mathbf{X}_n\}$ be a sequence of mutually independent random variables with a common distribution. Suppose that the $\mathbf{X}_n$ do not have a finite expectation and let A be a positive constant. The probability is one that infinitely many among the events $|\mathbf{X}_n| > An$ occur.

17. *Converse to the strong law of large numbers.* Under the assumption of problem 16 there is probability one that $|\mathbf{S}_n| > An$ for infinitely many n.

18. *A converse to Kolmogorov's criterion.* If $\Sigma \sigma_k^2/k^2$ diverges, then there exists a sequence $\{\mathbf{X}_k\}$ of mutually independent random variables with $\text{Var}\{\mathbf{X}_k\} = \sigma_k^2$ for which the strong law of large numbers does not apply. (*Hint:* Prove first that the convergence of $\Sigma \mathbf{P}\{|\mathbf{X}_n| > \epsilon n\}$ is a necessary condition for the strong law to apply.)

CHAPTER XI

Integral Valued Variables. Generating Functions

1. GENERALITIES

Among discrete random variables those assuming only the integral values $k = 0, 1, 2, \ldots$ are of special importance. Their study is facilitated by the powerful method of generating functions which will later be recognized as a special case of the method of characteristic functions on which the theory of probability depends to a large extent. More generally, the subject of generating functions belongs to the domain of operational methods which are widely used in the theory of differential and integral equations. In the theory of probability generating functions have been used since DeMoivre and Laplace, but the power and the possibilities of the method are rarely fully utilized.

Definition. *Let a_0, a_1, a_2, $\ldots$ be a sequence of real numbers. If*

$$(1.1) \qquad A(s) = a_0 + a_1 s + a_2 s^2 + \ldots$$

converges in some interval $-s_0 < s < s_0$, then $A(s)$ is called the generating function of the sequence $\{a_j\}$.

The variable s itself has no significance. If the sequence $\{a_j\}$ is bounded, then a comparison with the geometric series shows that (1.1) converges at least for $|s| < 1$.

Examples. If $a_j = 1$ for all j, then $A(s) = 1/(1 - s)$. The generating function of the sequence $(0, 0, 1, 1, 1, \ldots)$ is $s^2/(1 - s)$. The sequence $a_j = 1/j!$ has the generating function e^s. For fixed n the sequence $a_j = \binom{n}{j}$ has the generating function $(1 + s)^n$. If $\mathbf{X}$ is the number scored in a throw of a perfect die, the probability distribution of $\mathbf{X}$ has the generating function $(s + s^2 + s^3 + s^4 + s^5 + s^6)/6$.

Let $\mathbf{X}$ be a random variable assuming the values 0, 1, 2, ... It will be convenient to have a notation both for the distribution of $\mathbf{X}$ and for its tails, and we shall write

(1.2) $$\mathbf{P}\{\mathbf{X} = j\} = p_j, \qquad \mathbf{P}\{\mathbf{X} > j\} = q_j.$$

Then

(1.3) $$q_k = p_{k+1} + p_{k+2} + \cdots, \qquad\qquad k \geq 0.$$

The generating functions of the sequences $\{p_j\}$ and $\{q_k\}$ are

(1.4) $$P(s) = p_0 + p_1 s + p_2 s^2 + p_3 s^3 + \cdots$$

(1.5) $$Q(s) = q_0 + q_1 s + q_2 s^2 + q_3 s^3 + \cdots.$$

As $P(1) = 1$, *the series for $P(s)$ converges absolutely at least for* $-1 \leq s \leq 1$. The coefficients of $Q(s)$ are less than unity, and so *the series for $Q(s)$ converges at least in the open interval* $-1 < s < 1$.

Theorem 1. *For* $-1 < s < 1$ *we have*

(1.6) $$Q(s) = \frac{1 - P(s)}{1 - s}.$$

Proof. The coefficient of s^n in $(1 - s) \cdot Q(s)$ equals $q_n - q_{n-1} = -p_n$ when $n \geq 1$, and equals $q_0 = p_1 + p_2 + \cdots = 1 - p_0$ when $n = 0$. Therefore $(1 - s) \cdot Q(s) = 1 - P(s)$ as asserted.

Next we examine the derivative

(1.7) $$P'(s) = \sum_{k=1}^{\infty} k p_k s^{k-1}.$$

The series converges at least for $-1 < s < 1$. For $s = 1$ the right side reduces formally to $\Sigma k p_k = \mathbf{E}(\mathbf{X})$. Whenever this expectation exists, the derivative $P'(s)$ will be continuous in the closed interval $-1 \leq s \leq 1$. If $\Sigma k p_k$ diverges, then $P'(s) \to \infty$ as $s \to 1$. In this case we say that $\mathbf{X}$ *has an infinite expectation* and write $P'(1) = \mathbf{E}(\mathbf{X}) = \infty$. (All quantities being positive, there is no danger in the use of the symbol ∞.) Applying the mean value theorem to the right side in (1.6), we see that $Q(s) = P'(\sigma)$ where σ is a point lying between s and 1. The function $Q(s)$ increases monotonically as $s \to 1$, and so $Q(s) \to \mathbf{E}(\mathbf{X})$ (finite or infinite). This proves

Theorem 2. *For* $\mathbf{E}(\mathbf{X})$ *we have the two expressions*

(1.8) $$\mathbf{E}(\mathbf{X}) = \sum_{j=1}^{\infty} j p_j = \sum_{k=0}^{\infty} q_k.$$

In terms of the generating functions

$$(1.9) \qquad\qquad \mathbf{E}(\mathbf{X}) = P'(1) = Q(1).$$

By differentiation of (1.7) and of the relation $P'(s) = Q(s) - (1 - s)Q'(s)$ we find in the same way

$$(1.10) \qquad \mathbf{E}(\mathbf{X}(\mathbf{X} - 1)) = \Sigma k(k - 1)p_k = P''(1) = 2Q'(1).$$

To obtain the variance of $\mathbf{X}$ we have to add $\mathbf{E}(\mathbf{X}) - \mathbf{E}^2(\mathbf{X})$ which leads us to

Theorem 3. *We have*

$$(1.11) \qquad \mathrm{Var}(\mathbf{X}) = P''(1) + P'(1) - P'^2(1) =$$
$$= 2Q'(1) + Q(1) - Q^2(1).$$

In the case of an infinite variance $P''(s) \to \infty$ as $s \to 1$.

Frequently the formulas (1.9) and (1.11) provide the simplest means to calculate $\mathbf{E}(\mathbf{X})$ and $\mathrm{Var}(\mathbf{X})$.

2. CONVOLUTIONS

Let $\mathbf{X}$ and $\mathbf{Y}$ be non-negative independent integral-valued random variables with probability distributions $\mathbf{P}\{\mathbf{X} = j\} = a_j$ and $\mathbf{P}\{\mathbf{Y} = j\} = b_j$. The event $(\mathbf{X} = j, \mathbf{Y} = k)$ has probability $a_j b_k$. The sum $\mathbf{S} = \mathbf{X} + \mathbf{Y}$ is a new random variable, and the event $\mathbf{S} = r$ is the union of the mutually exclusive events

$$(\mathbf{X}{=}0, \mathbf{Y}{=}r), \quad (\mathbf{X}{=}1, \mathbf{Y}{=}r{-}1), \quad (\mathbf{X}{=}2, \mathbf{Y}{=}r{-}2), \quad \ldots, \quad (\mathbf{X}{=}r, \mathbf{Y}{=}0).$$

Therefore the distribution $c_r = \mathbf{P}\{\mathbf{S} = r\}$ is given by

$$(2.1) \qquad c_r = a_0 b_r + a_1 b_{r-1} + a_2 b_{r-2} + \ldots + a_{r-1} b_1 + a_r b_0.$$

The operation (2.1), leading from the two sequences $\{a_k\}$ and $\{b_k\}$ to a new sequence $\{c_k\}$, occurs so frequently that it is convenient to introduce a special name and notation for it.

Definition. *Let $\{a_k\}$ and $\{b_k\}$ be any two number sequences (not necessarily probability distributions). The new sequence $\{c_r\}$ defined by (2.1) is called the convolution* [1] *of $\{a_k\}$ and $\{b_k\}$ and will be denoted by*

$$(2.2) \qquad\qquad \{c_k\} = \{a_k\} * \{b_k\}.$$

---

[1] Some writers prefer the German word *faltung*. The French equivalent is *composition*.

Examples. (a) If $a_k = b_k = 1$ for all $k \geq 0$, then $c_k = k + 1$. If $a_k = k$, $b_k = 1$, then $c_k = 1 + 2 + \ldots + k = k(k + 1)/2$. Finally, if $a_0 = a_1 = \frac{1}{2}$, $a_k = 0$ for $k \geq 2$, then $c_k = (b_k + b_{k-1})/2$, etc.

The sequences $\{a_k\}$ and $\{b_k\}$ have generating functions $A(s) = \Sigma a_k s^k$ and $B(s) = \Sigma b_k s^k$. The product $A(s)B(s)$ can be obtained by termwise multiplication of the power series for $A(s)$ and $B(s)$. Collecting terms with equal powers of s, we find that the coefficient c_r of s^r in the expansion of $A(s)B(s)$ is given by (2.1). We have thus the

Theorem. *If* $\{a_k\}$ *and* $\{b_k\}$ *are sequences with generating functions* $A(s)$ *and* $B(s)$, *and* $\{c_k\}$ *is their convolution, then the generating function* $C(s) = \Sigma c_k s^k$ *is the product*

$$(2.3) \qquad\qquad\qquad C(s) = A(s)B(s).$$

If **X** *and* **Y** *are non-negative integral-valued mutually independent random variables with generating functions* $A(s)$ *and* $B(s)$, *then their sum* **X** + **Y** *has the generating function* $A(s)B(s)$.

Let now $\{a_k\}$, $\{b_k\}$, $\{c_k\}$, $\{d_k\}$, $\ldots$ be any sequences. We can form the convolution $\{a_k\} * \{b_k\}$, and then the convolution of this new sequence with $\{c_k\}$, etc. The generating function of $\{a_k\} * \{b_k\} * \{c_k\} * \{d_k\}$ is $A(s)B(s)C(s)D(s)$, and this fact shows that the order in which the convolutions are performed is immaterial. For example, $\{a_k\} * \{b_k\} * \{c_k\} = \{c_k\} * \{b_k\} * \{a_k\}$, etc. *Thus the convolution is an associative and commutative operation* (exactly as the summation of random variables).

In the study of sums of independent random variables $\mathbf{X}_n$ the special case where the $\mathbf{X}_n$ have a common distribution is of particular interest. *If* $\{a_j\}$ *is the common probability distribution of the* $\mathbf{X}_n$, *then the distribution of* $\mathbf{S}_n = \mathbf{X}_1 + \ldots + \mathbf{X}_n$ *will be denoted by* $\{a_j\}^{n*}$. Thus

$$(2.4) \qquad \{a_j\}^{2*} = \{a_j\} * \{a_j\}, \qquad \{a_j\}^{3*} = \{a_j\}^{2*} * \{a_j\}, \ldots$$

and generally

$$(2.5) \qquad\qquad\qquad \{a_j\}^{n*} = \{a_j\}^{(n-1)*} * \{a_j\}.$$

In words, $\{a_j\}^{n*}$ *is the sequence of numbers whose generating function is* $A^n(s)$. In particular, $\{a_j\}^{1*}$ *is the same as* $\{a_j\}$, *and* $\{a_j\}^{0*}$ *is defined as the sequence whose generating function is* $A^0(s) = 1$, *that is, the sequence* $(1, 0, 0, 0, \ldots)$.

Examples. (b) *Binomial distribution.* The generating function of the binomial distribution $b(k; n, p) = \binom{n}{k} p^k q^{n-k}$ is

(2.6) $$\sum_{k=0}^{n} \binom{n}{k} (ps)^k q^{n-k} = (q + ps)^n.$$

The fact that this generating function is the nth power of $q + ps$ shows that $\{b(k; n, p)\}$ is the distribution of a sum $\mathbf{S}_n = \mathbf{X}_1 + \ldots + \mathbf{X}_n$ of n independent random variables with the common generating function $q + ps$; each variable $\mathbf{X}_j$ assumes the value 0 with probability q and the value 1 with probability p. Thus

(2.7) $$\{b(k; n, p)\} = \{b(k; 1, p)\}^{n*}.$$

The representation $\mathbf{S}_n = \mathbf{X}_1 + \ldots + \mathbf{X}_n$ has already been used [e.g., in examples IX(3.a) and IX(5.a)]. The preceding argument may be reversed to obtain a new derivation of the binomial distribution. The multiplicative property $(q + ps)^m (q + ps)^n = (q + ps)^{m+n}$ shows also that

(2.8) $$\{b(k; m, p)\} * \{b(k; n, p)\} = \{b(k; m+n, p)\}$$

which is the same as formula VI(10.4). Differentiation of $(q + ps)^n$ leads also to a simple proof that $\mathbf{E}(\mathbf{S}_n) = np$ and $\mathrm{Var}(\mathbf{S}_n) = npq$.

(c) *Poisson distribution.* The generating function of the distribution $p(k; \lambda) = e^{-\lambda} \lambda^k / k!$ is

(2.9) $$\sum_{k=0}^{\infty} e^{-\lambda} \frac{(\lambda s)^k}{k!} = e^{-\lambda + \lambda s}.$$

It follows that

(2.10) $$\{p(k; \lambda)\} * \{p(k; \mu)\} = \{p(k; \lambda + \mu)\},$$

which is the same as formula VI(10.5). By differentiation we find again that both mean and variance of the Poisson distribution equal λ [cf. example IX(4.c)].

(d) *Geometric and negative binomial distributions.* Let $\mathbf{X}$ be a random variable with the geometric distribution

(2.11) $$\mathbf{P}\{\mathbf{X} = k\} = q^k p, \qquad\qquad k = 0, 1, 2, \ldots$$

where p and q are positive constants with $p + q = 1$. The corresponding generating function is

(2.12) $$p \sum_{k=0}^{\infty} (qs)^k = \frac{p}{1 - qs}.$$

Using the results of section 1 we find easily $\mathbf{E}(\mathbf{X}) = q/p$ and $\mathrm{Var}(\mathbf{X}) = q/p^2$, in agreement with the findings in example IX(3.c).

In a sequence of Bernoulli trials the probability that the *first success* occurs after exactly k failures (i.e., at the $k+1$st trial) is $q^k p$, and so $\mathbf{X}$ may be interpreted as the *waiting time for the first success*. Strictly speaking, such an interpretation refers to an infinite sample space, and the advantage of the formal definition (2.11) and the terminology of random variables is that we need not worry about the structure of the original sample space. The same is true of *the waiting time for the rth success*. If $\mathbf{X}_k$ denotes the number of failures following the $(k-1)$st and preceding the kth success, then $\mathbf{S}_r = \mathbf{X}_1 + \mathbf{X}_2 + \ldots + \mathbf{X}_r$ is the total number of failures preceding the rth success (and $\mathbf{S}_r + r$ is the number of trials up to and including the rth success). The notion of Bernoulli trials requires that the $\mathbf{X}_k$ should be mutually independent with the same distribution (2.11), and we can *define* the $\mathbf{X}_k$ by this property. Then $\mathbf{S}_r$ has the generating function

$$(2.13) \qquad \left(\frac{p}{1 - qs}\right)^r.$$

and the binomial expansion II(8.7) shows at once that the coefficient of s^k equals

$$(2.14) \qquad f(k; r, p) = \binom{-r}{k} p^r (-q)^k, \qquad k = 0, 1, 2, \ldots.$$

It follows that $\mathbf{P}\{\mathbf{S}_r = k\} = f(k; r, p)$, in agreement with the formula for the number of failures preceding the rth success derived in chapter VI, section 8. We can restate this result by saying that *the distribution $\{f(k; r, p)\}$ is the r-fold convolution of the geometric distribution with itself*, in symbols

$$(2.15) \qquad \{f(k; r, p)\} = \{q^k p\}^{r*}.$$

So far we have considered r as an integer. It will be recalled from chapter VI, section 8, that $\{f(k; r, p)\}$ defines the *negative binomial distribution* also when $r > 0$ is not an integer. The generating function is still defined by (2.13), and we see that for arbitrary $r > 0$ the *mean and variance of the negative binomial distribution are rq/p and rq/p^2 and that*

$$(2.16) \qquad \{f(k; r_1, p)\} * \{f(k; r_2, p)\} = \{f(k; r_1 + r_2, p)\}.$$

3. APPLICATION TO FIRST PASSAGE AND RECURRENCE TIMES IN BERNOULLI TRIALS

This section is inserted mainly for illustration. The results will be derived by different methods (see example XIII(3.b) and problem XIII.7; chapter XIV, section 5, and problems 11 and 15–17). For the special case $p = \frac{1}{2}$ the results are contained in chapter III. However, the following derivation provides an excellent example for the method of generating functions; and, in addition, it is instructive to compare the different approaches.

We consider Bernoulli trials with the probability of success p and put $\mathbf{X}_k = 1$ if the kth trial results in success, $\mathbf{X}_k = -1$ otherwise. Then $\mathbf{S}_n = \mathbf{X}_1 + \ldots + \mathbf{X}_n$ is the accumulated excess of successes over failures in n trials. In the more picturesque gambling language $\mathbf{S}_n$ is called Peter's net gain in the first n trials. It is convenient to put $\mathbf{S}_0 = 0$.

(a) First Passages

Suppose that Peter decides to quit at the first moment when he has a *positive* net gain (necessarily of a unit amount). A direct enumeration of all possibilities reveals that this will happen at trials number 1, 3, 5, 7, ... with probabilities p, qp^2, $2q^2p^3$, $5q^3p^4$, ... but a general rule is not discernible. The sum σ of these probabilities equals *the probability that Peter's net gain will ever become positive.* Not even this quantity can be obtained by a direct argument, but we shall show that $\sigma = 1$ *if* $p \geq q$ *and* $\sigma = p/q$ *if* $p \leq q$. Waiting for the net gain to increase to x units amounts to waiting x times in succession for an increase of a unit amount. *The probability that Peter's gain will ever reach the level of x units therefore equals* σ^x. We proceed to calculate σ and the probabilities $\lambda_n^{(x)}$ that it will take exactly n trials until the net gain reaches the level x for the first time.

In more formal language *we seek the probability* λ_n *that* $\mathbf{S}_1 \leq 0$, $\mathbf{S}_2 \leq 0$, ..., $\mathbf{S}_{n-1} \leq 0$, $\mathbf{S}_n = 1$. More generally, we shall say that *a first passage through the point $x > 0$ occurs at the nth trial if*

$$(3.1) \qquad \mathbf{S}_1 < x, \qquad \mathbf{S}_2 < x, \ldots, \mathbf{S}_{n-1} < x, \qquad \mathbf{S}_n = x.$$

The probability of this event will be denoted by $\lambda_n^{(x)}$, *and for brevity we put* $\lambda_n^{(1)} = \lambda_n$. In gambling (3.1) signifies that Peter's net gain reaches the level $x > 0$ for the first time at the nth trial. The term first passage is suggested by applications to diffusion theory.

Suppose now that the first passage through $x = 1$ occurs at the rth trial. The later trials produce the cumulative net gains $\mathbf{S'}_1 = \mathbf{X}_{r+1}$,

$S'_2 = X_{r+1} + X_{r+2}, \ldots$, which are independent of the first r trials. A first passage through $x = 2$ at time n occurs if, and only if, $S'_1 \leq 0$, $\ldots, S'_{n-r-1} \leq 0$, $S'_{n-r} = 1$, and the probability of this event is λ_{n-r}. In other words, the probability that the first passages through $x = 1$ and $x = 2$ occur at trials number r and $n > r$ is $\lambda_r \lambda_{n-r}$. We conclude that the first passage through $x = 2$ at time n has probability

$$(3.2) \qquad \lambda_n^{(2)} = \lambda_1 \lambda_{n-1} + \lambda_2 \lambda_{n-2} + \ldots + \lambda_{n-1} \lambda_1.$$

Remembering that $\lambda_0 = 0$, we see that $\{\lambda_n^{(2)}\} = \{\lambda_n\} * \{\lambda_n\}$ is the convolution of $\{\lambda_n\}$ with itself. Introducing the generating functions

$$(3.3) \qquad \lambda(s) = \sum_{n=1}^{\infty} \lambda_n s^n, \qquad \lambda^{(x)}(s) = \sum_{n=1}^{\infty} \lambda_n^{(x)} s^n$$

we have $\lambda^{(2)}(s) = \lambda^2(s)$ and, repeating the argument by induction,

$$(3.4) \qquad \lambda^{(x)}(s) = \lambda^x(s) \qquad\qquad x > 0.$$

It follows that our task has been reduced to finding the probabilities λ_n for the first passage through $x = 1$. If $X_1 = 1$ then this first passage takes place at the first trial. If $X_1 = -1$ the cumulative net gains X_2, $X_2 + X_3$, $\ldots$ after the first trial must increase by two units, and we conclude that

$$(3.5) \qquad \lambda_1 = p, \qquad \lambda_n = q\lambda_{n-1}^{(2)}, \qquad\qquad n > 1.$$

This is obviously equivalent to

$$(3.6) \qquad \lambda(s) = ps + qs\lambda^2(s),$$

which is a quadratic equation for $\lambda(s)$. Of the two roots one is unbounded near $s = 0$, and the unique bounded solution of (3.6) is

$$(3.7) \qquad \lambda(s) = \frac{1 - \{1 - 4pqs^2\}^{\frac{1}{2}}}{2qs}.$$

We have thus found the generating functions (3.4) of all first passage times. The binomial expansion II(8.7) enables us to write down the coefficients

$$(3.8) \qquad \lambda_{2m-1} = \frac{1}{2q}\binom{\frac{1}{2}}{m}(4pq)^m(-1)^{m-1}, \qquad \lambda_{2m} = 0$$

but we are not interested in explicit expressions; it is more instructive to extract the relevant information directly from the generating function.

First note that

$$(3.9) \qquad \lambda(1) = \frac{1 - |p - q|}{2q}$$

and so $\lambda(1) = 1$ if $p \geq q$ but $\lambda(1) = p/q$ if $p < q$. We conclude that $\Sigma \lambda_k$ equals 1 or p/q, *whichever is smaller*; when q is larger than p (a game unfavorable to Peter), *the probability that the sums $\mathbf{S}_n$ remain negative forever equals $(q - p)/q$.*

In the symmetric case $p = q = \frac{1}{2}$ and $\Sigma \lambda_k = 1$; in a prolonged sequence of coin tossings Peter is sure that he will sooner or later realize a positive gain. The question is: How long will it take? From $\lambda'(1) = \infty$ we conclude that *in coin tossing the number of trials preceding the first passage through 1 has infinite expectation.* If Peter hopes to realize a unit gain by participating in a coin-tossing game and quitting at the first opportune moment, he should expect that an enormous number of trials (and, in consequence, an enormous capital) will be required. Needless to say that the infinite expectation of the first-passage time is closely connected with the unexpected characteristics of the fluctuations in coin tossing discussed at great length in chapter III.

Note. We are now in possession of an explicit formula for λ_n but there remains the task to calculate the first passage probabilities $\lambda_n^{(x)}$ from (3.3) or (3.4). The standard analytic procedure for that consists in applying complex variable methods. It is therefore interesting to remark that simple applications of the reflection principle enabled us in theorem 2 of chapter III, section 4, to write down an explicit expression for $\lambda_n^{(x)}$ at least in the symmetric case $p = q = \frac{1}{2}$. (With the notations used in chapter III we have $f_{2n}^{(x)} = \lambda_{2n-x}^{(x)}$.) A glance at (3.4) and (3.7) reveals the pleasing feature that for arbitrary p the probability $\lambda_n^{(x)}$ equals the corresponding probability in the symmetric case multiplied by $(4pq)^{\frac{1}{2}n}(p/q)^{\frac{1}{2}x}$. It is instructive to follow this case in detail and realize that *a most elementary combinatorial argument enabled us to solve a difficult technical problem and that it replaces a formidable analytical apparatus.*

(b) Recurrence Times

We shall say that *a first return to zero occurs at the nth trial if* $\mathbf{S}_1 \neq 0$, $\mathbf{S}_2 \neq 0$, ..., $\mathbf{S}_{n-1} \neq 0$, $\mathbf{S}_n = 0$ (i.e., if the first equalization of the accumulated numbers of successes and failures occurs). Let f_n be the probability of this event. (Clearly $f_{2n+1} = 0$ for all n. The first few f_{2n} are easily found by direct enumeration: $f_2 = 2pq$, $f_4 = 2p^2q^2$, $f_6 = 4p^3q^3$, $f_8 = 10p^4q^4$.)

Let $\lambda_n^{(-1)}$ be the probability of a first passage through $x = -1$ at the nth trial; in other words, $\lambda_n^{(-1)}$ is the quantity obtained from $\lambda_n^{(1)} = \lambda_n$ by interchanging p and q. As above we note that a return to zero at the nth trial is equivalent to a first passage through either $+1$

or -1 in the $n - 1$ trials following the first trial, and we conclude

$$(3.10) \qquad f_n = q\lambda_{n-1} + p\lambda_{n-1}^{(-1)}.$$

Multiply by s^n and add. Observing that the generating functions of $\{\lambda_n^{(-1)}\}$ and $\{\lambda_n\}$ are obtained from each other by interchanging p and q, we get

$$(3.11) \qquad F(s) = \Sigma f_n s^n = 1 - (1 - 4pqs^2)^{\frac{1}{2}}.$$

We conclude: *The probability Σf_n that the accumulated numbers of successes and failures will ever equalize is $1 - |p - q|$.*

In the special case $p = q = \frac{1}{2}$ we find that $\Sigma f_n = 1$ *but the probability distribution $\{f_n\}$ has infinite expectation.* The probabilities f_{2n} were calculated, by entirely different methods, in chapter III, section 4. It is illuminating to note that several theorems of chapter III can be obtained without calculation and without explicit expressions for f_{2n} directly from the generating function $F(s)$. (See problems 6–10.)

Note. Conceptually, the problem of this section is analogous to the waiting time problem of example (2.d). In the sample space of *infinite sequences* of Bernoulli trials we may consider the random variable $\mathbf{N}_r$ defined as the number of trials from the first passage through $r - 1$ up to and including the first passage through r. The $\{\mathbf{N}_r\}$ are mutually independent variables with the common generating function $\lambda(s)$. The sum $\mathbf{N}^{(x)} = \mathbf{N}_1 + \ldots + \mathbf{N}_x$ is the waiting time for the first passage through x and has the generating function $\lambda^x(s)$. We have formally avoided referring to infinite sample spaces by *defining* the random variables in terms of their distributions. From an analytic point of view the theory is rigorous and self-contained, but for the probabilistic interpretation and for the intuition it is preferable to keep the natural infinite sample space in mind.

4. PARTIAL FRACTION EXPANSIONS

Given a generating function $P(s) = \Sigma p_k s^k$ the coefficients p_k can be found by differentiations from the obvious formula $p_k = P^{(k)}(0)/k!$. In practice it may be impossible to obtain explicit expressions and, anyhow, such expressions are frequently so complicated that reasonable approximations are preferable. The most common method for obtaining such approximations is based on partial fraction expansions. It is known from the theory of complex variables that a large class of functions admits of such expansions, but we shall limit our exposition to the simple case of *rational functions*.

Suppose then that the generating function is of the form

$$(4.1) \qquad P(s) = \frac{U(s)}{V(s)}$$

where $U(s)$ and $V(s)$ are polynomials without common roots. For simplicity let us first assume that the degree of $U(s)$ is lower than the degree of $V(s)$, say m. Moreover, suppose that the equation $V(s) = 0$ has m distinct (real or imaginary) roots $s_1, s_2, \ldots, s_m$. Then

$$(4.2) \qquad V(s) = (s - s_1)(s - s_2) \cdots (s - s_m),$$

and it is known from algebra that $P(s)$ can be decomposed into *partial fractions*

$$(4.3) \qquad P(s) = \frac{\rho_1}{s_1 - s} + \frac{\rho_2}{s_2 - s} + \ldots + \frac{\rho_m}{s_m - s}$$

where $\rho_1, \rho_2, \ldots, \rho_m$ are constants. To find ρ_1 multiply (4.3) by $s_1 - s$; as $s \to s_1$ the product $(s_1 - s)P(s)$ tends to ρ_1. On the other hand, from (4.1) and (4.2) we get

$$(4.4) \qquad (s_1 - s)P(s) = \frac{-U(s)}{(s - s_2)(s - s_3) \cdots (s - s_m)}.$$

As $s \to s_1$ the numerator tends to $-U(s_1)$ and the denominator to $(s_1 - s_2)(s_1 - s_3) \ldots (s_1 - s_m)$, which is the same as $V'(s_1)$. Thus $\rho_1 = -U(s_1)/V'(s_1)$. The same argument applies to all roots, so that for $k \le m$

$$(4.5) \qquad \rho_k = \frac{-U(s_k)}{V'(s_k)}.$$

Unfortunately, extensive numerical calculation is usually required to put (4.1) into the form (4.3). However, once the expansion (4.3) is obtained, we can easily derive an exact expression for the coefficient of s^n in $P(s)$. Write

$$(4.6) \qquad \frac{1}{s_k - s} = \frac{1}{s_k} \cdot \frac{1}{1 - s/s_k}.$$

For $|s| < |s_k|$ we expand the last fraction into a geometric series

$$(4.7) \qquad \frac{1}{1 - s/s_k} = 1 + \frac{s}{s_k} + \left(\frac{s}{s_k}\right)^2 + \left(\frac{s}{s_k}\right)^3 + \ldots.$$

Introducing these expressions into (4.3), we find for the *coefficient p_n of s^n*

$$(4.8) \qquad p_n = \frac{\rho_1}{s_1^{n+1}} + \frac{\rho_2}{s_2^{n+1}} + \ldots + \frac{\rho_m}{s_m^{n+1}}.$$

Thus, to get p_n we have first to find the roots $s_1, \ldots, s_m$ of the denominator and then to determine the coefficients $\rho_1, \ldots, \rho_m$ from (4.5).

In (4.8) we have an *exact* expression for the probability p_n. The labor involved in calculating all m roots is usually prohibitive, and therefore formula (4.8) is primarily of theoretical interest. Fortunately a single term in (4.8) almost always provides a satisfactory approximation. In fact, suppose that s_1 is a root which is *smaller* in absolute value than all other roots. Then the first denominator in (4.8) is smallest. Clearly, as n increases, the proportionate contributions of the other terms decrease and the first term preponderates. In other words, *if s_1 is a root of $V(s) = 0$ which is smaller in absolute value than all other roots, then, as $n \to \infty$,*

$$(4.9) \qquad\qquad p_n \sim \frac{\rho_1}{s_1^{n+1}}$$

(the sign $\sim$ indicating that the ratio of the two sides tends to 1). Usually this formula provides surprisingly good approximations even for relatively small values of n. The main advantage of (4.9) lies in the fact that it requires the computation of only one root of an algebraic equation.

It is easy to remove the restrictions under which we have derived the asymptotic formula (4.9). To begin with, the degree of the numerator in (4.1) may exceed the degree m of the denominator. Let $U(s)$ be of degree $m + r$ $(r \geq 0)$; a division reduces $P(s)$ to a polynomial of degree r plus a fraction $U_1(s)/V(s)$ in which $U_1(s)$ is a polynomial of a degree lower than m. The polynomial affects only the first $r + 1$ terms of the distribution $\{p_n\}$, and $U_1(s)/V(s)$ can be expanded into partial fractions as explained above. Thus (4.9) remains true. Secondly, the restriction that $V(s)$ should have only simple roots is unnecessary. It is known from algebra that every rational function admits of an expansion into partial fractions. If s_k is a double root of $V(s)$, then the partial fraction expansion (4.3) will contain an additional term of the form $a/(s - s_k)^2$, and this will contribute a term of the form $a(n + 1)s_k^{-(n+2)}$ to the exact expression (4.8) for p_n. However, this does not affect the asymptotic expansion (4.9), provided only that s_1 is a simple root. We note this result for future reference as a

Theorem. *If $P(s)$ is a rational function with a simple root s_1 of the denominator which is smaller in absolute value than all other roots, then the coefficient p_n of s^n is given asymptotically by $p_n \sim \rho_1 s_1^{-(n+1)}$, where ρ_1 is defined in (4.5).*

A similar asymptotic expansion exists also in the case where s_1 is a multiple root. (See problem 25.)

Examples. (a) Let a_n be the probability that n Bernoulli trials result in an *even number of successes*. This event occurs if an initial failure at the first trial is followed by an even number of successes or if an initial success is followed by an odd number. Therefore

$$(4.10) \qquad a_n = q a_{n-1} + p(1 - a_{n-1}), \qquad a_0 = 1.$$

Multiplying by s^n and adding we get the relation $A(s) - 1 = qsA(s) + ps(1 - s)^{-1} - psA(s)$ for the generating function $A(s)$. Hence

$$(4.11) \quad 2A(s) = \{1 - s\}^{-1} + \{1 - (q - p)s\}^{-1}, \quad 2a_n = 1 + (q - p)^n.$$

Observe that the last formula is in every way preferable to the obvious answer $a_n = b(0; n, p) + b(2; n, p) + \ldots$.

(b) Let q_n be the probability that in n tosses of an ideal coin no run of three consecutive heads appears. (Note that $\{q_n\}$ is not a probability distribution; if p_n is the probability that the first run of three consecutive heads ends at the nth trial, then $\{p_n\}$ is a probability distribution, and q_n represents its "tails," $q_n = p_{n+1} + p_{n+2} + \ldots$.)

We can easily show that q_n satisfies the recurrence formula

$$(4.12) \qquad q_n = \tfrac{1}{2} q_{n-1} + \tfrac{1}{4} q_{n-2} + \tfrac{1}{8} q_{n-3}.$$

In fact, the event that n trials produce no sequence HHH can occur only when the trials begin with T, HT, or HHT. The probabilities that the following trials lead to no run HHH are q_{n-1}, q_{n-2}, and q_{n-3}, respectively, and the right side of (4.12) therefore contains the probabilities of the three mutually exclusive ways in which the event "no run HHH" can occur.

Evidently $q_0 = q_1 = q_2 = 1$, and hence the q_n can be calculated successively from (4.12). To obtain the generating function $Q(s) = \Sigma q_n s^n$ we multiply both sides by s^n and add. We get

$$Q(s) - 1 - s - s^2 = \frac{s}{2}\{Q(s) - 1 - s\} + \frac{s^2}{4}\{Q(s) - 1\} + \frac{s^3}{8}Q(s)$$

or

$$(4.13) \qquad Q(s) = \frac{2s^2 + 4s + 8}{8 - 4s - 2s^2 - s^3}.$$

The denominator has the root $s_1 = 1.0873778\ldots$ and two complex roots. For $|s| < s_1$ we have $|4s + 2s^2 + s^3| < 4s_1 + 2s_1{}^2 + s_1{}^3 = 8$, and the same inequality holds also when $|s| = s_1$ unless $s = s_1$. Hence the other two roots exceed s_1 in absolute value. Thus, from (4.9)

$$(4.14) \qquad q_n \sim \frac{1.236840}{(1.0873778)^{n+1}},$$

where the numerator equals $(2s_1^2 + 4s_1 + 8)/(4 + 4s_1 + 3s_1^2)$. This formula gives remarkably good approximations even for small values of n. It approximates $q_3 = 0.875$ by 0.8847 and $q_4 = 0.8125$ by 0.81360. The percentage error decreases steadily, and $q_{12} = 0.41626\ldots$ is given correct to five decimal places.

5. BIVARIATE GENERATING FUNCTIONS

For a pair of integral-valued random variables $\mathbf{X}$, $\mathbf{Y}$ with a joint distribution of the form

$$(5.1) \qquad \mathbf{P}\{\mathbf{X} = j, \mathbf{Y} = k\} = p_{jk} \qquad j, k = 0, 1, \ldots$$

we define a generating function depending on two variables

$$(5.2) \qquad P(s_1, s_2) = \sum_{j,k} p_{jk} s_1^j s_2^k.$$

Such generating functions will be called bivariate for short.

The considerations of the first two sections apply without essential modifications, and it will suffice to point out three properties evident from (5.2):

(a) *The generating function of the marginal distributions* $\mathbf{P}\{\mathbf{X} = j\}$ *and* $\mathbf{P}\{\mathbf{Y} = k\}$ *are* $A(s) = P(s, 1)$ *and* $B(s) = P(1, s)$.

(b) *The generating function of* $\mathbf{X} + \mathbf{Y}$ *is* $P(s, s)$.

(c) *The variables* $\mathbf{X}$ *and* $\mathbf{Y}$ *are independent if, and only if,* $P(s_1, s_2) = A(s_1) B(s_2)$ *for all* s_1, s_2.

Examples. (a) *Bivariate Poisson distribution.* It is obvious that

$$(5.3) \qquad P(s_1, s_2) = e^{-a_1 - a_2 - b + a_1 s_1 + a_2 s_2 + b s_1 s_2}, \qquad a_i > 0, b > 0$$

has a power-series expansion with positive coefficients adding up to unity. Accordingly $P(s_1, s_2)$ represents the generating function of a bivariate probability distribution. The marginal distributions are Poisson distributions with mean $a_1 + b$ and $a_2 + b$, respectively, but the sum $\mathbf{X} + \mathbf{Y}$ has the generating function $e^{-a_1 - a_2 - b + (a_1 + a_2)s + b s^2}$ and is *not* a Poisson variable. (It is a compound Poisson distribution; see chapter XII, section 2.)

(b) *Multinomial distributions.* Consider a sequence of n independent trials, each of which results in E_0, E_1, or E_2 with respective probabilities p_0, p_1, p_2. If $\mathbf{X}_i$ is the number of occurrences of E_i, then $(\mathbf{X}_1, \mathbf{X}_2)$ has a trinomial distribution with generating function $(p_0 + p_1 s_1 + p_2 s_2)^n$.

* 6. THE CONTINUITY THEOREM

We know from chapter VI that the Poisson distribution $\{e^{-\lambda}\lambda^k/k!\}$ is the limiting form of the binomial distribution with the probability p depending on n in such a way that $np \to \lambda$ as $n \to \infty$. Then $b(k; n, p) \to e^{-\lambda}\lambda^k/k!$. The generating function of $\{b(k; n, p)\}$ is $(q + ps)^n = \{1 - \lambda(1 - s)/n\}^n$. Taking logarithms, we see directly that this generating function tends to $e^{-\lambda(1-s)}$, which is the generating function of the Poisson distribution. We shall show that this situation prevails in general; a sequence of probability distributions converges to a limiting distribution if and only if the corresponding generating functions converge. Unfortunately, this theorem is of limited applicability, since the most interesting limiting forms of discrete distributions are continuous distributions (for example, the normal distribution appears as a limiting form of the binomial distribution).

Continuity Theorem. *Suppose that for every fixed n the sequence* $a_{0,n}, a_{1,n}, a_{2,n}, \ldots$ *is a probability distribution, that is,*

$$(6.1) \qquad a_{k,n} \geq 0, \qquad \sum_{k=0}^{\infty} a_{k,n} = 1.$$

In order that for every fixed k

$$(6.2) \qquad a_{k,n} \to a_k$$

as $n \to \infty$, it is necessary and sufficient that for every s with $0 \leq s < 1$

$$(6.3) \qquad A_n(s) \to A(s).$$

Here

$$(6.4) \qquad A_n(s) = \sum_{k=0}^{\infty} a_{k,n}s^k, \qquad A(s) = \sum_{k=0}^{\infty} a_k s^k$$

denote the corresponding generating functions.

Note. If (6.2) holds, then automatically $0 \leq a_k < 1$ and $\Sigma a_k \leq 1$. The generating function $A(s)$ exists therefore at least for $|s| \leq 1$. However, the limiting sequence $\{a_k\}$ is not necessarily a probability distribution; for example, if the first n terms of the distribution $\{a_{k,n}\}$ vanish, then the limiting sequence vanishes identically. For $\{a_k\}$ to be a probability distribution it is necessary and sufficient that $\Sigma a_k = 1$ or $A(1) = 1$.

---

* The contents of this section will not be used in the sequel.

Proof.[2] First, suppose that (6.2) holds. For fixed s $(0 < s < 1)$ and fixed ϵ we can choose r so that $s^r/(1-s) < \epsilon$. Then

$$(6.5) \qquad |A_n(s) - A(s)| \le \sum_{k=0}^{r} |a_{k,n} - a_k| s^k + 2\epsilon.$$

The sum on the right contains only finitely many terms, each of which tends to zero. Hence $|A_n(s) - A(s)|$ is arbitrarily small for n sufficiently large. Next, assume that (6.3) holds. We use the well-known fact [3] that it is always possible to find a subsequence $\{a_{k,n}\}$ of the given sequence of distributions which converges. If (6.2) were not true, then it would be possible to extract two subsequences converging to two different limiting sequences $\{a_k{}^*\}$ and $\{a_k{}^{**}\}$, and the corresponding subsequences of $\{A_n(s)\}$ would converge to $A^*(s) = \Sigma a_k{}^* s^k$ and $A^{**}(s) = \Sigma a_k{}^{**} s^k$, respectively. However, this is impossible in view of the assumption (6.3). Therefore (6.3) implies (6.2).

Examples. (a) *The negative binomial distribution.* We saw in example (2.*d*) that the generating function of the distribution $\{f(k; r, p)\}$ is $p^r(1 - qs)^{-r}$. Now let λ be fixed, and let $p \to 1$, $q \to 0$, so that $q = \lambda/r$. Then

$$(6.6) \qquad \left(\frac{p}{1-qs}\right)^r = \left(\frac{1-\lambda/r}{1-\lambda s/r}\right)^r.$$

Passing to logarithms, we see that the right side tends to $e^{-\lambda + \lambda s}$, which is the generating function of the Poisson distribution $\{e^{-\lambda}\lambda^k/k!\}$. Hence *if* $r \to \infty$ *and* $rq \to \lambda$, *then*

$$(6.7) \qquad f(k; r, p) \to e^{-\lambda}\frac{\lambda^k}{k!}.$$

(b) *Bernoulli trials with variable probabilities.* Consider n independent trials such that the kth trial results in success with probability p_k and in failure with probability $q_k = 1 - p_k$. The number $\mathbf{S}_n$ of successes can be written as the sum $\mathbf{S}_n = \mathbf{X}_1 + \ldots + \mathbf{X}_n$ of n mutually independent random variables $\mathbf{X}_k$ with the distributions $\mathbf{P}\{\mathbf{X}_k = 0\} = q_k$,

---

[2] The theorem is a special case of the continuity theorem for Laplace-Stieltjes transforms, and the proof follows the general pattern. In the literature the continuity theorem for generating functions is usually stated and proved under unnecessary restrictions.

[3] This is easily established by the "method of diagonals" due to G. Cantor and found in all books on set theory. The statement is, incidentally, a special case of a well-known theorem of Helly.

$\mathbf{P}\{\mathbf{X}_k = 1\} = p_k$. The generating function of $\mathbf{X}_k$ is $q_k + p_k s$, and hence the generating function of $\mathbf{S}_n$

(6.8) $P(s) = (q_1 + p_1 s)(q_2 + p_2 s) \cdots (q_n + p_n s).$

As an application of this scheme let us assume that each house in a city has a small probability p_k of burning on a given day. The sum $p_1 + \ldots + p_n$ is the expected number of fires in the city, n being the number of houses. We have seen in chapter VI that if all p_k are equal and if the houses are stochastically independent, then the number of fires is a random variable whose distribution is near the Poisson distribution. We show now that this conclusion remains valid also under the more realistic assumption that the probabilities p_k are not equal. This result should increase our confidence in the Poisson distribution as an adequate description of phenomena which are the cumulative effect of many improbable events ("successes"). Accidents and telephone calls are typical examples.

We use the now familiar model of an increasing number n of variables where the probabilities p_k depend on n in such a way that the largest p_k tends to zero, but the sum $p_1 + p_2 + \ldots + p_n = \lambda$ remains constant. Then from (6.8)

(6.9) $\log P(s) = \sum_{k=1}^{n} \log \{1 - p_k(1 - s)\}.$

Since $p_k \to 0$, we can use the fact that $\log (1 - x) = -x - \theta x$, where $\theta \to 0$ as $x \to 0$. It follows that

(6.10) $\log P(s) = -(1 - s)\left\{ \sum_{k=1}^{n} (p_k + \theta_k p_k) \right\} \to -\lambda(1 - s),$

so that $P(s)$ tends to the generating function of the Poisson distribution. Hence, $\mathbf{S}_n$ *has in the limit a Poisson distribution.* We conclude that for large n and moderate values of $\lambda = p_1 + p_2 + \ldots + p_n$ the distribution of $\mathbf{S}_n$ can be approximated by a Poisson distribution. [Cf. example IX(5.b).]

7. PROBLEMS FOR SOLUTION

1. Let $\mathbf{X}$ be a random variable with generating function $P(s)$. Find the generating functions of $\mathbf{X} + 1$ and $2\mathbf{X}$.

2. *Continuation.* Find the generating functions of (*a*) $\mathbf{P}\{\mathbf{X} \leq n\}$, (*b*) $\mathbf{P}\{\mathbf{X} < n\}$, (*c*) $\mathbf{P}\{\mathbf{X} \geq n\}$, (*d*) $\mathbf{P}\{\mathbf{X} > n + 1\}$, (*e*) $\mathbf{P}\{\mathbf{X} = 2n\}$.

3. In a sequence of Bernoulli trials let u_n be the probability that the first combination SF occurs at trials number $n - 1$ and n. Find the generating function, mean, and variance.

4. Discuss which of the formulas of chapter II, section 12, represent convolutions and where generating functions have been used.

5. Let a_n be the number of ways in which the score n can be obtained by throwing a die any number of times. Show that the generating function of $\{a_n\}$ is $\{1 - s - s^2 - s^3 - s^4 - s^5 - s^6\}^{-1} - 1$.

Note: *Problems 6–10 refer to coin tossing with the usual notations. They contain, among other things, a straightforward derivation of certain relations found in chapter III. We write $u_n = \mathbf{P}\{\mathbf{S}_n = 0\}$ and $f_n = \mathbf{P}\{\mathbf{S}_1 \neq 0, \mathbf{S}_2 \neq 0, \ldots, \mathbf{S}_{n-1} \neq 0, \mathbf{S}_n = 0\}$ (first return); by definition $u_0 = 1$, $f_0 = 0$. We assume known (from section 3) that $\{f_n\}$ has the generating function $F(s) = 1 - \{1 - s^2\}^{\frac{1}{2}}$, and nothing more. The calculations are practically nil, and no explicit formulas for the coefficients are required.*

6. The generating function of $\{u_n\}$ is $U(s) = \{1 - s^2\}^{-\frac{1}{2}}$.

7. The probability that no zero occurs up to time $2n$ is the same as the probability u_{2n} that $\mathbf{S}_{2n} = 0$.

8. The probability that $\mathbf{S}_{2n} = 0$ and that all the sums $\mathbf{S}_1, \mathbf{S}_2, \ldots, \mathbf{S}_{2n}$ are ≥ 0 equals $2f_{2n+2}$.

9. The probability that the first change of sign occurs following the $2n$th trial equals $2f_{2n+2}$.

10. The probability that exactly k among the sums $\mathbf{S}_1, \ldots, \mathbf{S}_n$ are zero has the generating function $F^k(s)\, U(s)(1 + s)$.

---

11. In a sequence of Bernoulli trials with $p > q$ let a_n be the probability that there exists an index $j > n$ such that $\mathbf{S}_j = 0$. Show that a_n has the generating function $4pq[p - q + (1 - 4pqs^2)^{\frac{1}{2}}]^{-1}(1 + s)$.

12. In the *waiting time example* IX(3.d) find the generating function of $\mathbf{S}_r$ (for r fixed). Verify formula IX(3.3) for the mean and calculate the variance.

13. *Continuation.* The following is an alternative method for deriving the same result. Let $p_n(r) = \mathbf{P}\{\mathbf{S}_r = n\}$. Prove the recursion formula

$$(7.1) \qquad p_{n+1}(r) = \frac{r - 1}{N}\, p_n(r) + \frac{N - r + 1}{N}\, p_n(r - 1).$$

Derive the generating function directly from (7.1).

14. Solve the two preceding problems for r preassigned elements (instead of r arbitrary ones).

15.[4] Let the sequence of Bernoulli trials up to the first failure be called a

---

[4] Problems 15–17 have a direct bearing on the *game of billiards*. The probability p of success is a measure of the player's skill. The player continues to play until he fails. Hence the number of successes he accumulates is the length of his "turn." The game continues until one player has scored N successes. Problem 15 therefore gives the probability distribution of the number of turns one player needs to score k successes, problem 16 the average duration, and problem 17 the probability of a tie between two players. For further details cf. O. Bottema and S. C. Van Veen, *Kansberekningen bij het biljartspel*, *Nieuw Archief voor Wiskunde* (in Dutch), vol. 22 (1943), pp. 16–33 and 123–158.

turn. Find the generating function and the probability distribution of the accumulated number $\mathbf{S}_r$ of successes in r turns.

16. *Continuation.* Let $\mathbf{R}$ be the number of successive turns up to the νth success (that is, the νth success occurs during the $\mathbf{R}$th turn). Prove that

$$\mathbf{P}\{\mathbf{R} = r\} = p^\nu q^{r-1} \binom{r + \nu - 2}{\nu - 1}. \quad \text{Find } \mathbf{E}(\mathbf{R}) \text{ and } \mathrm{Var}(\mathbf{R}).$$

17. *Continuation.* Consider *two* sequences of Bernoulli trials with probabilities p_1, q_1, and p_2, q_2, respectively. Show that the probability that the same number of turns will lead to the Nth success can be exhibited in either of the forms:

$$(p_1 p_2)^N \sum_{\nu=1}^\infty \binom{N + \nu - 2}{\nu - 1}^2 (q_1 q_2)^{\nu-1} =$$

$$= (p_1 p_2)^N (1 - q_1 q_2)^{1-2N} \sum_{k=0}^{N-1} \binom{N - 1}{k}^2 (q_1 q_2)^k.$$

18. Let $\{\mathbf{X}_k\}$ be mutually independent variables, each assuming the values $0, 1, 2, \ldots, a-1$ with probabilities $1/a$. Let $\mathbf{S}_n = \mathbf{X}_1 + \ldots + \mathbf{X}_n$. Show that the generating function of $\mathbf{S}_n$ is

$$P(s) = \left\{ \frac{1 - s^a}{a(1 - s)} \right\}^n$$

and hence

$$\mathbf{P}\{\mathbf{S}_n = j\} = \frac{1}{a^n} \sum_{\nu=0}^\infty (-1)^{\nu+j+a\nu} \binom{n}{\nu} \binom{-n}{j - a\nu}.$$

(Only finitely many terms in the sum are different from zero.)

Note: For $a = 6$ we get the probability of scoring the sum $j + n$ in a throw with n dice. The solution goes back to DeMoivre.

19. *Continuation.* The probability $\mathbf{P}\{\mathbf{S}_n \leq j\}$ has the generating function $P(s)/(1 - s)$ and hence

$$\mathbf{P}\{\mathbf{S}_n \leq j\} = \frac{1}{a^n} \sum_\nu (-1)^\nu \binom{n}{\nu} \binom{j - a\nu}{n}.$$

20. *Continuation: the limiting form.* If $a \to \infty$ and $j \to \infty$, so that $j/a \to x$, then

$$\mathbf{P}\{\mathbf{S}_n \leq j\} \to \frac{1}{n!} \sum_\nu (-1)^\nu \binom{n}{\nu} (x - \nu)^n,$$

the summation extending over all ν with $0 \leq \nu < x$.

Note: This result is due to Lagrange. In the theory of geometric probabilities the right-hand side represents the distribution function of the sum of n independent random variables with "uniform" distribution in the interval $(0, 1)$.

21. Let u_n be the probability that the number of successes in n Bernoulli trials is divisible by 3. Find a recursive relation for u_n and hence the generating function.

22. *Continuation: alternative method.* Let v_n and w_n be the probabilities that $\mathbf{S}_n$ is of the form $3v + 1$ and $3v + 2$, respectively (so that $u_n + v_n + w_n = 1$). Find three simultaneous recursive relations and hence three equations for the generating functions.

23. Let $\mathbf{X}$ and $\mathbf{Y}$ be independent variables with generating functions $U(s)$ and $V(s)$. Show that $\mathbf{P}\{\mathbf{X} - \mathbf{Y} = j\}$ is the coefficient of s^j in $U(s) V(1/s)$, where $j = 0, \pm 1, \pm 2, \ldots$.

24. *Moment generating functions.* Let $\mathbf{X}$ be a random variable with generating function $P(s)$, and suppose that $\Sigma p_n s^n$ converges for some $s_0 > 1$. Then all moments $m_r = \mathbf{E}(\mathbf{X}^r)$ exist, and the generating function $F(s)$ of the sequence $m_r/r!$ converges at least for $|s| < \log s_0$. Moreover

$$F(s) = \sum_{r=0}^{\infty} \frac{m_r}{r!} s^r = P(e^s).$$

Note: $F(s)$ is usually called the *moment generating function*, although in reality it generates $m_r/r!$.

25. Suppose that $A(s) = \Sigma a_n s^n$ is a rational function $U(s)/V(s)$ and that s_1 is a root of $V(s)$, which is smaller in absolute value than all other roots. If s_1 is of multiplicity r, show that

$$a_n \sim \frac{\rho_1}{s_1^{n+r}} \binom{n + r - 1}{r - 1}$$

where $\rho_1 = -r! U(s_1)/V^{(r)}(s_1)$.

26. *Bivariate negative binomial distributions.* Show that for positive values of the parameters $p_0{}^a\{1 - p_1 s_1 - p_2 s_2\}^{-a}$ is the generating function of the distribution of a pair $(\mathbf{X}, \mathbf{Y})$ such that the marginal distributions of $\mathbf{X}, \mathbf{Y}$, and $\mathbf{X} + \mathbf{Y}$ are negative binomial distributions.[5]

---

[5] Distributions of this type were used by G. E. Bates and J. Neyman in investigations of accident proneness. See *University of California Publications in Statistics*, vol. 1, 1952.

CHAPTER XII

Compound Distributions. Branching Processes

1. SUMS OF A RANDOM NUMBER OF VARIABLES

Let $\{X_k\}$ be a sequence of mutually independent random variables with the common distribution $P\{X_k = j\} = f_j$ and generating function $f(s) = \Sigma f_i s^i$. We are often interested in sums $S_N = X_1 + X_2 + \ldots + X_N$, where the number N of terms is a random variable independent of the X_j. Let $P\{N = n\} = g_n$ be the distribution of N and $g(s) = \Sigma g_n s^n$ its generating function. For the distribution $\{h_j\}$ of S_N we get from the fundamental formula for conditional probabilities

$$(1.1) \quad h_j = P\{S_N = j\} = \sum_{n=0}^{\infty} P\{N = n\} \, P\{X_1 + \ldots + X_n = j\}.$$

If N assumes only finitely many values, the random variable S_N is defined on the sample space of finitely many X_k. Otherwise the probabilistic definition of S_N as a sum involves the sample space of an infinite sequence $\{X_k\}$, but we shall be dealing only with the distribution function of S_N: for our purposes we take the distribution (1.1) as definition of the variable S_N on the sample space with points $0, 1, 2, \ldots$.

For a fixed n the distribution of $X_1 + X_2 + \ldots + X_n$ is given by the n-fold convolution of $\{f_j\}$ with itself, and therefore (1.1) can be written in the compact form

$$(1.2) \qquad \qquad \{h_j\} = \sum_{n=0}^{\infty} g_n \{f_j\}^{n*}.$$

This formula can be simplified by the use of generating functions. The generating function of $\{f_j\}^{n*}$ is $f^n(s)$ and it is obvious from (1.2) that

---

* The contents of this chapter will not be used in the sequel.

the generating function of the sum S_N is given by

$$(1.3) \qquad h(s) = \sum_{j=0}^{\infty} h_j s^j = \sum_{n=0}^{\infty} g_n f^n(s).$$

The right side is the Taylor expansion of $g(s)$ with s replaced by $f(s)$; hence it equals $g(f(s))$.   This proves the

Theorem.   *The generating function of the sum* $S_N = X_1 + \ldots + X_N$ *is the compound function* $g(f(s))$.

Two special cases are of interest.

(a) If the X_i are Bernoulli variables with $P\{X_i = 1\} = p$ and $P\{X_i = 0\} = q$, then $f(s) = q + ps$ and therefore $h(s) = g(q + ps)$.

(b) If N has a Poisson distribution with mean t then

$$(1.4) \qquad h(s) = e^{-t + tf(s)}.$$

The distribution with this generating function will be called the *compound Poisson distribution*.

If the X_i are Bernoulli variables *and* N has a Poisson distribution, then $h(s) = e^{-tp + tps}$; the *sum* S_N *has a Poisson distribution with mean* tp.

Examples.   (a) We saw in example VI(7.c) that X-rays produce chromosome breakages in cells; for a given dosage and time of exposure the number N of breakages in individual cells has a Poisson distribution.   Each breakage has a fixed probability q of healing whereas with probability $p = 1 - q$ the cell dies.   Here S_N is the number of *observable* breakages [1] and has a Poisson distribution with mean tp.

(b) In animal-trapping experiments [2] g_n represents the probability that a species is of size n.   If each animal has a fixed probability p of being trapped, then (assuming stochastic independence) the number of trapped representatives of one species in the sample is a variable S_N with generating function $g(q + ps)$.   This description can be varied in many ways.   For example, let g_n be the probability of an insect's laying n eggs, and p the probability of survival of an egg.   Then S_N is the number of surviving eggs.   Again, let g_n be the probability of a family's having n children and let the sex ratio of boys to girls be $p:q$.   Then S_N represents the number of boys in a family.

---

[1] See D. G. Catcheside, Genetic effects of radiations, *Advances in Genetics,* edited by M. Demerec, vol. 2, Academic Press, New York, 1948, pp. 271–358, in particular p. 339.

[2] D. G. Kendall, On some modes of population growth leading to R. A. Fisher's logarithmic series distribution, *Biometrika,* vol. 35 (1948), pp. 6–15.

(c) Each plant has a large number of seeds, but each seed has only a small probability of survival, and it is therefore reasonable to assume that the number of survivors of an individual plant has a Poisson distribution. If g_n represents the distribution of the number of parent plants, $g(e^{-\lambda+\lambda s})$ is the generating function of the number of surviving seeds.

2. THE COMPOUND POISSON DISTRIBUTION

We preface our considerations by two typical

Examples. (a) Suppose that the number of hits by lightning during any time interval of duration t is a Poisson variable with mean λt. If $\{f_n\}$ is the probability distribution of the damage caused by an individual hit by lightning, then (assuming stochastic independence) the probability distribution of the total damage during time t is a compound Poisson distribution $\{h_j\} = e^{-\lambda t} \sum \dfrac{(\lambda t)^n}{n!} \{f_j\}^{n*}$ with generating function

$$(2.1) \qquad\qquad h(s; t) = e^{-\lambda t + \lambda t\, f(s)}.$$

(b) In ecology it is assumed that the number of animal litters in a plot has a Poisson distribution with mean proportional to the area t of the plot. If $\{f_k\}$ is the distribution of the number of animals in a litter, then (2.1) is the generating function for the total number of animals in the plot.

We recall from chapter VI that many phenomena depending on time or space obey a Poisson distribution, and the preceding examples will explain why the compound Poisson distribution is also frequently connected with such phenomena.

The generating function (2.1) has the remarkable property that

$$(2.2) \qquad\qquad h(s; t_1+t_2) = h(s; t_1)h(s; t_2).$$

In an intuitive way we may describe this as follows. With each period of duration t there is associated a random variable with generating function $h(s; t)$ which we call the *contribution* of that period. The contributions of two non-overlapping periods are independent, which means that a partitioning $t = t_1 + t_2$ of a period into two parts induces a decomposition $\mathbf{X}(t) = \mathbf{X}(t_1) + \mathbf{X}(t_2)$ of its contribution into a sum of two independent variables.

In the next section it will be shown that (among integral-valued random variables) *only the compound Poisson distribution* has this property. Here we preface the formulation of the theorem by two

Examples.   (c) *The negative binomial distribution* with generating function

$$(2.3) \qquad\qquad h(t; s) = \left(\frac{p}{1 - qs}\right)^t \qquad\qquad p + q = 1$$

does have the property (2.2). Therefore *the negative binomial* (2.3) *is a compound Poisson distribution;* it takes on the form (2.1) with

$$(2.4) \qquad \lambda = \log\frac{1}{p}, \qquad f(s) = \frac{1}{\lambda}\log\frac{1}{1 - qs}, \qquad f_n = \frac{\lambda q^n}{n}.$$

The distribution $\{\lambda q^n/n\}$ is called the logarithmic distribution.

(d) *Multiple Poisson distributions.* Suppose that we classify automobile accidents according to the number of vehicles involved as singlets, doublets, etc. Suppose further that the numbers of singlets, doublets, etc., have Poisson distributions with means $\lambda_1 t$, $\lambda_2 t$, ... and that there is no stochastic dependence among them. The total number of vehicles involved in accidents during a period t has then the generating function

$$(2.5) \qquad\qquad e^{-\lambda_1 t(1-s)} e^{-\lambda_2 t(1-s^2)} e^{-\lambda_3 t(1-s^3)} \ldots.$$

This is again a compound Poisson distribution with $\lambda = \Sigma\lambda_i$ and $f_i = \lambda_i/\lambda$. Conversely, *every* compound Poisson distribution can be rewritten in the form (2.5) and therefore admits of the alternative interpretation as representing the cumulative effect of singlets, doublets, etc.

3. INFINITELY DIVISIBLE DISTRIBUTIONS

A probability distribution $\{h_i\}$, $i = 0, 1, \ldots,$ *is called infinitely divisible, if for each n it can be represented as the n-fold convolution of a probability distribution* $\{\phi_i\}$ *with itself, that is, if its generating function* $h(s)$ *has an nth root such that* $h^{1/n}(s) = \phi(s)$ *generates a probability distribution* $\{\phi_i\}$.

Note that if $h(s; t)$ satisfies (2.2), then $h(s; t) = h^n(s; t/n)$ and therefore $h(s; t)$ is infinitely divisible for each t. The assertion of the preceding section is contained in the following theorem (which is a special case of an important general theorem of P. Lévy concerning arbitrary probability distributions).

Theorem. *If* $\{h_i\}$ *is infinitely divisible, then its generating function can be written in the form (2.1) (say with* $t = 1$*).*

[Note that $h^t(s) = h(s; t)$ satisfies (2.2).]

Proof. Suppose that $h^{1/n}(s)$ is a probability generating function for each n. This is possible only if $h(0) = h_0 > 0$. Then $h(s)$ must be positive in some interval $|s| \leq a \leq 1$ and in it we have $0 < 1 - h(s) < < 1$. It follows that $\log h(s) = \log (1 - \{1 - h(s)\})$ has the Taylor series

$$(3.1) \qquad \log h(s) = \sum_{i=0}^{\infty} \chi_i s^i \qquad\qquad -a < s < a.$$

Putting $s = 0$, we see that $\chi_0 < 0$. We want to prove that all other χ_i are non-negative. Assume the contrary, and let $r \geq 1$ be the *smallest* index such that $\chi_r < 0$. To avoid clumsy formulas set

$$(3.2) \qquad A(s) = \sum_{\nu=1}^{r-1} \chi_\nu s^\nu \qquad B(s) = \sum_{\nu=r+1}^{\infty} \chi_\nu s^\nu, \qquad \frac{1}{n} = \epsilon$$

so that

$$(3.3) \qquad h^{1/n}(s) = e^{\epsilon\chi_0} \cdot e^{\epsilon A(s)} e^{\epsilon\chi_r s^r} \cdot e^{\epsilon B(s)}.$$

By assumption $h^{1/n}(s) = \Sigma\phi_k s^k$ where $\phi_k \geq 0$. Consider in particular the coefficient ϕ_r of s^r. The power series $B(s)$ contains only powers of order greater than r and hence does not contribute to ϕ_r. Therefore ϕ_r is the coefficient of s^r in

$$(3.4) \qquad e^{\epsilon\chi_0}(1 + \epsilon A(s) + \tfrac{1}{2}\epsilon^2 A^2(s) + \ldots)(1 + \epsilon\chi_r s^r).$$

Since $A(s)$ is a polynomial of degree $\leq r - 1$ we see that

$$(3.5) \qquad \phi_r = e^{\epsilon\chi_0}[\epsilon\chi_r + \epsilon^2 p(\epsilon)]$$

where $p(\epsilon)$ is a polynomial in ϵ. If $\chi_r < 0$ as assumed, the right side of (3.5) will be negative for ϵ sufficiently small, and thus $\phi_r < 0$ which is impossible. This proves that $\chi_r \geq 0$ for $r = 1, 2, \ldots$. Moreover, $h(1) = 1$ and hence $\log h(1) = \Sigma\chi_\nu = 0$, that is, $-\chi_0 = \chi_1 + + \chi_2 + \ldots$. To write $h(s)$ in the form (2.1) with $t = 1$ it suffices now to put $-\chi_0 = \lambda$ and $f_i = \chi_i/\lambda$.

4. EXAMPLES FOR BRANCHING PROCESSES

We shall describe a chance process which serves as a simplified model of many empirical processes and also illustrates the usefulness of generating functions. In words the process may be described as follows.

We consider particles which are able to produce new particles of like kind. A single particle forms the original, or zero, generation. Every particle has probability p_k $(k = 0, 1, 2, \ldots)$ of creating exactly k new particles; the direct descendants of the nth generation form the $(n+1)st$

generation.   The particles of each generation act independently of each other.   We are interested in the size of the successive generations.

A few illustrations may precede a rigorous formulation in terms of random variables.

(a) *Nuclear chain reactions.*   This application became familiar in connection with the atomic bomb.[3]   The particles are neutrons, which are subject to chance hits by other particles.   Let p be the probability that the particle sooner or later scores a hit, thus creating m particles; then $q = 1 - p$ is the probability that the particle has no descendants; that is, it remains inactive (is removed or absorbed in a different way). In this scheme the only possible numbers of descendants are 0 and m, and the corresponding probabilities are q and p (i.e., $p_0 = q$, $p_m = p$, $p_j = 0$ for all other j).   At worst, the first particle remains inactive and the process never starts.   At best, there will be m particles of the first generation, m^2 of the second, and so on.   If p is near one, the number of particles is likely to increase very rapidly.   Mathematically, this number may increase indefinitely.   Physically speaking, for very large numbers of particles the probabilities of fission cannot remain constant, and also stochastic independence no longer holds.   However, for ordinary chain reactions, the mathematical description "indefinitely increasing number of particles" may be translated by "explosion."

(b) *Survival of family names.*   Here (as often in life), only male descendants count; they play the role of particles, and p_k is the probability for a newborn boy to become the progenitor of exactly k boys. Our scheme introduces two artificial simplifications.   Fertility is subject to secular trends, and therefore the distribution $\{p_k\}$ in reality changes from generation to generation.   Moreover, common inheritance and common environment are bound to produce similarities among brothers which is contrary to our assumption of stochastic independence.   Our model can be refined to take care of these objections, but the essential features remain unaffected.   We shall derive the probability of finding k carriers of the family name in the nth generation and, in particular, the probability of an extinction of the line.   Survival of family names appears to have been the first chain reaction studied by probability methods.   The problem was first treated by F. Galton (1889); for a detailed account the reader is referred to A. Lotka's book.[4]

---

[3] The following description follows E. Schroedinger, Probability problems in nuclear chemistry, *Proceedings of the Royal Irish Academy,* vol. 51, sect. A, No. 1 (December 1945).   There the assumption of spatial homogeneity is removed.

[4] Théorie analytique des associations biologiques, vol. 2, *Actualités scientifiques et industrielles,* No. 780 (1939), pp. 123–136, Hermann et Cie, Paris.

Lotka shows that American experience is reasonably well described by the distribution $p_0 = 0.4825$, $p_k = (0.2126)(0.5893)^{k-1}(k \geq 1)$, which, except for the first term, is a geometric distribution.

(c) *Genes and mutations.* Every gene of a given organism (cf. chapter V, section 5) has a chance to reappear in 1, 2, 3, ... direct descendants, and our scheme describes the process, neglecting, of course, variations within the population and with time. This scheme is of particular use in the study of mutations,[5] or changes of form in a gene. A spontaneous mutation produces a single gene of the new kind, which plays the role of a zero-generation particle. The theory leads to estimates of the chances of survival and of the spread of the mutant gene. To fix ideas, consider (following R. A. Fisher) a corn plant which is father to some 100 seeds and mother to an equal number. If the population size remains constant, an average of two among these 200 seeds will develop to a plant. Each seed has probability $\frac{1}{2}$ to receive a particular gene. The probability of a mutant gene's being represented in exactly k new plants is therefore comparable to the probability of exactly k successes in 200 Bernoulli trials with probability $p = \frac{1}{200}$, and it appears reasonable to assume that $\{p_k\}$ is, approximately, a Poisson distribution with mean 1. If the gene carries a biological advantage, we get a Poisson distribution with mean $\lambda > 1$.

(d) *Waiting lines.*[6] The theory of branching processes is useful for the analysis of fluctuations in waiting lines (in post offices, telephones, etc.). A customer arriving at an empty counter and having no waiting time is termed ancestor; the customers arriving during the ancestor's service time and joining in the queue are his direct descendants. The process continues as long as the queue lasts. In this example we are interested in the total progeny up to the moment of expiration.

5. EXTINCTION PROBABILITIES IN BRANCHING PROCESSES

For a mathematical description of the process let $\mathbf{X}_n$ represent the size of the nth generation. By assumption $\mathbf{X}_0 = 1$, and $\mathbf{X}_1$ has the given probability distribution $\{p_k\}$ and generating function $P(s) = \Sigma p_k s^k$. The second generation consists of the direct descendants of the $\mathbf{X}_1$ members of the first generation; in other words, we consider $\mathbf{X}_2$ as the sum of $\mathbf{X}_1$ mutually independent variables each having the generating function $P(s)$. By the theorem of section 1 the generating function of

---

[5] R. A. Fisher, *The genetical theory of natural selection*, Oxford, 1930, pp. 73ff.

[6] D. G. Kendall, Stochastic processes and population growth, *Journal Royal Statistical Society*, vol. 11 (1949), pp. 230–265.

$\mathbf{X}_2$ is therefore $P_2(s) = P(P(s))$. In like manner $\mathbf{X}_3$ is the sum of $\mathbf{X}_1$ variables each having the same distribution as $\mathbf{X}_2$, and so the generating function of $\mathbf{X}_3$ is $P_3(s) = P(P_2(s))$. By induction we see that in general *the generating function $P_{n+1}(s)$ of the number $\mathbf{X}_{n+1}$ of particles in the $(n+1)$st generation is defined recursively by*

$$(5.1) \qquad P_1(s) = P(s), \qquad P_{n+1}(s) = P(P_n(s)).$$

In example $(4.a)$ $P(s) = q + ps^m$; and hence $P_2(s) = q + p(q + ps^m)^m$, $P_3(s) = q + p\{q + p(q + ps^m)^m\}^m$, etc. For a Poisson distribution $P(s) = e^{-\lambda(1-s)}$, $P_2(s) = e^{-\lambda+\lambda e^{-\lambda+\lambda s}}$, etc. These formulas are not very pleasing but enable us to draw important conclusions.

We seek the probability x_n that the process terminates at or before the nth generation, that is $x_n = \mathbf{P}\{\mathbf{X}_n = 0\} = P_n(0)$. No extinction is possible when $p_0 = 0$ and *we shall therefore assume that $0 < p_0 < 1$.* It is clear from its definition that x_n increases with n. This can be seen analytically as follows. In the interval $0 < s < 1$ the function $P(s)$ is increasing and we have $x_1 = P(0) = p_0$. Therefore $x_2 = P(x_1) > > P(0) = x_1$ and by induction $x_{n+1} = P(x_n) > P(x_{n-1}) = x_n$. It follows that the sequence x_n increases monotonically to a number ζ, and obviously ζ satisfies the equation

$$(5.2) \qquad \qquad \zeta = P(\zeta).$$

If $u > 0$ is an arbitrary root of the equation $u = P(u)$, then $x_1 = P(0) < P(u) = u$ and so by induction $x_{n+1} = P(x_n) < P(u) = u$, which shows that $\zeta < u$. Accordingly, x_n *tends to the smallest positive root of* (5.2).

The graph of $y = P(s)$ being convex, the curve and the bisector $y = s$ can intersect in at most two points. They do intersect at the point $(1, 1)$ and therefore the equation (5.2) can have at most one root $0 < \zeta < 1$. When such a root exists, the difference ratio $\{1 - P(\zeta)\}/ /\{1 - \zeta\}$ equals one, and by the mean value theorem there exists a point x lying between ζ and 1 such that the derivative $P'(x) = 1$. It follows that a root $\zeta < 1$ of (5.2) can exist only if $P'(1) > 1$. On the other hand, if $P'(1) \leq 1$ then $\{1 - P(s)\}/\{1 - s\} < 1$ for all $s < 1$, and this implies $P(s) > 1$; the graph of $P(s)$ lies above the bisector and hence (5.2) can have no root. This shows that a positive root $\zeta < 1$ of (5.2) exists if, and only if, $P'(1) > 1$, and that this root is unique. Now $P'(1) = \Sigma k p_k$ is the expected number of direct descendants of each particle, and we can formulate the basic result:

Let $\mu = \Sigma k p_k$ be the expected number of direct descendants of a single particle. If $\mu \leq 1$, then the probability tends to one that the process will *terminate before the nth generation* (that is, $\mathbf{X}_n = 0$). *If $\mu > 1$, then there exists a unique root $\zeta < 1$ of (5.2), and ζ is the limit of the probability that the process terminates after finitely many generations.*

The difference $1 - \zeta$ can be called the probability of an infinitely prolonged process. Usually x_n converges to ζ rapidly, so that a terminating process is likely to proceed for only very few generations. In practice, therefore, ζ is the probability of a rapid extinction. In example (4.c) we may call $1 - \zeta$ the probability that a mutant gene establishes itself. If we start with r particles instead of a single one, the probability that all r descendant lines die out is ζ^r, and the probability of at least one being successful is $1 - \zeta^r$. Even if ζ is relatively large, $1 - \zeta^r$ is near 1 if the initial number r is large. In the nuclear chain reaction of example (4.a) this is always the case, and hence we can say: If $\mu > 1$, the probability of an explosion is near 1, but for $\mu \leq 1$ the probability is 1 that the process stops after a finite number of generations.

We can also find the expected size of the nth generation $\mathbf{E}(\mathbf{X}_n) = P'_n(1)$. Since $P_n(s) = P(P_{n-1}(s))$, we find

$$P'_n(1) = P'(P_{n-1}(1))P'_{n-1}(1) = P'(1)P'_{n-1}(1) = \mu \mathbf{E}(\mathbf{X}_{n-1}),$$

and generally by induction

$$(5.3) \qquad\qquad \mathbf{E}(\mathbf{X}_n) = \mu^n.$$

Hence, if $\mu > 1$, we should expect an exponential growth. This argument can be amplified. It is easily seen that not only $P_n(0) \to \zeta$ but also $P_n(s) \to \zeta$ for all $s < 1$. This means that the coefficients of s, s^2, s^3, ... tend to zero. *After a large number of generations the probability that no descendants exist is near ζ, and the probability that the number of descendants exceeds any preassigned bound is near $1 - \zeta$;* it is exceedingly improbable to find a moderate number of descendants.[7]

6. PROBLEMS FOR SOLUTION

1. The distribution (1.1) has mean $\mathbf{E}(\mathbf{N})\mathbf{E}(\mathbf{X})$ and variance $\mathbf{E}(\mathbf{N})\operatorname{Var}(\mathbf{X}) + \operatorname{Var}(\mathbf{N})\,\mathbf{E}^2(\mathbf{X})$. Verify this (a) using the generating function, (b) directly from the definition and the notion of conditional expectations.

2. *Animal trapping* [example (1.b)]. If $\{g_n\}$ is a geometric distribution, so is the resulting distribution. If $\{g_n\}$ is a logarithmic distribution [cf. formula (2.4)], there results a logarithmic distribution with an added term.

---

[7] For the behavior of $\mathbf{X}_n$ see T. E. Harris, Branching processes, *Annals of Mathematical Statistics*, vol. 19 (1948), pp. 474–494.

3. In **N** Bernoulli trials, where **N** is a random variable with a Poisson distribution, the numbers of successes and failures are stochastically independent variables. Generalize this to the multinomial distribution (*a*) directly, (*b*) using multivariate generating functions. [Cf. example IX(1.*d*).]

4. *Randomization*. Let **N** have a Poisson distribution with mean λ, and let **N** balls be placed randomly into *n* cells. Show without calculation that the probability of finding exactly *m* cells empty is $\binom{n}{m} e^{-\lambda m/n}[(1 - e)^{-\lambda/n}]^{n-m}$.

5. *Continuation*.[8] Show that when a fixed number *r* of balls is placed randomly into *n* cells the probability of finding exactly *m* cells empty equals the coefficient of $e^{-\lambda}\lambda^r/r!$ in the expression above. (*a*) Discuss the connection with moment generating functions (problem XI, 24). (*b*) Use the result for an effortless derivation of formula II(11.7).

6. *Mixtures of probability distributions*. Let $\{f_i\}$ and $\{g_i\}$ be two probability distributions, $\alpha > 0$, $\beta > 0$, $\alpha + \beta = 1$. Then $\{\alpha f_i + \beta g_i\}$ is again a probability distribution. Discuss its meaning and the connection with the urn models of chapter V, section 2. Generalize to more than two distributions. Can such a mixture be a compound Poisson distribution?

7. In the branching process prove that $\mathrm{Var}(\mathbf{X}_{n+1}) = \mu\,\mathrm{Var}(\mathbf{X}_n) + \mu^{2n}\sigma^2$, using (*a*) generating functions, (*b*) conditional expectations. Conclude that $\mathrm{Var}(\mathbf{X}_n) = \sigma^2(\mu^{2n-2} + \mu^{2n-3} + \ldots + \mu^{n-1})$.

8. *Continuation*. If $n > m$ show that $\mathbf{E}(\mathbf{X}_n\mathbf{X}_m) = \mu^{n-m}\mathbf{E}(\mathbf{X}_m^2)$.

9. *Continuation*. Show that the bivariate generating function of $\mathbf{X}_m$, $\mathbf{X}_n$ is $P_m(s_1 P_{n-m}(s_2))$. Use this to verify the assertion in 8.

---

[8] This elegant derivation of various combinatorial formulas by randomizing a parameter is due to C. Domb, On the use of a random parameter in combinatorial problems, *Proceedings Physical Society*, Sec. A., vol. 65 (1952), pp. 305–309.

CHAPTER XIII

Recurrent Events.
The Renewal Equation

1. INFORMAL PREPARATIONS AND EXAMPLES

We shall be concerned with certain repetitive patterns connected with repeated trials. Roughly speaking, a pattern $\mathcal{E}$ qualifies for the following theory if after each occurrence of $\mathcal{E}$ the trials start from scratch in the sense that the trials following an occurrence of $\mathcal{E}$ form a replica of the whole experiment. The waiting times between successive occurrences of $\mathcal{E}$ are mutually independent random variables having the same distribution.

The simplest special case arises when $\mathcal{E}$ stands as abbreviation for "a success occurs" in a sequence of Bernoulli trials. The waiting time up to the first success has a geometric distribution; when the first success occurs, the trials start anew, and the number of trials between the rth and the $(r+1)$st success has the same geometric distribution. The waiting time up to the rth success is the sum of r independent variables [example IX(3.c)]. By contrast, suppose that people are sampled one by one and let $\mathcal{E}$ stand for "Two people in the sample have birthdays the same day of the year." Here $\mathcal{E}$ is not repetitive; once it has occurred it persists. The sampling may proceed until a second double birthday turns up, but this second phase is not a replica of the first one. The larger a sample, the greater the probability of a duplication of birthdays; therefore a long waiting time for the first double birthday promises a short interval between the first and the second duplication. The two consecutive waiting times not only have different distributions but are stochastically dependent. Such waiting times are not the object of the theory of recurrent events.

A phenomenon of a different type occurs when we are interested in the appearance of two consecutive successes in Bernoulli trials. The *first* occurrence of the pattern SS is well defined, but if $\mathcal{E}$ stands for "a run of exactly two successes," the third trial may undo the second; if four successive trials produce the sequence $SSSF$, then $\mathcal{E}$ occurs at the second trial, but the whole sequence contains no $\mathcal{E}$. For us it is important that the event "$\mathcal{E}$ occurs at the nth trial" depends solely on the outcome of the first n trials and not on the future.

A few typical problems to which the theory of recurrent events does apply are listed in the following

Examples. (a) *Success runs in Bernoulli trials.* The term "success run of length r" has been defined in several ways. It is largely a matter of convention and convenience whether a sequence of three consecutive successes is said to contain 0, 1, or 2 runs of length 2, and for different purposes different definitions have been adopted. However, if we are to use the theory of recurrent events, then the notion of runs of length r must be defined so that we start from scratch every time a run is completed. This means adopting the following definition. *A sequence of n letters S and F contains as many runs of length r as there are nonoverlapping uninterrupted successions of exactly r letters S. In a sequence of Bernoulli trials a run of length r occurs at the nth trial, if the nth trial adds a new run to the sequence.* Thus in $SSS|SF|SSS|SSS$ we have three runs of length 3, and they occur at trials number 3, 8, 11; there are five runs of length 2, and they occur at trials number 2, 4, 7, 9, 11. This definition has the advantage of a considerable simplification of the theory since runs *of a fixed length* become recurrent events. (This topic will be taken up in sections 7 and 8.)

(b) *A counter problem.* Counters of the type used for cosmic rays and α-particles may be described by the following simplified model.[1] Bernoulli trials are performed at a uniform rate. A counter is designed to register successes, but the mechanism is locked for exactly $r - 1$ trials following each registration. In other words, a success at the nth trial is registered if, and only if, no *registration* has occurred in the preceding $r - 1$ trials. The counter is then locked at the conclusion of trials number $n, \ldots, n + r - 1$, and is freed at the conclusion of the $(n + r)$th trial provided this trial results in failure. The output of the counter represents *dependent trials*; each registration has an aftereffect. However, whenever the counter is free (not locked) the situation is exactly the same, and the trials start from scratch. Letting $\mathcal{E}$ stand for "at the conclusion of the trial the counter is free," we have a typical recurrent pattern (cf. problems 9 and 10 and XV, 13).

---

[1] We are describing a discrete analogue of the so-called counters of type I. Type II is described in problem 10. For a description see H. Maier-Leibnitz, Die Koinzidenzmethode und ihre Anwendung auf kernphysikalische Probleme, *Physikalische Zeitschrift*, vol. 43 (1942), pp. 333–362.

(c) *Return to the origin.* In a sequence of Bernoulli trials with probability p of success let $\mathcal{E}$ stand as an abbreviation for "The cumulative numbers of successes and failures are equal." As we have done before, we describe Bernoulli trials in terms of independent variables $\{X_k\}$ with the common distribution $\mathbf{P}\{X_k = 1\} = p$ and $\mathbf{P}\{X_k = -1\} = q$, and put

$$(1.1) \qquad S_0 = 0, \qquad S_n = X_1 + X_2 + \ldots + X_n.$$

Then S_n is the accumulated excess of heads over tails, and our $\mathcal{E}$ *occurs at the nth trial if, and only if,* $S_n = 0$. We shall describe $\mathcal{E}$ as the *return to* 0. Given that $S_n = 0$, the subsequent partial sums

$$(1.2) \qquad S'_0 = S_n, \qquad S'_1 = S_{n+1}, \qquad S'_2 = S_{n+2}, \ldots.$$

are subject to exactly the same probability relations as the original sequence $\{S_k\}$, and a return to 0 for $\{S'_k\}$ means a return to 0 for $\{S_k\}$ and vice versa.

The event "$\mathcal{E}$ occurs for the first time at the nth trial" alias "The *first return to the origin* takes place at the nth trial" is defined as the aggregate of sequences $\{X_k\}$ such that

$$(1.3) \quad S_1 \neq 0, \qquad S_2 \neq 0, \qquad \ldots, \qquad S_{n-1} \neq 0, \qquad S_n = 0.$$

If this occurs we say that the *waiting time* $\mathbf{T}$ equals n, and for the probability of (1.3) we write $f_n = \mathbf{P}\{\mathbf{T} = n\}$. The first few terms are easily found by direct enumeration of all admissible sequences; clearly $f_n = 0$ whenever n is odd and $f_2 = 2pq$, $f_4 = 2p^2q^2$, $f_6 = 4p^3q^3$, $f_8 = 10p^4q^4$, $f_{10} = 28p^5q^5$. The same sequence $\{f_n\}$ represents the probability distribution of the waiting time between the rth and the $(r+1)$st occurrence of $\mathcal{E}$, and we call $\{f_n\}$ also the distribution of *recurrence times.* (The distribution $\{f_n\}$ has been found in chapter XI, section 3, by the use of generating functions. In chapter III the special case $p = q = \frac{1}{2}$ is treated, and the formulas apply in general since the number of outcomes satisfying (1.3) is independent of p. In the present chapter we give a new and independent derivation.)

(d) *Ladder points in Bernoulli trials.* Adhering to the same notations we define a new repetitive pattern $\mathcal{E}$ by "$\mathcal{E}$ *occurs at the nth trial if* S_n *exceeds all preceding sums*" that is, if

$$(1.4) \quad S_n > 0, \qquad S_n > S_1, \qquad S_n > S_2, \ldots, \qquad S_n > S_{n-1}.$$

In this case we shall say that the nth trial (or the index n) represents a *ladder point.* In the sequence of partial sums S_1, S_2, $\ldots$ given by $-1, 0, 1 | 2 | 1, 2, 3 | 2, 1, 2, 1, 2, 3, 4 | 5 |$ (see figure 3 of chapter III) ladder points occur at the trials number 3, 4, 7, 14, 15, and the waiting times between consecutive occurrences are 3, 1, 3, 7, 1. The rth occurrence of $\mathcal{E}$ can be described as the *first occurrence of the value r,* and therefore the ladder points may be described as moments of *first passages.*

If $\mathcal{E}$ occurs at the nth trial the process starts from scratch in the following sense. Assuming (1.4) to hold, *a later trial number $n + m$ is a ladder point if, and only if,*

$$(1.5) \quad \mathbf{S}_{n+m} > \mathbf{S}_n, \mathbf{S}_{n+m} > \mathbf{S}_{n+1}, \mathbf{S}_{n+m} > \mathbf{S}_{n+2}, \ldots, \mathbf{S}_{n+m} > \mathbf{S}_{n+m-1}.$$

Put

$$(1.6) \qquad \mathbf{S}_k{}^* = \mathbf{S}_{n+k} - \mathbf{S}_n = \mathbf{X}_{n+1} + \ldots + \mathbf{X}_{n+k}.$$

Then $n + m$ is a ladder point for the sequence $\mathbf{S}_1, \mathbf{S}_2, \ldots$ if, and only if, m is a ladder point for $\{\mathbf{S}_n{}^*\}$. Clearly the operation defined in (1.6) produces an independent replica of the original sample space, and $\mathcal{E}$ qualifies for the theory of recurrent events. Note that in this case the sequence (1.2) as such is probabilistically different from the original sequence: after the rth occurrence of $\mathcal{E}$ the partial sums $\mathbf{S}_j$ are bound to be close to r and not to 0. Nevertheless, as far as our pattern $\mathcal{E}$ is concerned, the trials following the occurrence of $\mathcal{E}$ start from scratch.

(The ladder points provide a means of reducing the study of first-passage times to recurrent events, that is, to the summation of independent random variables. A direct (equivalent) approach is given in chapter IX, section 3. The notion of ladder points can be used profitably for sequences of arbitrary random variables, for example in connection with the general arc sine law.)

(*e*) In a sequence of consecutive throws of a perfect die let $\mathcal{E}$ stand for "Ones, twos, ..., sixes appeared in equal numbers." Here the recurrent character of $\mathcal{E}$ requires no further comment.

2. DEFINITIONS

We consider a sequence of repeated trials with possible outcomes E_j ($j = 1, 2, \ldots$). They need not be independent (applications to Markov chains being of special interest). As usual, we suppose that it is in principle possible to continue the trials indefinitely, the probabilities $\mathbf{P}\{E_{j_1}, E_{j_2}, \ldots, E_{j_n}\}$ being defined consistently for all finite sequences. Let $\mathcal{E}$ be an attribute of finite sequences; that is, we suppose that it is uniquely determined whether a sequence $(E_{j_1}, \ldots, E_{j_n})$ has, or has not, the characteristic $\mathcal{E}$. We agree that the expression "$\mathcal{E}$ occurs at the nth place in the (finite or infinite) sequence $E_{j_1}, E_{j_2}, \ldots$" is an abbreviation for "The subsequence $E_{j_1}, E_{j_2}, \ldots, E_{j_n}$ has the attribute $\mathcal{E}$." This convention implies that the occurrence of $\mathcal{E}$ at the

nth trial depends solely on the outcome of the first n trials. It is also understood that *when speaking of a "recurrent event* $\mathcal{E}$," *we are really referring to a class of events* defined by the property that $\mathcal{E}$ occurs. Clearly $\mathcal{E}$ itself is a label rather than an event. We are here abusing the language in the same way as is generally accepted in terms such as "a two-dimensional problem"; the problem itself is dimensionless.

Definition 1. *The attribute* $\mathcal{E}$ *defines a recurrent event if:*

(a) *In order that* $\mathcal{E}$ *occurs at the* nth *and the* $(n+m)$th *place of the sequence* $(E_{j_1}, E_{j_2}, \ldots, E_{j_{n+m}})$ *it is necessary and sufficient that* $\mathcal{E}$ *occurs at the last place in each of the two subsequences* $(E_{j_1}, E_{j_2}, \ldots, E_{j_n})$ *and* $(E_{j_{n+1}}, E_{j_{n+2}}, \ldots, E_{j_{n+m}})$.

(b) *Whenever this is the case we have*

$$\mathbf{P}\{E_{j_1}, \ldots, E_{j_{n+m}}\} = \mathbf{P}\{E_{j_1}, \ldots, E_{j_n}\}\,\mathbf{P}\{E_{j_{n+1}}, \ldots, E_{j_{n+m}}\}.$$

It has now an obvious meaning to say that $\mathcal{E}$ occurs in the sequence $(E_{j_1}, E_{j_2}, \ldots)$ *for the first time* at the nth place, etc. It is also clear that with each recurrent event $\mathcal{E}$ there are associated the two sequences of numbers defined for $n = 1, 2, \ldots$ as follows

(2.1)
$$u_n = \mathbf{P}\{\mathcal{E} \text{ occurs at the } n\text{th trial}\},$$
$$f_n = \mathbf{P}\{\mathcal{E} \text{ occurs for the first time at the } n\text{th trial}\}.$$

It will be convenient to define

(2.2)
$$f_0 = 0, \qquad u_0 = 1,$$

and to introduce the generating functions

(2.3)
$$F(s) = \sum_{k=1}^{\infty} f_k s^k, \qquad U(s) = \sum_{k=0}^{\infty} u_k s^k.$$

Observe that $\{u_k\}$ is not a probability distribution; in fact, in representative cases we shall have $\Sigma u_k = \infty$. However, the events "$\mathcal{E}$ occurs for the first time at the nth trial" are mutually exclusive, and therefore

(2.4)
$$f = \sum_{n=1}^{\infty} f_n \leq 1.$$

It is clear that $1 - f$ should be interpreted as *the probability that* $\mathcal{E}$ *does not occur in an indefinitely prolonged sequence of trials.* If $f = 1$ we may introduce a random variable $\mathbf{T}$ with distribution

(2.5)
$$\mathbf{P}\{\mathbf{T} = n\} = f_n.$$

We shall use the same notation (2.5) even if $f < 1$. Then $\mathbf{T}$ *is an im-*

proper, or defective random variable, which with probability $1 - f$ *does not assume a numerical value.* (For our purposes we could assign to **T** the symbol ∞, and it should be clear that no new rules are required.)

The *waiting time for* $\mathcal{E}$, that is, the number of trials up to and including the first occurrence of $\mathcal{E}$, is a random variable with the distribution (2.5); however, this random variable is really defined only in the space of infinite sequences $(E_{j_1}, E_{j_2}, \ldots)$.

By the definition of recurrent events the probability that $\mathcal{E}$ occurs for the first time at trial number k and for the *second* time at the nth trial equals $f_k f_{n-k}$. Therefore the probability $f_n^{(2)}$ that $\mathcal{E}$ occurs for the second time at the nth trial equals

$$(2.6) \qquad f_n^{(2)} = f_1 f_{n-1} + f_2 f_{n-2} + \ldots + f_{n-1} f_1.$$

The right side is the convolution of $\{f_n\}$ with itself and therefore $\{f_n^{(2)}\}$ represents the probability distribution of the sum of two independent random variables each having the distribution (2.5). More generally, if $f_n^{(r)}$ is the probability that the rth occurrence of $\mathcal{E}$ takes place at the nth trial we have

$$(2.7) \qquad f_n^{(r)} = f_1 f_{n-1}^{(r-1)} + f_2 f_{n-2}^{(r-1)} + \ldots + f_{n-1} f_1^{(r-1)}.$$

This simple fact is expressed in the

Theorem. *Let* $f_n^{(r)}$ *be the probability that the rth occurrence of* $\mathcal{E}$ *takes place at the nth trial. Then* $\{f_n^{(r)}\}$ *is the probability distribution of the sum*

$$(2.8) \qquad\qquad \mathbf{T}^{(r)} = \mathbf{T}_1 + \mathbf{T}_2 + \ldots + \mathbf{T}_r$$

of r independent random variables $\mathbf{T}_1, \ldots, \mathbf{T}_r$ *each having the distribution* (2.5). *In other words: For fixed r the sequence* $\{f_n^{(r)}\}$ *has the generating function* $F^r(s)$.

It follows in particular that

$$(2.9) \qquad\qquad \sum_{n=1}^{\infty} f_n^{(r)} = F^r(1) = f^r:$$

the probability that $\mathcal{E}$ occurs at least r times equals f^r (a fact which could have been anticipated). We now introduce

Definition 2. *A recurrent event* $\mathcal{E}$ *will be called persistent* [2] *if* $f = 1$ *and transient if* $f < 1$.

---

[2] In the first edition the terms certain and uncertain were used, but the present terminology is preferable in applications to Markov chains.

For a transient $\mathcal{E}$ the probability that it occurs more than r times tends to zero, whereas for a persistent $\mathcal{E}$ this probability remains unity. This can be described by saying *with probability one: A persistent $\mathcal{E}$ is bound to occur infinitely often whereas a transient $\mathcal{E}$ occurs only a finite number of times.* (This statement not only is a description but is formally correct if interpreted in the sample space of infinite sequences $E_{j_1}, E_{j_2}, \ldots$.)

We require one more definition. In Bernoulli trials a return to the origin [example $(1.c)$] can occur only at an *even*-numbered trial. In this case $f_{2n+1} = u_{2n+1} = 0$, and the generating functions $F(s)$ and $U(s)$ are power series in s^2 rather than s. Similarly, in example $(1.e)$ $\mathcal{E}$ can occur only at trials number 6, 12, 18, ... We express this by saying that $\mathcal{E}$ is periodic. Such recurrent events have a great nuisance value; in each instance the situation is quite obvious, but all general theorems require mention of the nominally special case of periodicity.

Definition 3. *The recurrent event $\mathcal{E}$ is called periodic if there exists an integer $\lambda > 1$ such that $\mathcal{E}$ can occur only at trials number $\lambda, 2\lambda, 3\lambda, \ldots$ (i.e., $u_n = 0$ whenever n is not divisible by λ). The greatest λ with this property is called the period of $\mathcal{E}$.*

In conclusion let us remark that in the sample space of infinite sequences $E_{j_1}, E_{j_2}, \ldots$ the number of trials between the $(r-1)$st and the rth occurrence of $\mathcal{E}$ is a well-defined random variable (possibly a defective one), having the probability distribution of our $\mathbf{T}_r$. In other words, our variables $\mathbf{T}_r$ really stand for the *waiting times between the successive occurrences of $\mathcal{E}$ (the recurrence times).* We have defined the $\mathbf{T}_r$ analytically in order not to refer to sample spaces beyond the scope of this volume, but it is hoped that the probabilistic background appears in all its intuitive simplicity. The notion of recurrent events is designed to reduce a fairly general situation to sums of independent random variables. Conversely, *an arbitrary probability distribution $\{f_n\}$, $n = 1, 2, \ldots$ may be used to define a recurrent event.* We prove this assertion by the

Example. *Self-renewing aggregates.* Consider an electric bulb, fuse, or other piece of equipment with a finite life span. As soon as the piece fails, it is replaced by a new piece of like kind, which in due time is replaced by a third piece, and so on. We assume that the life span is a random variable which ranges only over multiples of a unit time interval (year, day, or second). Each time unit then represents a trial with possible outcomes "replacement" and "no replacement." The successive replacements may be treated as recurrent events. If f_n is the probability that a new piece will serve for exactly n time units, then $\{f_n\}$ is the distribution of the recurrence times. When it is certain that the life span is finite, then $\Sigma f_n = 1$ and the recurrent event is persistent. Usually it is known that the life span cannot exceed a fixed number m, in which case the generating function $F(s)$ is a polynomial of a degree not exceeding m. In applications we desire the probability u_n that a replacement takes place at time n. This u_n may be calculated from equation (3.1). Here we have a class of recurrent events defined solely in terms of an arbitrary distribution $\{f_n\}$. The case $f < 1$ is not excluded, $1 - f$ being the probability of an eternal life of our piece of equipment.

3. THE BASIC RELATIONS

We adhere to the notations (2.2)–(2.4) and propose to investigate the connection between the $\{f_n\}$ and the $\{u_n\}$. The probability that $\mathcal{E}$ occurs for the first time at trial number ν and then again at a later trial $n > \nu$ is, by definition, $f_\nu u_{n-\nu}$. The probability that $\mathcal{E}$ occurs at the nth trial for the first time is $f_n = f_n u_0$. Since these cases are mutually exclusive we have

$$(3.1) \qquad u_n = f_1 u_{n-1} + f_2 u_{n-2} + \ldots + f_n u_0, \qquad\qquad n \geq 1.$$

At the right we recognize the convolution $\{f_k\} * \{u_k\}$ with the generating function $F(s) U(s)$. At the left we find the sequence $\{u_n\}$ with the term u_0 missing, so that its generating function is $U(s) - 1$. Thus $U(s) - 1 = F(s) U(s)$, and we have proved

Theorem 1. *The generating functions of $\{u_n\}$ and $\{f_n\}$ are related by*

$$(3.2) \qquad\qquad U(s) = \frac{1}{1 - F(s)}.$$

Note. The right side in (3.2) can be expanded into a geometric series $\Sigma F^r(s)$ converging for $|s| < 1$. The coefficient $f_n^{(r)}$ of s^n in $F^r(s)$ being the probability that the rth occurrence of $\mathcal{E}$ takes place at the nth trial, equation (3.2) is equivalent to

$$(3.3) \qquad\qquad u_n = f_n^{(1)} + f_n^{(2)} + \ldots$$

and expresses the obvious fact that if $\mathcal{E}$ occurs at the nth trial, it has previously occurred 0, 1, 2, $\ldots$, $n-1$ times. (Clearly $f_n^{(r)} = 0$ for $r > n$.)

Theorem 2. *For $\mathcal{E}$ to be transient, it is necessary and sufficient that*

$$(3.4) \qquad\qquad u = \sum_{j=0}^{\infty} u_j$$

is finite. In this case the probability f that ε ever occurs is given by

$$(3.5) \qquad\qquad f = \frac{u-1}{u}.$$

Note. We can interpret u_j as the expectation of a random variable which equals 1 or 0 according to whether ε does or does not occur at the jth trial.   Hence $u_1 + u_2 + \ldots + u_n$ is the expected number of occurrences of ε in n trials, and $u - 1$ can be interpreted as the expected number of occurrences of ε in infinitely many trials.

Proof. The coefficients u_k being non-negative, it is clear that $U(s)$ increases monotonically as $s \to 1$ and that for each N

$$\sum_{n=0}^{N} u_n \le \lim_{s \to 1} U(s) \le \sum_{n=0}^{\infty} u_n = u.$$

Since $U(s) \to (1-f)^{-1}$ when $f < 1$ and $U(s) \to \infty$ when $f = 1$, the theorem follows.

The next theorem is of particular importance.[3] The proof is of an elementary nature, but since it does not contribute to a probabilistic understanding we defer it to the end of the chapter. (See, however, problem 1.)

Theorem 3.   *Let ε be persistent and not periodic and denote by μ the mean of the recurrence times $\mathbf{T}_\nu$, that is,*

$$(3.6) \qquad\qquad \mu = \Sigma j f_j = F'(1)$$

(possibly $\mu = \infty$).   Then

$$(3.7) \qquad\qquad u_n \to \mu^{-1}$$

as $n \to \infty$ ($u_n \to 0$ if the mean recurrence time is infinite).

---

[3] P. Erdös, W. Feller, and H. Pollard, A theorem on power series, *Bulletin of the American Mathematical Society*, vol. 55 (1949), pp. 201–204.   This theorem was conjectured and proved for the purpose of obtaining a better access to ergodic properties of infinite Markov chains established by Kolmogorov.   After the appearance of the first edition it was observed by K. L. Chung that theorem 3 is really equivalent to the ergodic theorem of Kolmogorov and could be deduced from it.   Previously a great many papers were devoted to various special cases and variants.   Later, theorem 3 was generalized to continuous random variables and made more precise in various ways by Blackwell, Chung, Erdös, and Wolfowitz.   Blackwell gave an elegant simple proof that (3.7) holds for all integral-valued random variables (not necessarily positive ones as in the text), provided they have a positive mean.   His method is based on the use of ladder points for arbitrary variables [cf. example (1.d)].   See D. Blackwell, Extension of a renewal theorem, *Pacific Journal of Mathematics*, vol. 3 (1953), pp. 315–320.

Theorem 4. *If $\mathcal{E}$ is persistent and has period $\lambda > 1$, then as $n \to \infty$*

$$(3.8) \qquad\qquad u_{n\lambda} \to \lambda\mu^{-1}$$

and $u_k = 0$ for every k not divisible by λ.

Proof. Since $\mathcal{E}$ has period λ, the series $F(s) = \Sigma f_n s^n$ contains only powers of s^λ, and so $F(s^{1/\lambda}) = F_1(s)$ where $F_1(s)$ is again a power series with positive coefficients, and $F_1(1) = 1$. Theorem 3 implies that the coefficients of $U_1(s) = \{1 - F_1(s)\}^{-1}$ tend to μ_1^{-1} where

$$\mu_1 = F'_1(1) = \lambda^{-1} F'(1) = \lambda^{-1}\mu.$$

(Clearly μ and μ_1 are either both finite or both infinite.) Now $U(s) = U_1(s^\lambda)$ and so (3.8) holds.

Examples. (a) For a trite example let $\mathcal{E}$ stand for "success" in Bernoulli trials. Then $u_n = p$, by the very definition. Theorem 3 states that the expected number of trials between two consecutive successes is p^{-1}. Here $U(s) = 1 + ps(1 - s)^{-1} = (1 - qs)(1 - s)^{-1}$, and from theorem 1 we conclude that $F(s) = ps(1 - qs)^{-1}$, showing that the waiting time between consecutive successes has a geometric distribution.

(b) *Return to the origin in Bernoulli trials* [*example* (1.c)]. If at the kth trial the cumulative numbers of successes and failures are equal, then k must be an even number, $k = 2n$, and n trials must have resulted in success, the other n in failure. Therefore we have for the probability of an equalization

$$(3.9) \qquad\qquad u_{2n} = \binom{2n}{n} p^n q^n.$$

We know from the normal approximation to the binomial distribution, and we can also readily verify using Stirling's formula, that

$$(3.10) \qquad\qquad \binom{2n}{n} 2^{-2n} \sim \frac{1}{(\pi n)^{\frac{1}{2}}},$$

so that

$$(3.11) \qquad\qquad u_{2n} \sim \frac{(4pq)^n}{(\pi n)^{\frac{1}{2}}},$$

the sign $\sim$ indicating that the ratio of the two sides tends to unity.

If $p \neq \frac{1}{2}$, then $4pq < 1$, and Σu_{2n} converges faster than the geometric series with ratio $4pq$. If $p = \frac{1}{2}$, then $u_{2n} \sim (\pi n)^{-\frac{1}{2}}$; hence Σu_{2n} diverges, but $u_{2n} \to 0$. Our theorems permit the conclusion that with probability one the following is true:

If $p \neq q$, then the cumulative sums $\mathbf{S}_n$ will vanish only finitely many times. If $p = q = \frac{1}{2}$, they will pass through 0 infinitely often, but the mean recurrence time is infinite.

In the case $p \neq q$ the assertion is obvious intuitively and follows also from the *strong* law of large numbers. In gambling language, if the game is favorable for Peter, he can rest assured that after a few initial fluctuations his net gain will be positive and remain so. When $p = q = \frac{1}{2}$, the situation is much less intuitive and is the source of the paradoxical features of the fluctuations in coin tossing described in chapter III, section 7.

The theorems above can supply additional information. Using the readily verified formula

$$(3.12) \qquad \binom{2n}{n} = \binom{-\frac{1}{2}}{n} \cdot (-4)^n$$

and the binomial expansion II(8.7), we get from (3.9)

$$(3.13) \qquad U(s) = \sum_{n=0}^{\infty} u_{2n} s^{2n} = (1 - 4pqs^2)^{-\frac{1}{2}}.$$

If $p \neq \frac{1}{2}$, then $u = U(1) = (1 - 4pq)^{-\frac{1}{2}} = |p - q|^{-1}$. From (3.5) we conclude that *the probability f that the accumulated numbers of successes and failures will ever equalize is given by*

$$(3.14) \qquad f = 1 - |p - q|.$$

(*This is the probability of at least one return to the origin.*)

From (3.2) we get for *the generating function of the recurrence times*

$$(3.15) \qquad F(s) = 1 - (1 - 4pqs^2)^{\frac{1}{2}}.$$

This formula is most interesting in the case $p = q = \frac{1}{2}$. Then

$$(3.16) \qquad F(s) = 1 - (1 - s^2)^{\frac{1}{2}}$$

and the binomial expansion shows that

$$(3.17) \qquad f_{2n} = (-1)^{n+1} \binom{\frac{1}{2}}{n} = \frac{1}{n} \binom{2n-2}{n-1} 2^{-2n+1}$$

(f_n vanishes whenever n is odd). Equation (3.17) *gives the distribution of the recurrence times for the return to the origin in the classical coin-tossing game.*

(We have obtained this formula by different methods in chapter III, section 4, and chapter XI, section 3. The present method, although not the most elementary, is the most straightforward.)

(c) *Ties in multiple coin games.* We consider repeated independent tossings of *two* coins and say that $\mathcal{E}$ has occurred whenever the accumulated number of heads (and therefore of tails) is the same for both coins. Clearly

$$(3.18) \qquad u_n = \frac{1}{2^{2n}} \left\{ \binom{n}{0}^2 + \binom{n}{1}^2 + \binom{n}{2}^2 + \ldots + \binom{n}{n}^2 \right\}.$$

Using II(12.11) and (3.10), we find that

$$(3.19) \qquad u_n = \binom{2n}{n} 2^{-2n} \sim \frac{1}{(n\pi)^{\frac{1}{2}}}.$$

Hence Σu_n diverges, but $u_n \to 0$. Therefore $\mathcal{E}$ *is persistent but has infinite mean recurrence time.*

More generally, consider the simultaneous tossing of r coins, and let $\mathcal{E}$ stand for the recurrent event that *all r coins are in the same phase* (accumulated numbers of heads are the same for all coins). Then

$$(3.20) \qquad u_n = \frac{1}{2^{rn}} \left\{ \binom{n}{0}^r + \binom{n}{1}^r + \ldots + \binom{n}{n}^r \right\}.$$

To estimate u_n note that the maximal term of the binomial distribution $\binom{n}{k} 2^{-n}$ is smaller than $n^{-\frac{1}{2}}$. Therefore

$$(3.21) \quad u_n < n^{-\frac{1}{2}(r-1)} 2^{-n} \left\{ \binom{n}{0} + \binom{n}{1} + \ldots + \binom{n}{n} \right\} = n^{-\frac{1}{2}(r-1)}.$$

Accordingly Σu_n converges if $r \geq 4$. For $r = 2$ we saw that Σu_n diverges. A special consideration is necessary for the case $r = 3$. From the normal approximation to the binomial distribution we know that for sufficiently large n and values of k lying between $\frac{1}{2}n - n^{\frac{1}{2}}$ and $\frac{1}{2}n + n^{\frac{1}{2}}$ we have $\binom{n}{k} 2^{-n} > cn^{-\frac{1}{2}}$, where c is a positive constant (say e^{-4}). Therefore, when $r = 3$,

$$(3.22) \qquad u_n > 2n^{\frac{1}{2}}(c^3 n^{-\frac{3}{2}}) = 2c^3/n,$$

and hence Σu_n diverges. In other words, the recurrent event $\mathcal{E}$ *that k coins show the same cumulative numbers of heads is persistent if, and only if, $k \leq 3$. The mean recurrence time is infinite in each case.*

(d) *Dice.* In example (1.e) we considered the recurrent event $\mathcal{E}$ that the accumulated numbers of aces, twos, threes, etc., are equal. Obviously $\mathcal{E}$ has period 6 and $u_{6n} = (6n)!(n!)^{-6} 6^{-6n}$. Using Stirling's formula, we readily find that u_{6n} is of the order of magnitude $n^{-\frac{3}{2}}$, so that Σu_n converges. Hence $\mathcal{E}$ is transient. From (3.5) it easy to calculate that the probability of a recurrence is about 0.022.

(e) For applications to the theory of runs see sections 7 and 8.

4. THE RENEWAL EQUATION

The basic equation (3.1) of the theory of recurrent events is a special case of the so-called renewal equation (4.1), which is encountered in many different connections. We proceed to show that the theorems of the last section apply without essential modification to this more general equation. The discussion will be of a purely analytic character, probabilistic interpretations and applications being reserved for the next section.

Let $\{a_n\}$ and $\{b_n\}$ be two bounded sequences such that $0 \leq a_n < 1$ and $b_n \geq 0$ (where $n = 0, 1, 2, \ldots$). A third sequence $\{u_n\}$ is defined by the recursive relations

$$(4.1) \qquad u_n = b_n + (a_0 u_n + a_1 u_{n-1} + \ldots + a_n u_0)$$

or

$$(4.2) \qquad \{u_n\} = \{b_n\} + \{a_n\} * \{u_n\}.$$

Solving (4.1) successively, we get

$$u_0 = b_0/(1 - a_0), \qquad u_1 = (b_1 + a_1 u_0)/(1 - a_0), \ldots,$$

so that no problem about the existence of a unique solution $\{u_n\}$ arises. We are interested in the behavior of $\{u_n\}$ as $n \to \infty$, a problem to which a great number of papers (mostly of controversial nature) have been devoted.

Setting $b_n = 0$, $a_n = f_n$ for $n = 1, 2, \ldots$ and $b_0 = 1$, $a_0 = 0$ reduces equation (4.1) to (3.1). Formally, therefore, the renewal equation (4.1) is more general, but we shall derive its properties from those of (3.1). Once more we introduce the generating functions

$$(4.3) \qquad A(s) = \Sigma a_n s^n, \qquad B(s) = \Sigma b_n s^n, \qquad U(s) = \Sigma u_n s^n.$$

The coefficients a_n and b_n being bounded, the first two series converge at least for $|s| < 1$; the convergence of the last series will presently become evident. Equation (4.1) can now be rewritten in the form $U(s) = B(s) + A(s)U(s)$ or

$$(4.4) \qquad U(s) = \frac{B(s)}{1 - A(s)}.$$

For $B(s) \equiv 1$ this reduces to (3.2) with the essential difference that now $\{a_n\}$ is not necessarily the distribution of a recurrence time, so that $A(s)$ can be larger as well as smaller than 1.

We shall say that we have the *periodic case if there exists an integer* $\lambda > 1$, *such that all a_k except, perhaps, a_λ, $a_{2\lambda}$, $a_{3\lambda}$, ... vanish.* Then $A(s)$ is a power series in s^λ. The largest integer λ with the said property is called the *period*.

Theorem 1. *Suppose that $\{a_n\}$ is not periodic and that $B(1) = \Sigma b_n$ is finite.*

(a) *If $\Sigma a_n = 1$, then*

$$(4.5) \qquad u_n \to B(1)\mu^{-1} \qquad where \qquad \mu = \Sigma n a_n.$$

(*In particular, $u_n \to 0$ if $\Sigma n a_n$ diverges.*)

(b) *If $\Sigma a_n < 1$, then the series*

$$(4.6) \qquad \Sigma u_n = B(1)\{1 - A(1)\}^{-1}$$

converges.

(c) *If $\Sigma a_n > 1$ and also if the series diverges, then there exists a unique positive root $x < 1$ of the equation $A(x) = 1$. In this case*

$$(4.7) \qquad u_n \sim \frac{B(x)}{A'(x)} x^{-n-1},$$

the sign $\sim$ indicating that the ratio of the two sides tends to unity. (Relation (4.7) implies that u_n increases geometrically; the derivative $A'(x)$ is finite since $A(s)$ is regular for $|s| < 1$.)

Proof. (a) If v_n is the coefficient of s^n in $\{1 - A(s)\}^{-1}$, then $v_n \to \mu^{-1}$ by theorem 3 of the last section. Now

$$(4.8) \qquad u_n = v_n b_0 + v_{n-1} b_1 + \ldots + v_0 b_n.$$

For every fixed k the term $v_{n-k} b_k$ tends to b_k/μ as $n \to \infty$. Moreover, the v_n are bounded. It follows that, for N sufficiently large, u_n differs arbitrarily little from

$$(4.9) \qquad u'_n = v_n b_0 + v_{n-1} b_1 + \ldots + v_{n-N} b_N,$$

and $u'_n \to (b_0 + \ldots + b_N)/\mu$ which in turn differs arbitrarily little from $B(1)/\mu$.

(b) Here the proof of theorem 2, section 3, applies without modification.

(c) Here it suffices to apply the result under (a) to the sequences $\{a_n x^n\}$, $\{b_n x^n\}$, and $\{u_n x^n\}$ which have the generating functions $A(xs)$,

$B(xs)$, and $U(xs)$, and which are obviously related in the same way as the original sequences.

Unfortunately completeness requires a special mention of *periodic* sequences $\{a_n\}$ where $A(s) = \Sigma a_n s^{n\lambda}$ is a power series in s^λ. In this case we divide the coefficients u_n into groups of equal phase, $\{u_0, u_\lambda, u_{2\lambda}, u_{3\lambda}, \ldots\}$, $\{u_1, u_{\lambda+1}, u_{2\lambda+1}, u_{3\lambda+1}, \ldots\}$, $\ldots$, $\{u_{\lambda-1}, u_{2\lambda-1}, u_{3\lambda-1}, \ldots\}$. It is obvious from (4.4) that the coefficients $u_{n\lambda}$ depend only on b_0, b_λ, $b_{2\lambda}$, $\ldots$ but not on the b_k with k not divisible by λ. This leads us to represent $U(s)$ and $B(s)$ as the sum of λ power series in s^λ

$$(4.10) \qquad U(s) = U_0(s) + sU_1(s) + \ldots + s^{\lambda-1}U_{\lambda-1}(s)$$

$$B(s) = B_0(s) + sB_1(s) + \ldots + s^{\lambda-1}B_{\lambda-1}(s),$$

where

$$(4.11) \qquad U_j(s) = \sum_{n=0}^{\infty} u_{n\lambda+j} s^{n\lambda}, \qquad B_j(s) = \sum_{n=0}^{\infty} b_{n\lambda+j} s^{n\lambda}.$$

Then, from (4.4) for $j = 0, 1, \ldots, \lambda-1$,

$$(4.12) \qquad\qquad U_j(s) = \frac{B_j(s)}{1 - A(s)}.$$

Here all functions are power series in s^λ, and the preceding theorem applies after the change of variables $s^\lambda = t$. This leads to

Theorem 2. *In the periodic case with period λ the sequence $\{u_n\}$ is asymptotically periodic; if $A(1) = 1$, each of the λ subsequences $\{u_{n\lambda+j}\}$ has a limit*

$$(4.13) \qquad\qquad \lim_{n\to\infty} u_{n\lambda+j} = \frac{\lambda B_j(1)}{\mu}$$

where $B_j(1) = b_j + b_{\lambda+j} + b_{2\lambda+j} + b_{3\lambda+j} + \ldots$.

Example. *Repeated averaging.* Given three positive numbers u_1, u_2, u_3, define an infinite sequence $\{u_n\}$ by taking running arithmetic means

$$(4.14) \quad u_4 = \tfrac{1}{3}(u_1 + u_2 + u_3), \qquad u_5 = \tfrac{1}{3}(u_2 + u_3 + u_4), \quad \ldots,$$

$$u_{n+3} = \tfrac{1}{3}(u_n + u_{n+1} + u_{n+2}), \quad \ldots.$$

We seek information concerning the asymptotic behavior of $\{u_n\}$. More precisely, *we propose to show that*

$$(4.15) \qquad\qquad u_n \to \tfrac{1}{6}(u_1 + 2u_2 + 3u_3).$$

Needless to say, the same argument will apply to arbitrary means (cf.

problems 5 and XV, 15). The point is that problems of this type are reducible to the renewal equation (4.1) and throw a new light on its nature.

If we put

$$(4.16) \quad a_0 = 0, \qquad a_1 = a_2 = a_3 = \tfrac{1}{3}, \qquad a_n = b_n = 0 \quad \text{for } n \geq 4,$$

then (4.14) and (4.1) agree for $n \geq 4$. To reduce (4.14) to (4.1) for all n we have to define $b_0 = u_0 = 0$ and determine b_1, b_2, b_3 from

$$(4.17) \quad b_1 = u_1, \qquad b_2 = u_2 - \tfrac{1}{3}u_1, \qquad b_3 = u_3 - \tfrac{1}{3}(u_1 + u_2).$$

Now we can apply theorem $1(a)$ to obtain (4.15) without further calculations. Since the generating function $U(s)$ is rational, we can expand it into partial fractions to see that the limit in (4.15) is approached with exponential rapidity and to estimate the difference of the two sides.

5. DELAYED RECURRENT EVENTS

We shall now introduce a slight extension of the notion of recurrent events which is so obvious that it could pass without special mention, except that it is convenient to have a term for it and to have the basic equations on record.

Perhaps the best informal description of delayed recurrent events is to say that they refer to trials where we have "missed the beginning and start in the middle." The waiting time up to the *first* occurrence of $\mathcal{E}$ has a distribution $\{b_n\}$ different from the distribution $\{f_n\}$ of the recurrence times between the following occurrences of $\mathcal{E}$. The theory applies without change except that the trials following each occurrence of $\mathcal{E}$ are exact replicas of a fixed sample space which is not identical with the original one.

The situation being so simple, we shall forego formalities and agree to speak of a *delayed recurrent $\mathcal{E}$ when the definition of recurrent events applies only if the trials leading up to the first occurrence of $\mathcal{E}$ are disregarded; it is understood that the waiting time up to the first appearance of $\mathcal{E}$ is a random variable independent of the following recurrence times, although its distribution $\{b_n\}$ may be different from the common distribution $\{f_n\}$ of the recurrence times.*

It is easy to calculate the probabilities u_n of the occurrence of $\mathcal{E}$ at the nth trial directly from the definition above and the results of section 3. However, it is preferable to proceed independently and to write down a new equation of the renewal type.

The probability that $\mathcal{E}$ occurs at trial number $n - k$ *and the next time* at the nth trial equals $u_{n-k}f_k$. These events are mutually exclusive, and their union for $k = 1, 2, \ldots, n-1$ is the event that $\mathcal{E}$ occurs at the nth trial *and* at some previous trial. The probability that $\mathcal{E}$ occurs at the nth trial for the first time equals b_n, and hence for $n \geq 1$

$$(5.1) \qquad u_n = b_n + u_{n-1}f_1 + u_{n-2}f_2 + \ldots + u_1 f_{n-1}.$$

For the delayed events it is most natural to set

$$(5.2) \qquad\qquad u_0 = f_0 = b_0 = 0;$$

this reduces (5.1) to the renewal equation

$$(5.3) \qquad\qquad \{u_n\} = \{b_n\} + \{u_n\} * \{f_n\},$$

and the corresponding generating functions satisfy

$$(5.4) \qquad\qquad U(s) = \frac{B(s)}{1 - F(s)}.$$

The results of the last section now contain as a special case the

Theorem. *If $\mathcal{E}$ is not periodic and if $\Sigma f_n = 1$ (that is, $\mathcal{E}$ is persistent), then*

$$(5.5) \qquad\qquad u_n \to \mu^{-1}\Sigma b_n \qquad \mu = \Sigma n f_n.$$

If $f = \Sigma f_n < 1$ (that is, $\mathcal{E}$ is transient), then

$$(5.6) \qquad\qquad \Sigma u_n = (1 - f)^{-1}\Sigma b_n.$$

In the periodic case theorem 2 of section 4 applies.

Examples. (a) In the *counter problem* (1.b) suppose that at time 0 the counter was locked for exactly two time units (in other words, the observations begin two trials after a registration). The counter is locked for at least $r - 2$ additional units and becomes free at trial number $r - 1$ if that trial results in failure; otherwise it registers and therefore remains locked for at least r additional trials, etc. It follows that $b_{r-2} = q$, $b_{2r-2} = pq$, $b_{3r-2} = p^2q$, $\ldots$.

(b) *Self-renewing aggregates.* In the example of section 2 we have considered a piece of equipment whose lifetime is a random variable with distribution $\{f_n\}$. When it expires, it is immediately replaced by a new piece, and the process continues in this way, $\mathcal{E}$ standing for "replacement at time n." In section 2 we assumed that at time 0 a *new* piece of equipment is installed. Suppose, instead, that at time 0 the age of the piece is k. Then $\mathcal{E}$ becomes a delayed recurrent event, and we have to calculate the probability distribution $\{b_n\}$ of the waiting time for the *first* replacement. Clearly b_n is the probability that a piece of equipment will expire at age $n + k$, given that it has attained age k. Thus

$$(5.7) \qquad b_n = \frac{f_{n+k}}{r_k}, \qquad r_k = f_k + f_{k+1} + f_{k+2} + \ldots.$$

In applications it is not natural to consider just one piece of equipment but a whole population. Suppose then that *the initial population (at time 0) consists of N elements, among which exactly v_k are of age k* (where $\Sigma v_k = N$). Each element originates a line of descendants, and at any time n there is a certain probability that a replacement is required in this line. The sum of these probabilities for all N elements is the *expected number u_n of replacements at time n*. Obviously u_n satisfies the basic equation (5.3) with

$$(5.8) \qquad b_n = \sum_{k=0}^{\infty} \frac{v_k f_{n+k}}{r_k},$$

and our theorems show that u_n will converge.

It is easy to calculate not only the limit of u_n but also the age distribution at time n and its asymptotic behavior. Let $v_k(n)$ be the *expected number of elements of age k at time n* (so that $v_k(0) = v_k$). Clearly

$$(5.9) \qquad \begin{aligned} v_k(n) &= u_{n-k} r_k & \text{if} \quad k < n, \\[2mm] v_k(n) &= \frac{v_{k-n} r_k}{r_{k-n}} & \text{if} \quad k \geq n. \end{aligned}$$

In the non-periodic case we know that $u_n \to B(1)/\mu = N/\mu$ as $n \to \infty$, and it follows from (5.9) that $v_k(n) \to N r_k/\mu$. Hence, in the non-periodic case, there is a stable *limiting age distribution*: In the limit the expected number of elements of age k is $N r_k/\mu$, where N is the (constant) population size, and $\mu = \Sigma r_k$ the mean duration of life (if $\mu = \infty$, then the population ages indefinitely). The basic fact is that the *limiting age distribution is independent of the initial age distribution* and depends only on the mortality distribution $\{a_n\}$ (cf. problems 17 and 18).

As a numerical illustration consider a population of $N = 1000$ elements with the initial age distribution $v_0 = 500$, $v_1 = 320$, $v_2 = 74$, $v_3 = 100$, $v_4 = 6$. Assume the survival probabilities $f_1 = 0.20$, $f_2 = 0.43$, $f_3 = 0.17$, $f_4 = 0.17$, $f_5 = 0.03$ (so that 5 is the maximal age). Here $U(s)$ is a rational function,

$$(5.10) \quad U(s) = s \frac{397 + 332s + 159s^2 + 97s^3 + 15s^4}{1 - 0.20s - 0.43s^2 - 0.17s^3 - 0.17s^4 - 0.03s^5},$$

and can be expanded into partial fractions,

$$U(s) = \frac{1250s}{3(1-s)} - \frac{972s}{61(1+3s/5)} + \frac{38s}{87(1+s/5)} - \frac{78,225s^2 + 22,125s}{5307(1+s^2/4)}.$$

The age distributions $\{v_k(n)\}$ for $n = 1, 2, 3, \ldots$ may be calculated directly from the renewal equation. The columns of table 1 give these

TABLE 1

k	\multicolumn{9}{c}{n}
	0	1	2	3	4	5	6	7	∞
0	500	397	411.4	412	423.8	414.3	417.0	416.0	416.7
1	320	400	317.6	329.1	329.6	339.0	331.5	333.6	333.3
2	74	148	185	146.9	152.2	152.4	156.8	153.3	154.2
3	100	40	80	100	79.4	82.3	82.4	84.8	83.3
4	6	15	6	12	15	11.9	12.3	12.4	12.5

age distributions $\{v_k(n)\}$ together with the limiting distribution and show that the approach to the limit is not monotonic.

(c) *Population theory.* This theory is analogous to renewal theory, except that the population size is variable and female births play the role of replacements. The essential novelty is that a mother can have zero, one, or more daughters, so that lines may become extinct or branch. We now define a_n as the probability that a newborn female will survive and at age n give birth to a female child (the dependence on the number and ages of previous children is neglected). Then Σa_n is the expected number of daughters, and hence all three possibilities $\Sigma a_n < 1$, $\Sigma a_n = 1$, $\Sigma a_n > 1$ are now possible. The preceding argument applies with this obvious modification.

6. THE NUMBER OF OCCURRENCES OF $\mathcal{E}$

Up to now we have considered the first, second, $\ldots$, rth occurrence of a recurrent event $\mathcal{E}$ and taken the number of trials as a random variable. Often it is more natural to take the opposite point of view, namely to fix the number n of trials and to consider *the number $\mathbf{N}_n$ of occurrences of $\mathcal{E}$ in n trials* as a random variable. We shall investigate the asymptotic behavior of $\mathbf{N}_n$ for large n.

As in (2.8) let $\mathbf{T}^{(r)}$ stand for the number of trials up to and including the rth occurrence of ε. The probability distributions of $\mathbf{T}^{(r)}$ and $\mathbf{N}_n$ are related by the obvious identity

$$(6.1) \qquad \mathbf{P}\{\mathbf{N}_n \geq r\} = \mathbf{P}\{\mathbf{T}^{(r)} \leq n\}.$$

We begin with the simple case where ε is persistent and the distribution $\{f_n\}$ of its recurrence times has finite mean μ and variance σ^2. Since $\mathbf{T}^{(r)}$ is the sum of r independent variables, the central limit theorem (chapter X, section 1) asserts that for each fixed x as $r \to \infty$

$$(6.2) \qquad \mathbf{P}\left\{\frac{\mathbf{T}^{(r)} - r\mu}{\sigma r^{\frac{1}{2}}} < x\right\} \to \Phi(x)$$

where $\Phi(x)$ is the normal distribution function. Now let $n \to \infty$ and $r \to \infty$ in such a way that

$$(6.3) \qquad \frac{n - r\mu}{\sigma r^{\frac{1}{2}}} \to x;$$

then (6.1) and (6.2) together lead to

$$(6.4) \qquad \mathbf{P}\{\mathbf{N}_n \geq r\} \to \Phi(x).$$

To write this relation in a more familiar form we introduce the *reduced variable*

$$(6.5) \qquad \mathbf{N}_n^* = \frac{\mathbf{N}_n - n\mu^{-1}}{\sigma n^{\frac{1}{2}}\mu^{-\frac{3}{2}}}.$$

The inequality $\mathbf{N}_n \geq r$ takes on the form

$$(6.6) \qquad \mathbf{N}_n^* \geq \frac{r - n\mu^{-1}}{\sigma n^{\frac{1}{2}}\mu^{-\frac{3}{2}}} = -\frac{n - r\mu}{\sigma r^{\frac{1}{2}}} \cdot \left(\frac{r\mu}{n}\right)^{\frac{1}{2}},$$

and (6.3) shows that the right side tends to $-x$. Thus

$$(6.7) \quad \mathbf{P}\{\mathbf{N}_n^* \geq -x\} \to \Phi(x) \qquad \text{or} \qquad \mathbf{P}\{\mathbf{N}_n^* < -x\} \to 1 - \Phi(x),$$

and we have proved the

Theorem 1. *Normal approximation. If the recurrent event ε is persistent and its recurrence times have finite mean μ and variance σ^2, then both the number $\mathbf{T}^{(r)}$ of trials up to the rth occurrence of ε and the number $\mathbf{N}_n$ of occurrences of ε in the first n trials are asymptotically normally distributed as indicated in (6.2) and (6.7).*

Note that in (6.7) we have the central limit theorem applied to a sequence of *dependent* variables $\mathbf{N}_n$. The relations (6.7) make it plausible that

(6.8) $$\mathbf{E}(\mathbf{N}_n) \sim \frac{n}{\mu}, \qquad \mathrm{Var}(\mathbf{N}_n) \sim \frac{n\sigma^2}{\mu^3}$$

but an exact proof requires an additional argument.

The usefulness of theorem 1 will be illustrated by an application to the theory of runs in the next section. However, it should be borne in mind that most recurrence times occurring in the fluctuation theory of random variables and in physical processes have *infinite means*, and that theorem 1 must be replaced by more general limit theorems.[4]

We expect intuitively that $\mathbf{E}(\mathbf{N}_n)$ should always increase linearly with n [as in (6.8)], simply "because in twice as many trials $\mathcal{E}$ should occur twice as often." *And yet this is not so.* The return to the origin in coin tossing [example (1.c)] is typical of the recurrence times in diffusion theory and may once more serve as an example for the unexpected features of fluctuations in general.

Theorem 2. *Recurrence paradox. Let $\mathcal{E}$ be the return to the origin in symmetric Bernoulli trials (coin tossing). The expected number $\mathbf{E}(\mathbf{N}_{2n})$ of occurrences of $\mathcal{E}$ in $2n$ trials is given by*

(6.9) $$\mathbf{E}(\mathbf{N}_{2n}) = (2n + 1) \binom{2n}{n} 2^{-2n} - 1$$

so that

(6.10) $$\mathbf{E}(\mathbf{N}_{2n}) \sim 2(n/\pi)^{\frac{1}{2}}$$

(and $\mathbf{E}(\mathbf{N}_n)$ is of the order of magnitude $n^{\frac{1}{2}}$ instead of increasing linearly with n).

Proof. Recalling formula XI(1.8) we may calculate $\mathbf{E}(\mathbf{N}_n)$ from the "tails" in (6.1) to obtain

(6.11) $$\mathbf{E}(\mathbf{N}_n) = \sum_{r=1}^{\infty} \mathbf{P}\{\mathbf{N}_n \geq r\} = \sum_{r=1}^{\infty} \mathbf{P}\{\mathbf{T}^{(r)} \leq n\}.$$

The generating function of $\mathbf{T}^{(r)}$ is $F^r(s)$ where $F(s)$ was found in (3.16) to be $F(s) = 1 - (1 - s^2)^{\frac{1}{2}}$. By theorem 1 of chapter XI, section 1, the generating function of the cumulative probabilities $\mathbf{P}\{\mathbf{T}^{(r)} \leq n\}$ is $F^r(s)(1 - s)^{-1}$ and so by (6.11) the sequence $\{\mathbf{E}(\mathbf{N}_n)\}$ has the generat-

---

[4] W. Feller, Fluctuation theory of recurrent events, *Transactions of the American Mathematical Society*, vol. 67 (1949), pp. 98–119.

ing function

$$(6.12) \quad \sum \mathbf{E}(\mathbf{N}_n)s^n = \frac{F(s)}{(1-s)(1-F(s))} = \frac{1+s}{(1-s^2)^{\frac{3}{2}}} - \frac{1}{1-s}.$$

It follows that

$$(6.13) \qquad \mathbf{E}(\mathbf{N}_{2n}) = \mathbf{E}(\mathbf{N}_{2n+1}) = (-1)^n \binom{-\frac{3}{2}}{n} - 1,$$

and this has been rewritten in the form (6.9) for convenience [using II(12.5)].

The curious implications of this theorem have been discussed at length in chapter III, section 6. Theorem 2 of that section shows that $\mathbf{N}_n \cdot n^{-2}$ has an asymptotic distribution given by the positive part of the normal distribution. The normalization $\mathbf{N}_n n^{-2}$ stands in sharp contrast to that of theorem 1 above.

*7. APPLICATION TO THE THEORY OF SUCCESS RUNS

In the sequel r will denote a fixed positive integer and $\mathcal{E}$ will stand for the occurrence of a success run of length r in a sequence of Bernoulli trials. It is important that the length of a run be defined as stated in example (1.a), for otherwise runs are not recurrent events, and the calculations become more involved. As in (2.1) and (2.2), u_n is the probability of $\mathcal{E}$ at the nth trial, and f_n is the probability that the first run of length r occurs at the nth trial.

The probability that the r trials number $n, n-1, n-2, \ldots, n-r+1$ result in success is obviously p^r. In this case $\mathcal{E}$ occurs at one among these r trials; the probability that $\mathcal{E}$ occurs at the trial number $n - k$ ($k = 0, 1, \ldots, r-1$) and the following k trials result in success is $u_{n-k}p^k$. Since these r possibilities are mutually exclusive, we get the following recurrence relation:[5]

$$(7.1) \qquad u_n + u_{n-1}p + \ldots + u_{n-r+1}p^{r-1} = p^r.$$

This equation is valid for $n \geq r$. Clearly

$$(7.2) \qquad u_1 = u_2 = \ldots = u_{r-1} = 0, \qquad u_0 = 1.$$

Now multiply (7.1) by s^n and sum over $n = r, r+1, r+2, \ldots$. In

---

* Sections 7 and 8 treat a special topic and may be omitted.

[5] The classical approach consists in deriving a recurrence relation for f_n. This method is more complicated and does not apply to, say, runs of either kind or patterns like *SSFFSS*, to which our method applies without change [cf. example (8.c)].

view of (7.2) we get on the left side

(7.3) $\{U(s) - 1\}(1 + ps + p^2s^2 + \ldots + p^{r-1}s^{r-1})$

and on the right side $p^r(s^r + s^{r+1} + \ldots)$. Summing the two geometric series, we find

(7.4) $$\{U(s) - 1\} \cdot \frac{1 - (ps)^r}{1 - ps} = \frac{p^r s^r}{1 - s}$$

or

(7.5) $$U(s) = \frac{1 - s + qp^r s^{r+1}}{(1 - s)(1 - p^r s^r)}.$$

Using equation (3.2), we get for *the generating function of the recurrence times*

(7.6) $$F(s) = \frac{p^r s^r(1 - ps)}{1 - s + qp^r s^{r+1}} = \frac{p^r s^r}{1 - qs(1 + ps + \ldots + p^{r-1}s^{r-1})}.$$

The fact that $F(1) = 1$ shows that in a prolonged sequence of trials the number of runs of any length is certain to increase over all bounds. The mean recurrence time μ can be obtained directly from (7.1) since we know that $u_n \to \mu^{-1}$. If we require also the variance, it is preferable to calculate the derivatives of $F(s)$. This is best done by implicit differentiation after clearing (7.6) of the denominator. An easy calculation then shows that *the mean and variance of the recurrence times of runs of length r are*

(7.7) $$\mu = \frac{1 - p^r}{qp^r}, \qquad \sigma^2 = \frac{1}{(qp^r)^2} - \frac{2r + 1}{qp^r} - \frac{p}{q^2},$$

respectively. Theorem 1 of the last section implies that for large n *the number $\mathbf{N}_n$ of runs of length r produced in n trials is approximately normally distributed,* that is, for fixed $\alpha < \beta$ the probability that

(7.8) $$\frac{n}{\mu} + \frac{\alpha\sigma n^{\frac{1}{2}}}{\mu^{\frac{3}{2}}} < \mathbf{N}_n < \frac{n}{\mu} + \frac{\beta\sigma n^{\frac{1}{2}}}{\mu^{\frac{3}{2}}}$$

tends to $\Phi(\beta) - \Phi(\alpha)$. This fact was first proved by von Mises, but

TABLE 2

MEAN RECURRENCE TIMES FOR SUCCESS RUNS IF TRIALS ARE
PERFORMED AT THE RATE OF ONE PER SECOND

Length of Run	$p = 0.6$	$p = 0.5$ (Coins)	$p = \frac{1}{6}$ (Dice)
$r = 5$	30.7 seconds	1 minute	2.6 hours
10	6.9 minutes	34.1 minutes	28.0 months
15	1.5 hours	18.2 hours	18,098 years
20	19 hours	24.3 days	140.7 million years

without the theory of recurrent events the proof requires rather lengthy calculations. Table 2 gives a few typical means of recurrence times.

The method of partial fractions of chapter XI, section 4, permits us to derive excellent approximations. The second representation in (7.6) shows clearly that the denominator has a unique *positive root* $s = x$. For every real or imaginary number with $|s| \leq x$ we have

$$(7.9) \quad |qs(1 + ps + \ldots + p^{r-1}s^{r-1})| \leq$$

$$\leq qx(1 + px + \ldots + p^{r-1}x^{r-1}) = 1$$

where the equality sign is possible only if all terms on the left have the same argument, that is, if $s = x$. Hence x is smaller in absolute value than any other root of the denominator in (7.6). We can, therefore, apply formulas (4.5) and (4.9) of chapter XI with $s_1 = x$. The coefficient ρ_1 is easily computed with $U(s) = p^r s^r (1 - ps)$ and $V(s) = 1 - s + qp^r s^{r+1}$. We find, using that $V(s) = 0$,

$$(7.10) \qquad f_n \sim \frac{(x - 1)(1 - px)}{(r + 1 - rx)q} \cdot \frac{1}{x^{n+1}}.$$

The probability of no run in n trials is $q_n = f_{n+1} + f_{n+2} + f_{n+3} + \ldots$. Equation (7.10) approximates q_n by a geometric series, and we get

$$(7.11) \qquad q_n \sim \frac{1 - px}{(r + 1 - rx)q} \cdot \frac{1}{x^{n+1}}.$$

We have thus found that the probability of no success run of length r in n trials is, asymptotically, given by (7.11). Table 3 shows that

TABLE 3

PROBABILITY OF HAVING NO SUCCESS RUN OF LENGTH $r = 2$ IN n TRIALS WITH $p = \frac{1}{2}$

n	q_n Exact	Approximation (7.11)	Error
2	0.75	0.76631	0.0163
3	.625	.61996	.0080
4	.500	.50156	.0016
5	.40625	.40577	.0005

the formula gives surprisingly good approximations even for very small n, and the approximation improves rapidly with n. This illustrates the power of the method of generating function and partial fractions.

Numerical Calculations. For the benefit of the practical-minded reader we use this occasion to show that the numerical calculations involved in partial fraction expansions are often less formidable than they appear at first sight, and that excellent estimates of the error can be obtained.

The asymptotic expansion (7.11) raises two questions: first, the contribution of the $r - 1$ neglected roots must be estimated, and second, the dominant root x must be evaluated.

The first representation in (7.6) shows that all roots of the denominator of $F(s)$ satisfy the equation

$$(7.12) \qquad\qquad s = 1 + qp^r s^{r+1},$$

although (7.12) has the additional extraneous root $s = p^{-1}$. For positive s the graph of $f(s) = 1 + qp^r s^{r+1}$ is convex; it intersects the bisector $y = s$ at x and p^{-1} and in the interval between x and p^{-1} the graph lies *below* the bisector. Furthermore, $f'(p^{-1}) = (r + 1)q$. If this quantity exceeds unity, the graph of $f(s)$ crosses the bisector at $s = p$ from below, and hence $p^{-1} > x$. To fix ideas we shall assume that

$$(7.13) \qquad\qquad (r + 1)q > 1;$$

in this case $x < p^{-1}$, and $f(s) < s$ for $x < s < p^{-1}$. It follows that for all complex numbers s such that $x < |s| < p^{-1}$ we have $|f(s)| \leq f(|s|) < |s|$ so that no root s_k can lie in the annulus $x < |s| < p^{-1}$. Since x was chosen as the root smallest in absolute value, this implies that

$$(7.14) \qquad\qquad |s_k| > p^{-1}$$

for each root $s_k \neq x$. By differentiation of (7.12) it is now seen that all roots are simple.

The contribution of each root to q_n is of the same form as the contribution (7.11) of the dominant root x, and therefore the $r-1$ terms neglected in (7.11) are of the form

$$(7.15) \qquad\qquad A_k = \frac{ps_k - 1}{rs_k - (r + 1)} \cdot \frac{1}{qs_k^{n+1}}.$$

We require an upper bound for the first fraction on the right. For that purpose note that for fixed $s > p^{-1} > (r + 1)r^{-1}$

$$(7.16) \qquad\qquad \left| \frac{pse^{i\theta} - 1}{rse^{i\theta} - (r + 1)} \right| \leq \frac{ps + 1}{rs + r + 1};$$

in fact, the quantity on the left obviously assumes its maximum and minimum for $\theta = 0$ and $\theta = \pi$, and a direct substitution shows that 0 corresponds to a minimum, π to a maximum. In view of (7.13) and (7.14) we have then

$$(7.17) \qquad\qquad |A_k| < \frac{2p^{n+1}}{(r + 1 + rp^{-1})q} < \frac{2p^{n+2}}{rq(1 + p)}.$$

We conclude that in (7.11) *the error committed by neglecting the $r-1$ roots different from x is less in absolute value than*

$$(7.18) \qquad\qquad \frac{2(r - 1)p}{rq(1 + p)}.$$

The root x is easily calculated from (7.12) by successive approximations putting $x_0 = 1$, $x_{\nu+1} = f(x_\nu)$. The sequence will converge monotonically to x, and each term provides a lower bound for x, whereas any value s such that $s > f(s)$ provides an upper bound. It is easily seen that

$$(7.19) \qquad x = 1 + qp^r + (r+1)(qp^r)^2 + \ldots.$$

*8. MORE GENERAL PATTERNS

Our method is applicable to more general problems which have been considered as considerably deeper than the theory of runs.

Examples. (a) *Runs of either kind.* Let $\mathcal{E}$ stand for "*either a success run of length r or a failure run of length ρ.*" We are dealing with *two* recurrent events $\mathcal{E}_1$ and $\mathcal{E}_2$, where $\mathcal{E}_1$ stands for "success run of length r" and $\mathcal{E}_2$ for "failure run of length ρ" and $\mathcal{E}$ means "either $\mathcal{E}_1$ or $\mathcal{E}_2$." To $\mathcal{E}_1$ there corresponds the generating function (7.5) which will now be denoted by $U_1(s)$. The corresponding generating function $U_2(s)$ for $\mathcal{E}_2$ is obtained from (7.5) by interchanging p and q and replacing r by ρ. The probability u_n that $\mathcal{E}$ occurs at the nth trial is the sum of the corresponding probabilities for $\mathcal{E}_1$ and $\mathcal{E}_2$, except that $u_0 = 1$. It follows that

$$(8.1) \qquad U(s) = U_1(s) + U_2(s) - 1.$$

The generating function $F(s)$ of the recurrence times of $\mathcal{E}$ is again $F(s) = 1 - U^{-1}(s)$ or

$$(8.2) \quad F(s) = \frac{(1 - ps)p^r s^r(1 - q^\rho s^\rho) + (1 - qs)q^\rho s^\rho(1 - p^r s^r)}{1 - s + qp^r s^{r+1} + pq^\rho s^{\rho+1} - p^r q^\rho s^{r+\rho}}.$$

The *mean recurrence time* follows by differentiation

$$(8.3) \qquad \mu = \frac{(1 - p^r)(1 - q^\rho)}{qp^r + pq^\rho - p^r q^\rho}.$$

As $\rho \to \infty$, this expression tends to the mean recurrence time of success runs as given in (7.7).

(b) In chapter VIII, section 1, we calculated the probability x that a *success run of length r occurs before a failure run of length ρ.* Define two recurrent events $\mathcal{E}_1$ and $\mathcal{E}_2$ as in example (a). Let x_n = probability that $\mathcal{E}_1$ occurs for the first time at the nth trial and no $\mathcal{E}_2$ precedes it; f_n = probability that $\mathcal{E}_1$ occurs for the first time at the nth trial (with no condition on $\mathcal{E}_2$). Define y_n and g_n as x_n and f_n, respectively, but with $\mathcal{E}_1$ and $\mathcal{E}_2$ interchanged.

The generating function for f_n is given in (7.6), and $G(s)$ is obtained by interchanging p and q and replacing r by ρ. For x_n and y_n we have the obvious recurrence relations

$$(8.4) \qquad x_n = f_n - (y_1 f_{n-1} + y_2 f_{n-2} + \ldots + y_{n-1} f_1)$$

$$y_n = g_n - (x_1 g_{n-1} + x_2 g_{n-2} + \ldots + x_{n-1} g_1).$$

These equations are of the convolution type, and for the corresponding generating functions we have, therefore,

$$(8.5) \qquad\qquad X(s) = F(s) - Y(s)F(s)$$

$$Y(s) = G(s) - X(s)G(s).$$

From these two linear equations we get

$$(8.6) \qquad X(s) = \frac{F(s)\{1 - G(s)\}}{1 - F(s)G(s)}, \qquad Y(s) = \frac{G(s)\{1 - F(s)\}}{1 - F(s)G(s)}.$$

Expressions for x_n and y_n can again be obtained by the method of partial fractions. For $s = 1$ we get $X(1) = \Sigma x_n = x$, the probability of $\mathcal{E}_1$ occurring before $\mathcal{E}_2$. Both numerator and denominator vanish, and $X(1)$ is obtained from L'Hospital's rule differentiating numerator and denominator: $X(1) = G'(1)/\{F'(1) + G'(1)\}$. Using the values $F'(1) = (1 - p^r)/qp^r$ and $G'(1) = (1 - q^\rho)/pq^\rho$ from (7.7), we find $X(1)$ as given in equation VIII(1.3).

(c) Consider the recurrent event defined by the pattern $SSFFSS$. Repeating the argument of section 7, we easily find that

$$(8.7) \qquad\qquad p^4 q^2 = u_n + p^2 q^2 u_{n-4} + p^3 q^2 u_{n-5}.$$

Since we know that $u_n \to \mu^{-1}$ we get for the mean recurrence time $\mu = p^{-4} q^{-2} + p^{-2} + p^{-1}$. For $p = q = \frac{1}{2}$ we find $\mu = 70$, whereas the mean recurrence time for a success run of length 6 is 126. This shows that, contrary to expectation, *there is an essential difference in coin tossing between head runs and other patterns of the same length.*

9. LACK OF MEMORY OF GEOMETRIC WAITING TIMES

The geometric distribution for waiting times has an interesting and important property not shared by any other distribution. Consider a sequence of Bernoulli trials and let $\mathbf{T}$ be the number of trials up to and including the first success. Then $\mathbf{P}\{\mathbf{T} > k\} = q^k$. Suppose we know that no success has occurred during the first m trials; the waiting time $\mathbf{T}$ from this mth failure to the first success has exactly the same distribution $\{q^k\}$ and is independent of the number of preceding failures. In other words, the probability that the waiting time will be prolonged by k always equals the initial probability of the total length exceeding

k. If the life span of an atom or a piece of equipment has a geometric distribution, then *no aging* takes place; as long as it lives, the atom has the same probability of decaying at the next trial. Radioactive atoms actually have this property (except that in the case of a continuous time the exponential distribution plays the role of the geometric distribution). Conversely, if it is known that a phenomenon is characterized by a complete lack of memory or aging, then the probability distribution of the duration must be geometric or exponential. Typical is a well-known type of telephone conversation often cited as the model of incoherence and depending entirely on momentary impulses; a possible termination is an instantaneous chance effect without relation to the past chatter. By contrast, the knowledge that no streetcar has passed for five minutes increases our expectation that it will come soon. In coin tossing, the probability that the cumulative numbers of heads and tails will equalize at the second trial is $\frac{1}{2}$. However, given that they did not, the probability that they equalize after two additional trials is only $\frac{1}{4}$. These are examples for aftereffect.

For a rigorous formulation of the assertion, suppose that a waiting time $\mathbf{T}$ assumes the values 0, 1, 2, ... with probabilities $p_0, p_1, p_2, \ldots$. Let the distribution of $\mathbf{T}$ have the following property: *The conditional probability that the waiting time terminates at the kth trial, assuming that it has not terminated before, equals p_0 (the probability at the first trial). We claim that $p_k = (1 - p_0)^k p_0$, so that $\mathbf{T}$ has a geometric distribution.*

For a proof we introduce again the "tails"

$$q_k = p_{k+1} + p_{k+2} + p_{k+3} + \ldots = \mathbf{P}\{\mathbf{T} > k\}.$$

Our hypothesis is $\mathbf{T} > k - 1$, and its probability is q_{k-1}. The conditional probability of $\mathbf{T} = k$ is therefore p_k/q_{k-1}, and the assumption is that for all $k \geq 1$

(9.1) $$\frac{p_k}{q_{k-1}} = p_0.$$

Now $p_k = q_{k-1} - q_k$, and hence

(9.2) $$\frac{q_k}{q_{k-1}} = 1 - p_0.$$

Since $q_0 = p_1 + p_2 + \ldots = 1 - p_0$, it follows that $q_k = (1 - p_0)^{k+1}$, and hence $p_k = q_{k-1} - q_k = (1 - p_0)^k p_0$, as asserted.

In the theory of stochastic processes the described lack of memory is connected with the *Markovian property*; we shall return to it in chapter XV, section 10.

* 10. PROOF OF THEOREM 3 OF SECTION 3

In section 3 we have omitted the proof of theorem 3. The latter can be formulated either as a "Tauberian" theorem on power series or in an elementary way as follows. *Given a sequence $\{f_n\}$ such that $f_0 = 0$, $f_n \geq 0$, $\Sigma f_n = 1$, and that the greatest common divisor of those n for which $f_n > 0$ is one. Let $u_0 = 1$ and define u_n for $n \geq 1$ by*

$$(10.1) \qquad u_n = f_1 u_{n-1} + f_2 u_{n-2} + \ldots + f_n u_0$$

Then $u_n \to 1/\mu$, where $\mu = \Sigma n f_n$ (and $u_n \to 0$ if $\Sigma n f_n$ diverges).
For the proof put

$$(10.2) \qquad r_n = f_{n+1} + f_{n+2} + \ldots,$$

so that by formula XI(1.8)

$$(10.3) \qquad \mu = \Sigma r_n.$$

From (10.2) we get $r_0 = 1$, $f_1 = r_0 - r_1$, $f_2 = r_1 - r_2$, etc. Substituting these values into (10.1), we find that $r_0 u_n + r_1 u_{n-1} + \ldots + r_n u_0 = r_0 u_{n-1} + r_1 u_{n-2} + \ldots + r_{n-1} u_0$. If the left side is called A_n, then the right side is A_{n-1}, and our equation states that all A_n are equal. Now $A_0 = r_0 u_0 = 1$, and hence $A_n = 1$ for all n. Thus we have for every n

$$(10.4) \qquad r_0 u_n + r_1 u_{n-1} + \ldots + r_n u_0 = 1.$$

From (10.1) it follows by induction that $u_n \leq 1$. Hence there exists a number $\lambda = \limsup u_n$ such that for any $\epsilon > 0$ and all sufficiently large n we have $u_n < \lambda + \epsilon$, and there exists some sequence n_1, n_2, n_3, ... such that $u_{n_\nu} \to \lambda$. Choose an integer $j > 0$ such that $f_j > 0$. We claim that $u_{n_\nu - j} \to \lambda$. If this were not so, we could find arbitrarily large subscripts n such that simultaneously

$$(10.5) \qquad u_n > \lambda - \epsilon, \qquad u_{n-j} < \lambda' < \lambda.$$

Now let N be so large that $r_N < \epsilon$. Since $u_k \leq 1$, we have then from (10.1) for $n > N$

$$(10.6) \qquad u_n \leq f_0 u_n + f_1 u_{n-1} + \ldots + f_N u_{n-N} + \epsilon.$$

For sufficiently large n each u_k on the right side is less than $\lambda + \epsilon$, and

---

* This section should be omitted at first reading.

$u_{n-j} < \lambda'$. Hence

$$u_n < (f_0 + f_1 + \ldots + f_{j-1} + f_{j+1} + \ldots + f_N)(\lambda + \epsilon) +$$

$$(10.7) \qquad + f_j\lambda' + \epsilon \le (1 - f_j)(\lambda + \epsilon) + f_j\lambda' + \epsilon <$$

$$< \lambda + 2\epsilon - f_j(\lambda - \lambda').$$

If we choose ϵ so small that $f_j(\lambda - \lambda') > 3\epsilon$, then the last inequality contradicts the first one in (10.5), so that the assumption $\lambda' < \lambda$ is impossible.

This proves that, whenever $u_{n_\nu} \to \lambda$, also $u_{n_\nu - j} \to \lambda$. Repeating the argument, we see: *If $f_j > 0$ and $u_{n_\nu} \to \lambda = \lim \sup u_n$, then also*

$$u_{n_\nu - j} \to \lambda, \qquad u_{n_\nu - 2j} \to \lambda, \qquad u_{n_\nu - 3j} \to \lambda, \qquad \text{etc.}$$

For simplicity let us first consider the case where $f_1 > 0$. Then we can take $j = 1$ and conclude that $u_{n_\nu - k} \to \lambda$ for every fixed k. From (10.4) we find for $n = n_\nu$

$$(10.8) \qquad 1 \ge r_0 u_{n_\nu} + r_1 u_{n_\nu - 1} + \ldots + r_N u_{n_\nu - N}.$$

For fixed N every $u_{n_\nu - k} \to \lambda$, so that $1 \ge \lambda(r_0 + r_1 + \ldots + r_N)$. Since N is arbitrary, we conclude that $1 \ge \lambda\mu$ or $\lambda \le 1/\mu$. This completes the proof for the case where (10.3) diverges, for then $u_n \to 0$.

If $\mu < \infty$, let $\gamma = \lim \inf u_n$. The same argument shows that, for every sequence n_ν for which $u_{n_\nu} \to \gamma$, also $u_{n_\nu - k} \to \gamma$. If N is large enough that $r_N < \epsilon$, then from (10.4)

$$(10.9) \qquad 1 \le r_0 u_{n_\nu} + \ldots + r_N u_{n_\nu - N} + \epsilon;$$

herein $u_{n_\nu - k} \to \gamma$ so that $1 \le (r_0 + \ldots + r_N)\gamma + \epsilon$ and hence $\mu\gamma \ge 1$. However, by definition, $\gamma \le \lambda$. Therefore $\gamma = \lambda = 1/\mu$, as was to be proved.

There remains the case where $f_1 = 0$. Consider then the collection of all integers j for which $f_j > 0$. Among them we can find a finite collection $a, b, c, \ldots, m$ whose greatest common divisor is 1. We know that, when $u_{n_\nu} \to \lambda$, also $u_{n_\nu - xa} \to \lambda$, $u_{n_\nu - yb} \to \lambda$, etc., for every fixed $x > 0, y > 0, \ldots, w > 0$; hence also $u_{n_\nu - xa - yb - \ldots - wm} \to \lambda$. In other words, if an integer k is of the form $k = xa + yb + \ldots + wm$ with positive integers $x, y, \ldots, w$, then $u_{n_\nu - k} \to \lambda$. Now it is known from elementary number theory that *every* integer k exceeding the product $abc \ldots m$ can be written in this form. This means that for $k > abc \ldots m$ we have $u_{n_\nu - k} \to \lambda$. To get the inequality (10.8) it suffices to apply (10.4) to $n = n_\nu + ab \ldots m$. The remaining part of the proof requires no change.

11. PROBLEMS FOR SOLUTION

1. Suppose that $F(s)$ is a polynomial. Prove for this case all theorems of section 3, using the partial fraction method of chapter XI, section 4.

2. Let r coins be tossed repeatedly and let $\mathcal{E}$ be the recurrent event that for each of the r coins the accumulated number of heads and tails are equal. Is $\mathcal{E}$ persistent or transient? For the smallest r for which $\mathcal{E}$ is transient, estimate the probability that $\mathcal{E}$ ever occurs.

3. Let $\{\mathbf{X}_k\}$ be a sequence of mutually independent random variables with the common distribution $\mathbf{P}\{\mathbf{X}_k = a\} = b/(a + b)$, $\mathbf{P}\{\mathbf{X}_k = -b\} = a/(a + b)$, where a and b are positive integers. Let $\mathcal{E}$ denote the event $\mathbf{S}_n = 0$. Prove that $\mathcal{E}$ is a persistent event.

4. Let $\{\mathbf{X}_k\}$ be an arbitrary sequence of mutually independent random variables with a common distribution, and let $\mathcal{E}$ stand for $\mathbf{S}_n = 0, \mathbf{S}_1 \leq 0$, $\mathbf{S}_2 \leq 0, \ldots, \mathbf{S}_{n-1} \leq 0$. Prove that $\mathcal{E}$ is a transient recurrent event except in the trivial case where $\mathbf{P}\{\mathbf{X}_k = 0\} = 1$.

5. *Repeated averaging.* Modify the example of section 4 so as to permit arbitrary weighted averages and find the limit.

Note: *Problems 6–8 refer to Bernoulli trials with $p = q = \frac{1}{2}$ (coin tossing). The generating function $F(s) = 1 - (1 - s^2)^{\frac{1}{2}}$ for the return to zero is assumed to be known.*

6. Let $\mathcal{E}_1$ be the recurrent event $\mathbf{S}_n = 0$, $\mathbf{S}_{n-1} < 0$. Find the generating function $F_1(s)$ of the recurrence times.

7. *Continuation.* Find the generating function of the recurrence time for *ladder points* (example 1.*d*). (Note that this is the same as the *waiting time for the first passage through* 1 discussed in chapter XI, section 3.)

8. *Continuation.* Prove the *theorem*: *The probability that at the 2nth or $(2n+1)$st trial* $\mathbf{S}_k$ *assumes a value not previously assumed (i.e., a first passage occurs) equals the probability that* $\mathbf{S}_{2n} = 0$.

9. In the *counter problem* (1.*b*): (*a*) Find the generating function of the recurrence time. (What is its physical significance?) (*b*) If $\mathbf{Z}_n$ is the number of registrations in the first n trials, discuss the relationship between $\mathbf{Z}_n$ and $\mathbf{N}_n$, and find asymptotic expressions for $\mathbf{E}(\mathbf{Z}_n)$ and $\mathrm{Var}(\mathbf{Z}_n)$.

10. *Counters of Type II* differ from those in example (1.*b*) in that each *success* locks the counter for r time units ($r - 1$ trials following the success) so that a success during a locked period prolongs that period. Do problem 9 for such counters.

11. Find an approximation to the probability that in 10,000 tossings of a coin the number of head runs of length 3 will lie between 700 and 730.

12. In a sequence of tossings of a coin let $\mathcal{E}$ stand for the pattern *HTH*. Let r_n be the probability that $\mathcal{E}$ does not occur in n trials. Find the generating function and use the partial fraction method to obtain an asymptotic expansion.

13. In example (8.*b*) show that the expected duration of the game is

$$\mu_1\mu_2/(\mu_1 + \mu_2),$$

where μ_1 and μ_2 are the mean recurrence times for success runs of length r and failure runs of length ρ, respectively.

14. The possible outcomes of each trial are A, B, and C; the corresponding probabilities are α, β, γ ($\alpha + \beta + \gamma = 1$). Find the generating function of the probability that in n trials there is no run of length r: (a) of A's, (b) of A's or B's, (c) of any kind.

15. *Continuation.* Find the probability that the first A-run of length r precedes the first B-run of length ρ and terminates at the nth trial. [Note that this problem does *not* reduce to that of example (8.b) with $p = \alpha/(\alpha + \beta)$, $q = \beta/(\alpha + \beta)$.]

Note: *The following problems refer to the renewal theory, specifically to example (5.b).*

16. *Constancy of the population.* For the quantities (5.9) prove by induction that $\sum_k v_k(n) = N$ for every n.

17. If the mortality distribution is given by $p_k = q^{k-1}p$ (with $p + q = 1$), find u_n and the limiting age distribution, assuming that the original population consists of N elements aged zero.

18. An age distribution is called *stationary* if $v_k(n)$ does not depend on n. Show that this is the case if, and only if, $v_k = Cr_k$, where C is a constant.

---

19. Let $\mathcal{E}$ be a persistent aperiodic recurrent event. Assume that the recurrence time has finite mean μ and variance σ^2. Put $q_n = f_{n+1} + f_{n+2} + \ldots$ and $r_n = q_{n+1} + q_{n+2} + \ldots$. Show that the generating functions $Q(s)$ and $R(s)$ converge for $s = 1$. Prove that

(11.1) $$\sum \left(u_n - \frac{1}{\mu} \right) s^n = \frac{R(s)}{\mu Q(s)}$$

and hence that

(11.2) $$\sum \left(u_n - \frac{1}{\mu} \right) = \frac{\sigma^2 - \mu + \mu^2}{2\mu^2}.$$

20. Let $\mathcal{E}$ be a persistent recurrent event and $\mathbf{N}_r$ the number of occurrences of $\mathcal{E}$ in r trials. Prove that $\mathbf{E}(\mathbf{N}_r) = u_1 + \ldots + u_r$ and hence

(11.3) $$\mathbf{E}(\mathbf{N}_r) \sim \frac{r}{\mu}.$$

21. *Continuation.* Prove that

$$\mathbf{E}(\mathbf{N}_r{}^2) = u_1 + \ldots + u_r + 2 \sum_{j=1}^{r-1} u_j(u_1 + \ldots + u_{r-j})$$

and hence that $\mathbf{E}(\mathbf{N}_r{}^2)$ is the coefficient of s^r in

(11.4) $$\frac{F^2(s) + F(s)}{(1 - s)\{1 - F(s)\}^2}.$$

(Note that this may be reformulated more elegantly using bivariate generating functions.)

22. Let $q_{k,n} = \mathbf{P}\{\mathbf{N}_k = n\}$. Show that $q_{k,n}$ is the coefficient of s^k in

(11.5) $$F^n(s) \frac{\{1 - F(s)\}}{1 - s}.$$

Deduce that $\mathbf{E}(\mathbf{N}_r)$ and $\mathbf{E}(\mathbf{N}_r{}^2)$ are the coefficients of s^r in

$$(11.6) \qquad \frac{F(s)}{(1-s)\{1-F(s)\}}$$

and (11.4), respectively.

23. Using the notations of problem 19, show that

$$(11.7) \qquad \frac{F(s)}{(1-s)\{1-F(s)\}} = -\frac{1}{1-s} + \frac{1}{\mu(1-s)^2} + \frac{R(s)}{\mu\{1-F(s)\}}.$$

Hence, using the last problem, conclude that

$$(11.8) \qquad \mathbf{E}(\mathbf{N}_r) = \frac{r+1}{\mu} + \frac{\sigma^2 - \mu - \mu^2}{2\mu^2} + \epsilon_r$$

with $\epsilon_r \to 0$.

24. *Continuation.* Using a similar argument, show that

$$(11.9) \qquad \mathbf{E}(\mathbf{N}_r{}^2) = \frac{(r+2)(r+1)}{\mu^2} + \frac{2\sigma^2 - 2\mu - \mu^2}{\mu^3}r + \alpha_r,$$

where α_r remains bounded. Hence

$$(11.10) \qquad \mathrm{Var}(\mathbf{N}_r) \sim \frac{\sigma^2}{\mu^3}r.$$

25. In a sequence of Bernoulli trials let $q_{k,n}$ be the probability that exactly n success runs of length r occur in k trials. Using problem 22, show that the generating function $Q_k(x) = \Sigma q_{k,n}x^n$ is the coefficient of s^k in

$$\frac{1 - p^r s^r}{1 - s + qp^r s^{r+1} - (1 - ps)p^r s^r x}.$$

Show, furthermore, that the root of the denominator which is smallest in absolute value is $s_1 \approx 1 + qp^r(1 - x)$.

26. *Continuation. The Poisson distribution of long runs.*[6] If the number k of trials and the length r of runs both tend to infinity, so that $kqp^r \to \lambda$, then the probability of having exactly n runs of length r tends to $e^{-\lambda}\lambda^n/n!$.

Hint: Using the preceding problem, show that the generating function is asymptotically $\{1 + qp^r(1 - x)\}^{-k} \sim e^{-\lambda(1-x)}$. Use the *continuity theorem* of chapter XI, section 6.

---

[6] The theorem was proved by von Mises, but the present method is considerably simpler.

CHAPTER XIV

Random Walk and Ruin Problems

1. GENERAL ORIENTATION

The first part of this chapter is devoted to Bernoulli trials, and once more the picturesque language of betting and random walks is used to simplify and enliven the formulations.

Consider the familiar gambler who wins or loses a dollar with probabilities p and q, respectively. Let his initial capital be z and let him play against an adversary with initial capital $a - z$, so that the combined capital is a. The game continues until the gambler's capital either is reduced to zero or has increased to a, that is, until one of the two players is ruined. We are interested in the probability of the gambler's ruin and the probability distribution of the duration of the game. This is *the classical ruin problem*.

Physical applications and analogies suggest the more flexible interpretation in terms of the motion of a variable point or *"particle"* on the x-axis. At time 0 this particle is at its *initial position* z, and at times 1, 2, 3, ... it moves a unit step in the positive or negative direction, depending on whether the corresponding trial resulted in success or failure. The position of the particle at time n represents the gambler's capital at the conclusion of the nth trial. The trials terminate when the particle for the first time reaches either 0 or a, and we describe this by saying that the particle performs *a random walk with absorbing barriers at 0 and a*. This random walk is *restricted* to the possible positions 1, 2, ..., $a-1$; in the absence of absorbing barriers the random walk is called *unrestricted*. Physicists use the random-walk model as a crude approximation to one-dimensional diffusion or Brownian motion, where a physical particle is exposed to a great number of molecular collisions which impart to it a random motion. The case $p > q$ corresponds to a *drift* to the right when shocks from the left are more probable; when $p = q = \frac{1}{2}$, the random walk is called *symmetric*.

In the limiting case $a \to \infty$ we get a random walk on a semi-infinite line: A particle starting at $z > 0$ performs a random walk up to the moment when it for the first time reaches the origin. In this formulation we recognize the *first-passage time problem;* it was solved by elementary methods in chapter III (at least for the symmetric case) and by the use of generating functions in chapter XI, section 3 (see also problem XIII, 7). We shall recognize formulas previously obtained, but the present derivation is new.[1]

In this chapter we shall use the method of *difference equations* which serves as an introduction to the differential equations of diffusion theory. This analogy leads in a natural way to various modifications and generalizations of the classical ruin problem, a typical and instructive example being the replacing of absorbing barriers by *reflecting* and *elastic* barriers. To describe a reflecting barrier, consider a random walk in the interval $(0, a)$ as defined before but with the modification that whenever the particle is at point 1 it has probability p of moving to position 2 and probability q to stay at 1. In gambling terminology this corresponds to a convention that whenever the gambler loses his last dollar it is generously replaced by his adversary so that the game can continue. The physicist imagines a wall placed at the point $\frac{1}{2}$ of the x-axis with the property that a particle moving from 1 toward 0 is reflected at the wall and returns to 1 instead of reaching 0. Both the absorbing and the reflecting barriers are special cases of the so-called elastic barrier. We define an *elastic barrier at the origin by the rule that from position 1 the particle moves with probability p to position 2; with probability δq it stays at 1; and with probability $(1 - \delta)q$ it moves to 0 and is absorbed* (i.e., the process terminates). For $\delta = 0$ we have the classical ruin problem or absorbing barriers, for $\delta = 1$ reflecting barriers. As δ runs from 0 to 1 we have a family of intermediate cases. The greater δ is, the more likely is the process to continue, and with two reflecting barriers the process can never terminate.

Sections 2 and 3 are devoted to an elementary discussion of the classical ruin problem and its implications. The next three sections are more technical (and may be omitted); in 4 and 5 we derive the relevant generating functions and from them explicit expressions for the distribution of the duration of the game, etc. Section 6 contains an outline of the passage to the limit to the diffusion equation (the formal solutions of the latter being the limiting distributions for the random walk).

---

[1] Conversely, some of the new results can be proved also by the method of chapter III. For the solution of the ruin problem by infinitely many reflections see problems 7–9.

In section 7 the discussion again turns elementary and is devoted to *random walks in two or more dimensions* where new phenomena are encountered. Section 8 treats a generalization of an entirely different type, namely a random walk in one dimension where the particle is no longer restricted to move in unit steps but is permitted to change its position in jumps which are arbitrary multiples of unity. Such generalized random walks have attracted widespread interest in connection with Wald's theory of *sequential sampling*.

In conclusion it must be emphasized that each random walk represents a special Markov chain, and so the present chapter serves partly as an introduction to the next where several random-walk problems (e.g., elastic barriers) will be reformulated.

The problem section contains essential complements to the text and outlines of alternative approaches. It is hoped that a comparison of the methods used will prove highly instructive. (Readers desiring to refer to the graphs and the text of chapter III are asked to visualize the time axis horizontally and the x-axis in the vertical position.)

2. THE CLASSICAL RUIN PROBLEM

We shall consider the problem stated at the opening of the present chapter. Let q_z be the probability of the gambler's ultimate [2] ruin and p_z the probability of his winning. In random-walk terminology q_z and p_z are the probabilities that a particle starting at z will be absorbed at 0 and a, respectively. We shall show that $p_z + q_z = 1$, so that we need not consider the possibility of an unending game.

After the first trial the gambler's fortune is either $z - 1$ or $z + 1$, and therefore we must have

$$(2.1) \qquad q_z = pq_{z+1} + qq_{z-1}$$

provided $1 < z < a - 1$. For $z = 1$ the first trial may lead to ruin, and (2.1) is to be replaced by $q_1 = pq_2 + q$. Similarly, for $z = a - 1$ the first trial may result in victory, and therefore $q_{a-1} = qq_{a-2}$. To unify our equations we define

$$(2.2) \qquad q_0 = 1, \qquad q_a = 0.$$

---

[2] Strictly speaking, the probability of ruin is defined in a sample space of infinitely prolonged games, but we can work with the sample space of n trials. The probability of ruin in less than n trials increases with n and has therefore a limit. We call this *limit* "the probability of ruin." All probabilities in this chapter may be interpreted in this way without reference to infinite sample spaces (cf. the introduction to chapter VIII).

With this convention the probability q_z of ruin satisfies (2.1) for $z = 1, 2, \ldots, a-1$.

Equation (2.1) is a *difference equation*, and (2.2) represents the *boundary conditions* on q_z. We shall derive an explicit expression for q_z by the *method of particular solutions*, which will also be used in more general cases.

Suppose first that $p \neq q$. It is easily verified that the difference equation (2.1) admits of the two particular solutions $q_z = 1$ and $q_z = (q/p)^z$. It follows that for arbitrary constants A and B the sequence

$$(2.3) \qquad q_z = A + B\left(\frac{q}{p}\right)^z$$

represents a formal solution of (2.1). The boundary conditions (2.2) will hold if, and only if, A and B satisfy the two linear equations $A + B = 1$ and $A + B(q/p)^a = 0$. Thus

$$(2.4) \qquad q_z = \frac{(q/p)^a - (q/p)^z}{(q/p)^a - 1}$$

is a formal solution of the difference equation (2.1), satisfying the boundary conditions (2.2). In order to prove that (2.4) is the required probability of ruin it remains to show that the solution is unique, that is, that *all* solutions of (2.1) are of the form (2.3). Now, given an arbitrary solution of (2.1), the two constants A and B can be chosen so that (2.3) will agree with it for $z = 0$ and $z = 1$. From these two values all other values can be found by substituting in (2.1) successively $z = 1, 2, 3, \ldots$. Therefore two solutions which agree for $z = 0$ and $z = 1$ are identical, and hence every solution is of the form (2.3).

Our argument breaks down if $p = q = \frac{1}{2}$, for then (2.4) is meaningless because in this case the two formal particular solutions $q_z = 1$ and $q_z = (q/p)^z$ are identical. However, when $p = q = \frac{1}{2}$ we have a second solution in $q_z = z$, and therefore $q_z = A + Bz$ is a solution of (2.1) depending on two constants. In order to satisfy the boundary conditions (2.2) we must put $A = 1$ and $A + Ba = 0$. Hence

$$(2.5) \qquad q_z = 1 - \frac{z}{a}.$$

(The same numerical value can be obtained formally from (2.4) by finding the limit as $p \to \frac{1}{2}$, using L'Hospital's rule.)

We have thus proved that the required *probability of the gambler's ruin is given by* (2.4) *if* $p \neq q$, *and by* (2.5) *if* $p = q = \frac{1}{2}$. The probability p_z of the gambler's winning the game equals the probability of his adversary's ruin and is therefore obtained from our formulas on replacing p, q, and z by q, p, and $a - z$, respectively. It is readily seen that $p_z + q_z = 1$, as stated previously.

We can reformulate our result as follows: *Let a gambler with an initial capital z play against an infinitely rich adversary who is always willing to play, although the gambler has the privilege of stopping at his pleasure. The gambler adopts the strategy of playing until he either loses his capital or increases it to a (with a net gain $a - z$). Then q_z is the probability of his losing and $1 - q_z$ the probability of his winning.*

Under this system the gambler's ultimate gain or loss is a random variable **G** which assumes the values $a - z$ and $-z$ with probabilities $1 - q_z$ and q_z, respectively. The expected gain is

(2.6) $$\mathbf{E(G)} = a(1 - q_z) - z.$$

Clearly $\mathbf{E(G)} = 0$ if, and only if, $p = q$. This means that, with the system described, *a "fair" game remains fair, and no "unfair" game can be changed into a "fair" one.*

From (2.5) we see that in the case $p = q$ a player with initial capital $z = 999$ has a probability $\frac{999}{1000}$ to win a dollar before losing his capital. With $q = 0.6$, $p = 0.4$ the game is unfavorable indeed, but still the probability (2.4) of winning a dollar before losing the capital is about $\frac{2}{3}$. In general, a gambler with a relatively large initial capital z has a reasonable chance to win a small amount $a - z$ before being ruined.[3]

Let us now investigate the effect of *changing stakes*. Changing the unit from a dollar to a half-dollar is equivalent to doubling the initial capitals. The corresponding probability of ruin $q_z{}^*$ is obtained from (2.4) on replacing z by $2z$ and a by $2a$:

(2.7) $$q_z{}^* = \frac{(q/p)^{2a} - (q/p)^{2z}}{(q/p)^{2a} - 1} = q_z \cdot \frac{(q/p)^a + (q/p)^z}{(q/p)^a + 1}.$$

For $q > p$ the last fraction is greater than unity and $q_z{}^* > q_z$. We restate this conclusion as follows: *If the stakes are doubled while the initial capitals remain unchanged, the probability of ruin decreases for*

---

[3] A certain man used to visit Monte Carlo year after year and was always successful in recovering the costs of his vacations. He firmly believed in a magic power over chance. Actually his experience is not surprising. Assuming that he started with ten times the ultimate gain, the chances of success in any year are nearly $\frac{9}{10}$. The probability of an unbroken sequence of ten successes is about $(1 - \frac{1}{10})^{10} \approx e^{-1} \approx 0.37$. Thus continued success is by no means improbable. Moreover, *one* failure would, of course, be blamed on an oversight or momentary indisposition.

the player whose probability of success is $p < \frac{1}{2}$ and increases for the adversary (for whom the game is advantageous). Suppose, for example, that Peter owns 90 dollars and Paul 10, and let $p = 0.45$, the game being unfavorable to Peter. If at each trial the stake is one dollar, table 1 shows the probability of Peter's ruin to be 0.866, approximately.

TABLE 1

ILLUSTRATING THE CLASSICAL RUIN PROBLEM

p	q	z	a	Probability of		Expected	
				Ruin	Success	Gain	Duration
0.5	0.5	9	10	0.1	0.9	0	9
.5	.5	90	100	.1	.9	0	900
.5	.5	900	1,000	.1	.9	0	90,000
.5	.5	950	1,000	.05	.95	0	47,500
.5	.5	8,000	10,000	.2	.8	0	16,000,000
.45	.55	9	10	.210	.790	−1.1	11
.45	.55	90	100	.866	.134	−76.6	765.6
.45	.55	99	100	.182	.818	−17.2	171.8
.4	.6	90	100	.983	.017	−88.3	441.3
.4	.6	99	100	.333	.667	−32.3	161.7

The initial capital is z. The game terminates with ruin (loss z) or capital a (gain $a - z$).

If the same game is played for a stake of 10 dollars, the probability of Peter's ruin drops to less than one fourth, namely about 0.210. Thus the effect of increasing stakes is more pronounced than might be expected. In general, if k dollars are staked at each trial, we find the probability of ruin from (2.4), replacing z by z/k and a by a/k; the probability of ruin decreases as k increases. In a game with constant stakes the gambler therefore minimizes the probability of ruin by selecting the stake as large as consistent with his goal of gaining an amount fixed in advance. The empirical validity of this conclusion has been challenged, usually by people who contended that every "unfair" bet is unreasonable. If this were to be taken seriously, it would mean the end of all insurance business, for the careful driver who insures against liability obviously plays a game that is technically "unfair." Actually, there exists no theorem in probability to discourage such a driver from taking insurance.

3. EXPECTED DURATION OF THE GAME

The probability distribution of the duration of the game will be deduced in the following sections. However, its expected value can be derived by a much simpler method which is of such wide applicability that it will now be explained at the cost of a slight duplication.

We are still concerned with the classical ruin problem formulated at the beginning of this chapter. We shall assume as known the fact that the duration of the game has a finite expectation $\mathbf{D}_z$. A rigorous proof will be given in the next section.

If the first trial results in success the game continues as if the initial position had been $z + 1$. The conditional expectation of the duration assuming success at the first trial is therefore $\mathbf{D}_{z+1} + 1$. This argument shows that the expected duration $\mathbf{D}_z$ satisfies the difference equation

$$(3.1) \qquad \mathbf{D}_z = p\mathbf{D}_{z+1} + q\mathbf{D}_{z-1} + 1, \qquad 0 < z < a$$

with the boundary conditions

$$(3.2) \qquad \mathbf{D}_0 = 0, \qquad \mathbf{D}_a = 0.$$

The appearance of the term 1 makes the difference equation (3.1) non-homogeneous. If $p \neq q$, then $\mathbf{D}_z = z/(q - p)$ is a formal solution of (3.1). The difference Δ_z of any two solutions of (3.1) satisfies the homogeneous equations $\Delta_z = p\Delta_{z+1} + q\Delta_{z-1}$, and we know already that all solutions of this equation are of the form $A + B(q/p)^z$. It follows that when $p \neq q$ all solutions of (3.1) are of the form

$$(3.3) \qquad \mathbf{D}_z = \frac{z}{q - p} + A + B\left(\frac{q}{p}\right)^z.$$

The boundary conditions (3.2) require that $A + B = 0$ and $A + B(q/p)^a = -a/(q - p)$. Solving for A and B, we find

$$(3.4) \qquad \mathbf{D}_z = \frac{z}{q - p} - \frac{a}{q - p} \cdot \frac{1 - (q/p)^z}{1 - (q/p)^a}.$$

Again the method breaks down if $q = p = \frac{1}{2}$. In this case we must replace $z/(q - p)$ by $-z^2$, which is now a solution of (3.1). It follows that when $p = q = \frac{1}{2}$ all solutions of (3.1) are of the form $\mathbf{D}_z = -z^2 + A + Bz$. The required solution $\mathbf{D}_z$ satisfying the boundary conditions (3.2) is

$$(3.5) \qquad\qquad\qquad \mathbf{D}_z = z(a - z).$$

The expected duration of the game in the classical ruin problem is given by (3.4) or (3.5), according as $p \neq q$ or $p = q = \frac{1}{2}$.

It should be noted that this duration is considerably longer than we would naively expect. If two players with 500 dollars each toss a coin until one is ruined, the average duration of the game is 250,000 trials. If a gambler has only one dollar and his adversary 1000, the average duration is 1000 trials. Further examples are found in table 1.

Passage to the limit $a \to \infty$. If in the formulas (2.4) and (2.5) for the probability of ultimate ruin we let $a \to \infty$, we find that

$$(3.6) \qquad\qquad q_z \to \begin{array}{ll} 1 & \text{if} \quad q \geq p \\ (q/p)^z & \text{if} \quad q < p \end{array}$$

Nobody would hesitate to interpret these limits as probabilities of *ruin in a game against an infinitely rich adversary,* but axiomatically a random walk on the semi-infinite interval $(0, \infty)$ should be considered on its own merits. Now saying that in such a random walk a particle starting at $z > 0$ reaches the origin is really the same as saying that in an unrestricted random walk a particle reaches a position z units to the left from its starting point. This probability has been calculated in chapter XI, section 3, and agrees with (3.6): In a game against an infinitely rich adversary the probability of ruin is one if $q \geq p$ and $(q/p)^z$ if $q < p$. In the second case there is no sense in talking about the expected duration of the game since the game may go on forever. When $q > p$ we get for the expected duration of the game the limit $z(q - p)^{-1}$, and if $q = p$ the limit is infinite. This agrees with our knowledge that in a symmetric random walk all first-passage times have an infinite expectation. (An independent derivation of these results is contained in the next section.)

*4. GENERATING FUNCTIONS FOR THE DURATION OF THE GAME AND FOR THE FIRST-PASSAGE TIMES

We shall use the method of generating functions to study the duration of the game in the classical ruin problem, that is, the restricted random walk with absorbing barriers at 0 and a. The initial position is z (with $0 < z < a$). Let $u_{z,n}$ denote the probability that the process ends with the nth step at the barrier 0 (gambler's ruin at the nth trial). After the first step the position is $z + 1$ or $z - 1$, and we conclude that for $1 < z < a - 1$ and $n \geq 1$

$$(4.1) \qquad\qquad u_{z,n+1} = p u_{z+1,n} + q u_{z-1,n}.$$

This is a difference equation analogous to (2.1), but depending on the

---

* This section together with the related section 5 may be omitted at first reading.

two variables z and n. In analogy with the procedure of section 2 we wish to define boundary values $u_{0,n}$, $u_{a,n}$, and $u_{z,0}$ so that (4.1) becomes valid also for $z = 1$, $z = a - 1$, and $n = 0$. For this purpose we put

$$(4.2) \qquad u_{0,n} = u_{a,n} = 0 \qquad \text{when} \quad n \geq 1$$

and

$$(4.3) \qquad u_{0,0} = 1, \qquad u_{z,0} = 0 \qquad \text{when} \quad z > 0.$$

Then (4.1) holds for all z with $0 < z < a$ and all $n \geq 0$.

We now introduce the generating function

$$(4.4) \qquad U_z(s) = \sum_{n=0}^{\infty} u_{z,n} s^n.$$

Multiplying (4.1) by s^{n+1} and adding for $n = 0, 1, 2, \ldots$, we find

$$(4.5) \qquad U_z(s) = psU_{z+1}(s) + qsU_{z-1}(s), \qquad 0 < z < a$$

and equations (4.2) and (4.3) lead to the boundary conditions

$$(4.6) \qquad U_0(s) = 1, \qquad U_a(s) = 0.$$

Equation (4.5) is a difference equation analogous to (2.1), and the boundary conditions (4.6) correspond to (2.2). The novelty lies in the circumstance that the coefficients and the unknown $U_z(s)$ now depend on the variable s, but as far as the difference equation is concerned, s is merely an arbitrary constant. We can again apply the method of section 2 provided we succeed in finding two particular solutions of (4.5). It is natural to inquire whether there exist two solutions $U_z(s)$ of the form $U_z(s) = \lambda^z(s)$. Substituting this expression into (4.5), we find that $\lambda(s)$ must satisfy the quadratic equation

$$(4.7) \qquad \lambda(s) = ps\lambda^2(s) + qs,$$

which has the two roots

$$(4.8) \quad \lambda_1(s) = \frac{1 + (1 - 4pqs^2)^{\frac{1}{2}}}{2ps}, \qquad \lambda_2(s) = \frac{1 - (1 - 4pqs^2)^{\frac{1}{2}}}{2ps}$$

(we take $0 < s < 1$ and the positive square root).

We have thus found two particular solutions of (4.5) and conclude as in section 2 that for arbitrary functions $A(s)$ and $B(s)$

$$(4.9) \qquad U_z(s) = A(s)\lambda_1^{z}(s) + B(s)\lambda_2^{z}(s)$$

is a solution of (4.5). To satisfy the boundary conditions (4.6), we must have $A(s) + B(s) = 1$ and $A(s)\lambda_1{}^a(s) + B(s)\lambda_2{}^a(s) = 0$, or

$$(4.10) \qquad U_z(s) = \frac{\lambda_1{}^a(s)\lambda_2{}^z(s) - \lambda_1{}^z(s)\lambda_2{}^a(s)}{\lambda_1{}^a(s) - \lambda_2{}^a(s)}.$$

Using the obvious relation $\lambda_1(s)\lambda_2(s) = q/p$, the last formula simplifies to

$$(4.11) \qquad U_z(s) = \left(\frac{q}{p}\right)^z \frac{\lambda_1^{a-z}(s) - \lambda_2^{a-z}(s)}{\lambda_1{}^a(s) - \lambda_2{}^a(s)}.$$

This is *the required generating function of the probability of ruin at the nth trial (absorption at 0)*. The corresponding generating function for the probability of absorption at a is obtained on replacing p, q, z by q, p, and $a - z$, respectively. The generating function of the *duration of game* is, of course, the sum of the two generating functions.

The Case $a = \infty$

Our method applies equally to the case $a = \infty$ which corresponds to a random walk on $(0, \infty)$ with an absorbing barrier at the origin (or playing against an infinitely rich adversary). We have now the sole boundary condition $U_0(s) = 1$. All solutions of (4.5) are of the form (4.9), but since $\lambda_1(s) > 1$ and $\lambda_2(s) < 1$ for $0 < s < 1$, we find that $U_z(s)$ is unbounded unless $A(s) = 0$. Hence the required solution is

$$(4.12) \qquad V_z(s) = \lambda_2{}^z(s).$$

This is *the generating function of the probability that, starting from a point $z > 0$, the particle will be absorbed at the origin exactly at the nth trial.*

In other words, in an *unrestricted random walk* (4.12) *is the generating function of the distribution of first-passage times through a point z units to the left from the initial position.* To get a formula for the first passages to the right we have only to interchange p and q. A glance at (4.8) will show that *in an unrestricted random walk starting from the origin the first-passage times through a point $z > 0$ have the generating functions*

$$(4.13) \qquad \lambda^z(s) = \left(\frac{p}{q}\lambda_2(s)\right)^z = \lambda_1^{-z}(s).$$

For the particular value $z = 1$ we find $\lambda(s)$ as the generating function for the first passages one unit to the right. The first passage from 0 through an arbitrary $z > 1$ is the sum of the first-passage times from 0 to 1, from 1 to 2, ..., from $z - 1$ to z, and is therefore the sum of z independent random variables each having the generating function

$\lambda(s)$. This explains why in (4.13) we find the zth power of a generating function.

Substituting $s = 1$ into (4.13), we find the probability of ruin in the case of an infinitely rich adversary. It is $(q/p)^z$ or 1, according as $q \leq p$ or $q \geq p$.

* 5. EXPLICIT EXPRESSIONS

We shall now derive an explicit formula for $u_{z,n}$ by expanding $U_z(s)$ into partial fractions. Formally, the expression (4.11) for $U_z(s)$ depends on a square root, but in reality $U_z(s)$ is a rational function. In fact, expanding the expressions (4.8) according to the binomial theorem, we see that the difference $\lambda_1{}^k(s) - \lambda_2{}^k(s)$ is a rational function in s multiplied by $(1 - 4pqs^2)^{\frac{1}{2}}$; this root appears as a factor in both the numerator and the denominator of (4.11), and hence $U_z(s)$ is the ratio of two polynomials. The degree of the denominator is $a - 1$ for a odd and $a - 2$ for a even; the degree of the numerator is $a - 1$ when $a - z$ is odd and $a - 2$ when $a - z$ is even. In no case can the degree of the numerator exceed the degree of the denominator by more than one. Hence for $n > 1$ we can compute $u_{z,n}$ from equation XI(4.8), provided all the roots of the denominator are distinct.

We could calculate the roots of the denominator and the corresponding coefficients ρ_ν directly, but the algebra simplifies if we introduce a new independent variable ϕ by

(5.1) $$\frac{1}{\cos \phi} = 2(pq)^{\frac{1}{2}}s.$$

From (4.8) we find

(5.2) $$\lambda_{1,2}(s) = \left(\frac{q}{p}\right)^{\frac{1}{2}} (\cos \phi \pm i \sin \phi) = \left(\frac{q}{p}\right)^{\frac{1}{2}} e^{\pm i\phi},$$

and hence from (4.11)

(5.3) $$U_z(s) = \left(\frac{q}{p}\right)^{\frac{1}{2}z} \frac{\sin (a - z)\phi}{\sin a\phi}.$$

The roots of the denominator are obviously $\phi = 0, \pi/a, 2\pi/a, \ldots$. The corresponding values of s are

(5.4) $$s_\nu = \frac{1}{2(pq)^{\frac{1}{2}} \cos \nu\pi/a}.$$

We get all possible values for s_ν, putting $\nu = 0, 1, \ldots, a$. However, to $\nu = 0$ and $\nu = a$ there correspond the extraneous values $\phi = 0, \pi$, which are also roots of the numerator in (5.3), and if a is even, no number s_ν corresponds to $\nu = \frac{1}{2}a$. Hence, when a is odd, we get all $a - 1$ roots s_ν, putting $\nu = 1, 2, \ldots, a-1$; when a is even, the value $\nu = \frac{1}{2}a$ must be omitted. We should disregard those s_ν which are also roots of the numerator, but for them (5.6) leads automatically to $\rho_\nu = 0$.

We know that

$$(5.5) \qquad \left(\frac{q}{p}\right)^{\frac{1}{2}z} \frac{\sin (a - z)\phi}{\sin a\phi} = As + B + \frac{\rho_1}{s_1 - s} + \ldots + \frac{\rho_{a-1}}{s_{a-1} - s}.$$

To find ρ_ν multiply both sides by $s_\nu - s$ and let $s \to s_\nu$. We get (putting $\phi_\nu = \pi\nu/a$) as in formula XI(4.5)

$$(5.6) \qquad \rho_\nu = -\left(\frac{q}{p}\right)^{\frac{1}{2}z} \frac{\sin (a - z)\pi\nu/a}{a \cdot \cos \nu\pi \cdot (d\phi/ds)_{s=s_\nu}}$$

$$= \left(\frac{q}{p}\right)^{\frac{1}{2}z} \frac{\sin z\pi\nu/a \cdot \sin \pi\nu/a}{2a(pq)^{\frac{1}{2}} \cos^2 \pi\nu/a}.$$

Hence we get finally from (5.5) for the coefficient $u_{z,n}$ of s^n when $n > 1$

$$(5.7) \quad u_{z,n} = a^{-1}2^n p^{\frac{1}{2}(n-z)}q^{\frac{1}{2}(n+z)} \sum_{\nu=1}^{a-1} \cos^{n-1}\frac{\pi\nu}{a} \cdot \sin \frac{\pi\nu}{a} \cdot \sin \frac{\pi z\nu}{a}.$$

(Strictly speaking, the term $\nu = \frac{1}{2}a$ should be omitted when a is even but it is zero anyway and therefore does no harm.)

For $n > 1$ formula (5.7) represents *the probability of ruin (absorption) at the nth trial.* It goes back to Lagrange and has been derived in many different ways.[4] Despite an honorable history and its availability in textbooks, the formula is rediscovered at frequent intervals. For an alternative explicit expression see problem 13; for limiting forms see section 6 and problem 14 (analogous formulas for reflecting barriers are derived in chapter XVI, section 3).

If we let $a \to \infty$, the sum in (5.7) may be interpreted as a Riemann sum approximating an integral. In this way we find that *in a game against an infinitely rich adversary (single absorbing barrier at 0) the probability $w_{z,n}$ that a player with initial capital $z > 0$ will be ruined*

---

[4] An elementary derivation using trigonometric interpolation was given by Ellis, *Cambridge Mathematical Journal*, vol. 4 (1844), or *The Mathematical and Other Writings of R. E. Ellis*, Cambridge and London, 1863.

exactly at the nth step is

$$(5.8) \qquad w_{z,n} = 2^n p^{\frac{1}{2}(n-z)} q^{\frac{1}{2}(n+z)} \int_0^1 \cos^{n-1} \pi x \sin \pi x \sin \pi x z \cdot dx.$$

This integral can be expressed in an elementary way [5] as follows

$$(5.9) \qquad w_{z,n} = \frac{z}{n} \binom{n}{\frac{1}{2}(n-z)} p^{\frac{1}{2}(n-z)} q^{\frac{1}{2}(n+z)};$$

where the binomial coefficient is to be interpreted as zero if $\frac{1}{2}(n-z)$ is not an integer of the interval $[0, n]$. The corresponding *generating function* was found to be $\lambda_2^z(s)$ (see end of section 4).

6. PASSAGE TO THE LIMIT; DIFFUSION PROCESSES

It has already been pointed out that our random-walk models serve as a first approximation to the theory of diffusion and Brownian motion, where small particles are exposed to a tremendous number of molecular shocks. Each shock has a negligible effect, but the superposition of many small actions produces an observable motion. Accordingly, we now want to study random walks where the individual steps are extremely small and occur in very rapid succession. In the limit the process will appear as a continuous motion. The point of interest is that in passing to this limit our formulas remain meaningful and agree with physically significant formulas of diffusion theory which can be derived under much more general conditions by more streamlined methods.[6] This explains partly why the random-walk model, despite its crudeness, describes diffusion processes reasonably well; only the limiting case is physically significant, and various discrete models lead to the same limiting formulas. The situation is in many ways analogous to the conditions of the central limit theorem where the cumulative

---

[5] For $p = q = \frac{1}{2}$ formula (5.9) reduces to the formula III(4.11) for the *first-passage time distribution*. It is by no means easy to verify that (5.8) and (5.9) agree. Perhaps the simplest way is to show that both formulas represent solutions of the difference equation (4.1) with the boundary conditions (4.2)–(4.3) at the origin.

[6] The limiting formulas of the present section agree with those of the now classical Einstein-Wiener theory. The newer, more refined theories (Uhlenbeck, Ornstein) are not considered here. Credit for discovering the connection between random walks and diffusion is due principally to L. Bachelier (1870–   ). His work is frequently of a heuristic nature, but he derived many new results. Kolmogorov's theory of stochastic processes of the Markov type is based largely on Bachelier's ideas. See in particular L. Bachelier, *Calcul des probabilités*, Paris, 1912.

effect of many chance components is practically independent of the nature of the individual components.

Let us begin with an *unrestricted random walk starting at the origin*, and let $v_{x,n}$ be the probability that the nth step takes the particle to the position x. If r among the n steps are directed to the right, $n - r$ are directed to the left, and the total displacement is $r - (n - r) = 2r - n$ units. This displacement can equal x only if n and x are either both even or both odd (which means that after an even number of steps the abscissa x is an even integer). Out of n steps r can be selected in $\binom{n}{r}$ ways, and therefore

$$(6.1) \qquad v_{x,n} = \binom{n}{\frac{1}{2}(n + x)} p^{\frac{1}{2}(n+x)} q^{\frac{1}{2}(n-x)};$$

again the binomial coefficient should be interpreted as 0 whenever $\frac{1}{2}(n + x)$ is not an integer in the interval $[0, n]$.

An alternative way of deriving (6.1) uses the argument which led to the difference equation (4.1) and the boundary conditions (4.2) and (4.3). It can be verified that $v_{x,n}$ must satisfy the difference equation

$$(6.2) \qquad v_{x,n+1} = p v_{x-1,n} + q v_{x+1,n}$$

with the boundary conditions

$$(6.3) \qquad v_{0,0} = 1, \qquad v_{x,0} = 0 \qquad \text{for} \quad x \neq 0.$$

Given (6.3), we put in (6.2) successively $n = 1, 2, \ldots$ and get first all values $v_{x,1}$, and then successively $v_{x,2}$, $v_{x,3}$, $\ldots$. This shows that the conditions (6.2) and (6.3) uniquely determine $v_{x,n}$. On the other hand, it is readily seen that (6.1) is a solution.

Let us now change the unit of length so that *each step has length* Δx *and suppose that the time between any two consecutive steps is* Δt. During time t the particle performs about $t/\Delta t$ jumps, and a displacement x is now equivalent to $x/\Delta x$ units. Only multiples of Δx and Δt represent meaningful coordinates, but in the limit $\Delta x \to 0$, $\Delta t \to 0$ every displacement and all times become possible.

We must not expect sensible results if Δx and Δt approach zero in an arbitrary manner, for the maximum possible displacement in time t amounts to $t\Delta x/\Delta t$, so that in the limit no motion exists if $\Delta x/\Delta t \to 0$. Physically speaking, we must keep the x- and t-scales in an appropriate ratio or the process will degenerate in the limit, the variances tending to zero or infinity. To find the proper ratio note that the total displacement during time t is the sum of about $t/\Delta t$ mutually independent random variables each having the mean $(p - q)\Delta x$ and variance

$\{1 - (p - q)^2\}(\Delta x)^2 = 4pq(\Delta x)^2$. The mean and variance of the total displacement in time t are therefore about $t(p - q)\Delta x/\Delta t$ and $4pqt(\Delta x)^2/\Delta t$, respectively. To obtain reasonable results we must let Δx and Δt approach zero in such a way that they remain finite for all t. The finiteness of the variance requires that $(\Delta x)^2/\Delta t$ should remain bounded; the finiteness of the mean implies that $p - q$ must be of the order of magnitude of Δx. This suggests putting

$$(6.4) \qquad \frac{(\Delta x)^2}{\Delta t} = 2D, \qquad p = \frac{1}{2} + \frac{c}{2D}\Delta x, \qquad q = \frac{1}{2} - \frac{c}{2D}\Delta x,$$

where D and c are constants. The value of D introduces only a scale factor; for mathematical simplicity it is best to put $D = 1$, but we keep D unspecified to facilitate comparison with physical theories. The constants D and c are, respectively, the *diffusion coefficient* and the *drift*. If $c = 0$, the random walk is symmetric; in general, the sign of c determines the direction of the drift. In the limit p and q approach $\frac{1}{2}$; with any other norming the particle would drift away so fast that the probability of finite displacements would tend to zero.

We use the norming (6.4) to pass to the limit $\Delta x \to 0$, $\Delta t \to 0$. The total displacement at time $t \approx n\Delta t$ is determined by n Bernoulli trials, and therefore the limiting form of $v_{x,n}$ is given by the normal distribution. For a fixed Δx the displacement is the sum of finitely many independent variables, and its mean is $t(p - q)\Delta x/\Delta t = 2ct$; its variance $4pqt(\Delta x)^2/\Delta t = 2Dt$. Therefore *the probability that at time t the displacement lies between* x_0 *and* x_1 $(x_0 < x_1)$ *tends to*

$$(6.5) \qquad (2\pi)^{-\frac{1}{2}} \int_{y_0}^{y_1} e^{-\frac{1}{2}\lambda^2}\, d\lambda$$

where $y_1 = (x_1 - 2ct)/(2Dt)^{\frac{1}{2}}$ and $y_0 = (x_0 - 2ct)/(2Dt)^{\frac{1}{2}}$.

As for equation (6.2), we pass to the usual functional notation and write it in the form $v(x, t+\Delta t) = p \cdot v(x-\Delta x, t) + q \cdot v(x+\Delta x, t)$. Expanding according to Taylor's theorem up to terms of second order, we get formally

$$(6.6) \quad \Delta t \cdot \frac{\partial v(x, t)}{\partial t} = (q - p)\Delta x \cdot \frac{\partial v(x, t)}{\partial x} + \frac{(\Delta x)^2}{2}\frac{\partial^2 v(x, t)}{\partial x^2} + \ldots.$$

Using (6.4), we get in the limit

$$(6.7) \qquad \frac{\partial v(x, t)}{\partial t} = -2c \cdot \frac{\partial v(x, t)}{\partial x} + D \cdot \frac{\partial^2 v(x, t)}{\partial x^2}.$$

This is the *Fokker-Planck* equation for diffusion with drift, which can be derived from more general and more convincing assumptions. In the usual theory, the solution (6.5) is derived from (6.7), but we have obtained both results by the same limiting process. Our procedure is only heuristic but can be justified rigorously. All formulas of the discrete random walk permit a similar passage to the limit.

As a further example, consider the limiting form of the probabilities for the *first passage*. For simplicity let us first consider formula (5.9) which corresponds to a single barrier. Of the two quantities $w_{z,n}$ and $w_{z,n+1}$, one is necessarily zero. The sum $w_{z,n} + w_{z,n+1}$ represents, asymptotically, the probability of absorption during the time interval $(t, t+2\Delta t)$. We shall show that $w_{z,n} + w_{z,n+1} \sim f(z, t)(2\Delta t)$, where $f(z, t)$ is a continuous function. Then the limiting probability of absorption within any time interval (t_1, t_2) is the integral of $f(z, t)$ extended over that interval. When $n - z$ is even, we have $w_{z,n+1} = 0$, and to find $f(z, t)$ we must replace z in (5.9) by $z/\Delta x$ and n by $t/\Delta t$, and apply (6.4). Using the normal approximation to the binomial distribution and the last equation (6.9), we find easily [7]

$$(6.8) \qquad f(z, t) \sim \frac{z}{2(\pi D t^3)^{\frac{1}{2}}} e^{-\frac{1}{4}(z+2ct)^2/Dt}.$$

This is the limiting form of (5.9); again it coincides with the corresponding formula of diffusion theory. In fact, it is easily verified that $f(-x, t)$ is a solution of (6.7). (In the definition of $w_{z,n}$ the variable z plays the role of $-x$ in $v_{x,n}$.)

A similar argument applies to (5.7). An inspection of this formula shows that the contributions of $\nu = k$ and $\nu = a - k$ cancel if $n - z$ is odd and add if $n - z$ is even. Hence we get the limiting form of $f(z, t) \sim (u_{z,n} + u_{z,n+1})/(2\Delta t)$ by extending in (5.7) the sum twice over $1 \le \nu < a/2$. Replacing z, a, n respectively by $z/\Delta x, a/\Delta x, t/\Delta t$ and observing that for fixed ν

$$\sin \frac{\pi\nu\Delta x}{a} \sim \frac{\pi\nu\Delta x}{a}$$

$$(6.9) \qquad \left(\cos\frac{\pi\nu\Delta x}{a}\right)^{t/\Delta t} \sim \left(1 - \frac{D\pi^2\nu^2\Delta t}{a^2}\right)^{z/\Delta t} \sim e^{-D\pi^2\nu^2 t/a^2},$$

$$(4pq)^{t/2\Delta t}\left(\frac{q}{p}\right)^{z/2\Delta x} \sim e^{-c(ct+z)/D},$$

---

[7] In the symmetric case $c = 0$ (i.e., $p = q$), formula (6.8) agrees with the limiting distribution for first-passage times derived by elementary methods in III(8.c).

we obtain formally the limiting form

$$(6.10) \qquad f(z, t) \sim 2\pi D a^{-2} e^{-c(ct+z)/D} \sum_{\nu=1}^{\infty} \nu e^{-D\pi^2\nu^2 t/a^2} \sin \frac{\pi z \nu}{a}.$$

The formal passage to the limit is justified because of uniform convergence: the contribution of the terms with large ν is negligible both in (6.10) and in the original sum (5.7) (where we have $\nu < a/2$).

In diffusion theory (6.10) is known as Fürth's formula for first passages and is derived directly from the Fokker-Planck equation. In free diffusion the integral over (6.10), extended over the time interval (t_1, t_2), gives the probability that a particle starting at $z > 0$ will within that time interval for the first time reach the origin without having previously passed the barrier a.

* 7. RANDOM WALKS IN THE PLANE AND SPACE

In a two-dimensional random walk the particle moves in unit steps in one of the four directions parallel to the x- and y-axes. For a particle starting at the origin the possible positions are all points of the plane with integral-valued coordinates. Each position has four *neighbors*. Similarly, in three dimensions each position has six neighbors. In order to define the random walk the corresponding four or six probabilities must be specified. For simplicity we shall consider only the *symmetric* case where all directions have the same probability. The complexity of problems is considerably greater than in one dimension, for now the domains to which the particle is restricted may have arbitrary shapes so that complicated boundaries take the place of the single-point barriers in the one-dimensional case.

We begin with an interesting theorem due to Polya.[8]

Theorem. *In the symmetric random walks in one and two dimensions there is probability one that the particle will sooner or later (and therefore infinitely often) return to its initial position. In three dimensions, however, this probability is only about* 0.35 (the expected number of returns is then $0.65\Sigma k(0.35)^k = 0.35/0.65 \approx 0.53$).

Before proving the theorem let us give two alternative formulations, both due to Polya. First, it is almost obvious that the theorem implies

---

* This section treats a special topic and may be omitted at first reading.

[8] G. Polya, Über eine Aufgabe der Wahrscheinlichkeitsrechnung betreffend die Irrfahrt im Strassennetz, *Mathematische Annalen*, vol. 84 (1921), pp. 149–160. The numerical value 0.35 was calculated by W. H. McCrea and F. J. W. Whipple, Random paths in two and three dimensions, *Proceedings of the Royal Society of Edinburgh*, vol. 60 (1940), pp. 281–298.

that in *one and two dimensions there is probability* 1 *that the particle will pass infinitely often through every possible point;* in three dimensions this is not true, however. Thus the statement "all roads lead to Rome" is, in a way, justified in two dimensions.

Alternatively, consider *two* particles performing independent symmetric random walks, the steps occurring simultaneously. Will they ever meet? To simplify language let us define the *distance* of two possible positions as the smallest number of steps leading from one position to the other. (Then distance = sum of absolute differences of the coordinates). If the two particles move one step each, their mutual distance either remains the same or changes by two units, and so their distance either is even at all times or else is always odd. In the second case the two particles can never occupy the same position. In the first case it is readily seen that the probability of their meeting at the nth step equals the probability of the first particle's reaching in $2n$ steps the initial position of the second particle. Hence our theorem states that in two, but not in three, dimensions the two particles are sure infinitely often to occupy the same position. If the initial distance of the two particles is odd, a similar argument shows that they will infinitely often occupy neighboring positions. If this is called meeting, then our theorem asserts that *in one and two dimensions the two particles are certain to meet infinitely often, but in three dimensions there is a positive probability that they never meet.*

Proof. For one dimension the theorem has been proved in example XIII(3.b), except that there we referred to a coin-tossing game rather than to a symmetric random walk. The proof for two and three dimensions proceeds along the same lines. Let u_n be the probability that the nth trial takes the particle to the initial position. According to theorem 2 of chapter XIII, section 3, we have to prove that in the case of two dimensions Σu_n diverges, whereas in the case of three dimensions $\Sigma u_n \approx 0.53$. In two dimensions a return to the initial position is possible only if the numbers of steps in the positive x- and y-directions equal those in the negative x- and y-directions, respectively. Hence $u_n = 0$ if n is odd and (using the multinomial distribution VI(9.2)

$$(7.1) \quad u_{2n} = \frac{1}{4^{2n}} \sum_{k=0}^{n} \frac{(2n)!}{k!\,k!\,(n-k)!\,(n-k)!} = \frac{1}{4^{2n}} \binom{2n}{n} \sum_{k=0}^{n} \binom{n}{k}^2$$

The last expression equals $4^{-2n} \binom{2n}{n}^2$, by formula II(12.11). Stirling's formula shows that u_{2n} is of the order of magnitude $1/n$, so that Σu_{2n} diverges as asserted.

In the case of three dimensions we find similarly

$$(7.2) \qquad u_{2n} = \frac{1}{6^{2n}} \sum_{j,k} \frac{(2n)!}{j!j!k!k!(n-j-k)!(n-j-k)!},$$

the summation extending over all j, k with $j + k \leq n$. It is easily verified that

$$(7.3) \qquad u_{2n} = \frac{1}{2^{2n}} \binom{2n}{n} \sum_{j,k} \left\{ \frac{1}{3^n} \frac{n!}{j!k!(n-j-k)!} \right\}^2.$$

Within the braces we have the terms of a trinomial distribution, and we know that they add to unity. Hence the sum of the squares is smaller than the maximum term within braces, and the latter is attained when both j and k are close to $n/3$. Stirling's formula shows that this maximum is of the order of magnitude n^{-1}, and therefore u_{2n} is of the magnitude $n^{-\frac{3}{2}}$ so that Σu_{2n} converges as asserted.

Polya's theorem is analogous to the facts concerning multiple coin tossings discussed in example XIII(3.c).

We conclude this section with another problem which generalizes the concept of *absorbing barriers*. Consider the case of two dimensions where instead of the interval $0 \leq x \leq a$ we have a plane domain D, that is, a collection of points with integral-valued coordinates. Each point has four neighbors, but for some points of D one or more of the neighbors lie outside D. Such points form the boundary of D, and all other points are called interior points. In the one-dimensional case the two barriers form the boundary, and our problem consisted in finding the probability that, starting from z, the particle will reach the boundary point 0 before reaching a. By analogy, we now ask for the probability that the particle will reach a certain section of the boundary before reaching any boundary point that is not in this section. This means that we divide all boundary points into two sets B' and B''. If (x, y) is an interior point, we ask for the probability $u(x, y)$ that, starting from (x, y), the particle will reach a point of B' before reaching a point of B''. In particular, if B' consists of a single point, then $u(x, y)$ is the probability that the particle will, sooner or later, be absorbed at that particular point.

Let (x, y) be an interior point. The first step takes the particle from (x, y) to one of the four neighbors $(x \pm 1, y)$, $(x, y \pm 1)$, and if all four of them are interior points, we must have

$$(7.4) \quad u(x, y) = \tfrac{1}{4}[u(x + 1, y) + u(x - 1, y) +$$

$$+ u(x, y + 1) + u(x, y - 1)].$$

This is a partial difference equation which takes the place of (2.1) (with $p = q = \frac{1}{2}$). If $(x+1, y)$ is a boundary point, then its contribution $u(x+1, y)$ must be replaced by 1 or 0, according to whether $(x+1, y)$ belongs to B' or B''. *Hence (7.4) will be valid for all interior points if we agree that for a boundary point (ξ, η) we put $u(\xi, \eta) = 1$ if (ξ, η) is in B' and $u(\xi, \eta) = 0$ if (ξ, η) is in B''. This convention takes the place of the boundary conditions (2.2).*

In (7.4) we have a system of linear equations for the unknowns $u(x, y)$; to each interior point there correspond one unknown and one equation. The system is non-homogeneous, since in it there appears at least one boundary point (ξ, η) of B' and it gives rise to a contribution $\frac{1}{4}$ on the right side. If the domain D is finite, there are as many equations as unknowns, and it is well known that the system has a unique solution if, and only if, the corresponding homogeneous system (with $u(\xi, \eta) = 0$ for all boundary points) has no non-vanishing solution. Now $u(x, y)$ is the mean of the four neighboring values $u(x\pm1, y)$, $u(x, y\pm1)$ and cannot exceed all four. In other words, $u(x, y)$ has neither a maximum nor a minimum in the strict sense, and the greatest and the smallest value occur at boundary points. Hence, if all boundary values vanish, so does $u(x, y)$ at all interior points, which proves the existence and uniqueness of the solution of (7.4). Since the boundary values are 0 and 1, all values $u(x, y)$ lie between 0 and 1, as is required for probabilities. These statements are true also for the case of infinite domains, as will be seen from a general theorem on infinite Markov chains.[9]

8. THE GENERALIZED ONE-DIMENSIONAL RANDOM WALK (SEQUENTIAL SAMPLING)

We now return to one dimension but abandon the restriction that the particle moves in unit steps. Instead, *at each step the particle shall have probability p_k to move from any point x to $x + k$, where the integer k may be zero, positive, or negative.* We shall investigate the following *ruin problem: The particle starts from a position z such that $0 < z < a$; we seek the probability u_z that the particle will arrive at some position ≤ 0 before reaching any position $\geq a$.* In other words, the position of the particle at time n is the point $z + \mathbf{X}_1 + \mathbf{X}_2 + \ldots + \mathbf{X}_n$ of the x-axis, where the $\{\mathbf{X}_k\}$ are mutually independent random variables with the common distribution $\{p_\nu\}$; the process stops when for the first time either $\mathbf{X}_1 + \ldots \mathbf{X}_n \leq -z$ or $\mathbf{X}_1 + \ldots \mathbf{X}_n \geq a - z$.

---

[9] Explicit solutions are known in only a few cases and are always very complicated. Solutions for the case of rectangular domains, infinite strips, etc., will be found in the paper by McCrea and Whipple cited in footnote 8.

This problem has attracted widespread interest in connection with *sequential sampling*. There the X_k represent certain characteristics of samples or observations. Measurements are taken until a sum $X_1 + +\ldots+ X_k$ falls outside two preassigned limits (our $-z$ and $a - z$). In the first case the procedure leads to what is technically known as *rejection*, in the second case to *acceptance*. The first sampling procedure of this kind was described by W. Bartky;[10] the general theory was outlined by A. Wald, to whom the formulation above is due.[11]

Without loss of generality we shall suppose that steps are possible in both the positive and negative directions. Otherwise we would have either $u_z = 0$ or $u_z = 1$ for all z.

The probability of ruin at the *first* step is obviously

$$(8.1) \qquad r_z = p_{-z} + p_{-z-1} + p_{-z-2} + \cdots$$

(a quantity which may be zero). The random walk continues only if the particle moved to a position x with $0 < x < a$; the probability of a jump from z to x is p_{x-z}, and the probability of subsequent ruin is then u_x. Therefore

$$(8.2) \qquad u_z = \sum_{x=1}^{a-1} u_x p_{x-z} + r_z.$$

Once more we have here $a - 1$ linear equations for $a - 1$ unknowns u_z. The system is non-homogeneous, since at least for $z = 1$ the probability r_1 is different from zero (steps in the negative direction being possible, which obviously implies $r_1 > 0$). We claim that the corresponding homogeneous system

$$(8.3) \qquad u_z = \sum_{x=1}^{a-1} u_x p_{x-z}$$

has no solution except 0.

In fact, if it had another solution, one of the values u_z would be largest in absolute value, say $u_z = M > 0$. Suppose first that $p_{-1} \neq 0$. Since the coefficients p_{x-z} in (8.3) add to at most unity, the equation is possible only if all those p_{x-z} which actually appear on the right side (with a coefficient different from zero) equal M, and if their coefficients add to 1. Hence $u_{z-1} = M$, and, arguing the same way,

[10] W. Bartky, Multiple sampling with constant probability, *Annals of Mathematical Statistics*, vol. 14 (1943), pp. 363–377. It is described in example XV (2.*j*).

[11] A. Wald, On cumulative sums of random variables, *Annals of Mathematical Statistics*, vol. 15 (1944), pp. 283–296. The methods described in the present book are different from Wald's. See also Wald's book, *Sequential analysis*, John Wiley & Sons, New York, 1947.

$u_{z-2} = u_{z-3} = \ldots = u_1 = M$. However, for $z = 1$ the coefficients p_{x-z} in (8.3) add to less than unity, so that M must be zero. The same argument obviously applies also if $p_{-1} = 0$, since we can replace p_{-1} by some positive coefficient p_k with $k < 0$.

It follows that (8.2) has a unique solution, and thus our problem is determined. Equation (8.2) plays the role of the difference equation (2.1). Again we can simplify the writing by introducing the boundary conditions

(8.4)
$$u_x = 1 \qquad \text{if} \quad x \leq 0$$
$$u_x = 0 \qquad \text{if} \quad x \geq a.$$

Then (8.2) can be written in the form

(8.5)
$$u_z = \Sigma u_x p_{x-z},$$

the summation now extending over all x (for $x \geq a$ we have no contribution owing to the second condition (8.4); the contributions for $x \leq 0$ add to r_z owing to the first condition).

For large a it is cumbersome to solve $a-1$ linear equations directly, and it is preferable to use the *method of particular solutions* analogous to the procedure of section 2. It works whenever the probability distribution $\{p_k\}$ has relatively few positive terms. Suppose that only the p_k with $-\nu \leq k \leq \mu$ are different from zero, so that the largest possible jumps in the positive and negative directions are μ and ν, respectively. The *characteristic equation*

(8.6)
$$\Sigma p_k s^k = 1$$

is equivalent to an algebraic equation of degree $\nu + \mu$. If s is a root of (8.6), then $u_z = s^z$ is a formal solution of (8.5) for all z, but this solution does not satisfy the boundary conditions (8.4). If (8.6) has $\mu+\nu$ distinct roots $s_1, s_2, \ldots$, then the linear combination

(8.7)
$$u_z = \Sigma A_k s_k{}^z$$

is again a formal solution of (8.5) for all z, but we must adjust the constants A_k to satisfy the boundary conditions. Now for $0 < z < a$ only values x with $-\nu + 1 \leq x \leq a + \mu - 1$ appear in (8.5). It suffices therefore to satisfy the boundary conditions (8.4) for $x = 0, -1, -2, \ldots, -\nu+1$, and $x = a, a+1, \ldots, a+\mu-1$, so that we have $\mu + \nu$ conditions in all. If s_k is a double root of (8.5), we lose one constant, but in this case it is easily seen that $u_z = zs_k{}^z$ is another formal solution. In every case the $\mu + \nu$ boundary conditions determine the $\mu + \nu$ arbitrary constants.

Example. Suppose that each individual step takes the particle to one of the four nearest positions, and we let $p_{-2} = p_{-1} = p_1 = p_2 = \frac{1}{4}$. The characteristic equation (8.6) is $s^{-2} + s^{-1} + s + s^2 = 4$. To solve it we put $t = s + s^{-1}$: with this substitution our equation becomes $t^2 + t = 6$, which has the roots $t = 2, -3$. Solving $t = s + s^{-1}$ for s, we find the four roots

$$(8.8) \quad s_1 = s_2 = 1, \quad s_3 = \frac{-3 + 5^{\frac{1}{2}}}{2} = s_4^{-1}, \quad s_4 = \frac{-3 - 5^{\frac{1}{2}}}{2} = s_3^{-1}.$$

Since s_1 is a double root, the general solution of (8.5) in our case is

$$(8.9) \quad u_z = A_1 + A_2 z + A_3 s_3^z + A_4 s_4^z.$$

The boundary conditions are $u_0 = u_{-1} = 1$, and $u_a = u_{a+1} = 0$. They lead to four linear equations for the coefficients A_j and to the final solution

$$(8.10) \quad u_z = 1 - \frac{z}{a} + \frac{(2z - a)(s_3^a - s_4^a) - a(s_3^{2z-a} - s_4^{2z-a})}{a\{(a + 2)(s_3^a - s_4^a) - a(s_3^{a+2} - s_4^{a+2})\}}$$

with s_3 and s_4 given by (8.8).

Numerical Approximations. Usually it is cumbersome to find all the roots, but rather satisfactory approximations can be obtained in a surprisingly simple way. Consider first the case where the probability distribution $\{p_k\}$ has mean zero. Then the characteristic equation (8.6) has a double root at $s = 1$, and $A + Bz$ is a formal solution of (8.5). Of course, the two constants A and B do not suffice to satisfy the $\mu + \nu$ boundary conditions (8.4). However, if we determine A and B so that $A + Bz$ vanishes for $z = a + \mu - 1$ and equals 1 for $z = 0$, then $A + Bx \geq 1$ for $x \leq 0$ and $A + Bx \geq 0$ for $a \leq x < a + \mu$ so that $A + Bz$ satisfies the boundary conditions (8.4) with the equality sign replaced by "greater than or equal to." The difference $A + Bz - u_z$ is therefore a formal solution of (8.5) with non-negative boundary values whence $A + Bz - u_z \geq 0$. In like manner we can get a lower bound for u_z by determining A and B so that $A + Bz$ vanishes for $z = a$ and equals 1 for $z = -\nu + 1$. Hence we have

$$(8.11) \quad \frac{a - z}{a + \nu - 1} \leq u_z \leq \frac{a + \mu - z - 1}{a + \mu - 1}.$$

This estimate is excellent provided a is large as compared to $\mu + \nu$. (Of course, $u_z \approx (1 - z/a)$ is a better approximation but does not give precise bounds.)

Next, consider the general case where the mean of the distribution $\{p_k\}$ is not zero. The characteristic equation (8.6) has then a simple root at $s = 1$. The left side of (8.6) approaches ∞ as $s \to 0$ and as $s \to \infty$. For positive s the curve $y = \Sigma p_k s^k$ is continuous and convex, and since it intersects the line $y = 1$ at $s = 1$, there exists exactly one more intersection. Therefore, the characteristic equation (8.6) has exactly two positive roots, 1 and s_1. As before, we see that $A + Bs_1^z$ is a formal solution of (8.5), and we can apply our previous argument to this solution instead of $A + Bz$. We find in this case

(8.12)
$$\frac{s_1{}^a - s_1{}^z}{s_1{}^a - s_1^{-\nu+1}} \leq u_z \leq \frac{s_1^{a+\mu-1} - s_1{}^z}{s_1^{a+\mu-1} - 1},$$

and have the

Theorem. *The solution of our ruin problem satisfies the inequalities* (8.11) *if* $\{p_k\}$ *has zero mean, and* (8.12) *otherwise. Here s_1 is the unique positive root different from 1 of* (8.6), *and μ and $-\nu$ are defined, respectively, as the largest and smallest subscript for which $p_k \neq 0$.*

Let $m = \Sigma k p_k$ be the *expected gain* in a single trial (or expected length of a single step). It is easily seen from (8.6) that $s_1 > 1$ or $s_1 < 1$ according to whether $m < 0$ or $m > 0$. Letting $a \to \infty$, we conclude from our theorem that *in a game against an infinitely rich adversary the probability of an ultimate ruin is one if and only if $m \leq 0$.*

The *duration of game* can be discussed by similar methods (cf. problem 4).

9. PROBLEMS FOR SOLUTION

1. Consider the ruin problem of sections 2 and 3 for the case of a modified random walk in which the particle moves a unit step to the right or left, or stays at its present position with probabilities α, β, γ, respectively ($\alpha + \beta + \gamma = 1$). (In gambling terminology, the bet may result in a tie.)

2. Consider the ruin problem of sections 2 and 3 for the case where the origin is an *elastic* barrier (as defined in section 1). The difference equations for the probability of ruin (absorption at the origin) and for the expected duration are the same, but with new boundary conditions.

3. A particle moves at each step *two* units to the right or *one* unit to the left, with corresponding probabilities p and q ($p + q = 1$). If the starting position is $z > 0$, find the probability that the particle will ever reach the origin. (This is the ruin problem against an infinitely rich adversary.)

Hint: The equation corresponding to (2.1) has the particular solution $q_z = 1$ and two particular solutions of the form λ^z, where λ satisfies a quadratic equation.

4. In the generalized random-walk problem of section 8 put [in analogy with (8.1)] $\rho_z = p_{a-z} + p_{a+1-z} + p_{a+2-z} + \ldots$, and let $d_{z,n}$ be the probability that the game lasts for exactly n steps. Show that for $n \geq 1$

$$d_{z,n+1} = \sum_{x=1}^{a-1} d_{x,n} p_{x-z}$$

with $d_{z,1} = r_z + \rho_z$. Hence prove that the generating function $d_z(s) = \Sigma d_{z,n} s^n$ is the solution of the system of linear equations

$$s^{-1} d_z(s) - \sum_{x=1}^{a-1} d_x(s) p_{x-z} = r_z + \rho_z.$$

By differentiation it follows that the expected duration e_z is the solution of

$$e_z - \sum_{x=1}^{a-1} e_x p_{x-z} = 1.$$

5. In the random walk with *absorbing* barriers at the points 0 and a and with initial position z, let $w_{z,n}(x)$ be the probability that the nth step takes the particle to the position x. Find the difference equations and boundary conditions which determine $w_{z,n}(x)$.

6. *Continuation.* Modify the boundary conditions for the case of two *reflecting barriers* (i.e., elastic barriers with $\delta = 1$).

Note: *In the following problems $v_{x,n}$ is the probability (6.1) that in an unrestricted random walk starting at the origin the nth step takes the particle to the position x.*

7. *Method of images.*[12] Let $p = q = \frac{1}{2}$. In a random walk in $(0, \infty)$ with an absorbing barrier at the origin and initial position at z, let $u_{z,n}(x)$ be the probability that the nth step takes the particle to the position x. Show that $u_{z,n}(x) = v_{x-z,n} - v_{x+z,n}$. (*Hint:* Show that a difference equation corresponding to (4.1) and the appropriate boundary conditions are satisfied.)

8. *Continuation.* If the origin is a *reflecting barrier*, then

$$u_{z,n}(x) = v_{x-z,n} + v_{x+z,n}.$$

9. *Continuation.* If the random walk is restricted to $(0, a)$ and both barriers are *absorbing*, then

$$(9.1) \qquad u_{z,n}(x) = \sum_k \{v_{x-z-2ka,n} - v_{x+z-2ka,n}\},$$

the summation extending over all k, positive or negative (only finitely many terms are different from zero). If both barriers are *reflecting*, equation (9.1) holds with *minus* replaced by *plus*.

10. *Distribution of maxima.* In a symmetric unrestricted random walk starting at the origin let $\mathbf{M}_n$ be the maximum abscissa of the particle at times $0, 1, 2, \ldots, n$. Using the formula of problem 7, show that

$$(9.2) \qquad \mathbf{P}\{\mathbf{M}_n = z\} = v_{z,n} + v_{z+1,n}.$$

11. Let $V_x(s) = \Sigma v_{x,n}s^n$ (cf. the note preceding problem 7). Prove that $V_x(s) = V_0(x)\lambda_2^{-x}(s)$ when $x \le 0$ and $V_x(s) = V_0(s)\lambda_1^{-x}(s)$ when $x \ge 0$, where $\lambda_1(s)$ and $\lambda_2(s)$ are defined in (4.8). Moreover, $V_0(s) = (1 - 4pqs^2)^{-\frac{1}{2}}$.

Note. These relations follow *directly* from the fact that $\lambda_1(s)$ and $\lambda_2(s)$ are generating functions of first-passage times as explained at the conclusion of section 4.

12. In a random walk in $(0, \infty)$ with an absorbing barrier at the origin and initial position at z, let $u_{z,n}(x)$ be the probability that the nth step takes the

---

[12] Problems 7–9 are examples of the *method of images*. The term $v_{x-z,n}$ corresponds to a particle in an unrestricted random walk, and $v_{x+z,n}$ to an "image point." In equation (9.1) we find image points starting from various positions, obtained by repeated reflections at both boundaries. In problems 12 and 13 we get the general result for the unsymmetric random walk using generating functions. In the theory of difference equations the method of images is always ascribed to Lord Kelvin. The equivalent reflection principle is generally attributed to D. André. See footnote 4 of chapter III.

particle to the position x, and let

(9.3)
$$U_z(s; x) = \sum_{n=0}^{\infty} u_{z,n}(x)s^n.$$

Using problem 11, show that $U_z(s; x) = V_{x-z}(s) - \lambda_2{}^z(s)V_x(s)$. Conclude

(9.4)
$$u_{z,n}(x) = v_{x-z,n} - (q/p)^z \cdot v_{x+z,n}.$$

Compare with the result of problem 7 and derive (9.4) from the latter by combinatorial methods.

13. *Alternative formula for the probability of ruin* (5.7). Expanding (4.11) into a geometric series, prove that

$$u_{z,n} = \sum_{k=0}^{\infty} \left(\frac{p}{q}\right)^{ka} w_{z+2ka,n} - \sum_{k=1}^{\infty} \left(\frac{p}{q}\right)^{ka-z} w_{2ka-z,n}$$

with $w_{z,n}$ defined in (5.9).

14. If the passage to the limit of section 6 is applied to the expression for $u_{z,n}$ given in the preceding problem, show that the probability of absorption during a short time interval of length Δt is asymptotically[13]

$$\frac{1}{2} \Delta t(\pi Dt^3)^{-\frac{1}{2}} e^{-c(ct+z)/D} \sum_{k=-\infty}^{+\infty} (z + 2ka)e^{-\frac{1}{4}(z+2ka)^2/Dt}.$$

(*Hint:* Apply the normal approximation to the binomial distribution.)

15.[14] *Renewal method for the ruin problem.* In the random walk with two absorbing barriers let $u_{z,n}$ and $u_{z,n}{}^*$ be, respectively, the probabilities of absorption at the left and the right barriers. By a proper interpretation prove the truth of the following two equations:

$$V_{-z}(s) = U_z(s)V_0(s) + U_z{}^*(s)V_{-a}(s),$$

$$V_{a-z}(s) = U_z(s)V_a(s) + U_z{}^*(s)V_0(s).$$

By solving this system for $U_z(s)$, derive (4.11).

16. Let $u_{z,n}(x)$ be the probability that the particle, starting from z, will at the nth step be at x without having previously touched the absorbing barriers. Using the notations of problem 15, show that for the corresponding generating function $U_z(s; x) = \Sigma u_{z,n}(x)s^n$ we have

$$U_z(s; x) = V_{x-z}(s) - U_z(s)V_x(s) - U_z{}^*(s)V_{x-a}(s).$$

(No calculations are required.)

17. *Continuation.* The generating function $U_z(s; x)$ of the preceding problem can be obtained by putting $U_z(s; x) = V_{x-z}(s) - A\lambda_1{}^z(s) - B\lambda_2{}^z(s)$ and determining the constants so that the boundary conditions $U_z(s; x) = 0$ for $z = 0$ and $z = a$ are satisfied. With *reflecting barriers* the boundary conditions are $U_0(s; x) = U_1(s; x)$ and $U_a(s; x) = U_{a-1}(s; x)$.

---

[13] The agreement of the new formula with the limiting form (6.10) is a well-known fact of the theory of theta functions.

[14] Problems 15–17 contain a new and independent derivation of the main results concerning random walks in one dimension.

18.[15] A symmetric unrestricted random walk starts at the origin. The probability that the rth return to the origin occurs at the nth step equals the probability that the first passage through r occurs at the $(n-r)$th step. (*Hint:* Compare the generating functions.)

19. Prove the formula

$$ v_{x,n} = (2\pi)^{-1} 2^n p^{(n+x)/2} q^{(n-x)/2} \int_{-\pi}^{\pi} \cos^n t \cdot \cos tx \cdot dt. $$

by showing that the appropriate difference equation is satisfied. Conclude that

$$ V_x(s) = (2\pi)^{-1} \left(\frac{p}{q}\right)^{x/2} \int_{-\pi}^{\pi} \frac{\cos tx}{1 - 2(pq)^{\frac{1}{2}} \cdot s \cdot \cos t} \, dt. $$

20. In a three-dimensional symmetric random walk the particle has probability one to pass infinitely often through any particular line $x = m$, $y = n$. (*Hint:* Cf. problem 1.)

21. In a two-dimensional symmetric random walk starting at the origin the probability that the nth step takes the particle to (x, y) is

$$ (2\pi)^{-2} 2^{-n} \int_{-\pi}^{\pi} \int_{-\pi}^{\pi} (\cos \alpha + \cos \beta)^n \cdot \cos x\alpha \cdot \cos y\beta \cdot d\alpha \, d\beta. $$

Verify this formula and find the analogue for three dimensions. (*Hint:* Check that the expression satisfies the proper difference equation.)

22. In a two-dimensional symmetric random walk let $\mathbf{D}_n^2 = x^2 + y^2$ be the square of the distance of the particle from the origin at time n. Prove $\mathbf{E}(\mathbf{D}_n^2) = n$. [*Hint:* Calculate $\mathbf{E}(\mathbf{D}_{n+1}^2 - \mathbf{D}_n^2)$.]

23. In a symmetric random walk in d dimensions the particle has probability 1 to return infinitely often to a position already previously occupied. (*Hint:* At each step the probability of moving to a new position is at most $(2d - 1) \div 2d$.)

---

[15] This is theorem 3 of chapter III, section 4.

CHAPTER XV

Markov Chains

1. DEFINITION

Up to now we have been concerned mostly with independent trials which can be described as follows. A set of possible outcomes E_1, E_2, ..., (finite or infinite in number) is given, and with each there is associated a probability p_k; the probabilities of sample sequences are defined by the multiplicative property $\mathbf{P}\{(E_{j_0}, E_{j_1}, \ldots, E_{j_n})\} = = p_{j_0} p_{j_1} \cdots p_{j_n}$. In the theory of Markov[1] chains we consider the simplest generalization which consists in permitting the outcome of any trial to depend on the outcome of the directly preceding trial (and only on it). The outcome E_k is no longer associated with a fixed probability p_k, but to every pair (E_j, E_k) there corresponds a *conditional probability* p_{jk}; given that E_j has occurred at some trial, the probability of E_k at the next trial is p_{jk}. In addition to the p_{jk} we must be given the probability a_k of the outcome E_k at the *initial* trial. For p_{jk} to have the meaning attributed to them, the probabilities of sample sequences corresponding to two, three, or four trials must be defined by

$$\mathbf{P}\{(E_j, E_k)\} = a_j p_{jk}, \qquad \mathbf{P}\{(E_j, E_k, E_r)\} = a_j p_{jk} p_{kr},$$

$$\mathbf{P}\{(E_j, E_k, E_r, E_s)\} = a_j p_{jk} p_{kr} p_{rs},$$

and generally

(1.1) $\quad \mathbf{P}\{(E_{j_0}, E_{j_1}, \ldots, E_{j_n})\} = a_{j_0} p_{j_0 j_1} p_{j_1 j_2} \cdots p_{j_{n-2} j_{n-1}} p_{j_{n-1} j_n}.$

Here the initial trial is numbered zero, so that trial number one is the second trial. (This convention is convenient and has been introduced tacitly in the preceding chapter.)

Examples. (a) Every Markov chain is equivalent to an *urn model* as follows. Each occurring subscript is represented by an urn, and

---

[1] A. A. Markov (1856–1922).

338

each urn contains balls marked E_1, E_2, ... The composition of the urns remains fixed, but it varies from urn to urn; in the jth urn the probability to draw a ball marked E_k is p_{jk}. At the *initial*, or zero-th, trial an urn is chosen in accordance with the probability distribution $\{a_i\}$. From that urn a ball is drawn at random, and if it is marked E_j, the next drawing is made from the jth urn, etc. Obviously with this procedure the probability of a sequence $(E_{j_0}, \ldots, E_{j_n})$ is given by (1.1). We see that the notion of a Markov chain is not more general than urn models, but the new symbolism will prove more practical and more intuitive.

(b) *Independent trials* are, of course, the special case of our scheme with $p_{jk} = a_k$ for each j.

If a_k is the probability of E_k at the initial (or zero-th) trial, we must have $a_k \geq 0$ and $\Sigma a_k = 1$. Moreover, whenever E_j occurs it must be followed by some E_k, and it is therefore necessary that for all j and k

$$(1.2) \qquad p_{j1} + p_{j2} + p_{j3} + \ldots = 1, \qquad p_{jk} \geq 0.$$

We want to show that for any numbers a_k and p_{jk} satisfying these conditions, the assignment (1.1) is a permissible definition of probabilities in the sample space corresponding to $n + 1$ trials. The numbers defined in (1.1) being non-negative, we need only prove that they add to unity. Fix first $j_0, j_1, \ldots, j_{n-1}$ and add the numbers (1.1) for all possible j_n. Using (1.2) with $j = j_{n-1}$, we see immediately that the sum equals $a_{j_0} p_{j_0 j_1} \cdots p_{j_{n-2} j_{n-1}}$. Thus the sum over all numbers (1.1) does not depend on n, and since $\Sigma a_{j_0} = 1$, the sum equals unity for all n.

The definition (1.1) depends formally on the number of trials, but our argument proves the mutual consistency of the definitions (1.1) for all n. For example, to obtain the probability of the event "the first two trials result in (E_j, E_k)," we have to fix $j_0 = j$ and $j_1 = k$, and add the probabilities (1.1) for all possible $j_2, j_3, \ldots, j_n$. We have just shown that the sum is $a_j p_{jk}$ and is thus independent of n. This means that it is usually not necessary explicitly to refer to the number of trials; the event $(E_{j_0}, \ldots, E_{j_r})$ has the same probability in all sample spaces of more than r trials. In connection with independent trials it has been pointed out repeatedly that, from a mathematical point of view, it is most satisfactory to introduce only the unique sample space of unending sequences of trials and to consider the result of finitely many trials as the beginning of an infinite sequence. This statement holds true also for Markov chains. Unfortunately, sample spaces of infinitely many trials lead beyond the theory of discrete probabilities to which we are restricted in the present volume.

To summarize, our starting point is the following

Definition. *A sequence of trials with possible outcomes E_1, E_2, ...
will be called a Markov chain* [2] *if the probabilities of sample sequences are
defined by (1.1) in terms of an initial probability distribution $\{a_k\}$ for
the states E_k at time 0 and fixed conditional probabilities p_{jk} of E_k, given
that E_j has occurred at the preceding trial.*

We shall now modify our terminology to conform to the usage in
physical applications. Instead of saying "the nth trial results in E_k,"
we shall say that *at time n the system is in state E_k*. The conditional
probability p_{jk} will be called the *probability of the transition $E_j \rightarrow E_k$*
(from state E_j to state E_k).

The transition probabilities p_{jk} will be arranged in a *matrix of transition probabilities*

$$(1.3) \qquad P = \begin{bmatrix} p_{11} & p_{12} & p_{13} & \cdots \\ p_{21} & p_{22} & p_{23} & \cdots \\ p_{31} & p_{32} & p_{33} & \cdots \\ \cdot & \cdot & \cdot & \cdots \\ \cdot & \cdot & \cdot & \cdots \\ \cdot & \cdot & \cdot & \cdots \end{bmatrix}$$

where the first subscript stands for row, the second for column. Clearly
P is a square matrix with non-negative elements and unit row sums.
Such a matrix (finite or infinite) is called a *stochastic matrix. Any
stochastic matrix can serve as a matrix of transition probabilities; together
with our initial distribution $\{a_k\}$ it completely defines a Markov chain
with states E_1, E_2, ...*

In some special cases it is convenient to number the states starting
with 0 rather than with 1. A zero row and zero column are then to
be added to P.

2. ILLUSTRATIVE EXAMPLES

This section contains examples which will familiarize the reader with
the notion of a Markov chain. To save space we shall refer to some
of them as the occasion arises, but the reader is advised not to store

---

[2] This is not the standard terminology. We are here considering only a special
class of Markov chains, and, strictly speaking, here and in the following sections
the term Markov chain should always be qualified by adding the clause "with
constant transition probabilities." Actually, the general type of Markov chain
is rarely studied. It will be defined in section 10, where the Markov property will
be discussed in relation to general stochastic processes. There the reader will also
find examples of dependent trials that do not form Markov chains.

the examples in his mind. For the classical example of card shuffling see section 9.

(a) Suppose that there are only two states E_1, E_2 also called "success" and "failure." The matrix P is of the form

$$P = \begin{bmatrix} p & q \\ p' & q' \end{bmatrix} \qquad p + q = p' + q' = 1$$

and p, p' are the probabilities of success following success, and success following failure, respectively. For a particular example, imagine a ball moving with velocity ± 1 in the direction of the x-axis. At times 1, 2, ... the ball reverses its direction with probability q, and keeps it with probability p. If E_1 stands for velocity $+1$ and E_2 for -1, the matrix of transition probabilities is of the form described with $q' = p$ and $p' = q$. (This experiment could be simulated by means of a large regular pegboard.)

(b) *Random walk with absorbing barriers.* Let the possible states be E_0, E_1, ..., E_a and consider the matrix of transition probabilities

$$P = \begin{bmatrix} 1 & 0 & 0 & 0 & \cdots & 0 & 0 & 0 \\ q & 0 & p & 0 & \cdots & 0 & 0 & 0 \\ 0 & q & 0 & p & \cdots & 0 & 0 & 0 \\ \cdot & \cdot & \cdot & \cdot & \cdots & \cdot & \cdot & \cdot \\ \cdot & \cdot & \cdot & \cdot & \cdots & \cdot & \cdot & \cdot \\ 0 & 0 & 0 & 0 & \cdots & q & 0 & p \\ 0 & 0 & 0 & 0 & \cdots & 0 & 0 & 1 \end{bmatrix}.$$

From each of the "interior" states E_1, ..., E_{a-1} transitions are possible to the right and the left neighbors (with $p_{i,i+1} = p$ and $p_{i,i-1} = q$). However, no transition is possible from either E_0 or E_a to any other state; the system may move from one state to another, but once E_0 or E_a is reached, the system stays there fixed forever. Clearly this Markov chain differs only terminologically from the model of a random walk with absorbing barriers at 0 and a discussed in the last chapter. There the random walk started from a fixed point z of the interval. In Markov chain terminology this amounts to choosing the initial distribution so that $a_z = 1$ (and hence $a_x = 0$ for $x \neq z$). If we had chosen the initial state at random we would have $a_k = (a + 1)^{-1}$ for $k = 0, 1, \ldots, a$.

(c) *Elastic barriers.* We next consider a matrix which differs from the preceding one only in the rows number 1 and $a - 1$. Choose

$0 \leq \delta_0 \leq 1$ and $0 \leq \delta_a \leq 1$ and set

$$P = \begin{bmatrix} 1 & 0 & 0 & 0 & \cdots & 0 & 0 & 0 \\ (1-\delta_0)q & \delta_0 q & p & 0 & \cdots & 0 & 0 & 0 \\ 0 & q & 0 & p & \cdots & 0 & 0 & 0 \\ \cdot & \cdot & \cdot & \cdot & \cdots & \cdot & \cdot & \cdot \\ \cdot & \cdot & \cdot & \cdot & \cdots & \cdot & \cdot & \cdot \\ 0 & 0 & 0 & 0 & \cdots & 0 & p & 0 \\ 0 & 0 & 0 & 0 & \cdots & q & \delta_a p & (1-\delta_a)p \\ 0 & 0 & 0 & 0 & \cdots & 0 & 0 & 1 \end{bmatrix}.$$

The transition probabilities are the same as before except that from E_1 a passage to E_0 has only probability $(1 - \delta_0)q$, and with probability $\delta_0 q$ the system stays at E_1; a similar statement holds for E_{a-1}. For $\delta_0 = \delta_a = 0$ our matrix is identical with the preceding one. When $\delta_0 = \delta_a = 1$, no passage into E_0 and E_a is possible; a system starting at an interior state E_j will move from state to state but *never* enter E_0 or E_a. In random-walk terminology this last situation corresponds to *reflecting barriers* (cf. chapter XIV). In betting language the state of the system represents the capital of a player in a game where the two players own between them the amount a. Each time the first player loses his last dollar, the adversary replaces it with probability δ_0, and with probability $1 - \delta_0$ the game terminates. With two reflecting barriers the game *never* terminates.

(d) *Cyclical random walks.* Again let the possible states be E_1, E_2, ..., E_a but order them cyclically so that E_a has the neighbors E_{a-1} and E_1. If, as before, the system always passes either to the right or to the left neighbor, the rows of the matrix P are as in example (b), except that the first row is $(0, p, 0, 0, \ldots, 0, q)$ and the last $(p, 0, 0, 0, \ldots, 0, q, 0)$.

More generally, we may permit transitions between any two states. Let $q_0, q_1, \ldots, q_{a-1}$ be, respectively, the probability of staying fixed or moving $1, 2, \ldots, a-1$ units to the right (where k units to the right is the same as $a - k$ units to the left). Then P is the cyclical matrix

$$P = \begin{bmatrix} q_0 & q_1 & q_2 & \cdots & q_{a-2} & q_{a-1} \\ q_{a-1} & q_0 & q_1 & \cdots & q_{a-3} & q_{a-2} \\ q_{a-2} & q_{a-1} & q_0 & \cdots & q_{a-4} & q_{a-3} \\ \cdot & \cdot & \cdot & \cdots & \cdot & \cdot \\ \cdot & \cdot & \cdot & \cdots & \cdot & \cdot \\ q_1 & q_2 & q_3 & \cdots & q_{a-1} & q_0 \end{bmatrix}.$$

If $q_1 = p$, $q_{a-1} = q$, and $q_k = 0$ for $1 < k < a - 1$, then this random walk reduces to the simple case discussed at the beginning of this example. [The discussion is continued in example XVI(2.d).]

(e) *Unrestricted random walks.* An unrestricted one-dimensional random walk is a Markov chain, but it is most natural to order the states in a doubly infinite sequence ($\ldots E_{-2}, E_{-1}, E_0, E_1, E_2, \ldots$). In order to write the matrix of transition probabilities in the familiar form, we must rearrange the states. For example, for the ordering ($E_0, E_1, E_{-1}, E_2, E_{-2}, \ldots$) the first row of P becomes $(0, p, q, 0, 0, \ldots)$, the second $(q, 0, 0, p, 0, 0, \ldots)$, etc. Unfortunately, the natural symmetry is lost, and the formulas become unpleasant. The situation grows even worse in two dimensions. In such cases the methods of this chapter are not convenient for deriving explicit formulas, but the general theorems apply and contain pertinent information.

(f) *The Ehrenfest model of diffusion.* Once more we consider a chain with the $a + 1$ states E_0, E_1, $\ldots$, E_a and transitions possible only to the right and to the left neighbor; however, this time we put $p_{j,j+1} = 1 - j/a$ and $p_{j,j-1} = j/a$, so that

$$P = \begin{bmatrix} 0 & 1 & 0 & 0 & \ldots & 0 & 0 \\ a^{-1} & 0 & 1 - a^{-1} & 0 & \ldots & 0 & 0 \\ 0 & 2a^{-1} & 0 & 1 - 2a^{-1} & \ldots & 0 & 0 \\ \cdot & \cdot & \cdot & \cdot & \ldots & \cdot & \cdot \\ \cdot & \cdot & \cdot & \cdot & \ldots & \cdot & \cdot \\ 0 & 0 & 0 & 0 & \ldots & 0 & a^{-1} \\ 0 & 0 & 0 & 0 & \ldots & 1 & 0 \end{bmatrix}.$$

This chain has two interesting physical interpretations. For a discussion of various recurrence problems in statistical mechanics P. and T. Ehrenfest [3] described a conceptual experiment where a molecules are distributed in two containers A and B. At time n a molecule is chosen at random and removed from its container to the other. The state of the system is determined by the number of molecules in A. Suppose that at a certain moment there are exactly k molecules in the

---

[3] P. and T. Ehrenfest, Über zwei bekannte Einwände gegen das Boltzmannsche H-Theorem, *Physikalische Zeitschrift*, vol. 8 (1907), pp. 311–314. Ming Chen Wang and G. E. Uhlenbeck, On the theory of the Brownian motion II, *Reviews of Modern Physics*, vol. 17 (1945), pp. 323–342. For a more complete discussion (by methods essentially equivalent to those of chapter XVI) see M. Kac, Random walk and the theory of Brownian motion, *American Mathematical Monthly*, vol. 54 (1947), pp. 369–391. See also B. Friedman, A simple urn model, *Communications on Pure and Applied Mathematics*, vol. 2 (1949), pp. 59–70.

container A. At the next trial the system passes into E_{k-1} or E_{k+1} according to whether a molecule in A or B is chosen; the corresponding probabilities are k/a and $(a - k)/a$, and therefore our chain describes Ehrenfest's experiment. However, our chain can also be interpreted as *diffusion with a central force*, that is, a random walk in which the probability of a step to the right varies with the position. From $x = j$ the particle is more likely to move to the right or to the left according as $j < a/2$ or $j > a/2$; this means that the particle has a tendency to move toward $x = a/2$, which corresponds to an attractive elastic force increasing in direct proportion to the distance. (The Ehrenfest model has been described in example V(2.c); see also example (6.a) and problem 12.)

(g) *Occupancy problems.* In chapter I we considered random placements of balls into a cells. Let the number of occupied cells determine the state of the system. If j cells are occupied, the probability that the next ball is placed into an empty cell is $(a - j)/a$. Hence the experiment is described by a chain with transition probabilities $p_{jj} = j/a$, $p_{j,j+1} = (a - j)/a$, and $p_{j,k} = 0$ for all other combinations of j and k. The initial distribution (all cells empty) is given by $p_0 = 1$, $p_k = 0$ for $1 \le k \le a$. [Cf. example XVI(2.e).]

(h) *Success runs.* In a sequence of Bernoulli trials we agree to say that at time n we observe the state E_0 if the nth trial results in failure, and the state E_k ($k = 1, 2, \ldots, n$) if the last failure occurred at trial number $n - k$ (the zero-th trial counting as failure). In other words, the index k of the state E_k indicates the length of the uninterrupted sequence of successes ending at the nth trial. It is obvious that we are dealing with a Markov chain in which only the transitions $E_k \to E_0$ and $E_k \to E_{k+1}$ are possible, and the matrix of transition probabilities takes on the form

$$P = \begin{bmatrix} q & p & 0 & 0 & 0 & \cdots \\ q & 0 & p & 0 & 0 & \cdots \\ q & 0 & 0 & p & 0 & \cdots \\ \cdot & \cdot & \cdot & \cdot & \cdot & \cdots \\ \cdot & \cdot & \cdot & \cdot & \cdot & \cdots \\ \cdot & \cdot & \cdot & \cdot & \cdot & \cdots \end{bmatrix}.$$

(i) *Recurrent events.* The example above is a special case of a more interesting Markov chain. Let $\mathcal{E}$ be an arbitrary recurrent event with the distribution of recurrence times given by $\{f_n\}$. Conventionally we say that at the zero-th trial $\mathcal{E}$ did occur. We say that at time n the system is in state E_0 if $\mathcal{E}$ occurs at the nth trial, and in state E_k if the last occurrence of $\mathcal{E}$ took place at trial number $n - k$. (In a manner of speaking, we are dealing with the waiting time in the negative direction.) As in the last example, it is clear that the state E_k at the nth trial can be succeeded only by E_0 (if $\mathcal{E}$ occurs) or by E_{k+1}. Put

$$(2.1) \quad s_k = f_1 + \ldots + f_k, \quad q_k = \frac{f_{k+1}}{1 - s_k}, \quad p_k = 1 - q_k = \frac{1 - s_{k+1}}{1 - s_k}.$$

Observing E_k means that the waiting time for $\mathcal{E}$ exceeds k, and the probability of $\mathcal{E}$ occurring at the next trial under this hypothesis equals q_k. Accordingly the transitions $E_k \rightarrow E_{k+1}$ and $E_k \rightarrow E_0$ have probabilities p_k and q_k, respectively. A typical sample sequence is of the form $E_0E_0E_1E_2E_3E_0E_1E_0E_1E_2E_0E_0$ (the first E_0 representing the zero-th trial). Here the waiting times are successively 1, 4, 2, 3, 1, and the probability of our sequence equals $f_1f_4f_2f_3f_1$. Now

$$(2.2) \qquad\qquad f_1f_4f_2f_3f_1 = q_0p_0p_1p_2q_3p_0q_1p_0p_1q_2q_0$$

in accordance with the rule (1.1) for probabilities in Markov chains. This reasoning applies to all sequences, and we see that the process is a Markov chain with the matrix

$$P = \begin{bmatrix} q_0 & p_0 & 0 & 0 & 0 & \cdots \\ q_1 & 0 & p_1 & 0 & 0 & \cdots \\ & & & & & \cdots \\ q_2 & 0 & 0 & p_2 & 0 & \cdots \\ q_3 & 0 & 0 & 0 & p_3 & \cdots \\ & & & & & \cdots \\ \cdot & \cdot & \cdot & \cdot & \cdot & \cdots \\ \cdot & \cdot & \cdot & \cdot & \cdot & \cdots \\ \cdot & \cdot & \cdot & \cdot & \cdot & \cdots \end{bmatrix}.$$

[Continued in example (6.c).]

(j) *Sequential sampling.* As we have seen in chapter XIV, section 8, the following problem occurs in sequential sampling. Let $\mathbf{S}_n = \mathbf{X}_1 + + \ldots + \mathbf{X}_n$, where the $\mathbf{X}_\nu$ are mutually independent random variables assuming only integral values and having a common distribution $\{p_k\}$, $k = 0, \pm 1, \pm 2, \ldots$. For preassigned $z > 0$, $b > 0$ there exists a *smallest* n for which either $\mathbf{S}_n \geq b$ or $\mathbf{S}_n \leq -z$. This n is, of course, a random variable, and we are interested in its distribution and in the probabilities of the two contingencies $\mathbf{S}_n \leq -z$ and $\mathbf{S}_n \geq b$.

The problem can be formulated in terms of a Markov chain with states $0, 1, 2, \ldots, b+z$ as follows. Let $a = b + z - 1$ and choose z for the initial state. We say that at time n the system is in the state x (where $x = 1, 2, \ldots, a$) if $z + \mathbf{S}_n = x$ *provided*, however, none of the sums $z+\mathbf{S}_1, \ldots, z+\mathbf{S}_{n-1}$ is ≤ 0 or $> a$; and *with the same proviso* we say that the system is in state 0 if $z + \mathbf{S}_n \leq 0$ and in state $a + 1$ if $z + \mathbf{S}_n \geq a + 1$. Once the system passes into one of the two limiting states 0 and $a + 1$, it remains there forever (that is, we put $p_{0,0} = p_{a+1,a+1} = 1$). The matrix of transition probabilities is

$$P = \begin{bmatrix} 1 & 0 & 0 & 0 & \cdots & 0 & 0 \\ r_1 & p_0 & p_1 & p_2 & \cdots & p_{a-1} & \rho_1 \\ r_2 & p_{-1} & p_0 & p_1 & \cdots & p_{a-2} & \rho_2 \\ r_3 & p_{-2} & p_{-1} & p_0 & \cdots & p_{a-3} & \rho_3 \\ \cdot & \cdot & \cdot & \cdot & \cdots & \cdot & \cdot \\ \cdot & \cdot & \cdot & \cdot & \cdots & \cdot & \cdot \\ \cdot & \cdot & \cdot & \cdot & \cdots & \cdot & \cdot \\ r_a & p_{-a+1} & p_{-a+2} & p_{-a+3} & \cdots & p_0 & \rho_a \\ 0 & 0 & 0 & 0 & \cdots & 0 & 1 \end{bmatrix}$$

where

$$r_k = p_{-k} + p_{-k-1} + p_{-k-2} + p_{-k-3} + \ldots$$

and

$$\rho_k = p_{a-k+1} + p_{a-k+2} + \ldots.$$

As an illustration, take Bartky's double-sampling inspection scheme. To test a consignment of items, samples of size N are taken and subjected to complete inspection. It is assumed that the samples are stochastically independent and that the number of defectives in each has the same binomial distribution. Allowance is made for one defective item per sample, and so we let $\mathbf{X}_k + 1$ equal the number of defectives in the kth sample. Then for $k \geq 0$

$$(2.3) \qquad p_k = \binom{N}{k+1} p^{k+1} q^{N-k-1};$$

and $p_{-1} = q^N$, $p_x = 0$ for $x < -1$. The procedural rule is as follows: A preliminary sample is drawn and, if it contains no defective, the whole consignment is accepted; if the number of defectives exceeds a, the whole lot is rejected. In either of these cases the process stops and we have no Markov chain. If, however, the number z of defectives lies in the range $1 \leq z \leq a$, the sampling continues in the described way as long as the state of the chain is contained between 1 and a. Sooner or later it will pass either into 0, in which case the consignment is accepted, or into $a + 1$, in which case the consignment is rejected.

(k) *An example from genetics.*[4] Consider a population kept constant in size by the selection of N individuals in each successive generation. A particular gene assuming the forms A and a has $2N$ representatives; if in the nth generation A occurs j times, then a occurs $2N - j$ times. In this case we say that the population is at time n in state j ($0 \leq j \leq 2N$). Assuming random mating, the composition of the following generation is determined by $2N$ Bernoulli trials in which the A-gene has probability $j/2N$. We have therefore a Markov chain with

$$p_{jk} = \binom{2N}{k} \left(\frac{j}{2N}\right)^k \left(1 - \frac{j}{2N}\right)^{2N-k}.$$

[Cf. example (8.c).]

(l) *A breeding problem.* In the so-called brother-sister mating two individuals are mated, and among their direct descendants two individuals of opposite sex are selected at random. These are again mated, and the process continues indefinitely. With three genotypes AA, Aa, aa for each parent, we have to distinguish six combinations of parents which we label as follows: $E_1 = AA \times AA$, $E_2 = AA \times Aa$, $E_3 = Aa \times Aa$, $E_4 = Aa \times aa$, $E_5 = aa \times aa$, $E_6 = AA \times aa$. Using the rules of chapter V, it is easily seen that the matrix of transition probabilities is in this case

$$\begin{bmatrix} 1 & 0 & 0 & 0 & 0 & 0 \\ \frac{1}{4} & \frac{1}{2} & \frac{1}{4} & 0 & 0 & 0 \\ \frac{1}{16} & \frac{1}{4} & \frac{1}{4} & \frac{1}{4} & \frac{1}{16} & \frac{1}{8} \\ 0 & 0 & \frac{1}{4} & \frac{1}{2} & \frac{1}{4} & 0 \\ 0 & 0 & 0 & 0 & 1 & 0 \\ 0 & 0 & 1 & 0 & 0 & 0 \end{bmatrix}.$$

[The discussion is continued in problem 4; a complete treatment is given in example XVI(4.b).]

3. HIGHER TRANSITION PROBABILITIES

A transition from E_j to E_k in exactly n steps can occur via different paths $E_j \to E_{j_1} \to E_{j_2} \to \ldots \to E_{j_{n-1}} \to E_k$. The conditional prob-

---

[4] This problem was discussed at length by R. A. Fisher and S. Wright. The formulation in terms of Markov chains is due to G. Malécot, Sur un problème de probabilités en chaine que pose la génétique, *Comptes rendus de l'Académie des Sciences*, vol. 219 (1944), pp. 379–381.

ability that the system passes through this particular path given that
it is at E_j is $p_{jj_1}p_{j_1j_2} \cdots p_{j_{n-1}k}$. The sum of the corresponding expressions for all possible paths is the *probability of finding the system at
time $r + n$ in state E_k, given that at time r it was in state E_j. We denote
it by $p_{jk}^{(n)}$.*

We have, in particular, $p_{jk}^{(1)} = p_{jk}$, and

$$(3.1) \qquad\qquad p_{jk}^{(2)} = \sum_{\nu} p_{j\nu}p_{\nu k}.$$

By induction we find easily the *recursion formula*

$$(3.2) \qquad\qquad p_{jk}^{(n+1)} = \sum_{\nu} p_{j\nu}p_{\nu k}^{(n)};$$

a further induction on m shows that more generally

$$(3.3) \qquad\qquad p_{jk}^{(m+n)} = \sum_{\nu} p_{j\nu}^{(m)}p_{\nu k}^{(n)}.$$

This equation reflects the simple fact that the first m steps lead the
system from E_j to some intermediate state E_ν, and the last n steps
from E_ν to E_k. The identity (3.3) is characteristic for Markov chains.
For more general processes (cf. section 10) an analogous equation holds,
but the last factor depends not only on ν and k but also on j.

In the same way as the p_{jk} form the matrix P, *we arrange the $p_{jk}^{(n)}$ in
a matrix to be denoted by P^n.* Equation (3.2) states that to obtain the
element $p_{jk}^{(n+1)}$ of P^{n+1} we have to multiply the elements of the jth
row of P by the corresponding elements of the kth column of P^n and
add all products. This operation is called row-into-column multiplication of the matrices P and P^n and is expressed symbolically by the
equation $P^{n+1} = PP^n$. This suggests calling P^n the nth power of P;
equation (3.3) expresses the associative law $P^{m+n} = P^mP^n$.

In order to have (3.3) true for all $n \geq 0$ we define $p_{jk}^{(0)}$ by $p_{jj}^{(0)} = 1$
and $p_{jk}^{(0)} = 0$ for $j \neq k$ as is natural.

Examples. (*a*) In the trivial case of *independent trials* all rows of
P are identical, and it is clear without calculations that $P^n = P$ for
all n.

(*b*) In the *success run*, example (2.*h*), the n-step transition probabilities can be written down directly. For example, in three steps the
system can pass from E_k only into E_{k+3}, E_0, E_1, E_2 and the corresponding probabilities are clearly p^3, q, qp, qp^2. Thus

$$P^2 = \begin{bmatrix} q & qp & p^2 & 0 & 0 & \cdots \\ q & qp & 0 & p^2 & 0 & \cdots \\ q & qp & 0 & 0 & p^2 & \cdots \\ \cdot & \cdot & \cdot & \cdot & \cdot & \cdots \\ \cdot & \cdot & \cdot & \cdot & \cdot & \cdots \\ \cdot & \cdot & \cdot & \cdot & \cdot & \cdots \end{bmatrix}, \quad P^3 = \begin{bmatrix} q & qp & qp^2 & p^3 & 0 & 0 & \cdots \\ q & qp & qp^2 & 0 & p^3 & 0 & \cdots \\ q & qp & qp^2 & 0 & 0 & p^3 & \cdots \\ \cdot & \cdot & \cdot & \cdot & \cdot & \cdot & \cdots \\ \cdot & \cdot & \cdot & \cdot & \cdot & \cdot & \cdots \\ \cdot & \cdot & \cdot & \cdot & \cdot & \cdot & \cdots \end{bmatrix}.$$

In this case it is clear that P^n converges to a matrix such that all elements in the column number k equal qp^k.

Absolute Probabilities

Let again a_j stand for the probability of the state E_j at time 0. The (unconditional) probability of finding the system at time n in state E_k is then

$$(3.4) \qquad\qquad a_k^{(n)} = \sum_j a_j p_{jk}^{(n)}.$$

Usually we let the process start from a fixed state E_i, that is, we put $a_i = 1$. In this case $a_k^{(n)} = p_{ik}^{(n)}$.

We feel intuitively that the influence of the initial state on the probability distribution at time n should gradually wear off so that for large n the distribution (3.4) should be nearly independent of the initial distribution $\{a_j\}$. This is the case if (as in the last example) $p_{jk}^{(n)}$ converges to a limit independent of j, that is, if P^n converges to a matrix with identical rows. We shall see that this is usually so, but once more we shall have to take into account the annoying exception caused by periodicities.

4. CLOSURES AND CLOSED SETS

We shall say that E_k *can be reached from* E_j if there exists some $n \geq 0$ such that $p_{jk}^{(n)} > 0$ (i.e., if there is a positive probability of reaching E_k from E_j including the case $E_k = E_j$). For example, in an unrestricted random walk each state can be reached from every other state, but from an absorbing barrier no other state can be reached.

Definition. *A set C of states is closed if no state outside C can be reached from any state E_j in C. The smallest closed set containing C is called the closure of C.*

A single state E_k forming a closed set will be called absorbing.

A Markov chain is irreducible if there exists no closed set other than the set of all states.

Clearly C is closed if, and only if, $p_{jk} = 0$ whenever j is in C and k outside C, for in this case we see from (3.2) that $p_{jk}^{(n)} = 0$ for every n. We have then the obvious

Theorem. *If in the matrices P^n all rows and all columns corresponding to states outside the closed set C are deleted, there remain stochastic matrices for which the fundamental relations (3.2) and (3.3) again hold.*

This means that we have a Markov chain defined on C, and this *subchain can be studied independently of all other states.*

The state E_k is absorbing if, and only if, $p_{kk} = 1$; in this case the matrix of the last theorem reduces to a single element. The *closure of a single state E_j is the set of all states which can be reached from it* (including E_j). This remark may be reformulated in the form of the following useful

Criterion. *A chain is irreducible if, and only if, every state can be reached from every other state.*

Example. In order to find all closed sets it suffices to know which p_{jk} vanish and which are positive. Accordingly, we use a * to denote positive elements and consider a typical matrix, say

$$
P = \begin{bmatrix}
0 & 0 & 0 & * & 0 & 0 & 0 & 0 & * \\
0 & * & * & 0 & * & 0 & 0 & 0 & * \\
0 & 0 & 0 & 0 & 0 & 0 & 0 & * & 0 \\
* & 0 & 0 & 0 & 0 & 0 & 0 & 0 & 0 \\
0 & 0 & 0 & 0 & * & 0 & 0 & 0 & 0 \\
0 & * & 0 & 0 & 0 & 0 & 0 & 0 & 0 \\
0 & * & 0 & 0 & 0 & * & * & 0 & 0 \\
0 & 0 & * & 0 & 0 & 0 & 0 & 0 & 0 \\
0 & 0 & 0 & * & 0 & 0 & 0 & 0 & *
\end{bmatrix}.
$$

In the fifth row a * appears only at the fifth place, and therefore $p_{55} = 1$: the state E_5 is *absorbing*. The third and the eighth row contain only one positive element each, and it is clear that E_3 and E_8 form a *closed* set. From E_1 passages are possible into E_4 and E_9, and from there only to E_1, E_4, E_9. Accordingly the three states E_1, E_4, E_9 form another *closed* set.

It is now apparent that the complication of P arises mainly from an inconvenient notation. Let us relabel the states as follows:

$$E'_1 = E_5; \quad E'_2 = E_3; \quad E'_3 = E_8; \quad E'_4 = E_1; \quad E'_5 = E_9;$$

$$E'_6 = E_4; \quad E'_7 = E_2; \quad E'_8 = E_7; \quad E'_9 = E_6.$$

The elements of the matrix P are rearranged in like manner, and P takes on the form

$$P' = \begin{bmatrix} * & 0 & 0 & 0 & 0 & 0 & 0 & 0 & 0 \\ 0 & 0 & * & 0 & 0 & 0 & 0 & 0 & 0 \\ 0 & * & 0 & 0 & 0 & 0 & 0 & 0 & 0 \\ 0 & 0 & 0 & 0 & * & * & 0 & 0 & 0 \\ 0 & 0 & 0 & 0 & * & * & 0 & 0 & 0 \\ 0 & 0 & 0 & * & 0 & 0 & 0 & 0 & 0 \\ * & * & 0 & 0 & * & 0 & * & 0 & 0 \\ 0 & 0 & 0 & 0 & 0 & 0 & * & * & * \\ 0 & 0 & 0 & 0 & 0 & 0 & * & 0 & 0 \end{bmatrix}.$$

In this form the closed sets (E'_1), (E'_2, E'_3) and (E'_4, E'_5, E'_6) are evident. From E'_7 a passage is possible into each of these three closed sets, and therefore the closure of E'_7 is the set of states E'_1, E'_2, E'_3, E'_4, E'_5, E'_6, E'_7. From E'_8 a passage is possible into E'_7 and E'_9 and hence into each closed set: the closures of E'_8 and of E'_9 consist of all nine states.

Deleting all rows and all columns outside a closed set, we obtain the three stochastic submatrices

$$(4.1) \qquad\qquad [*] \qquad \begin{bmatrix} 0 & * \\ * & 0 \end{bmatrix} \qquad \begin{bmatrix} 0 & * & * \\ 0 & * & * \\ * & 0 & 0 \end{bmatrix}$$

and P' contains no other stochastic submatrices.

The reader is asked to find for himself the absorbing states and the closed sets in the matrices of the examples of section 2.

5. CLASSIFICATION OF STATES

Consider an arbitrary, but fixed, state E_j and suppose that initially the system is in E_j. Every time the system passes through E_j the process recommences from scratch exactly as it has begun. It is therefore clear that the *return to E_j is a recurrent event* as defined in chapter XIII. If the system starts from another state E_i, then the passage through E_j becomes a *delayed recurrent event* as defined in chapter XIII, section 5. It should therefore be clear that Markov chains are but a special case of recurrent events; the only new feature is that we are dealing with many recurrent events simultaneously.

Each state E_j is characterized by its *recurrence time distribution* $\{f_j^{(n)}\}$. Here $f_j^{(n)}$ is the probability that the *first return* to E_j occurs at time n. Starting from the $p_{jj}^{(n)}$, we can calculate the $f_j^{(n)}$ using the obvious recurrence relations [5]

$$(5.1) \qquad f_j^{(1)} = p_{jj}, \qquad f_j^{(2)} = p_{jj}^{(2)} - f_j^{(1)} p_{jj}, \qquad \cdots,$$
$$f_j^{(n)} = p_{jj}^{(n)} - f_j^{(1)} p_{jj}^{(n-1)} - f_j^{(2)} p_{jj}^{(n-2)} - \cdots - f_j^{(n-1)} p_{jj}$$

which, of course, are only a special case of the basic relation XIII(3.1) for recurrent events. The sum

$$(5.2) \qquad f_j = \sum_{n=1}^{\infty} f_j^{(n)}$$

is the probability that, starting from E_j, the system ever returns to E_j. The state E_j is persistent if $f_j = 1$; in this case the mean recurrence time is

$$(5.3) \qquad \mu_j = \sum_{n=1}^{\infty} n f_j^{(n)}$$

We shall call E_j a *null state* if $\mu_j = \infty$.

If the system starts at E_i, the waiting time up to the first passage through E_j has a distribution $f_{ij}^{(n)}$ where

$$(5.4) \qquad f_{ij}^{(1)} = p_{ij}, \qquad f_{ij}^{(n)} = p_{ij}^{(n)} - \sum_{\nu=1}^{n-1} f_{ij}^{(n-\nu)} p_{jj}^{(\nu)}.$$

Again this equation is not specific to Markov chains but is valid for arbitrary delayed recurrent events. Of course, if E_j cannot be reached from E_i, then $f_{ij}^{(n)} = 0$ for all n. In general,

$$(5.5) \qquad f_{ij} = \sum_{n=1}^{\infty} f_{ij}^{(n)}$$

is the probability that, starting from E_i, the system ever reaches E_j.

We can now summarize the basic facts proved in chapter XIII, sections 3 and 5, as follows:

---

[5] They state that the probability of a first return to E_j at time n equals the probability of a return at time n minus the probability that the first return takes place at some time $\nu = 1, 2, \ldots, n-1$ and is followed by a repeated return at time n. In the notation of XIII(3.1), we have $p_{jj}^{(n)} = u_n$ and $f_j^{(n)} = f_n$.

(i) *A state E_j is transient if $f_j < 1$. Necessary and sufficient for this is the condition that $\sum_{n=1}^{\infty} p_{jj}^{(n)} < \infty$. In this case automatically*[6] $\sum_{n=1}^{\infty} p_{ij}^{(n)} < \infty$ *for each i.*

(ii) *A state E_j is a persistent null state if $f_j = 1$, but the mean recurrence time $\mu_j = \infty$. Necessary and sufficient for this is the condition that $\sum_{n=1}^{\infty} p_{jj}^{(n)} = \infty$ but $p_{jj}^{(n)} \to 0$. In this case*[6]

$$(5.6) \qquad p_{ij}^{(n)} \to 0 \qquad as \quad n \to \infty$$

for each i.

(iii) *The state E_j has period $t > 1$ if $p_{jj}^{(n)} = 0$ whenever n is not divisible by t and t is the smallest integer with this property (i.e., a return to E_j is impossible except, perhaps, in t, $2t$, $3t$, ... steps).*

(iv) *If E_j is persistent and aperiodic (not periodic), then*[6]

$$(5.7) \qquad p_{ij}^{(n)} \to \mu_j^{-1} f_{ij} \qquad as \quad n \to \infty$$

and, in particular,

$$(5.8) \qquad p_{jj}^{(n)} \to \mu_j^{-1} \qquad as \quad n \to \infty.$$

(If E_j is a null state, set $\mu_j^{-1} = 0$.)

(v) *If E_j is persistent and has period t, then (5.8) is to be replaced by*

$$(5.9) \qquad p_{jj}^{(nt)} \to t\mu_j^{-1} \qquad as \quad n \to \infty.$$

Persistent states which are neither periodic nor null states will be called ergodic.[7]

Examples. (*a*) Consider the matrix P' of the example in section 4 (omitting the dashes). The state E_1, being absorbing, is persistent. From E_2 the system necessarily passes into E_3 and from there back into E_2. Therefore E_2 and E_3 are persistent states, with period 2 and mean recurrence time 2. The states E_4, E_5, E_6 form a closed subset,

---

[6] This follows trivially from (5.4) but is really a special case of the theorem in chapter XIII, section 5.

[7] Unfortunately, no generally accepted terminology exists. In the first edition the *persistent* states were called *recurrent*, which causes confusion by obscuring the parallelism between Markov chains and recurrent events. Kolmogorov calls transient states *unessential*, but new research has shown that the main interest, both theoretical and practical, centers on transient states. The term ergodic, being synonymous with "persistent, non-null, non-periodic," is rather generally accepted, but *"positive"* state is one of the existing alternatives, and sometimes "ergodic" is equated to persistent.

and the transitions between them are regulated by the last matrix shown in (4.1). It is clear that these states are persistent and non-periodic. (We shall see later on that in a finite Markov chain no persistent null states are possible.)

From E_7 a passage into one of these closed sets is possible, and then the system stays in that closed set forever. Therefore E_7 is *transient*. From E_9 the system passes into E_7 and no return to E_9 is possible; therefore E_9 too is transient. Finally, starting from E_8, the system will sooner or later pass into E_7 or E_9, never to return. Accordingly E_7, E_8, E_9 are transient.

(b) We recall that in an unrestricted random walk [example (2.e)] all states are persistent if $p = q$ and are transient otherwise [see example (8.d)].

It is not always easy to decide whether or not a given state is persistent, and the criterion that $\Sigma p_{jj}^{(n)}$ should diverge is usually too difficult to apply. A better criterion is contained in the theorem of the next section.

Let E_j be a fixed *persistent* state and E_k some other state which can be reached from it. Furthermore, let N be the length of the *shortest* possible path from E_j to E_k, and put $p_{jk}^{(N)} = \alpha > 0$. A return from E_k to E_j must have positive probability, for otherwise the probability of the system's not returning to E_j would be at least α, and $f_j \leq 1 - \alpha < 1$ contrary to the assumption that E_j is persistent. It follows that there exists an index M such that $p_{kj}^{(M)} = \beta > 0$. Now for any n we have obviously

$$(5.10) \qquad p_{jj}^{(n+N+M)} \geq p_{jk}^{(N)} p_{kk}^{(n)} p_{kj}^{(M)} = \alpha\beta \cdot p_{kk}^{(n)}$$

and

$$(5.11) \qquad p_{kk}^{(n+N+M)} \geq p_{kj}^{(M)} p_{jj}^{(n)} p_{jk}^{(N)} = \alpha\beta \cdot p_{jj}^{(n)}.$$

These relations imply that the sequences $p_{jj}^{(n)}$ and $p_{kk}^{(n)}$ have the same asymptotic behavior, and from this we can draw important conclusions. To begin with, E_j was assumed persistent, and therefore the series $\Sigma p_{jj}^{(n)}$ diverges. From (5.11) it follows that also $\Sigma p_{kk}^{(n)}$ diverges, so that E_k must be persistent. If $p_{jj}^{(n)} \to 0$, then also $p_{kk}^{(n)} \to 0$, and vice versa. Finally, suppose that E_j has period t. Since a return to E_j is possible in $N + M$ steps, $N + M$ must be a multiple of t. It follows then from (5.10) and (5.11) that E_j and E_k must have the same period.

We see thus that *from a persistent state only persistent states can be reached, and they are all of the same type:* Either they are all null states, or all ergodic, or all periodic non-null states with the same period. The closure C of a persistent state E_j is an *irreducible* set, and its submatrix defines a Markov chain on it which can be treated independently of the rest. We have thus proved the important

Theorem. *In an irreducible Markov chain all states belong to the same class: they are all transient, all persistent null states, or all persistent non-null states. In every case they have the same period. Moreover, every state can be reached from every other state.*

In every chain the persistent states can, in a unique manner, be divided into closed sets C_1, C_2, ... such that from any state of a given set C_ν all states of that set and no other can be reached. All states belonging to the same closed set C_ν are necessarily of the same class.

In addition to the closed sets C_ν the chain will in general contain transient states from which states of the closed sets C_ν can be reached (but not vice versa).

This theorem has the interesting

Corollary. *In a finite Markov chain there exist no null states, and it is impossible that all states are transient.*

Proof. It suffices to consider irreducible chains. If all states were either transient or null states, we would have $p_{jk}^{(n)} \to 0$ as $n \to \infty$ for each fixed pair j, k. Each row of P^n would tend to zero while the row sums equal unity. This is clearly impossible in the case of finitely many terms, and we conclude that in an irreducible chain there exist neither transient nor null states.

It follows that after an appropriate renumbering of the states (such as was used in the example of section 4) the matrix P corresponding to a chain with, say, two closed sets C_1 and C_2 and additional transient states can be written schematically in the form of a partitioned matrix

$$(5.12) \qquad P = \begin{bmatrix} P_1 & 0 & 0 \\ 0 & P_2 & 0 \\ A & B & C \end{bmatrix}$$

where P_1 and P_2 are the matrices of transition probabilities within the two closed sets. The matrix P^n is then of the same type with P_1, P_2, C replaced by $P_1{}^n$, $P_2{}^n$, C^n (and A and B by more complicated matrices to be studied in section 8). Note that P_1, P_2, and C are square matrices, but A and B may be rectangular matrices as in the example.

6. ERGODIC PROPERTIES OF IRREDUCIBLE CHAINS

In this section we restrict the discussion to *aperiodic* chains; as with recurrent events in general, the modifications required for periodic chains are rather trite, but the formulations become unpleasantly involved.

Definition. *A probability distribution $\{v_k\}$ is called stationary if*

$$(6.1) \qquad\qquad v_j = \sum_i v_i p_{ij}.$$

If the initial distribution $\{a_k\}$ happens to be stationary, then the absolute probabilities $\{a_k^{(n)}\}$ are independent of the time n, that is, $a_k^{(n)} = a_k$. The physical significance of stationarity becomes apparent if we imagine a large number of processes going on simultaneously. Let, for example, N particles perform independently the same type of random walk. At time n the expected number of particles in state E_k is $Na_k^{(n)}$. With a stationary distribution these expected numbers remain constant, and we observe (if N is large so that the law of large numbers applies) a state of *macroscopic equilibrium* maintained by a large number of transitions in opposite directions. Most statistical equilibria in physics are of this kind; that is, they are due exclusively to the simultaneous observation of many independent particles. Typical is the case of a symmetric random walk (or diffusion): if many particles are observed, then, after a sufficiently long time, roughly half of them will be to the right, the other to the left of the origin. Nevertheless, we know from the arc sine law of chapter III, section 5, that *the majority of the particles individually will misbehave* and spend a disproportionately large part of the time on the same side of the origin. Many protracted discussions and erroneous conclusions could be avoided by the realization that the notion of statistical equilibrium (or the steady state) does not say anything concerning the behavior of the individual particle. This should be borne in mind in connection with the next theorem which is frequently described as asserting a "tendency toward equilibrium."

Theorem. *An irreducible aperiodic Markov chain belongs to one of the following two classes:*

(a) *Either the states are all transient or all null states; in this case $p_{jk}^{(n)} \to 0$ as $n \to \infty$ for each pair j, k and there exists no stationary distribution.*

(b) *Or else, all states are ergodic, that is*

$$(6.2) \qquad\qquad \lim_{n \to \infty} p_{jk}^{(n)} = u_k > 0$$

where u_k is the reciprocal of the mean recurrence time of E_k. In this case $\{u_k\}$ is a stationary distribution and there exists no other stationary distribution.

A slight reformulation may explain the implications of this theorem. If (6.2) holds, then for an arbitrary initial distribution $\{a_k\}$

$$(6.3) \qquad a_k^{(n)} = \sum_j a_j p_{jk}^{(n)} \to u_k.$$

Therefore: *If there exists a stationary distribution, it is necessarily unique and the distribution at time n tends to it irrespective of the initial distribution.* The only alternative to this situation is that $p_{jk}^{(n)} \to 0$.

Proof. The preceding theorem assures us that (6.2) holds whenever the states are ergodic. To prove assertion (b) above we first note that

$$(6.4) \qquad \Sigma u_k \leq 1.$$

This follows directly from the fact that for fixed j and n the quantities $p_{jk}^{(n)}$ ($k = 1, 2, \ldots$) add to unity, so that $u_1 + u_2 + \ldots + u_N \leq 1$ for every N. Now put $n = 1$ in (3.3) and let $m \to \infty$. The left side tends to u_k, and the general term of the sum on the right side tends to $u_\nu p_{\nu k}$. Adding an arbitrary finite number of terms, we see that

$$(6.5) \qquad u_k \geq \sum_\nu u_\nu p_{\nu k}.$$

Summing these inequalities over all k, we obtain the finite quantity Σu_k on each side. This shows that in (6.5) the inequality is impossible and therefore

$$(6.6) \qquad u_k = \Sigma u_j p_{jk}.$$

Putting $v_k = u_k \cdot (\Sigma u_j)^{-1}$ we see that $\{v_k\}$ is a stationary distribution and hence at least one such distribution exists.

Let $\{v_k\}$ be any distribution satisfying equations (6.1). Multiplying (6.1) by $p_{jk}^{(n)}$ and adding over j we see by induction that for each n

$$(6.7) \qquad v_r = \sum_\nu v_\nu p_{\nu r}^{(n)}.$$

Letting $n \to \infty$ we get

$$(6.8) \qquad v_r = (v_1 + v_2 + \ldots)u_r = u_r.$$

This completes the proof of assertion (b). If the states are transient or null states and $\{v_k\}$ is a stationary distribution, then equations (6.7) hold and $p_{\nu r}^{(n)} \to 0$, which is clearly impossible. Accordingly, a stationary distribution can exist only in the ergodic case, and the proof is completed.

Examples. (*a*) *The Ehrenfest model.* In example (2.*f*), the conditions (6.1) for a stationary distribution take on the form

$$u_k = \left(1 - \frac{k-1}{a}\right)u_{k-1} + \frac{k+1}{a}u_{k+1} \qquad (k = 1, \ldots, a-1)$$

(6.9)

$$u_0 = \frac{u_1}{a}, \qquad u_a = \frac{u_{a-1}}{a}.$$

It is easily verified that the solution is given by the binomial distribution

(6.10) $$u_k = \binom{a}{k} 2^{-a}.$$

This result can be interpreted as follows: Whatever the initial number of molecules in the first container, after a long time the probability of finding k molecules in it is nearly the same as if the a molecules had been distributed at random, each molecule having probability $\frac{1}{2}$ to be in the first container. This is a typical example of how our result gains physical significance.

For large a the normal approximation to the binomial distribution shows that, once the limiting distribution (6.10) is established, we are practically certain to find about one-half the molecules in each container. To the physicist $a = 10^6$ is a small number, indeed. But even with $a = 10^6$ molecules the probability of finding more than 505,000 molecules in one container (density fluctuation of about 1 per cent) is of the order of magnitude 10^{-23}. With $a = 10^8$ a density fluctuation of one in a thousand has the same negligible probability. It is true that the system will occasionally pass into very improbable states, but their recurrence times are fantastically large as compared to the recurrence times of states near the equilibrium. Physical irreversibility manifests itself in the fact that, whenever the system is in a state far removed from equilibrium, it is much more likely to move toward equilibrium than in the opposite direction.

(*b*) *Doubly stochastic matrices.* The matrix P is called doubly stochastic if not only the row sums but also the column sums are unity. Suppose that the chain contains only a finite number, a, of states. The system (6.1) has then obviously the solution $v_k = 1/a$. It follows that, *if a finite irreducible aperiodic chain has a doubly stochastic matrix* P, *then* $v_k = 1/a$ (*i.e., in the limit all states become equally probable*). In this case no transient states are possible. By contrast, in an irreducible *infinite chain with doubly stochastic matrix all elements are either transient or null states.* To prove this assertion suppose that (6.2) holds. The matrix P being doubly stochastic, we have for each fixed k and arbitrarily large N

$$(6.11) \qquad 1 = \sum_{j=1}^{\infty} p_{jk}^{(n)} \geq \sum_{j=1}^{N} p_{jk}^{(n)} \rightarrow N u_k$$

and this clearly implies $u_k = 0$ against the assumption. (This proof applies also in the periodic case.)

(c) *Recurrent events.* In example (2.*i*) we have introduced a Markov chain associated with an arbitrary recurrent event $\mathcal{E}$, and we proceed now to show that (as could be expected) the states of the chain are always of the same type as $\mathcal{E}$.

First consider the case of a transient $\mathcal{E}$; that is, suppose $f < 1$. The chain of transitions $E_i \rightarrow E_{i+1} \rightarrow E_{i+2} \rightarrow \ldots \rightarrow E_{i+n}$ has probability

$$(6.12) \qquad \frac{1 - s_{i+1}}{1 - s_i} \cdot \frac{1 - s_{i+2}}{1 - s_{i+1}} \cdots \frac{1 - s_{i+n}}{1 - s_{i+n-1}} = \frac{1 - s_{i+n}}{1 - s_i} \geq \frac{1 - f}{1 - s_i}.$$

The probability that the system will never enter E_0 is thus seen to be positive, and therefore all states are transient. On the other hand, when $f = 1$, the left-hand term in (6.12) tends to zero; with probability one the system will sooner or later pass through E_0. It follows that E_0 is persistent, and since every state can be reached from E_0, the chain is irreducible. We see thus: *If $\mathcal{E}$ is transient, so are all states of the chain; if $\mathcal{E}$ is persistent, then the chain is irreducible and all states are persistent.*

It is clear that the chain and $\mathcal{E}$ have the same period, and we shall suppose that $\mathcal{E}$ is aperiodic and persistent. We have to decide whether there exists a stationary distribution, that is, a probability distribution $\{v_k\}$ satisfying (6.1). In the present case (6.1) reduces to

$$(6.13) \qquad v_0 = \sum_{i=0}^{\infty} \frac{f_{i+1}}{1 - s_i} v_i, \qquad v_k = \frac{1 - s_k}{1 - s_{k-1}} v_{k-1}.$$

There exists a unique solution of these equations, namely

$$(6.14) \qquad v_k = (1 - s_k) v_0 = r_k v_0 \qquad \text{where} \qquad r_k = \sum_{n=k+1}^{\infty} f_n.$$

In order that $\Sigma v_k < \infty$ it is necessary and sufficient that $\Sigma r_k < \infty$. But $\Sigma r_k = \Sigma n f_n$ equals the mean recurrence time [cf. XI(1.8)]. This shows that *the states of the Markov chain are null states if the mean recurrence time is infinite, and they have finite mean recurrence times if $\mathcal{E}$ has.*

We have derived the asymptotic properties of Markov chains from similar properties of recurrent events. Now we have shown that each recurrent event may be described in terms of a particular Markov chain. The three topics, asymptotic behavior of Markov chains, asymptotic behavior of recurrent events (i.e., summation theory of integral-valued independent random variables), and renewal theory, are therefore different versions of the same analytic background and are substantially equivalent.

In concluding this section, let us remark that it is usually comparatively easy to decide whether a stationary distribution exists and hence whether a given irreducible chain is ergodic. In section 8 we shall derive a similar criterion to discriminate between transient states and persistent null states. In principle this could be decided by discussing the convergence of the series $\Sigma p_{jk}^{(n)}$, but in practice this question cannot be attacked directly.

* 7. PERIODIC CHAINS

In the preceding section we have excluded the case of periodic chains, but this was done only to avoid obscuring salient facts by complicated descriptions. A characterization of the asymptotic behavior of $p_{jk}^{(n)}$ in irreducible periodic chains can be derived easily from the theorems of the preceding sections. We give such a derivation for the sake of completeness, but the results of this section will not be used in the sequel.

By the theorem of section 5 all states of an irreducible chain have the same period t. Consider any two states E_j and E_k of an irreducible chain with period t. Since every state can be reached from every other, there exist integers a, b such that $p_{jk}^{(a)} > 0$ and $p_{kj}^{(b)} > 0$. Now $p_{jj}^{(a+b)} \geq p_{jk}^{(a)} p_{kj}^{(b)}$, which shows that a return to E_j in $a+b$ steps is possible, so that $a + b$ is necessarily divisible by the period t. It follows that, if E_k can be reached from E_j in a_1 and in a_2 steps, $a_2 - a_1$ must be divisible by t, and hence a division of a_1 and a_2 by t will leave the same remainder.

Accordingly, for fixed E_j each state E_k belongs to a certain remainder ν (where $0 \leq \nu < t - 1$) such that a transition from E_j to E_k is possible only in ν, $\nu+t$, $\nu+2t$, $\nu+3t$, ... steps. Choosing $j = 1$, we get a classification of all states into t groups G_0, G_1, ..., G_{t-1} so that E_k belongs to G_ν if $p_{1k}^{(a)} > 0$ implies that $a = \nu + nt$. We order the G_ν cyclically so that G_0 and G_{t-1} become neighbors.

It follows in particular that a *one-step* transition from a state in G_ν will always lead to a state in the next following group $G_{\nu+1}$ (or G_0 in

---

* This section treats a special topic and should be omitted at first reading.

case $\nu = t - 1$); a two-step transition will lead to a state in $G_{\nu+2}$ (from G_{t-2} it leads to G_0, from G_{t-1} to G_1), etc. Finally, a t-step transition leads necessarily to a state belonging to the same group. This means that, in a Markov chain whose matrix of transition probabilities is P^t, each group G_ν forms a closed set. Since the original chain is irreducible, each state can be reached from every other. This implies that in the chain with transition probabilities P^t each G_ν forms an irreducible closed set. We have thus the

Theorem. *In an irreducible periodic Markov chain the states can be divided into t groups G_0, ..., G_{t-1}, so that a one-step transition from a state of G_ν always leads to a state of $G_{\nu+1}$ (to G_0 if $\nu = t - 1$). If we consider the chain only at times $t, 2t, 3t, \ldots$, then we get a new chain whose matrix of transition probabilities is P^t. In it each G_ν forms an irreducible closed set.*

Our theorem contains complete information concerning the *asymptotic behavior* of $p_{jk}^{(n)}$. If all states are transient or null states, then $p_{jk}^{(n)} \to 0$ for every pair j, k. Otherwise each state E_k has a finite mean recurrence time μ_k. Suppose that E_j belongs to G_ν. On G_ν we have an irreducible non-periodic Markov chain with transition probabilities $p_{jk}^{(t)}$, and hence there exist the limits

$$(7.1) \qquad \lim_{n \to \infty} p_{jk}^{(nt)} = \begin{cases} u_k & \text{if } E_k \text{ is in } G_\nu \\ 0 & \text{otherwise} \end{cases}$$

where u_k is the reciprocal mean recurrence time of E_k in the new chain, one step of which corresponds to t steps of the original chain. Thus

$$(7.2) \qquad u_k = \frac{t}{\mu_k}.$$

Using (3.2), we find from (7.1),

$$(7.3) \qquad \lim_{n \to \infty} p_{jk}^{(nt+1)} = \begin{cases} u_k & \text{if } E_k \text{ is in } G_{\nu+1} \\ 0 & \text{otherwise}. \end{cases}$$

Similarly, $p_{jk}^{(nt+2)} \to u_k$ if E_k is in $G_{\nu+2}$, etc. In other words, *for fixed E_j and E_k the sequence $p_{jk}^{(n)}$ is asymptotically periodic; in it blocks of $t - 1$ consecutive zeros alternate with a positive element which converges to $u_k = t/\mu_k$.*

By the theorem of section 6, the u_k within each group G_ν add to unity. Since there are t blocks, it follows from (7.2) that the sequence $\{1/\mu_k\}$

represents a probability distribution. The argument of section 6 shows directly that *this distribution is stationary and that no other stationary distributions exist.*

8. TRANSIENT STATES

From a persistent state E_j the system can pass only into a persistent E_k in the closure of E_j, and we have obtained complete information concerning the asymptotic behavior of $p_{jk}^{(n)}$ in this case.

If E_j is transient and E_k ergodic, then by (5.7)

$$(8.1) \qquad\qquad p_{jk}^{(n)} \to \mu_k^{-1} f_{jk}$$

where μ_k is the mean recurrence time of E_k and f_{jk} the probability that, starting from E_j, the system will sooner or later enter E_k. However, E_k belongs to an irreducible subchain C, and from E_k the system is bound to pass through each state of C. Therefore, for each fixed j the probability f_{jk} is the same for all states of C. In other words, *if C is an irreducible subchain with ergodic states and E_j is transient, then for each E_k of C*

$$(8.2) \qquad\qquad p_{jk}^{(n)} \to \mu_k^{-1} x_j$$

where x_j is the probability that, starting from E_j, the system will ever enter C. Needless to say that for null states the right-hand side in (8.2) must be replaced by 0, and that the case of periodic E_k necessitates only the usual routine modification.

To complete the picture of the asymptotic behavior of Markov chains, it remains to solve the following

Three Problems. (a) *Given a transient state E_j and a persistent closed set C, find the probability x_j that, starting from E_j, the system will ever enter C (i.e., pass through a state of C).*

(b) *Find the probability y_j that the system will forever remain in the set of transient states.*

(c) *Given an irreducible chain, decide whether its states are transient or persistent.*

It will be seen presently that, after a slight reformulation, problem (c) becomes a special case of (a).

Let T be the set of all transient states and suppose that *the system is initially in the transient state E_j*; let $x_j^{(n)}$ be the probability that at time n, and not sooner, the system reaches the closed set C. Then

$$(8.3) \qquad\qquad x_j = \sum_{n=1}^{\infty} x_j^{(n)}$$

is the probability that the system will ultimately reach C and stay in C.
By analogy with the simple random walk *we shall call x_j the probability
of absorption in C.* The difference $1 - x_j$ accounts for the possibility
of absorption in other closed sets and (in the case of some infinite
chains) of an indefinite continuation in transient states.

It is clear that

$$(8.4) \qquad\qquad x_j^{(1)} = \sum_C p_{jk},$$

the summation extending over those k for which E_k is contained in C.
If the system reaches C at the $(n+1)$st step, then the first step must
lead from E_j to another transient state. It is therefore clear that

$$(8.5) \qquad\qquad x_j^{(n+1)} = \sum_T p_{j\nu} x_\nu^{(n)},$$

the summation now extending over those ν for which E_ν is transient.
*Equations (8.4) and (8.5) are recurrence relations which uniquely deter-
mine the $x_j^{(n)}$.* Adding (8.5) for $n = 1, 2, 3, \ldots$, we find that *the absorption probabilities x_j are solutions of the system of linear equations*

$$(8.6) \qquad\qquad x_j - \sum_T p_{j\nu} x_\nu = x_j^{(1)}.$$

We have thus an answer to problem (a); the probability x_j can be
obtained constructively from (8.3)–(8.5), but it is preferable to characterize it as a solution of the system of linear equations (8.6). In
this connection the problem of uniqueness arises, but it fortunately
turns out to be a special case of problem (b).

Let $y_j^{(n)}$ be *the probability that the system is at time n in a transient
state.* Obviously

$$y_j^{(1)} = \sum_T p_{j\nu},$$

$$(8.7)$$

$$y_j^{(n+1)} = \sum_T p_{j\nu} y_\nu^{(n)},$$

the summations again extending over all ν for which E_ν is transient.
It follows from (8.7) that $y_j^{(1)} \leq 1$ and hence $y_j^{(2)} \leq y_j^{(1)}$, and generally
$y_j^{(n+1)} \leq y_j^{(n)}$. Therefore a limit

$$(8.8) \qquad\qquad y_j = \lim_{n \to \infty} y_j^{(n)}$$

exists; y_j is the probability of the system's forever staying in transient states.   From (8.7) we have

(8.9)
$$y_j = \sum_T p_{j\nu} y_\nu.$$

The probabilities y_j are thus seen to satisfy equations (8.9), but this
does not solve the main question, namely, whether or not $y_j = 0$ for
all j. Suppose that there exists a bounded solution of the system (8.9),
say

(8.10)
$$z_j = \sum_T p_{j\nu} z_\nu \qquad\qquad |z_\nu| \leq 1.$$

A comparison of (8.10) and (8.7) shows then that $|z_j| \leq y_j^{(1)}$ and hence
by induction $|z_j| \leq y_j^{(n)}$ for all n. It follows that $y_j = 0$ for all j if,
and only if, the system (8.10) has no non-zero solution. Finally, if
the linear equations (8.6) had two distinct solutions, their difference
would be a solution of the linear equations in (8.10). We have thus

Theorem 1.   *The probabilities x_j of problem (a) are a solution of the
linear equations (8.6). This solution is unique except when there exists a
state E_j such that, starting from E_j, the system has a positive probability
y_j of staying forever in the transient states. The $\{y_j\}$ satisfy (8.9).*

Note: We have seen that the probabilities y_j may be characterized
as the *maximal* solution of (8.9) bounded by 1; a similar property
attaches to $\{x_j\}$.

Corollary.   *In a finite Markov chain the probability of the system's
staying forever in the transient states is zero. The probabilities x_j of passing from a transient E_j into a closed set C are determined as the unique
solution of the linear equations (8.6).*

Proof.   We have to prove that the equations (8.9) admit of no solution. Suppose the contrary and let M be the maximum of the finitely
many y_j. There is no loss of generality in ordering the states so that
the y_j appear in *decreasing* order, say that $y_1 = y_2 = \ldots = y_a = M >$
$> y_{a+1} \geq y_{a+2} \geq \ldots$.   From (8.9) we have then for $i \leq a$

(8.11)
$$M = \sum_T p_{i\nu} y_\nu = \sum_{\nu=1}^{a} p_{i\nu} + \sum_{\nu \geq a+1} p_{i\nu} y_\nu,$$

and the equality sign can hold only if $p_{i\nu} = 0$ for each $\nu > a$. In this
case $E_1, \ldots, E_a$ form a closed set, and this is impossible since a finite
chain necessarily contains persistent states (corollary, section 5).

Theorem 1 is used to calculate *absorption probabilities*, that is, the
probabilities of entering a given absorbing state.

Examples. (a) *Random walk with absorbing barriers* [example (2.b)].
Take for C the absorbing state E_0. Then $x_1^{(1)} = q$ and $x_j^{(1)} = 0$ if $j > 1$.
The system (8.6) therefore reduces to

$$x_1 - px_2 = q,$$

(8.12) $$x_j - qx_{j-1} - px_{j+1} = 0 \quad (j = 2, 3, \ldots, a-2),$$

$$x_{a-1} - qx_{a-2} = 0.$$

This is the same as the system XIV (2.1)–(2.2) and the solution is given
in XIV(2.4).

(b) *Sequential sampling* [example (2.j)]. Again let C be the state E_0.
Then $x_j^{(1)} = r_j$, and the equations (8.6) reduce to XIV(8.2) (where u_x
stands for the present x_j; cf. also problem XIV, 4).

(c) *Genetics* [example (2.k)]. Here each of the two states E_0 and
E_{2N} forms a closed set. Absorption in E_0 and in E_{2N} signifies, respectively, that the population ultimately consists only of aa- or only of
AA-individuals. For the absorption in E_0 we have $x_j^{(1)} = p_{j0} =$
$= (1 - j/2N)^{2N}$, and hence (8.6) assumes the form

(8.13) $$x_j - \sum_{\nu=1}^{2N-1} \binom{2N}{\nu}\left(\frac{j}{2N}\right)^{\nu}\left(1 - \frac{j}{2N}\right)^{2N-\nu} x_{\nu} = \left(1 - \frac{j}{2N}\right)^{2N}.$$

It is plausible that at a moment when the A- and a-genes are in the
proportion $j:2N - j$ their survival chances should be in the same ratio.
If this is true, the solution to (8.13) must be $x_j = 1 - j(2N)^{-1}$. That
these x_j really satisfy (8.13) is easily verified upon recognizing in (8.13)
the terms of the binomial distribution with mean j.

Finally we give a solution to problem (c).

Theorem 2. *Let an irreducible chain have states E_0, E_1, $\ldots$. In
order that the states be transient, it is necessary and sufficient that the system of equations*

(8.14) $$y_i = \sum_{j=1}^{\infty} p_{ij}y_j, \qquad i = 1, 2, \ldots$$

admits of a non-zero bounded solution.

Proof. In the construction (8.7)–(8.8) of $\{y_j\}$ interpret T as the set
of the states E_1, E_2, $\ldots$ (the complement of E_0). The proof applies
without change to this case, and it is seen that the probability of staying in T (i.e., of not entering E_0) is given by (8.8) and satisfies (8.9).

Examples. (*d*) *Unrestricted random walk.* Example (2.*e*) requires a trivial change of notations since the states are numbered from $-\infty$ to $+\infty$. It is clear, however, that our criterion depends on the existence of solutions of the equations

$$(8.15) \qquad y_i = py_{i+1} + qy_{i-1}, \qquad y_0 = 0, \quad i = \pm 1, \pm 2, \dots.$$

Clearly all y_i can be calculated recursively from y_1 and y_{-1}. If $p > q$,

$$(8.16) \qquad y_i = \frac{\left(1 - \left(\dfrac{q}{p}\right)^i\right)}{1 - \dfrac{q}{p}} \, y_1, \qquad y_{-i} = 0, \qquad i = 1, 2, \dots$$

is the unique solution and is bounded. If $p = q$, the solution is $y_i = iy_1$ and is unbounded. We have here a Markov chain derivation of the old result that the states are transient if $p \neq q$, persistent if $p = q$.

(*e*) Consider the matrix

$$P = \begin{bmatrix} q_0 & p_0 & 0 & 0 & 0 & \cdots \\ q_1 & 0 & p_1 & 0 & 0 & \cdots \\ 0 & q_2 & 0 & p_2 & 0 & \cdots \\ 0 & 0 & q_3 & 0 & p_3 & \cdots \\ \cdot & \cdot & \cdot & \cdot & \cdot & \cdots \\ \cdot & \cdot & \cdot & \cdot & \cdot & \cdots \\ \cdot & \cdot & \cdot & \cdot & \cdot & \cdots \end{bmatrix}$$

which represents a random walk on $(0, \infty)$ with variable transition probabilities. It plays an important role in the theory of *birth-and-death processes* to be discussed in chapter XVII. The equations (8.14) reduce to

$$(8.17) \qquad y_1 = p_1 y_2, \qquad y_i = q_i y_{i-1} + p_i y_{i+1}, \qquad i = 2, 3, \dots$$

and can be solved recursively since

$$(8.18) \qquad \frac{y_{i+1} - y_i}{y_i - y_{i-1}} = \frac{q_i}{p_i}.$$

and hence

$$(8.19) \qquad y_{i+1} - y_i = y_1 \cdot \frac{q_1}{p_1} \cdot \frac{q_2}{p_2} \cdots \frac{q_i}{p_i}.$$

Adding these equations, we see that a bounded solution exists if, and only if, $\Sigma L_i < \infty$ where $L_i = (q_1 \cdots q_i)(p_1 \cdots p_i)^{-1}$. Therefore, the states are transient if $\Sigma L_i < \infty$ and persistent otherwise.

9. APPLICATION TO CARD SHUFFLING

A deck of N cards numbered 1, 2, ..., N can be arranged in $N!$ different orders, and each represents a possible state of the system. Every particular shuffling operation effects a transition from the existing state into some other state. For example, "cutting" will change the order $(1, 2, ..., N)$ into one of the N cyclically equivalent orders $(r, r+1, ..., N, 1, 2, ..., r-1)$. The same operation applied to the inverse order $(N, N-1, ..., 1)$ will produce $(N-r+1, N-r, ..., 1, N, N-1, ..., N-r+2)$. In other words, we conceive of each particular shuffling operation as a transformation $E_j \to E_k$. If *exactly* the same operation is repeated, the system will pass (starting from the given state E_j) through a well-defined succession of states, and after a finite number of steps the original order will be re-established. From then on the same succession of states will recur periodically. For most operations the period will be rather small, and in *no* case can all states be reached by this procedure.[8] For example, a perfect "lacing" would change a deck of $2m$ cards from $(1, ..., 2m)$ into $(1, m+1, 2, m+2, ..., m, 2m)$. With six cards four applications of this operation will re-establish the original order. With ten cards the initial order will reappear after six operations, so that repeated perfect lacing of a deck of ten cards can produce only six out of the $10! = 3,628,800$ possible orders.

In practice the player may wish to vary the operation, and at any rate accidental variations will be introduced by chance. We shall assume that we can account for the player's habits and the influence of chance variations by assuming that every particular operation has a certain probability (possibly zero). We need assume nothing about the numerical values of these probabilities but shall suppose that the player operates without regard to the past and does not know the order of the cards.[9] This implies that the successive operations correspond to independent trials with fixed probabilities; for the actual deck of cards we then have a Markov chain.

We now show that the matrix P of transition probabilities is *doubly stochastic* [example (6.b)]. In fact, if an operation changes a state (order of cards) E_j to E_k, then there exists another state E_r which it will change into E_j. This means that the elements of the jth column

---

[8] In the language of group theory this amounts to saying that the permutation group is not cyclic and can therefore not be generated by a simple operation.

[9] This assumption corresponds to the usual situation at bridge. It is easy to devise more complicated shuffling techniques in which the operations depend on previous operations and the final outcome is not a Markov chain [cf. example (10.e)].

of P are identical with the elements of the jth row, except that they appear in a different order. All column sums are therefore unity.

It follows that no state can be transient. *If the chain is irreducible and aperiodic, then in the limit all states become equally probable.* In other words, *any* kind of shuffling will do, provided only that it produces an irreducible and aperiodic chain. It is safe to assume that this is usually the case. Suppose, however, that the deck contains an even number of cards and the procedure consists in dividing them equally into two parts and shuffling them separately by any method. If the two parts are put together in their original order, then the Markov chain is reducible (since not every state can be reached from every other state). If the order of the two parts is inverted, the chain will have period 2. Thus both contingencies can arise in theory, but hardly in practice, since chance precludes perfect regularity.

It is seen that continued shuffling may reasonably be expected to produce perfect "randomness" and to eliminate all traces of the original order. It should be noted, however, that the number of operations required for this purpose is extremely large.[10]

10. THE GENERAL MARKOV PROCESS

In applications it is usually convenient to describe Markov chains in terms of random variables. This can be done by the simple device of replacing in the preceding sections the symbol E_k by the integer k. The state of the system at time n then is a random variable $\mathbf{X}^{(n)}$, which assumes the value k with probability $a_k^{(n)}$; the joint distribution of $\mathbf{X}^{(n)}$ and $\mathbf{X}^{(n+1)}$ is given by $\mathbf{P}\{\mathbf{X}^{(n)} = j, \mathbf{X}^{(n+1)} = k\} = a_j^{(n)}p_{jk}$, and the joint distribution of $(\mathbf{X}^{(0)}, \ldots, \mathbf{X}^{(n)})$ is given by (1.1). It is also possible and sometimes preferable to assign to E_k a numerical value e_k different from k. With this notation a Markov chain becomes a special stochastic process,[11] or in other words, a sequence of (dependent) random variables [12] $(\mathbf{X}^{(0)}, \mathbf{X}^{(1)}, \ldots)$. The superscript n plays the role of

---

[10] For an analysis of unbelievably poor results of shuffling in records of extrasensory perception experiments, see W. Feller, Statistical aspects of ESP, *Journal of Parapsychology*, vol. 4 (1940), pp. 271–298. In their amusing A review of Dr. Feller's critique, *ibid.*, pp. 299–319, J. A. Greenwood and C. E. Stuart try to show that these results are due to chance. Both their arithmetic and their experiments have a distinct tinge of the supernatural.

[11] The terms "stochastic process" and "random process" are synonyms and cover practically all the theory of probability from coin tossing to harmonic analysis. In practice, the term "stochastic process" is used mostly when a time parameter is introduced.

[12] This formulation refers to an infinite product space, but in reality we are concerned only with joint distributions of finite collections of the variables.

time. In chapter XVII we shall get a glimpse of more general stochastic processes in which the time parameter is permitted to vary continu-
ously. The term "Markov process" is applied to a very large and important class of stochastic processes (with both discrete and continuous
time parameters). Even in the discrete case there exist more general
Markov processes than the simple chains we have studied so far. It
will, therefore, be useful to give a definition of the Markov property,
to point out the special condition characterizing our Markov chains,
and, finally, to give a few examples of non-Markovian processes.

   Conceptually, a Markov process is the probabilistic analogue of the
processes of classical mechanics, where the future development is completely determined by the present state and is independent of the way
in which the present state has developed. The processes of mechanics
are in contrast to processes with aftereffect (or hereditary processes),
such as occur in the theory of plasticity, where the whole past history
of the system influences its future. In stochastic processes the future
is never uniquely determined, but we have at least probability relations
enabling us to make predictions. For the Markov chains studied in
this chapter it is clear that probability relations relating to the future
depend on the present state, but not on the manner in which the present state has emerged from the past. In other words, if two independent systems subject to the same transition probabilities happen to be
in the same state, then all probabilities relating to their future develop-
ments are identical. This is a rather vague description which is for-
malized in the following

   Definition. *A sequence of discrete-valued random variables is a
Markov process if, for every finite collection of integers $n_1 < n_2 < \ldots <$
$< n_r < n$, the joint distribution of $(\mathbf{X}^{(n_1)}, \mathbf{X}^{(n_2)}, \ldots, \mathbf{X}^{(n_r)}, \mathbf{X}^n)$ is defined
in such a way that the conditional probability of the relation $\mathbf{X}^{(n)} = x$ on
the hypothesis $\mathbf{X}^{(n_1)} = x_1, \ldots, \mathbf{X}^{(n_r)} = x_r$ is identical with the conditional
probability of $\mathbf{X}^{(n)} = x$ on the single hypothesis $\mathbf{X}^{(n_r)} = x_r$. Here
$x_1, \ldots, x_r$, are arbitrary numbers for which the hypothesis has a positive probability.*

   Reduced to simpler terms, this definition states that, given the state
x_r at time n_r, no additional data concerning states of the system at
previous times can alter the (conditional) probability of the state x at
a future time n.

   The Markov chains studied in this chapter are obviously Markov
processes, but they have the following additional property not implied
by the definition. *For the Markov chains studied in the preceding sec-
tions the transition probabilities $p_{jk} = \mathbf{P}\{\mathbf{X}^{(m+1)} = k \,|\, \mathbf{X}^{(m)} = j\}$ are in-*

dependent of m. The more general transition probabilities

(10.1) $$p_{jk}^{(n-m)} = \mathbf{P}\{\mathbf{X}^{(n)} = k \mid \mathbf{X}^{(m)} = j\} \qquad (m < n)$$

then depend only on the difference $n - m$. We say in this case that the transition probabilities are *stationary* (or constant). For a general integral-valued Markov chain the right side in (10.1) depends on m and n. We shall denote it by $p_{jk}(m, n)$ so that $p_{jk}(n, n+1)$ is the one-step transition probability at time n. Instead of (1.1) we get now for the probability of the path $(j_0, j_1, \ldots, j_n)$ the expression

(10.2) $$a_{j_0}^{(0)} p_{j_0 j_1}(0, 1)\, p_{j_1 j_2}(1, 2) \cdots p_{j_{n-1} j_n}(n-1, n).$$

The proper generalization of (3.3) is obviously the identity

(10.3) $$p_{jk}(m, n) = \sum_{\nu} p_{j\nu}(m, r)\, p_{\nu k}(r, n)$$

which is valid for all r with $m < r < n$. This identity follows directly from the definition of a Markov process and also from (10.2); it is called the *Chapman-Kolmogorov* equation.

In the present chapter we have dealt mostly with the asymptotic behavior of the higher transition probabilities, and few of the established properties are common to the most general discrete Markov process. We shall, therefore, not dwell on the general theory.

Examples of Non-Markovian Processes. (a) *The Polya urn scheme* [example V(2.c)]. Let $\mathbf{X}^{(n)}$ equal 1 or 0 according to whether the nth drawing results in a black or red ball. The sequence $\{\mathbf{X}^{(n)}\}$ is *not* a Markov process. For example,

$$\mathbf{P}\{\mathbf{X}^{(3)} = 1 \mid \mathbf{X}^{(2)} = 1\} = (b + c)/(b + r + c),$$

but

$$\mathbf{P}\{\mathbf{X}^{(3)} = 1 \mid \mathbf{X}^{(2)} = 1, \mathbf{X}^{(1)} = 1\} = (b + 2c)/(b + r + 2c).$$

(Cf. problems V, 19–20.) On the other hand, if $\mathbf{Y}^{(n)}$ is the number of black balls in the urn at time n, then $\{\mathbf{Y}^{(n)}\}$ is an ordinary Markov chain with constant transition probabilities.

(b) *Higher sums.* Let $\mathbf{Y}_0, \mathbf{Y}_1, \ldots$ be mutually independent random variables, and put $\mathbf{S}_n = \mathbf{Y}_0 + \ldots + \mathbf{Y}_n$. The difference $\mathbf{S}_n - \mathbf{S}_m$ (with $m < n$) depends only on $\mathbf{Y}_{m+1}, \ldots, \mathbf{Y}_n$, and it is therefore easily seen that the sequence $\{\mathbf{S}_n\}$ is a Markov process. Now let us go one step further and define a new sequence of random variables $\mathbf{U}_n$ by $\mathbf{U}_n = \mathbf{S}_0 + \mathbf{S}_1 + \ldots + \mathbf{S}_n$ (which means that

$$\mathbf{U}_n = \mathbf{Y}_n + 2\mathbf{Y}_{n-1} + 3\mathbf{Y}_{n-2} + \ldots).$$

The sequence $\{\mathbf{U}_n\}$ forms a stochastic process whose probability relations can, in principle, be expressed in terms of the distributions of the $\mathbf{Y}_k$. The $\{\mathbf{U}_n\}$ process is in general not of the Markov type, since there is no reason why, for example, $\mathbf{P}\{\mathbf{U}_n = 0 \,|\, \mathbf{U}_{n-1} = a\}$ should be the same as $\mathbf{P}\{\mathbf{U}_n = 0 \,|\, \mathbf{U}_{n-1} = a, \mathbf{U}_{n-2} = b\}$; the knowledge of $\mathbf{U}_{n-1}$ and $\mathbf{U}_{n-2}$ permits better predictions than the sole knowledge of $\mathbf{U}_{n-1}$.

In the case of a continuous time parameter the preceding summations are replaced by integrations. In diffusion theory the $\mathbf{Y}_n$ play the role of accelerations; the $\mathbf{S}_n$ are then velocities, and the $\mathbf{U}_n$ positions. If only positions can be measured, we are compelled to study a non-Markovian process, even though it is indirectly defined in terms of a Markov process.

(c) *Moving averages.* Again let $\{\mathbf{Y}_n\}$ be a sequence of mutually independent random variables. Moving averages of order r are defined by $\mathbf{X}^{(n)} = (\mathbf{Y}_n + \mathbf{Y}_{n+1} + \ldots + \mathbf{Y}_{n+r-1})/r$. It is easily seen that the $\mathbf{X}^{(n)}$ are not a Markov process. Processes of this type are common in many applications (cf. problem 26).

(d) *A traffic problem.* For an empirical example of a non-Markovian process R. Fürth [13] made extensive observations on the number of pedestrians on a certain segment of a street. An idealized mathematical model of this process can be obtained in the following way. For simplicity we assume that all pedestrians have the same speed v; also, we consider only pedestrians moving in one direction. At time $t = 0$ we divide the positive x-axis into segments of fixed length δ, each of which may or may not contain a pedestrian. We suppose that the distribution of pedestrians in our segments is determined by a sequence of Bernoulli trials. In other words, we have a sequence of independent random variables $\mathbf{Y}_k$, each of which assumes the values 1 or 0 with probabilities p and q, respectively. The segment $(k - 1)\delta \leq x < k\delta$ contains a pedestrian if $\mathbf{Y}_k = 1$. Let now the whole axis move with velocity v in the negative direction, and let us observe the number of pedestrians in the fixed interval of length $N\delta$, which at time $t = 0$ is covered by the interval $0 \leq x < N\delta$ of the moving x-axis. At time t this fixed interval is covered by the interval $vt \leq x < vt + N\delta$ of the x-axis. Let observations be made at times $n\delta/v$ and let $\mathbf{X}^{(n)}$ be the number of pedestrians in our fixed interval observed at time n. Then $\mathbf{X}^{(n)} = \mathbf{Y}_n + \mathbf{Y}_{n+1} + \ldots + \mathbf{Y}_{n+N-1}$, so that our process is, except for the factor $1/N$, a moving average process. It is therefore non-Mar-

---

[13] R. Fürth, Schwankungserscheinungen in der Physik, *Sammlung Vieweg*, Braunschweig, 1920, pp. 17ff. The original observations appeared in *Physikalische Zeitschrift*, vols. 19 (1918) and 20 (1919).

kovian. (Passing to the limit $\delta \to 0$, we obtain a continuous model, in which a Poisson distribution takes over the role of the binomial distribution.)

(e) *Superposition of Markov processes (composite shuffling).* There exist many technical devices (such as groups of selectors in telephone exchanges, counters, filters) whose action can be described as a superposition of two Markov processes with an output which is non-Markovian. A fair idea of such mechanisms may be obtained from the study of the following method of card shuffling.

In addition to the target deck of N cards we have an equivalent auxiliary deck, and the usual shuffling technique is applied to this auxiliary deck. If its cards appear in the order $(a_1, a_2, \ldots, a_N)$, we permute the cards of the target deck so that the first, second, $\ldots$, Nth cards are transferred to the places number $a_1, a_2, \ldots, a_N$. Thus the shuffling of the auxiliary deck indirectly determines the successive orderings of the target deck. The latter form *a stochastic process which is not of the Markov type.* To prove this, it suffices to show that the knowledge of two successive orderings of the target deck conveys in general more clues to the future than the sole knowledge of the last ordering. We show this in a simple special case.

Let $N = 4$, and suppose that the auxiliary deck is initially in the order (2431). Suppose, furthermore, that the shuffling operation always consists of a true "cutting," that is, the ordering (a_1, a_2, a_3, a_4) is changed into one of the three orderings (a_2, a_3, a_4, a_1), (a_3, a_4, a_1, a_2), (a_4, a_1, a_2, a_3); we attribute to each of these three possibilities probability $\frac{1}{3}$. With these conventions the auxiliary deck will at any time be in one of the four orderings (2431), (4312), (3124), (1243). On the other hand, a little experimentation will show that the target deck will gradually pass through all 24 possible orderings and that each of them will appear in combination with each of the four possible orderings of the auxiliary deck. This means that the ordering (1234) of the target deck will recur infinitely often, and it will always be succeeded by one of the four orderings (2431), (4312), (3124), (1243). Now the auxiliary deck can never remain in the same ordering, and hence the target deck cannot twice in succession undergo the same permutation. Hence, if at times $n - 1$ and n the orderings are (1234) and (1243), respectively, then at time $n + 1$ the state (1234) is impossible. Thus the knowledge of the state at times $(n - 1)$ and n conveys more information than the sole knowledge of the state at time n.

* 11. MISCELLANY

(a) Inverse Probabilities

Although it is most natural to investigate the future development of a system, it is occasionally necessary to study its past. Consider a Markov chain with states E_k and constant transition probabilities p_{jk}, whose absolute probabilities at time n are $a_k^{(n)} = \Sigma a_\nu^{(0)} p_{\nu k}^{(n)}$. *The conditional probability that the system was at time $m < n$ in state E_j, given that at time n it is in E_k, is (independently of the states at times after n)*

$$(11.1) \qquad\qquad q_{kj}(n, m) = \frac{a_j^{(m)}}{a_k^{(n)}} p_{jk}^{(n-m)}, \qquad\qquad m < n.$$

This formula makes sense only if $a_k^{(n)} > 0$; otherwise the conditional probability in question is not defined. If all $a_k^{(n)}$ are positive, then (11.1) defines a system of transition probabilities with all the properties required for a Markov process. In particular, the $q_{kj}(n, m)$ satisfy the Chapman-Kolmogorov identity (10.3) with the time direction reversed, namely,

$$(11.2) \qquad\qquad q_{kj}(n, m) = \sum_\nu q_{k\nu}(n, r)\, q_{\nu j}(r, m)$$

$(m < r < n)$. The $q_{kj}(n, m)$ are called *inverse probabilities*.[14] Consider, in particular, an irreducible chain with stationary probabilities $\{u_k\}$. Then $a_k^{(n)} = u_k$ for all n, and $u_k > 0$ (cf. sections 6 and 7). In this case the *one-step* transitions $q_{k,j}(n+1, n)$ are independent of n and reduce to

$$(11.3) \qquad\qquad q_{kj} = \frac{u_j}{u_k} p_{jk}.$$

The matrix $\{q_{kj}\}$ is stochastic, so that here the inverse probabilities define a Markov chain with constant transition probabilities. If $q_{jk} = p_{jk}$, the original chain is called *reversible;* its probability relations are then symmetric in time.

(b) The Central Limit Theorem

The theory of recurrent events contains further information concerning Markov chains. Let E_k be a fixed persistent state whose recurrence time has finite variance σ_k^2 (this condition is always satisfied if the

---

* This section may be omitted at first reading.

[14] A. Kolmogoroff, Zur Theorie der Markoffschen Ketten, *Mathematische Annalen*, vol. 112 (1935), pp. 155–160.

chain is finite). Let $\mathbf{N}_n$ denote the number of passages up to time n of the system through E_k. Then we know from chapter XIII, section 6, that the variable $\mathbf{N}_n$ is asymptotically normally distributed. In the notations of the present chapter we have $\mathbf{E}(\mathbf{N}_n) = n/\mu_k = nu_k$; a way to calculate the variance in the case of finite chains will be indicated in the next chapter. In particular, as $n \to \infty$, the probability tends to one that $\left| \dfrac{\mathbf{N}_n}{n} - u_k \right| < \epsilon$ for every arbitrary $\epsilon > 0$. This is the *weak law of large numbers* for the number of passages through E_k. Similarly, the strong law of large numbers and the law of the iterated logarithm hold and require no special proof. In the case of an infinite chain, the recurrence time of E_k need not have a finite variance, even if its mean is finite. However, the general limit theorems for recurrent events apply in this case.

The random variable $\mathbf{N}_n$ may be defined by $\mathbf{N}_n = \mathbf{X}_1 + \ldots + \mathbf{X}_n$, where $\mathbf{X}_n$ equals one if the system is, at time n, in state E_k and zero otherwise. This suggests the following generalization. We assign to the state E_k an arbitrary number x_k and let the random variable $\mathbf{X}_n$ equal x_k if at time n the system is in state E_k. As usual, we put $\mathbf{S}_n = \mathbf{X}_1 + \ldots + \mathbf{X}_n$. For *finite* Markov chains Doeblin [15] has shown that in general the central limit theorem and the law of the iterated logarithm hold for $\mathbf{S}_n$. An exception occurs only if the numbers x_k are chosen so that for every shortest path leading from E_k back to E_k the sum of the x_ν equals a constant c independent of the path.

(c) Non-stochastic Matrices

The theorems of this chapter describe the asymptotic behavior of the powers P^n of an arbitrary stochastic matrix P, that is, of a matrix whose elements satisfy the conditions (1.2). It is easy to generalize these theorems to a more general class of matrices. Let P be an arbitrary *(finite or infinite) matrix with non-negative elements and denote its row sums by S_j so that $S_j = \Sigma_k p_{jk}$. We assume that the sequence S_j is bounded, that is, that there exists a constant M such that $S_j \le M$.* Under these conditions the asymptotic behavior of P^n is still described by our theorems, inasmuch as P can be reduced to a stochastic matrix.

To fix ideas suppose that the rows and columns of P are numbered starting with 1, and consider first the case where $S_j \le 1$ for all j. In this case we enlarge (border) the matrix P by adding a row and a col-

---

[15] W. Doeblin, Sur les propriétés asymptotiques de mouvements régis par certains types de chaines simples, Thesis, Paris, 1937.

umn number zero whose elements are defined by $p_{00} = 1$, $p_{01} = p_{02} =$
$= \ldots = 0$, and $p_{j0} = 1 - S_j$ for $j \geq 1$. The new matrix Q is stochastic, and its asymptotic behavior is given by our theorems. On the
other hand, P^n is the submatrix of the corner element $p_{00}^{(n)}$ of Q^n. In
the general case the row sums S_j may exceed unity, but we may replace
the matrix P by the matrix P^* whose elements are p_{jk}/M. The row
sums S_j^* of P^* satisfy the condition $S_j^* \leq 1$, and we are able to describe the asymptotic behavior of the powers P^{*n}. However, the matrices P^n and P^{*n} differ only by the factor M^n, so that our theorems
actually describe the asymptotic behavior of $p_{jk}^{(n)}$ in all cases.

Matrices of the described type occur in the theory of generalized
random walks with creation or destruction of masses.

(d) Literature

There exists a huge literature on *finite* Markov chains. A detailed
account of the various methods of attack and references to earlier work
will be found in the comprehensive treatise by M. Fréchet.[16] An algebraic treatment of finite chains will be described in the next chapter.
The entire theory of finite chains can be derived from Frobenius' theory
of matrices with positive elements. This method has been exploited
in particular by V. Romanovsky. Unfortunately these methods do
not carry over to the more interesting case of infinite chains, first considered by A. Kolmogorov.[17] His work was continued by W. Doeblin [18]
and J. L. Doob.[19] The latter derived the ergodic properties from general group theory. Recent papers by K. L. Chung [20] investigate in
particular transitions from one state to another when certain states

[16] *Recherches théoriques modernes sur le calcul des probabilités*, vol. 2 (théorie des
événements en chaine dans le cas d'un nombre fini d'états possibles), Paris, 1938.
Another monograph on Markov chains is due to B. Hostinsky, *Méthodes générales
du calcul des probabilités*, fasc. 52 of the *Mémorial des sciences mathématiques*, Paris,
1931.

[17] Anfangsgründe der Theorie der Markoffschen Ketten mit unendlich vielen
möglichen Zuständen, *Matematičeskii Sbornik*, N.S., vol. 1 (1936), pp. 607–610.
This paper contains no proofs. A complete exposition was given only in Russian,
in *Bulletin de l'Université d'État à Moscou*, Sect. A, vol. 1 (1937), pp. 1–15.

[18] Sur deux problèmes de M. Kolmogoroff concernant les chaines dénombrables,
Bulletin Société Mathématique de France, vol. 66 (1939), pp. 1–11.

[19] Topics in the theory of Markoff chains, and also Markoff chains—denumerable case, *Transactions American Mathematical Society*, vol. 52 (1942), pp. 37–64,
and vol. 58 (1945), pp. 455–473.

[20] K. L. Chung, Contributions to the theory of Markov chains I, *Journal of Research*, National Bureau of Standards, vol. 50 (1953), pp. 203–208, and II, *Transactions American Mathematical Society*, vol. 76 (1954), pp. 397–419.

are forbidden. This leads in turn to more elegant formulas for the central limit theorem.

It has been shown by C. Derman [21] that in an irreducible chain with null states the equations (6.1) for stationary distributions admit of a unique solution $\{v_k\}$ such that $\Sigma v_k = \infty$. The inversion formula (11.3) makes sense also for such solutions, and the modern theory pays increasing attention to similar uses of unbounded solutions.[22] Certain very general classes of non-Markovian processes related to Markov chains are treated systematically by T. E. Harris.[23]

12. PROBLEMS FOR SOLUTION

1. In a sequence of Bernoulli trials we say that at time n the state E_1 is observed if the trials number $n - 1$ and n resulted in SS. Similarly E_2, E_3, E_4 stand for SF, FS, FF. Find the matrix P and all its powers. Generalize the scheme.

2. Classify the states for the four chains whose matrices P have the rows given below. Find in each case P^2 and the asymptotic behavior of $p_{jk}^{(n)}$.

(a) $(0, \frac{1}{2}, \frac{1}{2})$, $(\frac{1}{2}, 0, \frac{1}{2})$, $(\frac{1}{2}, \frac{1}{2}, 0)$;

(b) $(0, 0, 0, 1)$, $(0, 0, 0, 1)$, $(\frac{1}{2}, \frac{1}{2}, 0, 0)$, $(0, 0, 1, 0)$;

(c) $(\frac{1}{2}, 0, \frac{1}{2}, 0, 0)$, $(\frac{1}{4}, \frac{1}{2}, \frac{1}{4}, 0, 0)$, $(\frac{1}{2}, 0, \frac{1}{2}, 0, 0)$, $(0, 0, 0, \frac{1}{2}, \frac{1}{2})$, $(0, 0, 0, \frac{1}{2}, \frac{1}{2})$;

(d) $(0, \frac{1}{2}, \frac{1}{2}, 0, 0, 0)$, $(0, 0, 0, \frac{1}{3}, \frac{1}{3}, \frac{1}{3})$, $(0, 0, 0, \frac{1}{3}, \frac{1}{3}, \frac{1}{3})$, $(1, 0, 0, 0, 0, 0)$, $(1, 0, 0, 0, 0, 0)$, $(1, 0, 0, 0, 0, 0)$.

3. We consider throws of a true die and agree to say that at time n the system is in state E_j if j is the highest number appearing in the first n throws. Find the matrix P^n and verify that formula (3.3) holds.

4. In example (2.l) find the (absorption) probabilities x_k and y_k that, starting from E_k, the system will end in E_1 or E_5, respectively ($k = 2, 3, 4, 6$). (Do this problem from the basic definitions without referring to the formulas of section 8.)

5. Treat example I(5.b) as a Markov chain. Calculate the probability of winning for each player.

6. The first row of P is $\{p_1, p_2, \ldots\}$. In the following rows $p_{j,j-1} = 1$, all other entries being zero. Discuss the character of the states and find the stationary distribution, if any.

7. The first column of P is $\{q_0, q_1, \ldots\}$ and $p_{i,i+1} = 1 - q_i$ for $i = 0, 1, \ldots$. Prove that the states are transient if, and only if, $\Sigma q_j < \infty$. When are the states null states? Find the stationary distribution, if any.

8. *One reflecting barrier.* Consider the random-walk matrix with $p_{k,k+1} = p$, $p_{k,k-1} = q$ for $k = 2, 3, \ldots$ and $p_{12} = p$, $p_{11} = q$. Prove that the states are

[21] C. Derman, A solution to a set of fundamental equations in Markov chains, *Proceedings American Mathematical Society*, vol. 5 (1954), pp. 332–334.

[22] W. Feller, Boundaries induced by positive matrices, *Transactions American Mathematical Society*, vol. 83 (1956), pp. 19–54.

[23] T. E. Harris, On chains of infinite order, *Pacific Journal of Mathematics*, vol. 5 (1955), Supplement 1, pp. 707–724.

transient if $p > q$, persistent null states if $p = q$, and ergodic if $p < q$. Find the stationary distribution.

9. *Two reflecting barriers.* A chain with states 1, 2, ... a has a matrix whose first and last rows are $(q, p, 0, \ldots, 0)$ and $(0, \ldots, 0, q, p)$. In all other rows $p_{k,k+1} = p$, $p_{k,k-1} = q$. Find the stationary distribution. Can the chain be periodic?

10. N black and N white balls are placed in two urns so that each urn contains N balls. The number of black balls in the first urn is the state of the system. At each step one ball is selected at random from each urn, and the two balls thus selected are interchanged. Find the p_{jk}. Show that in the limiting distribution the term u_k equals the probability of getting exactly k black balls if N balls are selected at random out of a collection of N black and N white balls.[24]

11. A chain with states E_0, E_1, ... has transition probabilities

$$p_{jk} = e^{-\lambda} \sum_{\nu=0}^{j} \binom{j}{\nu} p^\nu q^{j-\nu} \frac{\lambda^{k-\nu}}{(k - \nu)!}$$

where the terms in the sum should be replaced by zero if $\nu > k$. Show that

$$p_{jk}^{(n)} \to e^{-\lambda/q} \frac{(\lambda/q)^k}{k!}.$$

Note: This chain occurs in statistical mechanics [25] and can be interpreted as follows. The state of the system is defined by the number of particles in a certain volume of space. During each time interval of unit length each particle has probability q to leave the volume, and the particles are stochastically independent. Moreover, new particles may enter the volume, and the probability of r entrants is given by the Poisson expression $e^{-\lambda}\lambda^r/r!$. The stationary distribution is then a Poisson distribution with parameter λ/q.

12. *Ehrenfest model.* In example $(2.f)$ let there initially be j molecules in the first container, and let $\mathbf{X}^{(n)} = 2k - a$ if at time n the system is in state k (so that $\mathbf{X}^{(n)}$ is the difference of the number of molecules in the two containers). Let $e_n = \mathbf{E}(\mathbf{X}^{(n)})$. Prove that $e_{n+1} = (a - 2)e_n/a$, whence $e_n = = (1 - 2/a)^n(2j - a)$. (Note that $e_n \to 0$ as $n \to \infty$.)

13. Treat the counter problem, example XIII$(1.b)$, as a Markov chain.

14. *Plane random walk with reflecting barriers.* Consider a *symmetric* random walk in a bounded region of the plane. The boundary is reflecting in the sense that, whenever in an unrestricted random walk the particle would leave the region, it is forced to return to the last position. Show that, if every point of the region can be reached from every other point, there exists a stationary distribution and that $u_k = 1/a$, where a is the number of positions in the region.

15. *Repeated averaging.* Let $\{x_1, x_2, \ldots\}$ be a bounded sequence of numbers and P the matrix of an ergodic chain. Prove that $\sum_j p_{ij}^{(n)} x_j \to \Sigma u_j x_j$.

---

[24] This problem goes back to Laplace; see Fréchet's book (cited in footnote 16), p. 49.

[25] S. Chandrasekhar, Stochastic problems in physics and astronomy, *Reviews of Modern Physics*, vol. 15 (1943), pp. 1–89, in particular p. 45.

Show that the repeated averaging procedure of chapter XIII, section 4, and of problem XIII, 5 is a special case.

16. In the theory of *waiting lines* we encounter the chain matrix

$$\begin{bmatrix} p_0 & p_1 & p_2 & p_3 & \cdots \\ p_0 & p_1 & p_2 & p_3 & \cdots \\ 0 & p_0 & p_1 & p_2 & \cdots \\ 0 & 0 & p_0 & p_1 & \cdots \end{bmatrix}$$

where $\{p_k\}$ is a probability distribution. Using generating functions, discuss the character of the states. Find the generating function of the stationary distribution, if any.

17. *Waiting time to absorption.* For transient E_j let $\mathbf{Y}_j$ be the time when the system for *the first time* passes into a persistent state. Assuming that the probability of staying forever in transient states is zero, prove that $d_j = \mathbf{E}(\mathbf{Y}_j)$ is uniquely determined as the solution of the system of linear equations

$$d_j - \sum_T p_{j\nu} d_\nu = 1,$$

the summation extending over all ν such that E_ν is transient. However, d_ν need not be finite.

18. If the number of states is $a < \infty$ and if E_k can be reached from E_j, then it can be reached in a steps or less.

19. Let the chain contain a states and let E_j be persistent. There exists a number $q < 1$ such that for $n \geq a$ the probability of the recurrence time of E_j exceeding n is smaller than q^n. (*Hint:* Use problem 18.)

20. In a finite chain E_j is transient if and only if there exists an E_k such that E_k can be reached from E_j but not E_j from E_k. (For infinite chains this is false, as shown by problem 7.)

21. An irreducible chain for which *one* diagonal element p_{jj} is positive cannot be periodic.

22. A finite irreducible chain is non-periodic if and only if there exists an n such that $p_{jk}^{(n)} > 0$ for all j and k.

23. In a chain with a states let $(x_1, \ldots, x_a)$ be a solution of the system of linear equations $x_j = \Sigma p_{j\nu} x_\nu$. Prove: (*a*) the states E_r for which $x_r > 0$ form a closed (not necessarily irreducible) set; (*b*) if E_j and E_k belong to the same irreducible set, then $x_j = x_k$.

24. *Continuation.* If $(x_1, \ldots, x_a)$ is a solution of $x_j = s\Sigma p_{j\nu} x_\nu$ with $|s| = 1$ but $s \neq 1$, then there exists an integer $t > 1$ such that $s^t = 1$. If the chain is irreducible, then the smallest integer of this kind is the period of the chain.

25. *Mean ergodic theorem.*[26] In an arbitrary chain let

$$A_{jk}^{(n)} = \frac{1}{n} \sum_{\nu=1}^{n} p_{jk}^{(\nu)}.$$

---

[26] This theorem is a simple consequence of the results of the present chapter. However, it is much weaker and can therefore be proved by simpler methods; see K. Yosida and S. Kakutani, Markoff processes with an enumerable infinite number of possible states, *Japanese Journal of Mathematics*, vol. 16 (1939), pp. 47–55.

If E_j and E_k belong to the same irreducible closed set, then $A_{jk}^{(n)}$ tends to a limit which is independent of j and equals the stationary probability u_k, whenever the latter exists. If E_j and E_k belong to different closed sets, then $A_{jk}^{(n)} = 0$ for all n. If E_k is transient, then $A_{jk}^{(n)} \to 0$ for all j.

26. *Moving averages.* Let $\{Y_k\}$ be a sequence of mutually independent random variables, each assuming the values ± 1 with probability $\frac{1}{2}$. Put $X^{(n)} = (Y_n + Y_{n+1})/2$. Find the transition probabilities

$$p_{jk}(m, n) = \mathbf{P}\{X^{(n)} = k \mid X^{(m)} = j\},$$

where $m < n$ and $j, k = -1, 0, 1$. Conclude that $\{X^{(n)}\}$ is not a Markov process and that (10.3) does not hold.

27. In a sequence of Bernoulli trials say that the state E_1 is observed at time n if the trials number $n - 1$ and n resulted in success; otherwise the system is in E_2. Find the n-step transition probabilities and discuss the non-Markovian character.

Note: This process is obtained from the chain of problem 1 by lumping together three states. Such a *grouping* procedure can be applied to any Markov chain and destroys the Markovian character. Processes of this type are studied in the paper by Harris.

28. *Mixing of Markov chains.* Given two Markov chains with the same number of states, and matrices P_1 and P_2. A new process is defined by an initial distribution and n-step transition probabilities $\frac{1}{2}P_1{}^n + \frac{1}{2}P_2{}^n$. Discuss the non-Markovian character and the relation to the urn models of chapter V.

CHAPTER XVI

Algebraic Treatment
of Finite Markov Chains

In this chapter we consider a Markov chain with finitely many states $E_1, \ldots, E_a$ and a given matrix of transition probabilities p_{jk}. Our main aim is to derive explicit formulas for the n-step transition probabilities $p_{jk}^{(n)}$. We shall not require the results of the preceding chapter, except the general concepts and notations of section 3.

We shall make use of the method of generating functions and shall obtain the desired results from the partial fraction expansions of chapter XI, section 4. Our results can also be obtained directly from the theory of canonical decompositions of matrices [1] (which in turn can be derived from our results). Moreover, for *finite* chains the ergodic properties proved in chapter XV follow from the results of the present chapter. However, for simplicity, we shall slightly restrict the generality and disregard exceptional cases which complicate the general theory and do not occur in practical examples.

The general method is outlined in section 1 and illustrated in sections 2 and 3. In section 4 special attention is paid to transient states and absorption probabilities. In section 5 the theory is applied to finding the variances of the recurrence times of the states E_j.

1. GENERAL THEORY

For every fixed j, k we define a generating function

$$(1.1) \qquad P_{jk}(s) = \sum_{n=1}^{\infty} p_{jk}^{(n)} s^{n-1}.$$

---

* This chapter treats a special topic and may be omitted.
[1] See the treatise by Fréchet cited in chapter XV, section 11.

Multiplying this equation by $sp_{\nu j}$ and adding over all j, we get

(1.2) $$s \sum_{j=1}^{a} p_{\nu j} P_{jk}(s) = P_{\nu k}(s) - p_{\nu k}.$$

For every fixed k we have here a system of a non-homogeneous linear equations for the a unknowns $P_{1k}(s), \ldots, P_{ak}(s)$. Theoretically, this system can be solved by means of determinants or by successive elimi-nations of unknowns. We use only the fact that the determinant $D(s)$ of the system is a polynomial of degree not exceeding a, and that the $P_{\nu k}(s)$ are *rational functions* of s with the common denominator $D(s)$. We shall consider only the case where the equation $D(s) = 0$ has no multiple roots; this is a slight restriction of generality, but the theory will cover most cases of practical interest.

Since the $P_{\nu k}(s)$ are rational functions, the partial fraction expansion of chapter XI, section 4, shows that there exist coefficients $\rho_{\nu k}^{(1)}, \ldots, \rho_{\nu k}^{(a)}$ such that

(1.3) $$p_{\nu k}^{(n)} = \frac{\rho_{\nu k}^{(1)}}{s_1^{\,n}} + \frac{\rho_{\nu k}^{(2)}}{s_2^{\,n}} + \ldots + \frac{\rho_{\nu k}^{(a)}}{s_a^{\,n}}$$

where $s_1, s_2, \ldots$ are the roots of $D(s) = 0$. If the degree of $D(s)$ is smaller than a, then (1.3) will contain fewer than a terms. It is also possible that for some particular values of ν and k one or more roots s_r are common to the numerator and denominator and hence cancel. We take care of such cases by letting the corresponding $\rho_{\nu k}^{(r)}$ be zero.

We could calculate the roots s_r and the coefficients $\rho_{\nu k}^{(r)}$ by the methods of chapter XI, but it is preferable to take advantage of certain par-ticular properties of Markov chains. Multiply equation (1.3) by $p_{j\nu}$ and sum over $\nu = 1, 2, \ldots$. The result is

(1.4) $$p_{jk}^{(n+1)} = \sum_{\nu=1}^{a} p_{j\nu} \left\{ \frac{\rho_{\nu k}^{(1)}}{s_1^{\,n}} + \ldots + \frac{\rho_{\nu k}^{(a)}}{s_a^{\,n}} \right\}.$$

If the left side is expressed by means of (1.3), we get an identity which can hold for all n only if the coefficients of $s_1^{-n}, \ldots, s_a^{-n}$ on both sides are equal. This means that for every fixed r we must have

(1.5a) $$\rho_{jk}^{(r)} = s_r \sum_{\nu=1}^{a} p_{j\nu} \rho_{\nu k}^{(r)}, \qquad\qquad r = 1, \ldots, a.$$

In like manner we get, on multiplying (1.3) by p_{km} and adding over all k,

(1.5b) $$\rho_{\nu m}^{(r)} = s_r \sum_{k=1}^{a} \rho_{\nu k}^{(r)} p_{km}.$$

The relations (1.5a) show that for k and r fixed the a quantities $\rho_{1k}^{(r)}, \ldots, \rho_{ak}^{(r)}$ are a solution of the system of a linear equations

$$(1.6a) \qquad\qquad x_j^{(r)} = s_r \sum_{\nu=1}^{a} p_{j\nu} x_\nu^{(r)} \qquad\qquad (j = 1, \ldots, a)$$

Similarly, relations (1.5b) imply that for ν and r fixed, the $\rho_{\nu 1}^{(r)}, \ldots, \rho_{\nu a}^{(r)}$ satisfy the a linear equations

$$(1.6b) \qquad\qquad y_m^{(r)} = s_r \sum_{k=1}^{a} y_k^{(r)} p_{km} \qquad\qquad (m = 1, \ldots, a).$$

For a better understanding let us replace s_r by an arbitrary s and study the two more general systems

$$(1.7a) \qquad\qquad x_j = s \sum_{\nu=1}^{a} p_{j\nu} x_\nu \qquad\qquad (j = 1, \ldots, a)$$

and

$$(1.7b) \qquad\qquad y_m = s \sum_{k=1}^{a} y_k p_{km} \qquad\qquad (m = 1, \ldots, a).$$

A system of a homogeneous equations in a unknowns can have a non-trivial [2] solution only if its determinant vanishes. Now the matrices of the two systems (1.7a) and (1.7b) are the same except that rows and columns are interchanged. Their determinants are therefore equal. Moreover, the determinant of (1.7a) obviously equals the determinant of the system (1.2), which means that the determinants of the two systems (1.7a) and (1.7b) vanish for $s = s_1, s_2, \ldots, s_a$. We can now forget about the generating functions $P_{jk}(s)$ and define the roots s_r as those numbers (real or complex) for which the systems (1.7a) and (1.7b) admit of non-trivial solutions. The assumption that s_r is a simple root means that for every fixed r the solutions $(x_1^{(r)}, \ldots, x_a^{(r)})$ and $(y_1^{(r)}, \ldots, y_a^{(r)})$ are uniquely determined except, of course, for a numerical factor. However, our starting point was the discovery that, for k and r fixed, $(\rho_{1k}^{(r)}, \ldots, \rho_{ak}^{(r)})$ is a solution of (1.7a), while for ν and r fixed $(\rho_{\nu 1}^{(r)}, \ldots, \rho_{\nu a}^{(r)})$ is a solution of (1.7b). Since these solutions are determined up to a numerical factor, we must have

$$(1.8) \qquad\qquad \rho_{jk}^{(r)} = c_r x_j^{(r)} y_k^{(r)}.$$

There remains only the calculation of the constants $c_1, \ldots, c_a$.

---

[2] As usual we call an identically vanishing solution trivial and disregard it.

From (1.8) and (1.3) we have

$$(1.9) \qquad p_{jk}^{(n)} = \sum_{r=1}^{a} c_r x_j^{(r)} y_k^{(r)} s_r^{-n}.$$

Therefore

$$(1.9a) \qquad P_{jk}(s) = c_1 \frac{x_j^{(1)} y_k^{(1)}}{s_1 - s} + \ldots + c_a \frac{x_j^{(a)} y_k^{(a)}}{s_a - s}.$$

Using (1.6a) we get from (1.1)

$$(1.10) \qquad \sum_{k=1}^{a} P_{jk}(s) x_k^{(r)} = x_j^{(r)} \sum_{n=1}^{\infty} s^{n-1} s_r^{-n} = \frac{x_j^{(r)}}{s_r - s}.$$

On the other hand, if we evaluate the left side using (1.9a), we are lead to a sum of a fractions with denominators $s_\nu - s$. It follows that for $\nu \neq r$ the numerators must vanish and

$$(1.11) \qquad 1 = c_r \sum_{\nu=1}^{a} x_\nu^{(r)} y_\nu^{(r)},$$

and thus we have found c_r. It is true that the solutions $x_\nu^{(r)}$ and $y_\nu^{(r)}$ are determined only up to a numerical factor. However, if we replace the $x_j^{(r)}$ by $A x_j^{(r)}$, and the $y_k^{(r)}$ by $B y_k^{(r)}$, then c_r will be changed into c_r/AB and the quantity $\rho_{jk}^{(r)}$ of (1.8) remains unchanged.

Summarizing, we have the following procedure to calculate $p_{jk}^{(n)}$.

Write down the two systems of linear equations (1.7a) and (1.7b). They have a common determinant and admit of non-trivial solutions only for values of s for which this determinant vanishes. We suppose that the roots s_1, s_2, ... (of which there are at most a) are simple; then for each r, the solutions $(x_1^{(r)}, \ldots, x_a^{(r)})$ and $(y_1^{(r)}, \ldots, y_a^{(r)})$ are determined up to an arbitrary multiplicative constant. Find these solutions and the constants c_r from (1.11). Then $p_{jk}^{(n)}$ is given by (1.9).

For every fixed r the $\rho_{jk}^{(r)}$ form a matrix which may be constructed in the following way. Form a multiplication table with the $x_j^{(r)}$ heading the rows and the $y_k^{(r)}$ heading the columns. Multiplying all a^2 elements of this square table by c_r, we get the matrix $\rho_{jk}^{(r)}$. To construct the matrix $(p_{jk}^{(n)})$ we have to divide all elements of $\rho_{jk}^{(r)}$ by s_r^n and add the matrices thus obtained for $r = 1, 2, \ldots, a$. Note that the roots s_r may be simple even if there are fewer than a roots.

The case of multiple roots requires certain changes but may be treated by similar methods. The case of greatest interest will be discussed in section 4.

In algebra the reciprocals $\lambda_r = 1/s_r$ are called *characteristic values* (or eigen values or latent roots) of the matrix P. Zero is a possible characteristic value, but to it there corresponds no root s_r. This explains why there may be fewer than a roots s_r even though there are always a characteristic values. The use of s_r rather than of their reciprocals is more convenient for the method of generating functions. Moreover, it corresponds to the general usage in the theory of integral equations and is therefore more natural in probability theory.

The value $s = 1$ *always occurs among the* s_r, *and to it there corresponds the solution* $(1, 1, \ldots, 1)$ of $(1.7a)$. For all r we have $|s_r| \geq 1$. In fact,[3] a root s_r with $|s_r| < 1$ would lead to a divergent development in (1.3). If $s_1 = 1$ is the only root with $|s_r| = 1$, then $p_{jk}^{(n)} \to c_1 x_j^{(1)} y_k^{(1)}$. It is not difficult to show that if there exist other roots with $|s_r| = 1$, then they are necessarily tth roots of unity, where t is an integer; in this case the chain has period t. For details the reader is referred to Fréchet's treatise quoted in chapter XV, section 11.

Often it is cumbersome or impossible to find *all* roots s_r. However, it is clear that the asymptotic behavior of $p_{jk}^{(n)}$ is determined in first approximation by the s_r with $|s_r| = 1$, and in second approximation by the roots s_r with the next smallest absolute value.

The final formula (1.9) can be written more elegantly in matrix notation. Let $X^{(r)}$ be the *column vector* (or an $a \times 1$ matrix) with elements $x_j^{(r)}$ and let $Y^{(r)}$ be the *row vector* (or a $1 \times a$ matrix) with elements $y_k^{(r)}$. Then $X^{(r)}Y^{(r)}$ is the $a \times a$ matrix with elements $x_j^{(r)}y_k^{(r)}$ and (1.9) takes on the form

$$(1.12) \qquad P^n = \sum_{r=1}^{a} c_r s_r^{-n} X^{(r)} Y^{(r)} \qquad \text{where} \quad c_r^{-1} = Y^{(r)} X^{(r)}.$$

The vectors $X^{(r)}$ and $Y^{(r)}$ are called *latent vectors or eigen vectors*, and c_r^{-1} is their inner product.

2. EXAMPLES

(a) Consider first a chain with only two states. The matrix of transition probabilities assumes the simple form

$$P = \begin{pmatrix} 1 - p & p \\ \alpha & 1 - \alpha \end{pmatrix}$$

where $0 < p < 1$ and $0 < \alpha < 1$. The equations $(1.7a)$ reduce to $s(1 - p)x_1 + spx_2 = x_1$ and $s\alpha x_1 + s(1 - \alpha)x_2 = x_2$. Equating the two ratios x_1/x_2, it is found that a solution exists only if either $s = 1$ or $s = 1/(1 - \alpha - p)$. The solution corresponding to $s_1 = 1$ is $(1, 1)$; the solution corresponding to $s_2 = 1/(1 - \alpha - p)$ is $(p, -\alpha)$. Next take the system $(1.7b)$ which now reduces to $s(1 - p)y_1 + s\alpha y_2 = y_1$ and $spy_1 + s(1 - \alpha)y_2 = y_2$. We know that it can be solved only when $s = s_1$ or $s = s_2$. The corresponding solutions are (α, p) and $(1, -1)$. From (1.11) we get $c_1 = c_2 = 1/(\alpha + p)$. Equations (1.9) and (1.11) now enable us to write down explicit formulas for the quan-

---

[3] A direct proof is as follows. Let M be the largest term in the sequence $|x_1^{(r)}|, \ldots, |x_a^{(r)}|$ (r fixed). Then from $(1.6a)$ $M \leq |s_r| \Sigma p_{j\nu} M = |s_r| M$ or $|s_r| \geq 1$.

tities $p_{jk}^{(n)}$. The final result can be written in matrix form

$$P^n = \frac{1}{\alpha + p}\begin{pmatrix} \alpha & p \\ \alpha & p \end{pmatrix} + \frac{(1 - \alpha - p)^n}{\alpha + p}\begin{pmatrix} p & -p \\ -\alpha & \alpha \end{pmatrix}$$

(where factors common to all four elements have been taken out as factors to the matrices). Since $|1 - \alpha - p| < 1$, the second matrix tends to zero as $n \to \infty$, and the first matrix represents the limiting form of P^n.

(b) Let

$$(2.1) \qquad P = \begin{bmatrix} 0 & 0 & 0 & 1 \\ 0 & 0 & 0 & 1 \\ \frac{1}{2} & \frac{1}{2} & 0 & 0 \\ 0 & 0 & 1 & 0 \end{bmatrix}$$

[this is the matrix of problem XV,2(b)]. The system (1.7a) reduces to

$$(2.2) \quad x_1 = sx_4, \qquad x_2 = sx_4, \qquad x_3 = \frac{s(x_1 + x_2)}{2}, \qquad x_4 = sx_3.$$

Since a multiplicative constant remains arbitrary, we may put $x_4 = 1$. Then $x_1 = s$, $x_2 = s$, $x_3 = s^2$, $x_4 = s^3$, and therefore we must have $s^3 = 1$. Now if we put

$$(2.3) \qquad \theta = e^{2\pi i/3} = \cos\frac{2\pi}{3} + i\sin\frac{2\pi}{3},$$

then the three roots of $s^3 = 1$ are $s_1 = 1$, $s_2 = \theta$, $s_3 = \theta^2$. (Note that we have only three roots, even though there are four states.) The solutions $x_j^{(r)}$ corresponding to the three roots are $(1, 1, 1, 1)$, $(\theta, \theta, \theta^2, 1)$, $(\theta^2, \theta^2, \theta, 1)$.

From system (1.7b) we get $y_1 = sy_3/2$, $y_2 = sy_3/2$, $y_3 = sy_4$, $y_4 = s(y_1 + y_2)$. The three sets of solutions corresponding to $s_1 = 1$, $s_2 = \theta$, and $s_3 = \theta^2$ are $(1, 1, 2, 2)$, $(\theta, \theta, 2, 2\theta^2)$, $(\theta^2, \theta^2, 2, 2\theta)$. Therefore from (1.11) $c_1 = \frac{1}{6}$, $c_2 = 1/(6\theta^2) = \theta/6$, $c_3 = 1/(6\theta) = \theta^2/6$. We are now able to express all $p_{jk}^{(n)}$. For example,

$$p_{11}^{(n)} = p_{22}^{(n)} = \frac{1 + \theta^n + \theta^{2n}}{6}$$

$$(2.4) \qquad p_{13}^{(n)} = \frac{1 + \theta^{2n+2} + \theta^{n+1}}{3}$$

$$p_{14}^{(n)} = \frac{1 + \theta^{2n+1} + \theta^{n+2}}{3}$$

etc. The chain is obviously periodic with period 3.

(c) Let $p + q = 1$, and

$$(2.5) \qquad P = \begin{bmatrix} 0 & p & 0 & q \\ q & 0 & p & 0 \\ 0 & q & 0 & p \\ p & 0 & q & 0 \end{bmatrix}.$$

[This matrix describes a cyclical random walk; see example XV(2.d).] The equations (1.7a) reduce to $x_1 = s(px_2 + qx_4)$, $x_2 = s(qx_1 + px_3)$, $x_3 = s(qx_2 + px_4)$, $x_4 = s(px_1 + qx_3)$. Suppose that $p \neq q$. From the first and the third equations we find $x_1 + x_3 = s(x_2 + x_4)$, and from the remaining equations $x_2 + x_4 = s(x_1 + x_3)$. Hence we have either $s^2 = 1$ or $x_1 + x_3 = x_2 + x_4 = 0$. The first alternative leads to the two roots $s_1 = 1$, $s_2 = -1$. On the other hand, substituting $x_3 = -x_1$, $x_4 = -x_2$ into the first two equations, we find $s^2(p - q)^2 = -1$, which yields the remaining two roots s_3 and s_4. Thus

$$(2.6) \quad s_1 = 1, \qquad s_2 = -1, \qquad s_3 = \frac{i}{q - p}, \qquad s_4 = -\frac{i}{q - p},$$

(where $i^2 = -1$). The corresponding solutions $x_j^{(r)}$ contain an arbitrary factor, and we are free to put $x_4^{(r)} = 1$. Then the four sets of solutions are easily found to be $(1, 1, 1, 1)$, $(-1, 1, -1, 1)$, $(i, -1, -i, 1)$, $(-i, -1, i, 1)$. The system (1.7b) reduces in our case to $y_1 = s(qy_2 + py_4)$, $y_2 = s(py_1 + qy_3)$, $y_3 = s(py_2 + qy_4)$, $y_4 = s(qy_1 + py_3)$. To the four roots (2.6) there correspond the solutions $(1, 1, 1, 1)$, $(-1, 1, -1, 1)$, $(-i, -1, i, 1)$, $(i, -1, -i, 1)$. For the constants c_r we find from (1.11) $c_1 = c_2 = c_3 = c_4 = \frac{1}{4}$. Using (1.3) and (1.8), we can now write an explicit formula for each sequence $p_{jk}^{(n)}$ ($n = 1$, 2, 3, ...). In the present case the solutions $x_j^{(r)}$ and $y_j^{(r)}$ are of the simple form $(\alpha, \alpha^2, \alpha^3, \alpha^4)$, where α is one of the four numbers 1, -1, i, or $-i$. This enables us to express the $p_{jk}^{(n)}$ by the single formula

$$(2.7) \qquad p_{jk}^{(n)} = \tfrac{1}{4}\{1 + (q - p)^n(i)^{j-k-n}\}\{1 + (-1)^{k+j-n}\}.$$

This formula is valid also for $p = q = \frac{1}{2}$.

It is seen that the term involving $(q - p)^n$ tends to zero, and that the other term has period 2.

(d) General cyclical random walk [example XV(2.d)]. In the preceding example we were able to express the $x_k^{(r)}$ and $y_k^{(r)}$ as powers of the four fourth roots of unity. This suggests trying a similar procedure for the general matrix of example XV(2.d). It is convenient to number the states from 0 to $a - 1$. For brevity we put

$$(2.8) \qquad\qquad \theta = e^{2i\pi/a}.$$

This is an ath root of unity, and all ath roots are represented by the sequence $1, \theta, \theta^2, \ldots, \theta^{a-1}$. It is easily seen that the systems $(1.7a)$ and $(1.7b)$ are satisfied by the a sets of solutions

$$(2.9) \qquad\qquad x_j^{(r)} = \theta^{rj}, \qquad y_k^{(r)} = \theta^{-rk}$$

with $r = 0, 1, 2, \ldots, a-1$; they correspond to

$$(2.10) \qquad\qquad s_r = \left\{ \sum_{\nu=0}^{a-1} q_\nu \theta^{\nu r} \right\}^{-1}.$$

From equations (1.11) and (2.9) we find $c_r = 1/a$ for all r, and thus finally

$$(2.11) \qquad\qquad p_{jk}^{(n)} = \frac{1}{a} \sum_{r=0}^{a-1} \theta^{r(j-k)} \left(\sum_{\nu=0}^{a-1} q_\nu \theta^{\nu r} \right)^n.$$

It is interesting to verify this formula for $n = 1$. The factor of q_ν is

$$(2.12) \qquad\qquad \sum_{r=0}^{a-1} \theta^{r(j-k+\nu)}.$$

This sum is zero except when $j - k + \nu = 0$ or a, in which case each term equals one. Hence $p_{jk}^{(1)}$ reduces to q_{k-j} if $k \geq j$ and to q_{a+k-j} if $k < j$, and this is the given matrix (p_{jk}).

(e) *The occupancy problem.* Example XV$(2.g)$ shows that the classical occupancy problem can be treated by the method of Markov chains. The system is in state j if there are j occupied and $a - j$ empty cells. If this is the initial situation and n additional balls are placed at random, then $p_{jk}^{(n)}$ is the probability that there will be k occupied and $a - k$ empty cells (so that $p_{jk}^{(n)} = 0$ if $k < j$). For $j = 0$ this probability follows from formula II(11.7). We now derive a formula for $p_{jk}^{(n)}$, thus generalizing the result of chapter II.

Since $p_{jj} = j/a$ and $p_{j,j+1} = (a - j)/a$, it is easily seen that the system of equations $(1.7a)$ reduces to

$$(2.13) \qquad (a - sj)x_j = s(a - j)x_{j+1}, \qquad j = 0, \ldots, a.$$

For $s = 1$ we get the solution $x_j = 1$. It is clear that if $s \neq 1$ then $x_a = 0$, so that $s = 1$ is the only value of s for which all x_j are different from zero. If s is any other value for which (2.13) has a solution, then there must exist some index $r < a$ such that $x_{r+1} = 0$ but $-x_r \neq 0$; from (2.13) it then follows that $sr = a$. Thus the roots s_r

for which (2.13) has solutions are $s_r = a/r$ with $r = 1, 2, \ldots, a$. The corresponding solutions of (2.13) are obtained successively, putting $x_0^{(r)} = 1$, and $j = 0, 1, \ldots$. We find

$$(2.14) \qquad x_j^{(r)} = \binom{r}{j} \div \binom{a}{j}$$

so that $x_j^{(r)} = 0$ when $j > r$.

For $s = s_r$ the system (1.7b) reduces to

$$(2.15) \qquad (r - j)y_j^{(r)} = (a - j + 1)y_{j-1}^{(r)}$$

and has the solution

$$(2.16) \qquad y_j^{(r)} = \binom{a - r}{j - r}(-1)^{j-r}$$

where, of course, $y_j^{(r)} = 0$ if $j < r$. Since $x_j^{(r)} = 0$ for $j > r$ and $y_j^{(r)} = 0$ for $j < r$, we easily find from equation (1.11) that $c_r = (x_r^{(r)}y_r^{(r)})^{-1} = $

$= \binom{a}{r}$, and hence

$$(2.17) \qquad p_{jk}^{(n)} = \sum_{r=j}^{k} \left(\frac{r}{a}\right)^n \binom{a}{r}\binom{r}{j}\binom{a - r}{k - r}(-1)^{k-r} \div \binom{a}{j}.$$

On expressing the binomial coefficients in terms of factorials, this formula simplifies to

$$(2.18) \qquad p_{jk}^{(n)} = \binom{a - j}{a - k}\sum_{\nu=0}^{k-j}\left(\frac{\nu + j}{a}\right)^n(-1)^{k-j-\nu}\binom{k - j}{\nu},$$

with $p_{jk}^{(n)} = 0$ if $k < j$.

(Further examples are found in the following two sections.)

3. RANDOM WALK WITH REFLECTING BARRIERS

The application of Markov chains will now be illustrated by a complete discussion of a random walk with states $1, 2, \ldots, a$ and two reflecting barriers.[4] The rows number $2, 3, \ldots, a-1$ of the matrix P are determined by $p_{k,k+1} = p$ and $p_{k,k-1} = q$; the first and the last rows are defined by $(q, p, 0, \ldots, 0)$ $(0, \ldots, 0, q, p)$. The matrix of

---

[4] Part of what follows is a repetition of the theory of chapter XIV. Our quadratic equation occurs there as (4.7); the quantities $\lambda_1(s)$ and $\lambda_2(s)$ of the text were given in (4.8), and the general solution (3.3) appears in chapter XIV as (4.9). The two methods are related, but in many cases the computational details will differ radically.

example XV($2.c$) reduces to this when $\delta = 1$. In the terminology of random walks, $p_{jk}^{(n)}$ is the probability that the particle which starts from $x = j$ is at time n at $x = k$.

The equations ($1.7a$) take on the form

$$x_1 = s(qx_1 + px_2)$$

(3.1) $$x_j = s(qx_{j-1} + px_{j+1}) \quad (j = 2, 3, \ldots, a-1)$$

$$x_a = s(qx_{a-1} + px_a).$$

This system admits the solution $x_j \equiv 1$ corresponding to the root $s = 1$. To find all other solutions we apply the method of particular solutions (which we have used for similar equations in chapter XIV, section 4). The middle equation in (3.1) is satisfied by $x_j = \lambda^j$ provided that λ is a root of the quadratic equation $\lambda = qs + \lambda^2 ps$. The two roots of this equation are

(3.2) $$\lambda_1(s) = \frac{1 + (1 - 4pqs^2)^{\frac{1}{2}}}{2ps}, \qquad \lambda_2(s) = \frac{1 - (1 - 4pqs^2)^{\frac{1}{2}}}{2ps},$$

and the most general solution of the middle equation in (3.1) is therefore

(3.3) $$x_j = A(s)\lambda_1{}^j(s) + B(s)\lambda_2{}^j(s),$$

where $A(s)$ and $B(s)$ are arbitrary. The first and the last equation in (3.1) will be satisfied by (3.3) if and only if $x_0 = x_1$ and $x_a = x_{a+1}$. This requires that $A(s)$ and $B(s)$ satisfy the conditions

(3.4)
$$A(s)\{1 - \lambda_1(s)\} + B(s)\{1 - \lambda_2(s)\} = 0$$
$$A(s)\lambda_1{}^a(s)\{1 - \lambda_1(s)\} + B(s)\lambda_2{}^a(s)\{1 - \lambda_2(s)\} = 0.$$

However, these two equations are compatible only if

(3.5) $$\lambda_1{}^a(s) = \lambda_2{}^a(s),$$

and we have to determine the values of s for which (3.5) is possible.

From the definition (3.2) we have $\lambda_1(s)\lambda_2(s) = q/p$, and (3.5) implies that $\lambda_1(s)(p/q)^{\frac{1}{2}}$ and $\lambda_2(s)(p/q)^{\frac{1}{2}}$ must be ($2a$)th roots of unity. These roots can be written in the form

(3.6) $$e^{i\pi r/a} = \cos\frac{\pi r}{a} + i \sin\frac{\pi r}{a},$$

where $i^2 = -1$ and $r = 0, 1, 2, \ldots, 2a-1$. Thus all solutions of (3.5) are among the roots of

$$\lambda_1(s) = \left(\frac{q}{p}\right)^{\frac{1}{2}} e^{i\pi r/a}, \qquad \lambda_2(s) = \left(\frac{q}{p}\right)^{\frac{1}{2}} e^{-i\pi r/a}.$$

To each value r we can find a root s_r, namely

(3.7) $$s_r = \{2(pq)^{\frac{1}{2}} \cos \pi r/a\}^{-1}.$$

The value $r = a$ must be disregarded, since for it $\lambda_1(s) = \lambda_2(s)$, $A(s) = -B(s)$, so that it leads only to the trivial solution $x_j \equiv 0$. To $r = 0$ there corresponds the solution $x_j \equiv 1$, which we have already considered. To $r = 1, 2, \ldots, a-1$ there correspond $a - 1$ distinct solutions; if we let $r = a+1, a+2, \ldots, 2a-1$, we get the same solutions with $\lambda_1(s)$ and $\lambda_2(s)$ interchanged. Thus we have found a distinct sets of solutions of (3.1), and we know that there can be no more.

For $s = s_r$ with $r = 1, 2, \ldots, a-1$ we get from (3.4) $2A(s) = 1 - \lambda_2(s)$ and $2B(s) = -\{1 - \lambda_1(s)\}$. (Remember that a multiplicative constant remains arbitrary.) Substituting into (3.3), we find the $a - 1$ sets of solutions

(3.8) $$x_j^{(r)} = \left(\frac{q}{p}\right)^{\frac{1}{2}j} \sin \frac{\pi r j}{a} - \left(\frac{q}{p}\right)^{\frac{1}{2}(j+1)} \sin \frac{\pi r(j - 1)}{a}$$

$(r = 1, 2, \ldots, a-1)$. To this we add the solution previously found

(3.9) $$x_j^{(0)} = 1.$$

It is easy to verify that (3.8) and (3.9) represent solutions of the given system (3.1).

We have now to find solutions of the second system of linear equations. In the present case (1.7b) takes on the form

(3.10)
$$y_1 = sq(y_1 + y_2),$$
$$y_k = s(py_{k-1} + qy_{k+1}), \qquad (k = 2, \ldots, a-1)$$
$$y_a = sp(y_{a-1} + y_a).$$

The middle equation is the same as (3.1) with p and q interchanged, and its general solution is therefore obtained from (3.3) simply by interchanging p and q. The first and the last equations can be satisfied if $s = s_r$, and a simple calculation shows that for $r = 1, 2, \ldots,$ $a-1$ the solution of (3.10) is

(3.11) $$y_k^{(r)} = \left(\frac{p}{q}\right)^{\frac{1}{2}k} \sin \frac{\pi r k}{a} - \left(\frac{p}{q}\right)^{\frac{1}{2}(k-1)} \sin \frac{\pi r(k - 1)}{a}.$$

For $s = 1$ we find similarly

$$(3.12) \qquad y_k^{(0)} = \left(\frac{p}{q}\right)^k.$$

The next step consists in evaluating the coefficients c_r in (1.11). The sum simplifies if $\sin^2 \pi rj/a$ is expressed in terms of the cosine of the double angle, and this in turn by means of complex exponentials. Then we have only to sum finite geometric series and find easily

$$(3.13) \qquad c_r = \frac{2p}{a} \left\{ 1 - 2(pq)^{\frac{1}{2}} \cos \frac{\pi r}{a} \right\}^{-1} \qquad (r = 1, 2, \ldots, a-1).$$

For $r = 0$ we get,

$$(3.14) \qquad c_0 = \frac{q}{p} \frac{(p/q) - 1}{(p/q)^a - 1},$$

provided that $p \neq q$. If $p = q = \frac{1}{2}$, then (3.13) remains valid, but (3.14) is to be replaced by $c_0 = 1/a$.

These formulas lead to the *final result*

$$(3.15) \qquad p_{jk}^{(n)} = \frac{(p/q) - 1}{(p/q)^a - 1} \left(\frac{p}{q}\right)^{k-1} + \frac{2^{n+1} p^{1+\frac{1}{2}(n-j+k)} q^{\frac{1}{2}(n+j-k)}}{a} \sum_{r=1}^{a-1} S_r$$

where S_r stands for

$$\frac{\cos^n \dfrac{\pi r}{a} \left\{ \sin \dfrac{\pi r j}{a} - \left(\dfrac{q}{p}\right)^{\frac{1}{2}} \sin \dfrac{\pi r(j - 1)}{a} \right\} \left\{ \sin \dfrac{\pi r k}{a} - \left(\dfrac{q}{p}\right)^{\frac{1}{2}} \sin \dfrac{\pi r(k - 1)}{a} \right\}}{1 - 2(pq)^{\frac{1}{2}} \cos \dfrac{\pi r}{a}}.$$

As $n \to \infty$, the second term in (3.15) tends to zero, and we find again that $p_{jk}^{(n)}$ tends to a stationary distribution independent of j. (This limiting distribution was derived by other methods in problem XV, 9.) Passing to the limit $a \to \infty$, we get the formula for a random walk with a single reflecting barrier; in the limit, the sum is replaced by an integral.[5]

---

[5] For analogous formulas in the case of one reflecting and one absorbing barrier see M. Kac, Random walk and the theory of Brownian motion, *American Mathematical Monthly*, vol. 54 (1947), pp. 369–391. The definition of the reflecting barrier is there modified so that the particle may reach 0; whenever this occurs, the next step takes it to 1. The explicit formulas are then more complicated. Kac also found formulas for p_k^n in the Ehrenfest model [example XV (2.f)].

4. TRANSIENT STATES; ABSORPTION PROBABILITIES

The theorem of section 1 was derived under the assumption that the roots $s_1, s_2, \ldots$ are distinct. The presence of multiple roots does not require essential modifications, but we shall discuss only a particular case of special importance. The root $s_1 = 1$ is multiple whenever the chain contains two or more closed subchains, and this is a frequent situation in problems connected with absorption probabilities. It is easy to adapt the method of section 1 to this case. For conciseness and clarity, we shall explain the procedure by means of examples which will reveal the main features of the general case.

Examples. (*a*) Consider the matrix of transition probabilities

$$
(4.1) \qquad P = \begin{bmatrix}
\frac{1}{3} & \frac{2}{3} & 0 & 0 & 0 & 0 \\
\frac{2}{3} & \frac{1}{3} & 0 & 0 & 0 & 0 \\
0 & 0 & \frac{1}{4} & \frac{3}{4} & 0 & 0 \\
0 & 0 & \frac{1}{5} & \frac{4}{5} & 0 & 0 \\
\frac{1}{4} & 0 & \frac{1}{4} & 0 & \frac{1}{4} & \frac{1}{4} \\
\frac{1}{6} & \frac{1}{6} & \frac{1}{6} & \frac{1}{6} & \frac{1}{6} & \frac{1}{6}
\end{bmatrix}.
$$

It is clear that E_1 and E_2 form a closed set (that is, no transition is possible to any of the remaining four states; compare chapter XV, section 4). Similarly E_3 and E_4 form another closed set. Finally, E_5 and E_6 are transient states. After finitely many steps the system passes into one of the two closed sets and remains there.

The matrix P has the form of a partitioned matrix

$$
(4.2) \qquad P = \begin{bmatrix}
A & 0 & 0 \\
0 & B & 0 \\
U & V & T
\end{bmatrix}
$$

where each letter stands for a two-by-two matrix and each zero for a matrix with four zeros. For example, A has the rows $(\frac{1}{3}, \frac{2}{3})$ and $(\frac{2}{3}, \frac{1}{3})$; this is the matrix of transition probabilities corresponding to the chain formed by the two states E_1 and E_2. This matrix can be studied by itself, and the powers A^n can be obtained from example (2.*a*) with $p = \alpha = \frac{2}{3}$. When the powers P^2, P^3, $\ldots$ are calculated, it will be found that the first two rows are in no way affected by the remaining four rows. More precisely, P^n has the form

$$
(4.3) \qquad P^n = \begin{bmatrix}
A^n & 0 & 0 \\
0 & B^n & 0 \\
U_n & V_n & T^n
\end{bmatrix}
$$

where A^n, B^n, T^n are the nth powers of A, B, and T, respectively, and can be calculated [6] by the method of section 1 (cf. example (2.a) where all calculations are performed). Instead of six equations with six unknowns we are confronted only with systems of two equations with two unknowns each.

It should be noted that the matrices U_n and V_n in (4.3) are not powers of U and V and cannot be obtained in the same simple way as A^n, B^n, and T^n. However, in the calculation of P^2, P^3, ... the third and fourth columns never affect the remaining four columns. In other words, if in P^n the rows and columns corresponding to E_3 and E_4 are deleted, we get the matrix

$$(4.4) \qquad \begin{pmatrix} A^n & 0 \\ U_n & T^n \end{pmatrix}$$

which is the nth power of the corresponding submatrix in P, that is, of

$$(4.5) \qquad \begin{pmatrix} A & 0 \\ U & T \end{pmatrix} = \begin{bmatrix} \frac{1}{3} & \frac{2}{3} & 0 & 0 \\ \frac{2}{3} & \frac{1}{3} & 0 & 0 \\ \frac{1}{4} & 0 & \frac{1}{4} & \frac{1}{4} \\ \frac{1}{6} & \frac{1}{6} & \frac{1}{6} & \frac{1}{6} \end{bmatrix}.$$

Therefore matrix (4.4) can be calculated by the method of section 1, which in the present case simplifies considerably. The matrix V_n can be obtained in a similar way.

Usually the explicit forms of U_n and V_n are of interest only inasmuch as they are connected with *absorption probabilities*. If the system starts from, say, E_5, what is the *probability* λ *that it will eventually pass into the closed set formed by* E_1 *and* E_2 (and not into the other closed set)? What is the *probability* λ_n *that this will occur exactly at the* nth *step?* Clearly $p_{51}^{(n)} + p_{52}^{(n)}$ is the probability that the considered event occurs at the nth step or before, that is,

$$p_{51}^{(n)} + p_{52}^{(n)} = \lambda_1 + \lambda_2 + \ldots + \lambda_n.$$

Letting $n \to \infty$, we get λ. A preferable way to calculate λ_n is as follows. The $(n-1)$st step must take the system to a state other than E_1 and E_2, that is, to either E_5 or E_6 (since from E_3 or E_4 no transition to E_1 and E_2 is possible). The nth step then takes the system to

---

[6] In T the rows do not add to unity so that T is not a stochastic matrix. However, the method of section 1 applies without change, except that $s = 1$ is no longer a root (so that $T^n \to 0$).

E_1 or E_2.　Hence

(4.6)
$$\lambda_n = p_{55}^{(n-1)}(p_{51} + p_{52}) + p_{56}^{(n-1)}(p_{61} + p_{62}) =$$
$$= \tfrac{1}{4}p_{55}^{(n-1)} + \tfrac{1}{3}p_{56}^{(n-1)}.$$

It will be noted that λ_n is completely determined by the elements of T^{n-1}, and this matrix is easily calculated.　In the present case

$$p_{55}^{(n)} = p_{56}^{(n)} = \tfrac{1}{4}(\tfrac{5}{12})^{n-1} \qquad \text{and hence} \qquad \lambda_n = \tfrac{7}{48}(\tfrac{5}{12})^{n-2}.$$

(b) *Brother-sister mating.*　As a second example we give a complete treatment of example XV(2.l).　A glance at the matrix shows that the states E_1 and E_5 form a closed set each (a fact which is clear from the biological meaning).　If the system starts from any other state E_j, it will eventually pass either into E_1 or into E_5 and then remain there. The breeder desires to know the corresponding probabilities and the expected duration of the process.

Deleting the first and fifth column and row, we get the reduced matrix

(4.7)
$$T = \begin{bmatrix} \tfrac{1}{2} & \tfrac{1}{4} & 0 & 0 \\ \tfrac{1}{4} & \tfrac{1}{4} & \tfrac{1}{4} & \tfrac{1}{8} \\ 0 & \tfrac{1}{4} & \tfrac{1}{2} & 0 \\ 0 & 1 & 0 & 0 \end{bmatrix}.$$

The powers T^n will now be calculated by the method of section 1. They represent the transition probabilities among transient states.

The equations (1.7a) reduce to

$$x_1 = \frac{s(2x_1 + x_2)}{4}, \qquad x_2 = \frac{s(2x_1 + 2x_2 + 2x_3 + x_4)}{8},$$

(4.8)

$$x_3 = \frac{s(x_2 + 2x_3)}{4}, \qquad x_4 = sx_2.$$

This has a solution only if the determinant vanishes, and this condition leads to a fourth-degree equation in s.　To simplify writing we put

(4.9)
$$\theta_1 = 5^{\frac{1}{2}} - 1, \qquad \theta_2 = 5^{\frac{1}{2}} + 1.$$

Then the four roots s_r are

(4.10)
$$s_1 = 2, \qquad s_2 = 4, \qquad s_3 = \theta_1, \qquad s_4 = -\theta_2,$$

and the corresponding solutions $(x_1^{(r)}, \ldots, x_4^{(r)})$ of (4.8) are

(4.11)　$(1, 0, -1, 0), \quad (1, -1, 1, -4), \quad (1, \theta_1, 1, \theta_1^2), \quad (1, -\theta_2, 1, \theta_2^2).$

The system of linear equations for $y_k^{(r)}$ is obtained by specialization from (1.7b), and the four sets of solutions are in proper order

(4.12) $(1, 0, -1, 0), \quad (1, -1, 1, -\tfrac{1}{2}),$

$(1, \theta_1, 1, \theta_1{}^2/8), \quad (1, -\theta_2, 1, \theta_2{}^2/8).$

From (1.11) we find the four constants $c_1 = \tfrac{1}{2}$, $c_2 = \tfrac{1}{5}$, $c_3 = \theta_2{}^2/40$, $c_4 = \theta_1{}^2/40$. From (1.8) we get the $\rho_{jk}^{(r)}$; and finally (1.3) gives us $p_{jk}^{(n)}$ for all transient states, that is, for $j, k = 2, 3, 4, 6$. For fixed j, k the sequence $p_{jk}^{(n)}$ is the sum of four geometric series with ratios $s_1, \ldots, s_4$.

An absorption in E_1 exactly at the nth step is possible only if the $(n-1)$st step takes the system into either E_2 or E_3, and the nth step into E_1. The probability for this is $p_{j2}^{(n-1)}/4 + p_{j3}^{(n-1)}/16$. Similarly, the probability of absorption at E_5 is $p_{j3}^{(n-1)}/16 + p_{j4}^{(n-1)}/4$. Summing over all n we get the probabilities that the system will eventually pass into and stay in E_1 and E_5, respectively. The actual calculation of these probabilities requires only the summation of four geometric series.

5. APPLICATION TO RECURRENCE TIMES

In problem XIII, 19 it is shown how the mean μ and the variance σ^2 of the recurrence time of a recurrent event $\mathcal{E}$ can be calculated in terms of the probabilities u_n that $\mathcal{E}$ occurs at the nth trial. If $\mathcal{E}$ is not periodic, then

(5.1) $u_n \to \dfrac{1}{\mu} \quad$ and $\quad \displaystyle\sum_{n=0}^{\infty} \left(u_n - \dfrac{1}{\mu}\right) = \dfrac{\sigma^2 - \mu + \mu^2}{2\mu^2},$

provided that σ^2 is finite.

If we identify $\mathcal{E}$ with a persistent state E_j, then $u_n = p_{jj}^{(n)}$ (and $u_0 = 1$). In a finite Markov chain all recurrence times have finite variance (cf. problem XV, 19), so that (5.1) applies. Suppose that E_j is not periodic and that formula (1.3) applies. Then $s_1 = 1$ and $|s_r| > 1$ for $r = 2, 3, \ldots$, so that $p_{jj}^{(n)} \to \rho_{jj}^{(1)} = 1/\mu_j$. To the term $u_n - 1/\mu$ of (5.1) there corresponds

(5.2) $p_{jj}^{(n)} - \dfrac{1}{\mu_j} = \displaystyle\sum_{r=2}^{a} \rho_{jj}^{(r)} s_r^{-n}.$

This formula is valid for $n \geq 1$; summing the geometric series with ratio s_r^{-1}, we find

(5.3) $\displaystyle\sum_{n=1}^{\infty} \left(p_{jj}^{(n)} - \dfrac{1}{\mu_j}\right) = \displaystyle\sum_{r=2}^{a} \dfrac{\rho_{jj}^{(r)}}{s_r - 1}.$

Introducing this into (5.1), we find that if E_j is a *non-periodic persistent state, then its mean recurrence time is given by* $\mu_j = 1/\rho_{jj}^{(1)}$, *and the variance of its recurrence time is*

$$(5.4) \qquad \sigma_j^2 = \mu_j - \mu_j^2 + 2\mu_j^2 \sum_{r=2}^{a} \frac{\rho_{jj}^{(r)}}{s_r - 1},$$

provided, of course, that formula (1.3) is applicable and $s_1 = 1$. The case of periodic states and the occurrence of double roots require only obvious modifications.

CHAPTER XVII

The Simplest Time-Dependent Stochastic Processes [1]

1. GENERAL ORIENTATION

Random walks and Markov chains are stochastic processes [2] where changes occur only at fixed times, say, $t = 1, 2, 3, \ldots$. On the other hand, in chapter VI, sections 5–6, we were concerned with phenomena such as telephone calls, radioactive disintegrations, and chromosome breakages, where changes may occur at any time. Obviously a complete description of such processes leads beyond the domain of discrete probabilities. To fix ideas, consider the incoming calls at a telephone exchange (or, rather, an idealized mathematical model of the actual process). Every instant t corresponds to a trial, and the result of an experiment may be described in terms of a function $\mathbf{X}(t)$ giving the number of calls up to time t. If the first call occurs at time t_1, the second at t_2, etc., the function $\mathbf{X}(t)$ equals 0 for $0 < t < t_1$, 1 for $t_1 < t < t_2$, 2 for $t_2 < t < t_3$, etc. Conversely, every non-decreasing function $\mathbf{X}(t)$, assuming only the values 0, 1, 2, $\ldots$, represents a possible development at our telephone exchange. In other words, a complete description of our conceptual experiment calls for a sample space whose points are functions $\mathbf{X}(t)$ (and not sequences as in the case of discrete trials). A compound event such as "seven calls within a minute on a certain day" is obviously the aggregate of those $\mathbf{X}(t)$ which satisfy the condition that for some point t of a specified interval we have $\mathbf{X}(t + h) - \mathbf{X}(t) \geq 7$, where h represents the span of one minute.

We cannot deal here with such complicated sample spaces and must defer the study of the more delicate aspects of the theory. Fortunately,

---

[1] This chapter is almost independent of chapters X–XVI.
[2] See footnote 11 of chapter XV.

certain interesting questions can be answered even with the simple means now at our disposal.

If we limit the consideration to the number of calls $\mathbf{X}(t)$ within an arbitrary but fixed period of duration t, then $\mathbf{X}(t)$ is a random variable of the familiar type, assuming the values 0, 1, 2, ... Let $P_n(t)$ be the probability that $\mathbf{X}(t) = n$. It is true that the distribution $\{P_n(t)\}$ depends on a continuous parameter, but so do most distributions introduced in this book.

The situation is best illustrated by the Poisson distribution

$$(1.1) \qquad P_n(t) = e^{-\lambda t} \frac{(\lambda t)^n}{n!}.$$

It was derived in chapter VI, section 5, as a limiting form of the binomial distribution; a more satisfactory derivation is contained in chapter XII, section 3. We shall not use the results of that chapter, but the situation analyzed there is so simple and so typical that a short summary may serve as the best introduction to the present chapter.

Consider a stochastic process represented by an integral-valued random variable $\mathbf{X}(t) \geq 0$. Intuitively we may interpret $\mathbf{X}(t)$, say, as the cumulative damage by lightning measured to the nearest dollar. We arrive at a particularly simple mathematical model if we introduce two postulates as follows. The increment $\mathbf{X}(t + s) - \mathbf{X}(0)$ during the time interval from 0 to $t + s$ is the sum of the increments $\mathbf{X}(s) - \mathbf{X}(0)$ and $\mathbf{X}(t + s) - \mathbf{X}(s)$ corresponding to the subintervals from 0 to s and from s to $t + s$. We postulate, first, that these increments $\mathbf{X}(s) - \mathbf{X}(0)$ and $\mathbf{X}(t + s) - \mathbf{X}(s)$ are stochastically independent and, secondly, that the distribution of $\mathbf{X}(t + s) - \mathbf{X}(s)$ depends only on t (i.e., only on the length of the interval, not on its position: this is the property of homogeneity in time).

Let $h_n(t)$ be the probability that $\mathbf{X}(t + s) - \mathbf{X}(s)$ assumes the value n (where $n = 0, 1, 2, \ldots$). Analytically, the independence of $\mathbf{X}(t + s) - \mathbf{X}(s)$ and $\mathbf{X}(s) - \mathbf{X}(0)$ is expressed by

$$(1.2) \qquad h_n(t + s) = \sum_{j=0}^{n} h_j(s) \cdot h_{n-j}(t).$$

It has been shown in chapter XII, section 3, that the only distribution $\{h_n(t)\}$ with the property (1.2) is the *compound Poisson distribution;* that is, $\mathbf{X}(t)$ has the distribution of a random variable

$$(1.3) \qquad \mathbf{S_N} \qquad \text{with} \qquad \mathbf{P}\{\mathbf{N} = n\} = e^{-\lambda t} \frac{(\lambda t)^n}{n!}$$

where $\mathbf{S}_n = \mathbf{Y}_1 + \mathbf{Y}_2 + \ldots + \mathbf{Y}_n$ is the sum of n mutually independent variables with the common distribution $\{f_i\}$, $i = 0, 1, 2, \ldots$. In our example $\{f_i\}$ represents the probability distribution of the damage from an individual hit by lightning; then (1.3) states that the number of hits in a time interval of length t obeys the Poisson distribution (1.1), and that the individual damages are independent random variables. The variable (1.3) has the same probability distribution as the change $\mathbf{X}(t + s) - \mathbf{X}(s)$ during an arbitrary interval of length t, and we see that this total change is the sum of a random number $\mathbf{N}$ of individual changes or *jumps*. The number $\mathbf{N}$ of changes has a Poisson distribution (1.1), and the individual jump has the probability distribution $\{f_i\}$. In particular, the Poisson distribution (1.1) itself represents the special case where all jumps are of unit length (that is, $f_1 = 1, f_0 = f_2 = \ldots = 0$, the variables $\mathbf{Y}_n$ assuming only the value 1).

It will be observed that we have found a characterization of the simple and the compound Poisson distribution by means of intrinsic probabilistic properties. The Poisson distribution no longer appears as an approximation or a limiting form of other distributions but stands in its own right (or, we might say, as the expression of a physical law). Its derivation is of a purely analytic character, the notion of a stochastic process and the random variable $\mathbf{X}(t)$ serving only to get a set of plausible postulates on the distribution $\{h_n(t)\}$. For many applications, nothing beyond the knowledge of $\{h_n(t)\}$ is required. Theoretically, it should be shown that $\{h_n(t)\}$ really determines a family of random variables $\mathbf{X}(t)$ and all relevant probability relations such as the probability of the event that $\mathbf{X}(t)$ will ever exceed $at + b$ (this is the ruin problem of the collective risk theory in insurance).

Questions of this type lead beyond the scope of this book. We shall be content to translate a physical description of a process into properties required of the basic probabilities $P_n(t)$ and to consider $\{P_n(t)\}$ as a family of discrete probability distributions depending on t.

This artificial limitation to discrete probabilities has unavoidable drawbacks. Consider, for example, the zero term in (1.1). We interpret

$$(1.4) \qquad\qquad P_0(t) = e^{-\lambda t}$$

as the probability that no call occurs within an observation period of duration t. This formulation suggests that $P_0(t)$ might be interpreted as the probability that the waiting time (starting at an arbitrary moment) up to the first call exceeds t. It can be shown that this interpretation is correct, but it will be noticed that it involves probabilities in a continuum. The operational meaning of our first formulation is as follows: Make a series of "identical observations" with a fixed observational period t. Each trial results in either "no call" (success) or "one or more calls" (failure). Then we have Bernoulli trials with the probability of success $e^{-\lambda t}$. With the second interpretation we are to wait until a call arrives. Every positive number is a possible waiting time, so that the sample space corresponding to each trial is the half-line $t > 0$. Formula (1.4) then represents a continuous probability distribution.

2. THE POISSON PROCESS

We begin by giving a new derivation of the Poisson distribution; it is by no means better than the derivation described above, but it lends itself more naturally to various generalizations which we propose to study.

Take a system subject to instantaneous changes due to the occurrence of random events such as splitting of physical particles, arrival of telephone calls, or breakage of a chromosome under harmful irradiation. All changes are assumed to be of the same kind, and we are concerned only with their total number. Each change is represented by a point on the time axis, so that we are studying certain random distributions of points on a line.

The physical processes which we have in mind are characterized by the two properties, that they are homogeneous in time and that future changes are independent of past changes. By this we mean that the forces and influences which determine the process remain absolutely unchanged, so that the probability of any particular event is the same for all time intervals of length t, independent of where this interval is situated and of the past history of the system.[3]

We now translate this description into mathematical language. The process is to be described in terms of probabilities [4] $P_n(t)$ that exactly n changes occur during a time interval of length t. In particular, $P_0(t)$ is the probability of no change, and $1 - P_0(t)$ the probability of one or more changes. We shall assume that [5] as $t \to 0$

---

[3] In a telephone exchange incoming calls are more frequent during the busiest hour of the day than, say, between midnight and 1 A.M.; the process is therefore not homogeneous in time. However, for obvious reasons telephone engineers are concerned mainly with the "busy hour" of the day, and for that period the process can be considered homogeneous. Experience shows also that during the busy hour the incoming traffic follows the Poisson distribution with surprising accuracy. Similar considerations apply to automobile accidents, which are more frequent on Sundays, etc.

[4] For a non-homogeneous process we should have to introduce the probability $P_n(t_1, t_2)$ that n changes occur in the interval $t_1 < t < t_2$.

[5] This condition can be dispensed with; see section 6.

$$(2.1) \qquad \frac{1 - P_0(t)}{t} \to \lambda$$

where λ is a positive constant. Then for a small interval of length h the probability of one or more changes is $1 - P_0(h) = \lambda h + o(h)$, where the term $o(h)$ denotes a quantity which is of smaller order of magnitude than h. We now formulate our

Postulates for the Poisson Process. *Whatever the number of changes during* $(0, t)$, *the probability that during* $(t, t+h)$ *a change occurs is* $\lambda h + o(h)$, *and the probability that more than one change occurs is* $o(h)$.

These conditions easily lead to a system of differential equations for $P_n(t)$. Consider two contiguous intervals $(0, t)$ and $(t, t+h)$, where h is small. If $n \geq 1$, then exactly n changes can occur in the interval $(0, t+h)$ in three mutually exclusive ways: (1) no change during $(t, t+h)$ and n changes during $(0, t)$; (2) one change during $(t, t+h)$ and $n - 1$ changes during $(0, t)$; (3) $x \geq 2$ changes during $(t, t+h)$ and $n - x$ changes during $(0, t)$. According to our hypotheses, the probability of the first contingency is $P_n(t)$ times the probability of no change during $(t, t+h)$ and this last is $1 - \lambda h - o(h)$. Similarly, the second contingency has probability $P_{n-1}(t)\lambda h + o(h)$, and the last has a probability of smaller order of magnitude than h. This means that

$$(2.2) \qquad P_n(t + h) = P_n(t)(1 - \lambda h) + P_{n-1}(t)\lambda h + o(h)$$

or

$$(2.3) \qquad \frac{P_n(t + h) - P_n(t)}{h} = -\lambda P_n(t) + \lambda P_{n-1}(t) + \frac{o(h)}{h}.$$

As $h \to 0$, the last term tends to zero; hence the limit [6] of the left side exists and

$$(2.4) \qquad P'_n(t) = -\lambda P_n(t) + \lambda P_{n-1}(t) \qquad\qquad (n \geq 1).$$

For $n = 0$ the second and third contingencies mentioned above do not

---

[6] Since we restricted h to positive values, $P'_n(t)$ in (2.4) should be interpreted as a right-hand derivative. It is really an ordinary two-sided derivative. In fact, the term $o(h)$ in (2.2) does not depend on t and therefore remains unchanged when t is replaced by $t - h$. Thus (2.2) implies continuity, and (2.3) implies differentiability in the ordinary sense. This remark applies throughout the chapter and will not be repeated.

arise, and therefore (2.4) is to be replaced by the simpler equation

(2.5) $$P_0(t + h) = P_0(t)(1 - \lambda h) + o(h),$$

which leads to

(2.6) $$P'_0(t) = -\lambda P_0(t).$$

From (2.6) and $P_0(0) = 1$ we get $P_0(t) = e^{-\lambda t}$. Substituting this $P_0(t)$ into (2.4) with $n = 1$, we get an ordinary differential equation for $P_1(t)$. Since $P_1(0) = 0$, we find easily that $P_1(t) = \lambda t e^{-\lambda t}$, in agreement with the Poisson distribution (1.1). Proceeding in the same way, we find successively all terms of (1.1).

3. THE PURE BIRTH PROCESS

In the Poisson process the probability of a change during $(t, t+h)$ is independent of the number of changes during $(0, t)$. The simplest generalization consists of dropping this assumption. Assume instead that, when n changes occur during $(0, t)$, the probability of a new change during $(t, t+h)$ equals $\lambda_n h$ plus terms of smaller order of magnitude than h; the single constant λ characterizing the process is replaced by the sequence $\lambda_0, \lambda_1, \lambda_2, \ldots$.

It is convenient to introduce a more flexible terminology. Instead of saying that n changes occur during $(0, t)$, we shall say that *the system is in state E_n*. A new change then becomes a *transition $E_n \to E_{n+1}$*. In a pure birth process transitions from E_n are possible only to E_{n+1}. Such a process is characterized by the following

Postulates. *If at time t the system is in state E_n ($n = 0, 1, 2, \ldots$), then the probability that during $(t, t+h)$ a transition to E_{n+1} occurs equals $\lambda_n h + o(h)$; the probability of any other change is $o(h)$.*

The salient feature of this assumption is that the time which the system spends in any particular state plays no role; there are sudden changes of state but no aging as long as the system remains within a single state.

Again let $P_n(t)$ be the probability that at time t the system is in state E_n. The functions $P_n(t)$ satisfy a system of differential equations which can be derived by the argument of the preceding section, with the only change that (2.2) is replaced by

(3.1) $$P_n(t + h) = P_n(t)(1 - \lambda_n h) + P_{n-1}(t)\lambda_{n-1}h + o(h).$$

In this way we get the *basic system of differential equations*

(3.2)
$$P'_n(t) = -\lambda_n P_n(t) + \lambda_{n-1}P_{n-1}(t) \qquad (n \geq 1),$$
$$P'_0(t) = -\lambda_0 P_0(t).$$

We can calculate $P_0(t)$ first and then, by recursion, all $P_n(t)$. If the state of the system represents the number of changes during $(0, t)$, then the initial state is E_0 so that $P_0(0) = 1$ and hence $P_0(t) = e^{-\lambda_0 t}$. However, the system need not start from state E_0 [see example $(3.b)$]. If at time zero the system is in E_i, then we have

$$(3.3) \qquad P_i(0) = 1, \qquad P_n(0) = 0 \qquad \text{for} \quad n \neq i.$$

These *initial conditions* uniquely determine the solution $\{P_n(t)\}$ of (3.2). (In particular, $P_0(t) = P_1(t) = \ldots = P_{i-1}(t) = 0$.) Explicit formulas for $P_n(t)$ have been derived independently by many authors but are of no interest to us. It is easily verified that for arbitrarily prescribed λ_n the system $\{P_n(t)\}$ has all required properties, except that under certain conditions $\Sigma P_n(t) < 1$. This phenomenon will be discussed in section 4.

Examples. (a) *Radioactive transmutations.* A radioactive atom, say uranium, may by emission of particles or γ-rays change to an atom of a different kind. Each kind represents a possible state of the system, and as the process continues, we get a succession of transitions $E_0 \to E_1 \to E_2 \to \ldots \to E_m$. According to accepted physical theories, the probability of a transition $E_n \to E_{n+1}$ remains unchanged as long as the atom is in state E_n, and this hypothesis is expressed by our starting supposition. The differential equations (3.2) therefore describe the process (a fact well known to physicists). If E_m is the terminal state from which no further transitions are possible, then $\lambda_m = 0$ and the system (3.2) terminates with $n = m$. (For $n > m$ we get automatically $P_n(t) = 0$.)

(b) *The Yule process.* Consider a population of members which can (by splitting or otherwise) give birth to new members but cannot die. Assume that during any short time interval of length h each member has probability $\lambda h + o(h)$ to create a new one; the constant λ determines the rate of increase of the population. If there is no interaction among the members and at time t the population size is n, then the probability of an increase during $(t, t+h)$ is $n\lambda h + o(h)$. The probability $P_n(t)$ that the population numbers exactly n elements therefore satisfies (3.2) with $\lambda_n = n\lambda$, that is,

$$(3.4) \qquad P'_n(t) = -n\lambda P_n(t) + (n - 1)\lambda P_{n-1}(t) \qquad (n \geq 1).$$

If i is the population size at time $t = 0$, then the initial conditions (3.3) apply. It is easily verified that for $n \geq i$ the solution is given by

$$(3.5) \qquad P_n(t) = \binom{n - 1}{n - i} e^{-i\lambda t}(1 - e^{-\lambda t})^{n-i}$$

404 STOCHASTIC PROCESSES [XVII.3

and, of course, $P_n(t) = 0$ for $n < i$. This distribution is a special case of the negative binomial distribution: using the definition VI(8.1) we may rewrite (3.5) as $P_n(t) = f(n-i;\ i,\ e^{-\lambda t})$. It follows [cf. example IX(3.c)] that the population size at time t is the sum of i independent random variables each having the distribution obtained from (3.5) on replacing i by 1. These i variables represent the progenies of the i original members of our population.

This type of process was first studied by Yule [7] in connection with the mathematical theory of evolution. The population consists of the species within a genus, and the creation of a new element is due to mutations. The assumption that each species has the same probability of throwing out a new species neglects the difference in species sizes. Since we have also neglected the possibility that a species may die out, formula (3.5) can be expected to give only a crude approximation. Furry [8] used the same model to describe a process connected with cosmic rays, but again the approximation is rather crude. The differential equations (3.4) apply strictly to a population of particles which can split into exact replicas of themselves, provided, of course, that there is no interaction among particles.

*4. DIVERGENT BIRTH PROCESSES

The solution $\{P_n(t)\}$ of the infinite system of differential equations (3.2) subject to initial conditions (3.3) can be calculated inductively, starting from $P_i(t) = e^{-\lambda_i t}$. The distribution $\{P_n(t)\}$ is therefore uniquely determined. From the familiar formulas for solving linear differential equations it follows also that $P_n(t) \geq 0$. The only question

---

[7] G. Udny Yule, A mathematical theory of evolution, based on the conclusions of Dr. J. C. Willis, F.R.S., *Philosophical Transactions of the Royal Society, London*, Series B, vol. 213 (1924), pp. 21–87. Yule does not introduce the differential equations (3.4) but derives $P_n(t)$ by a limiting process similar to the one used in chapter VI, section 5, for the Poisson process. Much more general, and more flexible, models of the same type were devised and applied to epidemics and population growth in an unpretentious and highly interesting paper by Lieutenant Colonel A. G. M'Kendrick, Applications of mathematics to medical problems, *Proceedings Edinburgh Mathematical Society*, vol. 44 (1925), pp. 1–34. It is very unfortunate that this remarkable paper passed practically unnoticed. In particular, it was unknown to the present author when he introduced various stochastic models for population growth in Die Grundlagen der Volterraschen Theorie des Kampfes ums Dasein in wahrscheinlichkeitstheoretischer Behandlung, *Acta Biotheoretica*, vol. 5 (1939), pp. 11–40.

[8] On fluctuation phenomena in the passage of high-energy electrons through lead, *Physical Reviews*, vol. 52 (1937), p. 569.

* This section treats a special topic and may be omitted.

left open is whether $\{P_n(t)\}$ is an honest probability distribution, that is, whether or not

(4.1) $\Sigma P_n(t) = 1$

for all t. We shall see that this is not always so: if the coefficients λ_n increase sufficiently fast, then it may happen that

(4.2) $\Sigma P_n(t) < 1.$

At first sight this possibility appears surprising and, perhaps, disturbing, but it finds a ready explanation. The left side in (4.2) may be interpreted as the probability that during time t only a *finite number* of changes takes place. Accordingly, the difference between the two sides in (4.2) accounts for the possibility of infinitely many changes, or a sort of explosion. For a better understanding of this phenomenon let us compare our probabilistic model of growth with the familiar deterministic approach.

The quantity λ_n in (3.2) could be called the average rate of growth at a time when the population size is n. For example, in the special case (3.4) we have $\lambda_n = n\lambda$, so that the average rate of growth is proportional to the actual population size. If growth is not subject to chance fluctuations and has a rate of increase proportional to the instantaneous population size, then $x(t)$ varies in accordance with the deterministic differential equation

(4.3) $$\frac{dx(t)}{dt} = \lambda x(t).$$

It follows that at time t the population size is

(4.4) $x(t) = ie^{\lambda t},$

where $i = x(0)$ is the initial population size. The connection between (3.4) and (4.3) is not purely formal. It is readily seen that (4.4) actually gives the expected value of the distribution (3.5), so that (4.3) describes the expected population size, whereas (3.4) takes account of chance fluctuations.

Let us now consider a deterministic growth process where the rate of growth increases faster than the population size. To a rate of growth proportional to $x^2(t)$ there corresponds the differential equation

(4.5) $$\frac{dx(t)}{dt} = \lambda x^2(t)$$

whose solution is

$$(4.6) \qquad x(t) = \frac{i}{1 - \lambda it}.$$

Note that $x(t)$ increases over all bounds as $t \to 1/\lambda i$. In other words, the assumption that the rate of growth increases as the square of the population size implies an infinite growth within a finite time interval. Similarly, if in (3.4) the λ_n increase too fast, there is a finite probability that infinitely many changes take place in a finite time interval. A precise answer about the conditions when such a divergent growth occurs is given by the

Theorem. *In order that (4.1) may hold for all t it is necessary and sufficient that the series*

$$(4.7) \qquad \sum \frac{1}{\lambda_n}$$

diverge.

Proof. Letting

$$(4.8) \qquad S_k(t) = P_0(t) + \ldots + P_k(t),$$

we get from (3.2)

$$(4.9) \qquad S'_k(t) = -\lambda_k P_k(t)$$

and hence for $k \geq i$

$$(4.10) \qquad 1 - S_k(t) = \lambda_k \int_0^t P_k(\tau)\, d\tau.$$

Since all terms in (4.8) are non-negative, the sequence $S_k(t)$—for fixed t—can only increase with k, and therefore the right side in (4.10) decreases monotonically with k. Call its limit $\mu(t)$. Then for $k \geq i$

$$(4.11) \qquad \lambda_k \int_0^t P_k(\tau)\, d\tau \geq \mu(t)$$

and hence

$$(4.12) \qquad \int_0^t S_n(\tau)\, d\tau \geq \mu(t) \left(\frac{1}{\lambda_i} + \frac{1}{\lambda_{i+1}} + \ldots + \frac{1}{\lambda_n} \right).$$

Because of (4.10) we have $S_n(t) \leq 1$, so that the left side in (4.12) is at most t. If the series (4.7) diverges, the second factor on the right in (4.12) tends to infinity, and the inequality can hold only if $\mu(t) = 0$ for all t. In this case the right side in (4.10) tends to zero as $k \to \infty$, and therefore $S_n(t) \to 1$, so that (4.1) holds. Conversely,[9] integrating (4.8) and using (4.10) we see that the left side of (4.12) is less than $\lambda_0^{-1} + \lambda_1^{-1} + \ldots + \lambda_n^{-1}$. If the series (4.7) converges, this expression is bounded and hence it is impossible that $S_n(t) \to 1$ for all t.

5. THE BIRTH AND DEATH PROCESS

The pure birth process of section 3 provides a satisfactory description of radioactive transmutations, but it cannot serve as a realistic model for changes in the size of populations whose members can die (or drop out). This suggests generalizing the model by permitting transitions from the state E_n not only to the next higher state E_{n+1} but also to the next lower state E_{n-1}. (More general processes will be defined in section 9.) Accordingly we start from the following

Postulates. *The system changes only through transitions from states to their next neighbors (from E_n to E_{n+1} or E_{n-1} if $n \geq 1$, but from E_0 to E_1 only). If at any time t the system is in state E_n, the probability that during $(t, t+h)$ the transition $E_n \to E_{n+1}$ occurs equals $\lambda_n h + o(h)$, and the probability of $E_n \to E_{n-1}$ (if $n \geq 1$) equals $\mu_n h + o(h)$. The probability that during $(t, t+h)$ more than one change occurs is $o(h)$.*

It is easy to adapt the method of section 2 to derive differential equations for the probabilities $P_n(t)$ of finding the system at time t in state E_n. To calculate $P_n(t + h)$, note that at time $t + h$ the system can be in state E_n only if one of the following conditions is satisfied: (1) At time t the system is in E_n and during $(t, t+h)$ no change occurs; (2) at time t the system is in E_{n-1} and a transition to E_n occurs; (3) at time t the system is in E_{n+1} and a transition to E_n occurs; (4) during $(t, t+h)$ two or more transitions occur. By assumption, the probability of the last event is $o(h)$. The first three contingencies are mutually exclusive, so that their probabilities add. Therefore

$$(5.1) \quad P_n(t + h) = P_n(t)\{1 - \lambda_n h - \mu_n h\} +$$
$$+ \lambda_{n-1} h P_{n-1}(t) + \mu_{n+1} h P_{n+1}(t) + o(h).$$

Transposing the term $P_n(t)$ and dividing the equation by h, we get on the left the difference ratio of $P_n(t)$. Letting $h \to 0$, we get

$$(5.2) \quad P'_n(t) = -(\lambda_n + \mu_n)P_n(t) + \lambda_{n-1}P_{n-1}(t) + \mu_{n+1}P_{n+1}(t).$$

---

[9] By a regrettable oversight the following three lines were missing in the first printing of the first edition and part of the preceding argument was repeated instead. The error was corrected after a few months. (The present discussion is continued in section 10.)

This equation holds for $n \geq 1$. For $n = 0$ in the same way

(5.3) $$P'_0(t) = -\lambda_0 P_0(t) + \mu_1 P_1(t).$$

If at time zero the system is in state E_i, the initial conditions are

(5.4) $$P_i(0) = 1, \qquad P_n(0) = 0 \qquad \text{for} \quad n \neq i.$$

The birth and death process is thus seen to depend on the infinite system of differential equations (5.2)–(5.3) together with the initial condition (5.4). The question of existence and of uniqueness of solutions is in this case by no means trivial. In a pure birth process the system (3.2) of differential equations was also infinite, but it had the form of recurrence relations; $P_0(t)$ was determined by the first equation and $P_n(t)$ could be calculated from $P_{n-1}(t)$. The new system (5.2) is not of this form, and all $P_n(t)$ must be found simultaneously. We shall here (and elsewhere in this chapter) state properties of the solutions without proof.[10]

For arbitrarily prescribed coefficients $\lambda_n \geq 0$, $\mu_n \geq 0$ there always exists a positive solution $\{P_n(t)\}$ of (5.2)–(5.4) such that $\Sigma P_n(t) \leq 1$. If the coefficients are bounded (or increase sufficiently slowly), this solution is unique and satisfies the regularity condition $\Sigma P_n(t) = 1$. However, it is possible to choose the coefficients in such a way that $\Sigma P_n(t) < 1$ and that there exist infinitely many solutions. In the latter case we encounter a phenomenon analogous to that studied in the preceding section for the pure birth process. This situation is of considerable theoretical interest,[11] but the reader may safely assume that in all

---

[10] A simple existence proof and uniqueness criterion (although using Laplace transforms) applicable to the most general equations of this chapter is contained in section 4 of W. Feller, On boundary conditions for the Kolmogorov differential equations, *Annals of Mathematics*, vol. 65 (1957), pp. 527–570. The first existence proof was given in The integrodifferential equations of completely discontinuous Markov processes, *Transactions American Mathematical Society*, vol. 48 (1940), pp. 488–515. Unfortunately this paper treats the general case of non-denumerable sample spaces and time dependent coefficients, and it has generally been overlooked that the specialization to the case of ordinary differential equations with constant coefficients treated in this chapter leads to a simple existence proof.

[11] Solutions of the birth and death process such that $\Sigma P_n(t) < 1$ have recently attracted wide attention. See W. Ledermann and G. E. Reuter, Spectral theory for the differential equations of simple birth and death processes, *Philosophical Transactions Royal Society*, London, Ser. A, vol. 246 (1954), pp. 321–369; S. Karlin and J. McGregor, Representation of a class of stochastic processes, *Proceedings National Academy Sciences*, USA (6) vol. 4 (1955), pp. 387–391; forthcoming papers by the same authors and another by B. O. Koopman, both in the *Transactions American Mathematical Society*.

cases of practical significance the conditions of uniqueness are satisfied; in this case automatically $\Sigma P_n(t) = 1$ (see section 10).

When $\lambda_0 = 0$ the transition $E_0 \to E_1$ is impossible. In the terminology of Markov chains E_0 is an *absorbing state* from which no exit is possible; once the system is in E_0 it stays there. From (5.3) it follows that in this case $P'_0(t) \geq 0$, so that $P_0(t)$ increases monotonically. The limit $P_0(\infty)$ is the probability of ultimate absorption.

More generally, it can be shown that *the limits*

$$(5.5) \qquad \lim_{t \to \infty} P_n(t) = p_n$$

exist and are independent of the initial conditions (5.4); they satisfy the system of linear equations obtained from (5.2)–(5.3) on putting $P'_n(t) = 0$. The relation (5.5) is usually interpreted as a "tendency toward the steady state condition" and this suggestive name has caused much confusion. It must be understood that, except when E_0 is an absorbing state, the chance fluctuations continue forever unabated and (5.5) shows only that in the long run the influence of the initial condition disappears. The remarks made in chapter XV, section 6, concerning the statistical equilibria apply here without change.

The truth of (5.5) can be proved either from explicit formulas for the $P_n(t)$ or from general ergodic theories. Intuitively the theorem becomes almost obvious by a comparison of our process with a simple Markov chain with transition probabilities

$$(5.6) \qquad p_{n,n+1} = \frac{\lambda_n}{\lambda_n + \mu_n}, \qquad p_{n,n-1} = \frac{\mu_n}{\lambda_n + \mu_n}.$$

In this chain the only direct transitions are $E_n \to E_{n+1}$ and $E_n \to E_{n-1}$, and they have the same conditional probabilities as in our process; the difference between the chain and our process lies in the fact that, with the latter, changes can occur at arbitrary times, so that the number of transitions during time t is a random variable. However, for large t this number is certain to be large, and hence it is plausible that for $t \to \infty$ the probabilities $P_n(t)$ behave as the corresponding probabilities of the simple chain.

The principal field of applications of the birth and death process is to problems of waiting times, trunking, etc.; see sections 6 and 7.

Examples. (a) *Linear growth.* Suppose that a population consists of elements which can split or die. During any short time interval of length h the probability for any living element to split into two is $\lambda h + o(h)$, whereas the corresponding probability of dying is $\mu h + o(h)$.

Here λ and μ are two constants characteristic of the population. If there is no interaction among the elements, we are led to a birth and death process with $\lambda_n = n\lambda$, $\mu_n = n\mu$. The basic differential equations take on the form

$$(5.7) \quad \begin{aligned} P'_0(t) &= \mu P_1(t), \\ P'_n(t) &= -(\lambda + \mu)nP_n(t) + \lambda(n-1)P_{n-1}(t) + \mu(n+1)P_{n+1}(t). \end{aligned}$$

Explicit solutions can be found [12] (cf. problems 9–11), but we shall not discuss this aspect. The limits (5.5) exist and satisfy (5.7) with $P'_n(t) = 0$. From the first equation we find $p_1 = 0$, and we see by induction from the second equation that $p_n = 0$ for all $n \geq 1$. If $p_0 = 1$, we may say that the probability of ultimate extinction is 1. If $p_0 < 1$, the relations $p_1 = p_2 \ldots = 0$ imply that with probability $1 - p_0$ the population increases over all bounds; ultimately the population must either die out or increase indefinitely. To find the probability p_0 of extinction we compare the process to the related Markov chain. In our case the transition probabilities (5.6) are independent of n, and we have therefore an ordinary random walk in which the steps to the right and left have probabilities $p = \lambda/(\lambda + \mu)$ and $q = \mu/(\lambda + \mu)$, respectively. The state E_0 (or $x = 0$) is an absorbing barrier. We know from the classical ruin problem (see chapter XIV, section 2) that the probability of extinction is 1 if $p \leq q$ and $(q/p)^r$ if $q < p$ and r is the initial state. We conclude that *in our process the probability* $p_0 = \lim P_0(t)$ *of ultimate extinction is* 1 *if* $\lambda \leq \mu$, *and* $(\mu/\lambda)^r$ *if* $\lambda > \mu$. (This is easily verified from the explicit solution; see problem 10.)

As in many similar cases, the explicit solution of (5.7) is rather complicated, and it is desirable to calculate the mean and the variance of the distribution $\{P_n(t)\}$ directly from the differential equations. We have for the mean

$$(5.8) \quad M(t) = \sum_{n=1}^{\infty} nP_n(t).$$

We shall omit a formal proof that $M(t)$ is finite and that the following formal operations are justified (again both points follow readily from

---

[12] A systematic way consists in deriving a partial differential equation for the generating function $\Sigma P_n(t)s^n$. A more general process where the coefficients λ and μ in (5.7) are permitted to depend on time is discussed in detail in David G. Kendall, The generalized "birth and death" process, *Annals of Mathematical Statistics*, vol. 19 (1948), pp. 1–15. See also the same author's Stochastic processes and population growth, *Journal of the Royal Statistical Society*, B, vol. 11 (1949), pp. 230–265 where the theory is generalized to take account of the age distribution in biological populations.

the solution given in problem 10). Multiplying the second equation in (5.7) by n and adding over $n = 1, 2, \ldots$, we find that the terms containing n^2 cancel, and we get

$$(5.9) \qquad M'(t) = \lambda\Sigma(n - 1)P_{n-1}(t) - \mu\Sigma(n + 1)P_{n+1}(t) =$$
$$= (\lambda - \mu)M(t).$$

This is a differential equation for $M(t)$. At time $t = 0$ the population size is i, and hence $M(0) = i$. Therefore

$$(5.10) \qquad\qquad M(t) = ie^{(\lambda-\mu)t}.$$

We see that the mean tends to 0 or infinity, according as $\lambda < \mu$ or $\lambda > \mu$. The variance of $\{P_n(t)\}$ can be calculated in a similar way (cf. problem 12).

(b) *Waiting lines for a single channel.* In the simplest case of constant coefficients $\lambda_n = \lambda$, $\mu_n = \mu$ the birth and death process reduces to a special case of the waiting line example (7.*b*) when $a = 1$.

6. EXPONENTIAL HOLDING TIMES

The principal field of applications of the pure birth and death process is connected with trunking in telephone engineering and various types of waiting lines for telephones, counters, or machines. This type of problem can be treated with various degrees of mathematical sophistication. The method of the birth and death process offers the easiest approach, but this model is based on a mathematical simplification known as the *assumption of exponential holding times*. We begin with a discussion of this basic assumption.

For concreteness of language let us consider a telephone conversation, and let us assume that its length is necessarily an integral number of seconds. We treat the length of the conversation as a random variable $\mathbf{X}$ and assume its probability distribution $p_n = \mathbf{P}\{\mathbf{X} = n\}$ known. The telephone line then represents a physical system with two possible states, "busy" (E_0) and "free" (E_1). If at an arbitrary moment t the line is busy, then the probability of a change in state during the next second depends on how long the conversation has been going on. In other words, the past has an influence on the future, and our process is therefore not a Markov process (see chapter XV, section 10). This circumstance is the source of most difficulties in more complicated problems. However, there exists a simple exceptional case discussed at length in chapter XIII, section 9.

Imagine that the decision whether or not the conversation is to be continued is made each second at random by means of a skew coin. In other words, a sequence of Bernoulli trials with probability p of success is performed at a rate of one per second and continued until the first success. The conversation ends when this first success occurs. In this case the total length of the conversation, the "holding time," has the geometric distribution $p_n = q^{n-1}p$. If at any time t the line is busy, the probability that it will remain busy for more than one second is q, and the probability of the transition $E_0 \to E_1$ at the next step is p. These probabilities are now independent of how long the line was busy.

Without discretizing the time parameter we have to deal with continuous random variables. The role of the geometric distribution for waiting times is then taken over by the *exponential distribution*. It is the only distribution having a Markovian character, that is, endowed with complete lack of memory. In other words, the probability that a conversation which goes on at time x continues beyond $x + h$ is independent of the past duration of the conversation if, and only if, the probability that the conversation lasts for longer than t time units is given by an exponential $e^{-\lambda t}$. We have encountered this "exponential holding time distribution" as the zero term in the Poisson distribution (1.1), that is, as the waiting time up to the occurrence of the first change.

The method of the birth and death process is applicable only if the transition probabilities in question do not depend on the past; for trunking and waiting line problems this means that all holding times must be exponential. From a practical point of view this assumption may at first sight appear rather artificial, but experience shows that it reasonably describes actual phenomena. In particular, many measurements have shown that telephone conversations within a city [13] follow the exponential law to a surprising degree of accuracy. The same situation prevails for other holding times (e.g., the duration of machine repairs).

It remains to characterize the so-called incoming traffic (arriving calls, machine breakdowns, etc.). We shall assume that during any time interval of length h the probability of an incoming call is λh plus negligible terms, and that the probability of more than one call is in the limit negligible. According to the results of section 2, this means that the number of incoming calls has a Poisson distribution with mean λt. We shall describe this situation by saying that *the incoming traffic is of the Poisson type with intensity* λ.

---

[13] For conversations between cities, companies usually charge by intervals of three minutes, and the holding times are therefore likely to be multiples of three minutes. This is a systematic deviation from the exponential law, and our theory does not apply.

It is easy to verify the described property of exponential holding times. Denote by $u(t)$ the probability that a conversation lasts for at least t time units. The probability $u(t + s)$ that a conversation starting at time 0 lasts beyond $t + s$ equals the probability that it lasts longer than t units multiplied by the conditional probability that a conversation lasts additional s units, given that its length exceeds t. If the past duration has no influence, the last conditional probability must equal $u(s)$; that is, we must have

$$(6.1) \qquad\qquad u(t + s) = u(t)\, u(s).$$

It remains to prove the

Theorem. *Let $u(t)$ be defined for $t > 0$ and bounded in each finite interval. If $u(t)$ satisfies (6.1), then either $u(t) = 0$ for all t, or $u = e^{-\lambda t}$ for some constant λ.*

Proof. If $u(t)$ does not vanish identically, there exists a point x such that $u(x) > 0$. Let $\lambda = -\log u(x)$ and $v(t) = e^{\lambda t} u(xt)$. Then

$$(6.2) \qquad\qquad v(t + s) = v(t)\, v(s), \qquad\qquad v(1) = 1$$

and we shall prove that $v(t) = 1$ for all $t > 0$. Clearly $v^2(\tfrac{1}{2}) = v(1) = 1$, and generally $v^n(1/n) = v(1) = 1$ for each integer $n > 0$. Therefore $v(1/n) = 1$ and thence $v(m/n) = v^m(1/n) = 1$ for each pair of integers $m > 0$, $n > 0$. Hence $v(r) = 1$ for each rational r. Suppose now that $v(\tau) = c \neq 1$. Then $v(\tau^{-1}) = c^{-1}$ and we may assume $c > 1$. In this case $v(N\tau) = v^N(\tau) = c^N$ can be made arbitrarily large by choosing N sufficiently large. Now choose a rational r in the interval

$$N\tau - 1 < r < N\tau.$$

Then

$$(6.3) \qquad v(N\tau - r) = v(N\tau - r)\, v(r) = v(N\tau) = c^N$$

which shows that there exist points $a = N\tau - r$ in the interval $0 < a < 1$ such that $v(a) > c^N$. This contradicts the assumption that $u(t)$, and therefore $v(t)$, are bounded in each finite interval.

7. WAITING LINE AND SERVICING PROBLEMS

(a) *The simplest trunking problem.*[14] Suppose that infinitely many trunks or channels are available, and that the probability of a conver-

---

[14] C. Palm, Intensitätsschwankungen im Fernsprechverkehr, *Ericsson Technics* (Stockholm), no. 44 (1943), pp. 1–189, in particular p. 57. Waiting line and trunking problems for telephone exchanges were studied long before the theory of stochastic processes was available and had a stimulating influence on the development of the theory. In particular, Palm's impressive work over many years has proved useful to several authors. The earliest worker in the field was A. K. Erlang (1878–1929). See E. Brockmeyer, H. L. Halström, and Arne Jensen, The life and works of A. K. Erlang, *Transactions of the Danish Academy Technical Sciences*, No. 2, Copenhagen, 1948. Independently valuable pioneer work has been done by T. C. Fry whose book, quoted in footnote 4 of chapter VI, did much for the development of engineering applications of probability.

sation ending during the interval $(t, t+h)$ is μh plus terms which are negligible as $h \to 0$ (exponential holding time). The incoming calls constitute a traffic of the Poisson type with parameter λ. The system is in state E_n if n lines are busy.

It is, of course, assumed that the durations of the conversations are mutually independent. If n lines are busy, the probability that one of them will be freed within time h is then $n\mu h + o(h)$. The probability that within this time two or more conversations terminate is obviously of the order of magnitude h^2 and therefore negligible. The probability of a new call arriving is $\lambda h + o(h)$. The probability of a combination of several calls, or of a call arriving and a conversation ending, is again $o(h)$. Thus, in the notation of section 5

$$(7.1) \qquad\qquad \lambda_n = \lambda, \qquad \mu_n = n\mu.$$

The basic differential equations (5.2)–(5.3) take the form $(n \geq 1)$

$$(7.2) \quad P'_0(t) = -\lambda P_0(t) + \mu P_1(t)$$

$$P'_n(t) = -(\lambda + n\mu)P_n(t) + \lambda P_{n-1}(t) + (n + 1)\mu P_{n+1}(t).$$

Explicit solutions can be obtained by deriving a partial differential equation for the generating function (cf. problem 13). We shall only determine the quantities $p_n = \lim P_n(t)$ of (5.5). They satisfy the equations

$$(7.3) \qquad \begin{aligned} \lambda p_0 &= \mu p_1 \\ (\lambda + n\mu)p_n &= \lambda p_{n-1} + (n + 1)\mu p_{n+1}. \end{aligned}$$

We find by induction that $p_n = p_0(\lambda/\mu)^n/n!$, and hence

$$(7.4) \qquad\qquad p_n = e^{-\lambda/\mu} \frac{(\lambda/\mu)^n}{n!}.$$

Thus, *the limiting distribution is a Poisson distribution with parameter* λ/μ. *It is independent of the initial state.*

It is easy to find the mean $M(t) = \Sigma n P_n(t)$. Multiplying the nth equation of (7.2) by n and adding, we get, taking into account that the $P_n(t)$ add to unity,

$$(7.5) \qquad\qquad M'(t) = \lambda - \mu M(t).$$

When the initial state is E_i, then $M(0) = i$, and

$$(7.6) \qquad\qquad M(t) = \frac{\lambda}{\mu}(1 - e^{-\mu t}) + ie^{-\mu t}.$$

As $t \to \infty$, we see that $M(t)$ approaches the mean of the Poisson distribution found above. Incidentally, the reader may verify that in the special case $i = 0$ the $P_n(t)$ are given exactly by a Poisson distribution with mean $M(t)$.

(b) *Waiting lines for a finite number of channels.*[15] We now modify the last example to obtain a more realistic model. The assumptions are the same, except that *the number a of trunklines or channels is finite. If all channels are busy, each new call joins a waiting line and waits until a channel is freed.* This means that all trunklines have a *common* waiting line.

The word "trunk" may be replaced by *counter* at a postoffice and "conversation" by *service.* We are actually treating the general waiting line problem for the case where a person has to wait only if all a channels are busy.

We say that *the system is in state E_n if there are exactly n persons either being served or in the waiting line.* Such a line exists only when $n > a$, and then there are $n - a$ persons in it.

As long as at least one channel is free, we are in exactly the same situation as in the preceding example. However, if the system is in a state E_n with $n > a$, only a conversations are going on, and we have therefore $\mu_n = a\mu$, for $n \geq a$. The basic system of differential equations is therefore given by (7.2) for $n < a$, but for $n \geq a$ by

$$(7.7) \qquad P'_n(t) = -(\lambda + a\mu)P_n(t) + \lambda P_{n-1}(t) + a\mu P_{n+1}(t).$$

In the special case of a single channel ($a = 1$) these equations reduce to those of a birth and death process with coefficients independent of n.

The limits p_n of (5.5) exist; they satisfy (7.3) for $n < a$, and

$$(7.8) \qquad\qquad (\lambda + a\mu)p_n = \lambda p_{n-1} + a\mu p_{n+1}$$

for $n \geq a$. By recursion we find again that

$$(7.9) \qquad\qquad p_n = p_0 \frac{(\lambda/\mu)^n}{n!}, \qquad\qquad n \leq a$$

$$(7.10) \qquad\qquad p_n = \frac{(\lambda/\mu)^n}{a!\,a^{n-a}} p_0, \qquad\qquad n \geq a.$$

The series $\Sigma\,(p_n/p_0)$ converges only if

$$(7.11) \qquad\qquad \frac{\lambda}{\mu} < a.$$

Hence, if (7.11) does not hold, a limiting distribution $\{p_k\}$ cannot exist. *In this case $p_n = 0$ for all n, which means that gradually the waiting line grows over all bounds.* On the other hand, if (7.11) holds, then we can

---

[15] A. Kolmogoroff, *Sur le problème d'attente, Recueil Mathématique [Sbornik]*, Vol. 38, 1931, pp. 101–106.

determine p_0 so that the sum of the expressions (7.9) and (7.10) equals unity. From the explicit expressions for $P_n(t)$, which we have not derived, however, it can be shown that the p_n thus obtained really represent the *limiting distribution* of the $P_n(t)$. Table 1 gives a numerical illustration for $a = 3$, $\lambda/\mu = 2$.

TABLE 1

LIMITING PROBABILITIES IN THE CASE OF $a = 3$ CHANNELS AND $\lambda/\mu = 2$

n	0	1	2	3	4	5	6	7
Lines busy	0	1	2	3	3	3	3	3
People waiting	0	0	0	0	1	2	3	4
p_n	0.1111	0.2222	0.2222	0.1481	0.0988	0.0658	0.0439	0.0293

(c) *Servicing of machines.*[16] The results derived in this and the next example are being successfully applied in Swedish industry. For orientation we begin with the simplest case and generalize it in the next example. The problem is as follows.

We consider automatic machines which normally require no human care. However, at any time a machine may break down and call for service. The time required for servicing the machine is again taken as a random variable with an exponential distribution. In other words, the machine is characterized by two constants λ and μ with the following properties. If at time t the machine is in working state, the probability that it will call for service before time $t + h$ is λh plus terms which are negligible in the limit $h \to 0$. Conversely, if at time t the machine is being serviced, the probability that the servicing time terminates before $t + h$ and the machine reverts to the working state is $\mu h + o(h)$. For an efficient machine λ should be relatively small and μ relatively large. The ratio λ/μ is called the *servicing factor*.

We suppose that *m machines with the same parameters λ and μ and working independently are serviced by a single repairman.* A machine which breaks down is serviced immediately unless the repairman is servicing another machine, in which case a waiting line is formed. We say that *the system is in state E_n* if n machines are not working. For $1 \leq n \leq m$ this means that one machine is being serviced and $n - 1$ are in the waiting line; in the state E_0 all machines work and the repairman is idle.

---

[16] Examples (c) and (d), including the numerical illustrations, are taken from an article by C. Palm, The distribution of repairmen in servicing automatic machines (in Swedish), *Industritidningen Norden*, vol. 75 (1947), pp. 75–80, 90–94, 119–123. Palm gives tables and graphs for the most economical number of repairmen.

A transition $E_n \to E_{n+1}$ is caused by a breakdown of one among the $m - n$ working machines, whereas a transition $E_n \to E_{n-1}$ occurs if the machine being serviced reverts to the working state. Hence we have a birth and death process with coefficients

(7.12) $\lambda_n = (m - n)\lambda, \qquad \mu_0 = 0, \qquad \mu_1 = \mu_2 = \ldots = \mu_m = \mu$

and the basic differential equations (5.2) and (5.3) become ($1 \leq n \leq$ $\leq m - 1$):

$$P'_0(t) = -m\lambda P_0(t) + \mu P_1(t),$$

$$P'_n(t) = -\{(m - n)\lambda + \mu\}P_n(t) + (m - n + 1)\lambda P_{n-1}(t) +$$

(7.13)

$$+ \mu P_{n+1}(t),$$

$$P'_m(t) = -\mu P_m(t) + \lambda P_{m-1}(t).$$

This is a *finite* system of differential equations and can be solved by ordinary methods. The limits (5.5) exist and satisfy the equations

$$m\lambda p_0 = \mu p_1,$$

(7.14) $\{(m - n)\lambda + \mu\}p_n = (m - n + 1)\lambda p_{n-1} + \mu p_{n+1},$

$$\mu p_m = \lambda p_{m-1}.$$

It follows easily that the recursion formula

(7.15) $(m - n)\lambda p_n = \mu p_{n+1}$

holds. Substituting successively $n = m-1, m-2, \ldots, 1, 0$, we get

(7.16) $p_{m-k} = \dfrac{1}{k!} \left(\dfrac{\mu}{\lambda}\right)^k \cdot p_m.$

The remaining unknown constant p_m can be obtained from the condition that the p_j add to unity:

(7.16a) $p_m = \left\{1 + \dfrac{1}{1!}\left(\dfrac{\mu}{\lambda}\right)^1 + \ldots + \dfrac{1}{m!}\left(\dfrac{\mu}{\lambda}\right)^m\right\}^{-1}.$

Formula (7.16) is well known among trunking engineers as *Erlang's loss formula.* Typical numerical values are exhibited in table 2.

TABLE 2

PROBABILITIES p_n FOR THE CASE $\lambda/\mu = 0.1$, $m = 6$
(ERLANG'S LOSS FORMULA)

n	Machines in Waiting Line	p_n
0	0	0.4845
1	0	.2907
2	1	.1454
3	2	.0582
4	3	.0175
5	4	.0035
6	5	.0003

The probability p_0 may be interpreted as the probability of the repairman's being idle (in the example of table 2 he should be idle about half the time). The *expected number of machines in the waiting line is*

$$(7.17) \qquad w = \sum_{k=1}^{m} (k-1)p_k = \sum_{k=1}^{m} kp_k - (1 - p_0).$$

This quantity can be calculated by adding the relations (7.15) for $n = 0, 1, \ldots, m$. Using the fact that the p_n add to unity, we get

$$m\lambda - \lambda w - \lambda(1 - p_0) = \mu(1 - p_0)$$

or

$$(7.18) \qquad w = m - \frac{\lambda + \mu}{\lambda}(1 - p_0).$$

In the example of table 2 we have $w = 6 \cdot (0.0549)$. Thus 0.0549 is the average contribution of a machine to the waiting line.

(d) *Continuation: several repairmen.* We shall not change the basic assumptions of the preceding problem, except that the m *machines are now serviced by r repairmen* ($r < m$). Thus for $n \leq r$ the state E_n means that $r - n$ repairmen are idle, n machines are being serviced, and no machine is in the waiting line for repairs. For $n > r$ the state E_n signifies that r machines are being serviced and $n - r$ machines are in the waiting line. We can use the setup of the preceding example except that (7.12) is obviously to be replaced by

$$\lambda_0 = m\lambda, \qquad\qquad \mu_0 = 0,$$

(7.19) $\qquad \lambda_n = (m - n)\lambda, \qquad \mu_n = n\mu \qquad (1 \leq n \leq r),$

$$\lambda_n = (m - n)\lambda, \qquad \mu_n = r\mu \qquad (r \leq n \leq m).$$

We shall not write down the basic system of differential equations but only the equations for the limiting probabilities p_n. They are

$$m\lambda p_0 = \mu p_1,$$

(7.20) $\quad \{(m - n)\lambda + n\mu\}p_n = (m - n + 1)\lambda p_{n-1} + (n + 1)\mu p_{n+1}$

$$(1 \leq n < r),$$

$$\{(m - n)\lambda + r\mu\}p_n = (m - n + 1)\lambda p_{n-1} + r\mu p_{n+1}$$

$$(r \leq n \leq m).$$

From the first equation we get the ratio of p_1/p_0. From the second equation we get by induction for $n < r$

(7.21) $\qquad\qquad (n + 1)\mu p_{n+1} = (m - n)\lambda p_n;$

finally, for $n \geq r$ we get from the last equation in (7.20)

(7.22) $\qquad\qquad r\mu p_{n+1} = (m - n)\lambda p_n.$

These equations permit calculating successively the ratios p_n/p_0. Finally, p_0 follows from the condition $\Sigma p_k = 1$. The values in table 3 are obtained in this way.

TABLE 3

PROBABILITIES p_n FOR THE CASE $\lambda/\mu = 0.1$, $m = 20$, $r = 3$

n	Machines Serviced	Machines Waiting	Repairmen Idle	p_n
0	0	0	3	0.13625
1	1	0	2	.27250
2	2	0	1	.25888
3	3	0	0	.15533
4	3	1	0	.08802
5	3	2	0	.04694
6	3	3	0	.02347
7	3	4	0	.01095
8	3	5	0	.00475
9	3	6	0	.00190
10	3	7	0	.00070
11	3	8	0	.00023
12	3	9	0	.00007

A comparison of tables 2 and 3 reveals surprising facts. Note that both tables refer to the same machines ($\lambda/\mu = 0.1$), but in the second case we have $m = 20$ machines and $r = 3$ repairmen. The number of machines per repairman has increased from 6 to $6\frac{2}{3}$, but at the same time, the machines are serviced more efficiently. Let us define a *coefficient of loss for machines* by

$$(7.23) \qquad \frac{w}{m} = \frac{\text{average number of machines in waiting line}}{\text{number of machines}}$$

and a coefficient of loss for repairmen by

$$(7.24) \qquad \frac{\rho}{r} = \frac{\text{average number of repairmen idle}}{\text{number of repairmen}}.$$

For practical purposes we may identify the probabilities $P_n(t)$ with their limits p_n. In table 3 we have then $w = p_4 + 2p_5 + 3p_6 + \ldots + 17p_{20}$ and $\rho = 3p_0 + 2p_1 + p_2$. Table 4 proves conclusively that

TABLE 4

COMPARISON OF EFFICIENCIES OF TWO SYSTEMS DISCUSSED IN
EXAMPLES (c) AND (d)

	I	II
Number of machines	6	20
Number of repairmen	1	3
Machines per repairman	6	$6\frac{2}{3}$
Coefficient of loss for repairmen	0.4845	0.4042
Coefficient of loss for machines	0.0549	0.01694

for our particular machines for which ($\lambda/\mu = 0.1$) *three repairmen per twenty machines are ever so much more economical than one repairman per six machines.* Palm's tables referred to in footnote 16 enable us to find the most economical ratio of repairmen per machine.

(e) *A power-supply problem.*[17] One electric circuit supplies *a* welders who use the current only intermittently. If at time *t* a welder uses current, the probability that he ceases using it at time $t + h$ is $\mu h + o(h)$; if at time *t* he requires no current, the probability that he calls for current before $t + h$ is $\lambda h + o(h)$. The welders work independently of each other.

---

[17] This example was suggested by the problem treated (inadequately) by H. A. Adler and K. W. Miller, A new approach to probability problems in electrical engineering, *Transactions of the American Institute of Electrical Engineers*, vol. 65 (1946), pp. 630–632.

We say that the system is in state E_n if n welders are using current. Thus we have only finitely many states $E_0, \ldots, E_a$.

If the system is in state E_n, then $a - n$ welders are not using current and the probability for a new call for current within time h is $(a - n)\lambda h + o(h)$; on the other hand, the probability that one of the n welders ceases using current is $n\mu h + o(h)$. Hence we have a birth and death process with

$$(7.25) \qquad \lambda_n = (a - n)\lambda, \qquad \mu_n = n\mu, \qquad 0 \le n \le a.$$

The basic differential equations become $(1 \le n \le a - 1)$

$$P'_0(t) = -a\lambda P_0(t) + \mu P_1(t),$$
$$(7.26) \quad P'_n(t) = -\{n\mu + (a - n)\lambda\}P_n(t) + (n + 1)\mu P_{n+1}(t) +$$
$$+ (a - n + 1)\lambda P_{n-1}(t),$$
$$P'_a(t) = -a\mu P_a(t) + \lambda P_{a-1}(t).$$

It is easily verified that *the limiting probabilities are given by the binomial distribution*

$$(7.27) \qquad p_n = \binom{a}{n}\left(\frac{\lambda}{\lambda + \mu}\right)^n \left(\frac{\mu}{\lambda + \mu}\right)^{a-n},$$

a result which could have been anticipated on intuitive grounds.

8. THE BACKWARD (RETROSPECTIVE) EQUATIONS

In the preceding sections we were studying the probabilities $P_n(t)$ of finding the system at time t in state E_n. This notation is convenient but misleading, inasmuch as it omits mentioning the initial state E_i of the system at time zero. For theoretical purposes it is therefore more natural to introduce the notation $P_{in}(t)$; *this is the probability that the system is at time t in state E_n, given that at time zero it was in E_i.* The $P_{in}(t)$ will be called *transition probabilities*.

It must be emphasized that we have been studying these transition probabilities all along and that nothing is changed but notation. When the initial state is known to be E_i, then $\{P_{in}(t)\}$ is the absolute probability distribution at time t. When at time zero we have only a probability distribution $\{q_i\}$ for the initial state, then the probability of E_n at time t is

$$(8.1) \qquad Q_n(t) = \sum_i q_i P_{in}(t).$$

In the case of the pure birth process and of the birth and death process, we found that *for an arbitrary fixed i the transition probabilities*

$P_{in}(t)$ *satisfy the basic differential equations* (3.2) *and* (5.2). The subscript i appears only in the initial conditions, which should now be written

$$(8.2) \qquad P_{in}(0) = \begin{matrix} 1 & \text{for} \quad n = i \\ 0 & \text{otherwise.} \end{matrix}$$

These basic differential equations were derived by prolonging the time interval $(0, t)$ to $(0, t+h)$ and considering the possible changes during the short time $(t, t+h)$. We could as well have prolonged the interval $(0, t)$ in the direction of the past and considered the changes during $(-h, 0)$. In this way we get a new system of differential equations in which n (instead of i) remains fixed.

Consider first the case of a pure birth process and let us neglect events whose probability tends to zero faster than h. If the system passed from E_i $(i > 0)$ at time $-h$ to E_n at time t, then at time 0 it was with probability $1 - o(h)$ either at E_i or at E_{i+1}. By the method of sections 2 and 3 we conclude that

$$(8.3) \qquad P_{in}(t + h) = P_{in}(t)(1 - \lambda_i h) + P_{i+1,n}(t)\lambda_i h + o(h).$$

Hence for $i \geq 0$ the new basic system now takes the form

$$(8.4) \qquad P'_{in}(t) = -\lambda_i P_{in}(t) + \lambda_i P_{i+1,n}(t).$$

These equations are called the *backward equations*, and, for distinction, equations (3.2) are called the *forward equations*. The initial conditions are (8.2). (Intuitively one should expect that

$$(8.5) \qquad P_{in}(t) = 0 \qquad \text{if } n < i,$$

but pathological exceptions exist; see section 10).

In the case of the birth and death process, if the system is at time $-h$ in E_i, then at time zero it should be in E_{i+1}, E_i, or E_{i-1}, and the same argument leads to the *backward equations*

$$(8.6) \quad P'_{in}(t) = -(\lambda_i + \mu_i)P_{i,n}(t) + \lambda_i P_{i+1,n}(t) + \mu_i P_{i-1,n}(t).$$

These equations correspond to (5.2).

It should be clear that the forward and backward equations are not independent of each other; the solution of the backward equations with the initial conditions (8.2) automatically satisfies the forward equations, except in the rare situations where the solution is not unique. These connections are mentioned here only as a preparation for the general theory of the next section.

Example. *The Poisson process.* In section 2 we have interpreted the Poisson expression (1.1) as the probability that exactly n calls arrive during any time interval of length t. Let us say that at time t the system is in state E_n if exactly n calls arrive within the time interval from 0 to t. A transition from E_i at t_1 to E_n at t_2 means that $n - i$ calls arrived during (t_1, t_2). This is possible only if $n \geq i$, and hence we have for the transition probabilities of the Poisson process

$$P_{in}(t) = e^{-\lambda t} \frac{(\lambda t)^{n-i}}{(n - i)!} \qquad \text{if} \quad n \geq i,$$

(8.7)

$$P_{in}(0) = 0 \qquad \text{if} \quad n < i.$$

The forward and backward equations are, respectively,

(8.8) $$P'_{in}(t) = -\lambda P_{in}(t) + \lambda P_{i,n-1}(t)$$

and

(8.9) $$P'_{in}(t) = -\lambda P_{in}(t) + \lambda P_{i+1,n}(t),$$

and it is easily verified that (8.7) is a solution of both systems and satisfies the initial condition (8.2).

9. GENERALIZATION; THE KOLMOGOROV EQUATIONS

So far the theory has been restricted to processes in which direct transitions from a state E_n are possible only to the neighboring states E_{n+1} and E_{n-1}. Moreover, the processes have been time-homogeneous, that is to say, the transition probabilities $P_{in}(t)$ have been the same for all time intervals of length t. We now consider more general processes in which both assumptions are dropped.

As in the theory of ordinary Markov chains, we shall permit direct transitions from any state E_i to any state E_n. The transition probabilities are permitted to vary in time. This necessitates specifying the two endpoints of any time interval instead of specifying just its length. Accordingly, we shall write $P_{in}(\tau, t)$ *for the conditional probability of finding the system at time t in state E_n, given that at a previous instant τ the state was E_i.* The symbol $P_{in}(\tau, t)$ is meaningless unless $\tau < t$. If the process is homogeneous in time, then $P_{in}(\tau, t)$ depends only on the difference $t - \tau$, and we can write $P_{in}(t)$ instead of $P_{in}(\tau, \tau+t)$ (which is then independent of τ).

The principal property of our processes is the Markov property discussed in chapter XV, section 10: Given the state of the system at any time, future changes are independent of the past. More precisely, consider three moments $\tau < s < t$ and suppose that at time τ the system is in state E_i and at time s in state E_ν. For an arbitrary process the (conditional) probability of finding the system at time t in state E_n depends on both i and ν; in other words, not only the "present state" E_ν, but also the past state E_i, has an influence on the state at time t. However, for a Markov process this is not so. For it the considered probability equals $P_{\nu n}(s, t)$, the probability of a transition from E_ν at time s to E_n at time t; the knowledge that at time $\tau < s$ the system was in state E_i permits no inference about the future. This assumption leads directly to an important conclusion. The passage from E_j at time τ to E_n at time t must occur via some state E_ν at time s, and for a Markov process the probability that the passage goes via a particular state E_ν is $P_{i\nu}(\tau, s)P_{\nu n}(s, t)$. It follows that we must have

$$(9.1) \qquad P_{in}(\tau, t) = \sum_\nu P_{i\nu}(\tau, s)P_{\nu n}(s, t)$$

identically for all $\tau < s < t$. This is the Chapman-Kolmogorov equation. It is the counterpart, for the case of a continuous time parameter, to equation XV(10.3), which is valid when the time parameter assumes integral values only.

It was shown in chapter XV, section 10, that the Chapman-Kolmogorov equation does not hold for all stochastic processes. For our purposes we could take (9.1) *as defining the class of processes with which we are concerned.*[18] In fact, we shall add only regularity restrictions and derive our basic differential equations from (9.1). There is a probabilistic background leading up to the Chapman-Kolmogorov equation, but we need not refer to it; once (9.1) is given we can easily derive differential equations which determine the probabilities $P_{in}(t)$ and can proceed in a purely analytical way.

In the case of time-homogeneous processes, equation (9.1) assumes the simpler form

$$(9.2) \qquad P_{in}(t + s) = \sum_\nu P_{i\nu}(t)P_{\nu n}(s).$$

For the Poisson process this equation reduces to the convolution property of the Poisson distribution [example XI(2.c)].

---

[18] The question of whether the Kolmogorov equation characterizes Markov processes poses difficult problems requiring the study of the actual sample functions $\mathbf{X}(t)$. It should be borne in mind that we are using a short cut to obtain differential equations for certain probabilities and are not analyzing the process in all its aspects.

We now introduce our fundamental regularity conditions which in an obvious way generalize the starting assumptions of the birth and death process.

Assumption 1. *To every state E_n there corresponds a continuous function $c_n(t) \geq 0$ such that as $h \to 0$*

$$(9.3) \qquad \frac{1 - P_{nn}(t, t+h)}{h} \to c_n(t).$$

The probabilistic interpretation of (9.3) is obvious; if at time t the system is in state E_n, the probability that during $(t, t+h)$ a change occurs is $c_n(t)h + o(h)$. Analytically, relations (9.3) require that $P_{nn}(t, s) \to 1$ as $s \to t$, and that $P_{nn}(t, x)$ has at $x = t$ a derivative. The function $c_n(t)$ plays the role of $\lambda_n + \mu_n$ in the birth and death process. In the case of a time-homogeneous process, c_n is independent of t.

Assumption 2. *To every pair of states E_j, E_k with $j \neq k$ there correspond transition probabilities $p_{jk}(t)$ (depending on time) such that as $h \to 0$*

$$(9.4) \qquad \frac{P_{jk}(t, t+h)}{h} \to c_j(t)p_{jk}(t) \qquad\qquad (j \neq k).$$

The $p_{jk}(t)$ are continuous in t, and for every fixed t, j

$$(9.5) \qquad \sum_k p_{jk}(t) = 1, \qquad\qquad p_{jj}(t) = 0.$$

Here $p_{jk}(t)$ can be interpreted as the conditional probability that, *if a change from E_j occurs during $(t, t+h)$, this change takes the system from E_j to E_k.* In the birth and death process

$$(9.6) \qquad p_{j,j+1}(t) = \frac{\lambda_j}{\lambda_j + \mu_j}, \qquad p_{j,j-1}(t) = \frac{\mu_j}{\lambda_j + \mu_j},$$

and $p_{jk}(t) = 0$ for all other combinations of j and k. For every fixed t the $p_{jk}(t)$ can be interpreted as transition probabilities of a Markov chain.

The two assumptions suffice to derive a system of backward equations for the $P_{jk}(\tau, t)$, but for the forward equations we require in addition

Assumption 3. *For fixed k the passage to the limit in (9.4) is uniform with respect to j.*

The necessity of this assumption is of considerable interest for the theory of infinite systems of differential equations and will be discussed in the next section.

We proceed to derive differential equations for the $P_{ik}(\tau, t)$ as functions of t and n (forward equations). From equation (9.1) we have

$$(9.7) \qquad P_{ik}(\tau, t+h) = \sum_j P_{ij}(\tau, t)P_{jk}(t, t+h).$$

Expressing the term $P_{kk}(t, t+h)$ on the right in accordance with (9.3), we get

$$(9.8) \qquad \frac{P_{ik}(\tau, t+h) - P_{ik}(\tau, t)}{h} = -c_k(t)P_{ik}(\tau, t) +$$

$$+ \frac{1}{h} \sum_{j \neq k} P_{ij}(\tau, t)P_{jk}(t, t+h) + \ldots$$

where the neglected terms tend to 0 with h, and the sum extends over all j except $j = k$. We can now apply (9.4) to the terms of the sum. Since (by assumption 3) the passage to the limit is uniform in j, the right side has a limit. Hence also the left side has a limit, which means that $P_{ik}(\tau, t)$ has a partial derivative with respect to t, and

$$(9.9) \qquad \frac{\partial P_{ik}(\tau, t)}{\partial t} = -c_k(t)P_{ik}(\tau, t) + \sum_j P_{ij}(\tau, t)c_j(t)p_{jk}(t).$$

This is the basic system of forward differential equations. Note that i and τ are fixed so that we have (despite the formal appearance of a partial derivative) a system of *ordinary* differential equations for the infinite system of functions $P_{ik}(\tau, t)$, $k = 0, 1, 2, \ldots$. The parameters i and τ appear only in the initial condition

$$(9.10) \qquad P_{ik}(\tau, \tau) = \begin{array}{ll} 1 & \text{for} \quad k = i \\ 0 & \text{otherwise.} \end{array}$$

A system of backward equations can be obtained on similar lines, and the derivation is actually simpler since we can dispense with assumption 3 entirely. As for equations (9.3) and (9.4), it is more natural to use the forms

$$(9.3a) \qquad \frac{1 - P_{nn}(t-h, t)}{h} \rightarrow c_n(t)$$

$$(9.4a) \qquad \frac{P_{jk}(t-h, t)}{h} \rightarrow c_j(t)p_{jk}(t) \qquad (j \neq k).$$

These relations can be shown to be equivalent to (9.3) and (9.4), but we shall simply start from (9.3a), (9.4a), and (9.5) as our basic assumptions. Rewriting the Chapman-Kolmogorov equation (9.1) in the form

$$(9.11) \qquad P_{ik}(\tau-h, t) = \sum_{\nu} P_{i\nu}(\tau-h, \tau)P_{\nu k}(\tau, t)$$

and using (9.3a) with $n = i$, we get

$$(9.12) \qquad \frac{P_{ik}(\tau-h, t) - P_{ik}(\tau, t)}{h} = -c_i(\tau)P_{ik}(\tau, t) +$$

$$+ \frac{1}{h} \sum_{\nu \neq i} P_{i\nu}(\tau-h, \tau)P_{\nu k}(\tau, t) + \frac{o(h)}{h}.$$

Here $h^{-1}P_{i\nu}(\tau-h, \tau) \to c_i(\tau)p_{i\nu}(\tau)$ and the passage to the limit in the sum to the right in (9.12) is always uniform. In fact, if $N > i$ we have

$$(9.13) \quad 0 \leq h^{-1} \sum_{\nu=N+1}^{\infty} P_{i\nu}(\tau-h, \tau)P_{\nu k}(\tau, t) \leq h^{-1} \sum_{\nu=N+1}^{\infty} P_{i\nu}(\tau-h, \tau) \leq$$

$$\leq h^{-1}\{1 - \sum_{\nu=0}^{N} P_{i\nu}(\tau-h, \tau)\} \to c_i(\tau)\{1 - \sum_{\nu=0}^{N} p_{i\nu}(\tau)\}.$$

In view of condition (9.5) the right side can be made arbitrarily small by choosing N sufficiently large. It follows that a termwise passage to the limit in (9.12) is permitted and we obtain

$$(9.14) \qquad \frac{\partial P_{ik}(\tau, t)}{\partial \tau} = c_i(\tau)P_{ik}(\tau, t) - c_i(\tau) \sum_{\nu} p_{i\nu}(\tau)P_{\nu k}(\tau, t).$$

This, together with the initial condition (9.10), is the *basic system of backward differential equations.*

The two systems of differential equations were first derived by A. Kolmogorov,[19] who laid the foundations of the theory of Markov processes. It has been shown [20] that there always exists a common solution $\{P_{ik}(\tau, t)\}$ of the two systems which satisfies the Chapman-Kolmogorov equation (9.1) and

$$(9.15) \qquad P_{ik}(\tau, t) \geq 0, \qquad \sum_{k} P_{ik}(\tau, t) \leq 1.$$

We know from the pure birth process (section 4) that the $P_{ik}(\tau, t)$ need not add to unity, the difference $1 - \Sigma P_{ik}(\tau, t)$ accounting for the pos-

[19] Über die analytischen Methoden in der Wahrscheinlichkeitsrechnung, *Mathematische Annalen*, vol. 104 (1931), pp. 415–458.
[20] See footnote 10.

sibility of infinitely many transitions within the finite time interval (τ, t). If $\Sigma P_{ik}(\tau, t) = 1$, the solution $\{P_{ik}(\tau, t)\}$ is unique, but in general different processes may satisfy the same forward and backward equation (see section 10). From the point of view of applications, the possibility of the inequality $\Sigma P_{ik}(\tau, t) < 1$ may be safely disregarded.

Example. *Generalized Poisson process.* Consider the case where *all* $c_i(t)$ *equal the same constant,* $c_i(t) = \lambda$, *and the* p_{jk} *are independent of* t. In this case the p_{jk} are the transition probabilities of an ordinary Markov chain and (as in chapter XV) we denote its higher transition probabilities by $p_{jk}^{(n)}$.

From $c_i(t) = \lambda$, it follows that the probability of a transition occurring during the interval $(t, t+h)$ is independent of the state of the system at time t and equals $\lambda h + o(h)$. This implies that the number of transitions within the interval (τ, t) has a Poisson distribution with parameter $\lambda(t - \tau)$. Given that exactly n transitions occurred, the (conditional) probability of a passage from j to k is $p_{jk}^{(n)}$. Hence

$$(9.16) \qquad P_{ik}(\tau, t) = e^{-\lambda(t-\tau)} \sum_{n=0}^{\infty} \frac{\lambda^n (t - \tau)^n}{n!} p_{ik}^{(n)}$$

(where, as usual, $p_{jj}^{(0)} = 1$ and $p_{jk}^{(0)} = 0$ for $j \neq k$). It is easily verified that (9.16) is in fact a solution of the two systems (9.9) and (9.14) of differential equations satisfying the boundary condition (9.10).

If, in particular,

$$(9.17) \quad p_{jk} = 0 \qquad \text{for} \quad k < j, \qquad p_{jk} = f_{k-j} \qquad \text{for} \quad k \geq j$$

(9.16) reduces to the *compound Poisson distribution* of chapter XII, section 1.

10. PROCESSES INVOLVING ESCAPES

The example of the pure birth process (sections 3 and 4) proves that the transition probabilities $P_{ik}(t)$ determined from the Kolmogorov differential equations do not necessarily add to unity; it can happen that

$$(10.1) \qquad\qquad \sum_k P_{ik}(t) < 1.$$

At the time of its discovery, in 1940, this phenomenon came as a disturbing surprise. A huge literature has been devoted to it and the related fact that the Kolmogorov differential equations do not always determine a unique set of transition probabilities $P_{ik}(t)$. Processes

with these properties are usually called pathological.[21]   With a better
understanding there came the realization that we are really confronted
with a simple and natural analogue to the familiar situation in diffusion
theory.   The occurrence of (10.1), no longer appeared disturbing, but
led to the gratifying discovery that the theory of the Kolmogorov differential equations shares the basic features of diffusion theory. Despite
the completely different appearance of the basic equations and the analytical apparatus involved, we encounter in both theories the same type
of boundary conditions and other similarities; each theory is better
understood in the light of the other, and no sharp boundaries can in
fact be drawn.   In this way the theory of Markov processes has
achieved an unexpected and pleasing internal unity.

Let us reconsider the simple pure birth process of section 3.   The
system spends some time at the initial state E_0, moves from there to
E_1, stays for a while there, moves on to E_2, etc.   The probability $P_0(t)$
that the sojourn time in E_0 exceeds t is obtained from (3.2) as $P_0(t) =$
$= e^{-\lambda_0 t}$.   This sojourn time, $\mathbf{T}_0$, is a random variable, but its range is
the positive t-axis and therefore formally out of bounds for this book.
However, the step from a geometric distribution to an exponential being trivial, we may with impunity trespass a trifle.   An approximation
to $\mathbf{T}_0$ by a discrete random variable with a geometric distribution shows
that it is natural to define the expected sojourn time at E_0 by

$$(10.2) \qquad \mathbf{E}(\mathbf{T}_0) = \int_0^\infty te^{-\lambda_0 t}\, dt = \lambda_0^{-1}.$$

At the moment when the system enters E_j, the state E_j takes over the
role of the initial state and the same conclusion applies to the sojourn
time $\mathbf{T}_j$ at E_j: The *expected sojourn time at E_j is* $\mathbf{E}(\mathbf{T}_j) = \lambda_j^{-1}$.   It follows that $\lambda_0^{-1} + \lambda_1^{-1} + \ldots + \lambda_n^{-1}$ is the expected duration of the
time it takes the system to pass through E_0, E_1, $\ldots$, E_n, and we can
restate the criterion of section 4 as follows:

In order that $\Sigma P_n(t) = 1$ for all t it is necessary and sufficient that

$$(10.3) \qquad \Sigma \mathbf{E}(\mathbf{T}_j) = \Sigma \lambda_j^{-1} = \infty;$$

that is, the total expected duration of the time spent at E_0, E_1, E_2, $\ldots$
must be infinite.   Of course, $L_0(t) = 1 - \Sigma P_n(t)$ is the probability that
the system has gone through *all* states before time t.

---

[21] The counterpart of this section in the first edition was entitled "degenerate
processes."

In this form the theorem is extremely plausible. If the expected sojourn time at E_j is 2^{-j}, the probability that the system has passed through all states within time $1 + 2^{-1} + 2^{-2} + \ldots = 2$ must be positive. Similarly, a particle moving along the x-axis at an exponentially increasing velocity traverses the entire axis in a finite time.

If the birth process serves as a model of population growth, the state E_n stands for an actual population size n and reaching infinity in a finite time expresses a sort of explosion. In this connection (10.1) represents indeed a singular anomaly, but for other applications it may appear as a regular affair. Geometrically speaking, there is no reason to place the states E_0, E_1, E_2, ... at the points 0, 1, 2, ... of the x-axis. Imagine instead E_n placed at the point x_n of the x-axis, where $0 = x_0 < x_1 < x_2 < \ldots$ and $x_n \to 1$. The birth process may then be pictured as the motion of a "particle" starting at $x_0 = 0$, jumping to x_1, jumping after a while to x_2 and so on. In this picture, a particle which has passed through all states has reached the limiting point 1; it is natural that this event can occur in a finite time. Compare the probabilistic movement with a deterministic motion of a particle starting at the origin and having at the place x velocity $f(x)$. Its position $x(t)$ at time t satisfies the differential equation $x'(t) = f(x(t))$ and the time τ when the point 1 is reached is

$$(10.4) \qquad \tau = \int_0^1 \frac{dx}{f(x)} \leq \infty.$$

Whether or not the point 1 is actually reached in a finite time (or only asymptotically approached) depends on the convergence of the integral over the reciprocal velocity. In the probabilistic model the motion goes by jumps, but λ_n^{-1} is the *average* time it takes to come from x_n to x_{n+1}. From this point of view (10.3) and (10.4) appear as twin criteria.

Let us continue with the simple birth process and show how the criterion (10.3) is related to the problem of *uniqueness* of the solutions of the Kolmogorov differential equations.

Considered as transition probabilities the $P_n(t)$ of section 3 should be written as $P_{in}(t)$. The basic differential equations (3.2) apply equally to $P_{ik}(t)$ for an arbitrary (but fixed) i, and we have the *forward equations*

$$(10.5) \quad P'_{i0}(t) = -\lambda_0 P_{i0}(t), \qquad P'_{ik}(t) = -\lambda_k P_{ik}(t) + \lambda_{k-1} P_{i,k-1}(t)$$

where $i \geq 0$ is fixed and $k = 1, 2, \ldots$. In (8.4) and (8.5) we have the corresponding *backward equations*

$$(10.6) \qquad P'_{ik}(t) = -\lambda_i P_{ik}(t) + \lambda_i P_{i+1,k}(t)$$

where $k \geq 0$ is fixed and $i = 0, 1, 2, \ldots$. The initial conditions are the obvious ones:

$$(10.7) \qquad P_{ii}(0) = 1, \qquad P_{ik}(0) = 0, \qquad\qquad k \neq i.$$

A glance at (10.5) shows that $P_{i0}(t)$ is determined uniquely by the first differential equation together with the boundary condition (10.7). We can then calculate $P_{ik}(t)$ successively for $k = 1, 2, \ldots$. How to solve a first order linear equation is well known, and we have the easily verified formula for the *unique solution of the forward equation* (10.5) with the initial condition (10.7):

$$(10.8)$$
$$P_{ik}(t) = 0 \quad \text{for} \quad k < i, \qquad P_{ii}(t) = e^{-\lambda_i t}$$
$$P_{ik}(t) = \lambda_{k-1} \int_0^t e^{-\lambda_k s} P_{i,k-1}(t-s)\, ds, \qquad (k > i).$$

The situation is completely different for the backward equations (10.6). We shall show that when $\Sigma \lambda_n^{-1} < \infty$ there is no uniqueness of the solution.

Lemma. *The unique solution $P_{ik}(t)$ of the forward equations* (10.5) *given by* (10.8) *is automatically a solution of the backward equations* (10.6). *If $\overline{P}_{ik}(t)$ is any non-negative solution of* (10.6)–(10.7) *then*

$$(10.9) \qquad\qquad \overline{P}_{ik}(t) \geq P_{ik}(t).$$

Proof. Consider (10.6) putting a bar over all $P_{ik}(t)$. The ith equation may be solved as a linear differential equation for $\overline{P}_{ik}(t)$ to obtain

$$\overline{P}_{ik}(t) = \lambda_i \int_0^t e^{-\lambda_i s} \overline{P}_{i+1,k}(t-s)\, ds \qquad k \neq i$$
$$(10.10)$$
$$\overline{P}_{kk}(t) = e^{-\lambda_k t} + \lambda_k \int_0^t e^{-\lambda_k s} \cdot \overline{P}_{k+1,k}(t-s)\, ds.$$

[Note that this is not a recursive system and cannot be used to solve the system of equations (10.6).]

Let $P_{ik}(t)$ stand for the solution of the forward equations given by (10.8). For each k and $i > k$ put $\overline{P}_{ik}(t) = P_{ik}(t) = 0$. These functions satisfy (10.10). Furthermore (10.10) defines $\overline{P}_{kk}(t) = e^{-\lambda_k t} = P_{kk}(t)$. Letting in (10.10) successively $i = k-1, k-2, \ldots$, we get $\overline{P}_{ik}(t)$ defined for all i and they are a solution of the backward equations (10.6) with the initial conditions (10.7). Clearly $\overline{P}_{k-1,k}(t) = P_{k-1,k}(t)$. We shall verify by induction that $\overline{P}_{ik}(t) = P_{ik}(t)$. Suppose that this identity holds for all combinations i, k such that $k - i \leq$

$\leq r$ where $r \geq 1$ is an integer (we know this to be true for $r = 1$), and let $k - i = r + 1$. The integral in (10.10) expresses $\bar{P}_{ik}$ in terms of $\bar{P}_{i+1,k} = P_{i+1,k}$ and (10.8) in turn expresses $P_{i+1,k}$ as an integral involving $P_{i+1,k-1} = \bar{P}_{i+1,k-1}$. We get thus $\bar{P}_{ik}$ as a double integral over $\bar{P}_{i+1,k-1}$. Reversing the order of integration we get

$$\bar{P}_{ik}(t) = \lambda_i \lambda_{k-1} \int_0^t e^{-\lambda_k x}\, dx \int_0^{t-x} e^{-\lambda_i s} \bar{P}_{i+1,k-1}(t - x - s)\, ds =$$

(10.11)

$$= \lambda_{k-1} \int_0^t e^{-\lambda_k x} \bar{P}_{i,k-1}(t - x)\, dx.$$

By the induction hypothesis $\bar{P}_{i,k-1}(t) = P_{i,k-1}(t)$, and a comparison of (10.8) and (10.11) proves that $\bar{P}_{ik}(t) = P_{ik}(t)$ as asserted.

It remains to prove that (10.9) holds for an arbitrary solution $\bar{P}_{ik}(t) \geq 0$ of the backward equations (10.6). Now both $\bar{P}_{ik}(t)$ and $P_{ik}(t)$ satisfy (10.10). For $i > k$ we have $\bar{P}_{ik}(t) \geq P_{ik}(t) = 0$. Letting successively $i = k, k-1, k-2, \ldots$ we find that (10.9) holds for all i, k and the lemma is proved.

We can now sum up the situation in the following way. Two contingencies can arise.

(a) *The case* $\Sigma \lambda_n^{-1} = \infty$. We know from section 4 that in this case $\sum_k P_{ik}(t) = 1$. It follows that any other positive solution of the backward equations necessarily adds to more than unity, which is inadmissible. Accordingly, in this case *we have the uniqueness for the admissible solutions both of the forward and the backward equations. The common solution represents the transition probabilities of a birth process such that* $\Sigma P_{ik}(t) = 1$. (It is easy to verify by differentiation that the Chapman-Kolmogorov equation (9.1) holds.)

(b) *The case* $\Sigma \lambda_n^{-1} < \infty$. We know that in this case $\Sigma P_{ik}(t) < 1$. Then

(10.12)
$$L_i(t) = 1 - \sum_{k=0}^{\infty} P_{ik}(t)$$

is the *probability that, starting from* E_i, *"infinity" is reached before time* t. We know that (10.10) is satisfied by $\bar{P}_{ik}(t) = P_{ik}(t)$ and by summation we see that

(10.13)
$$L_i(t) = \lambda_i \int_0^t e^{-\lambda_i s} L_{i+1}(t - s)\, ds$$

or

(10.14)
$$L'_i(t) = -\lambda_i L_i(t) + \lambda_i L_{i+1}(t) \qquad\qquad L_i(0) = 0.$$

It follows that *in this case the infinite system of differential equations* (10.14) *has a non-zero solution* $\{L_i(t)\}$ *with* $L_i(0) = 0$. *With arbitrary* $A_k(t)$ *the matrix*

$$(10.15) \qquad \overline{P}_{ik}(t) = P_{ik}(t) + L_i(t)A_k(t)$$

is a solution of the backward equations (10.6) *satisfying the initial conditions* (10.7).

The question arises whether the $A_k(t)$ can be defined in such a way that the $\overline{P}_{ik}(t)$ become transition probabilities satisfying the Chapman-Kolmogorov equation (9.1). The answer is in the affirmative. We refrain from proving this assertion but shall give a probabilistic interpretation.

The $P_{ik}(t)$ define the so-called *absorbing barrier process: When the system reaches infinity, the process terminates.* Doob [22] was the first to study a *return process* in which, on reaching infinity, the system instantaneously returns to E_0 (or some other prescribed state) and the process starts from scratch. In such a process the system may pass from E_0 to E_5 either in five steps or in infinitely many, having completed one or several complete runs from E_0 to "infinity." The transition probabilities of this process are of the form (10.15). They *satisfy the backward equations* (10.6) *but not the forward equations* (10.5).

This explains why in the derivation of the forward equations we were forced to introduce the strange-looking assumption 3, which was unnecessary for the backward equations: The probabilistically and intuitively simple assumptions 1–2 are compatible with return processes, for which the forward equations (10.5) do not hold. In other words, if we start from the assumptions 1–2 then *Kolmogorov's backward equations are satisfied, but to the forward equations another term must be added.* [23]

The pure birth process is admittedly too trite to be really interesting, but the conditions as described are typical for the most general case of the Kolmogorov equations. Two essentially new phenomena occur, however. First, the birth process involves only one escape route out to "infinity" or, in abstract terminology, a single *boundary* point. By contrast, the general process may involve boundaries of a complicated topological structure. Second, in the birth process the motion is directed toward the boundary because only transitions $E_n \to E_{n+1}$ are

---

[22] J. L. Doob, Markoff chains—denumerable case, *Transactions American Mathematical Society*, vol. 58 (1945), pp. 455–473.

[23] Its form is given in the more recent paper cited in footnote 10, where the various types of processes and the appropriate boundary conditions are studied.

possible. Processes of a different type can be constructed; for example, the direction may be reversed to obtain a process in which only transitions $E_{n+1} \to E_n$ are possible. Such a process can *originate* at the boundary instead of ending there. In the birth and death process, transitions are possible in both directions just as in one-dimensional diffusion. It turns out that in this case there exist processes analogous to the elastic and reflecting barrier processes of diffusion theory, but their description would lead beyond the scope of this book.

11. PROBLEMS FOR SOLUTION

1. In the pure birth process defined by (3.2) let $\lambda_n > 0$ for all n. Prove that for every fixed $n \geq 1$ the function $P_n(t)$ first increases, then decreases to 0. If t_n is the place of the maximum, then $t_1 < t_2 < t_3 < \dots$. *Hint:* Use induction; differentiate (3.2).

2. *Continuation.* If $\Sigma \lambda_n^{-1} = \infty$ show that $t_n \to \infty$. *Hint:* If $t_n \to \tau$, then for fixed $t > \tau$ the sequence $\lambda_n P_n(t)$ increases. Use (4.10).

3. *The Yule process.* Derive the mean and the variance of the distribution defined by (3.4). [Use only the differential equations, not the explicit form (3.5).]

4. *Pure death process.* Find the differential equations of a process of the Yule type with transitions only from E_n to E_{n-1}. Find the distribution $P_n(t)$, its mean, and its variance, assuming that the initial state is i.

5. *Parking lots.* In a parking lot with N spaces the incoming traffic is of the Poisson type with intensity λ, but only as long as empty spaces are available. Find the appropriate differential equations for the probabilities $P_n(t)$ of finding exactly n spaces occupied.

6. In a waiting line *the customer who came last is served first.*[24] Find the appropriate differential equations for the probabilities $P_n(t)$ that exactly n newcomers will be served during the waiting time of a customer picked at random.

7. *The Polya process.*[25] This is a non-stationary pure birth process with λ_n depending on time:

$$(11.1) \qquad \lambda_n(t) = \frac{1 + an}{1 + at}.$$

Show that the solution with initial condition $P_0(0) = \mathbf{1}$ is

$$(11.2) \qquad \begin{aligned} &P_0(t) = (1 + at)^{-1/a} \\ &P_n(t) = t^n (1 + at)^{-n-1/a} \frac{(1 + a)(1 + 2a) \cdots \{1 + (n-1)a\}}{n!}. \end{aligned}$$

---

[24] E. Vaulot, Delais d'attente des appels téléphoniques dans l'ordre inverse de leur arrivée, *Comptes Rendues*, Académie des Sciences, Paris, vol. 238 (1954), pp. 1188–1189.

[25] O. Lundberg, *On random processes and their applications to sickness and accident statistics*, Uppsala, 1940.

Show from the differential equations that the mean and variance are t and $t(1 + at)$, respectively.

8. *Continuation.* The Polya process can be obtained by a passage to the limit from the Polya urn scheme, example V(2.c). If the state of the system is defined as the number of red balls, then the transition probability $E_k \to E_{k+1}$ at the $(n+1)$st drawing is

$$(11.3) \qquad p_{k,n} = \frac{r + kc}{r + b + nc} = \frac{p + k\gamma}{1 + n\gamma}$$

where $p = r/(r + b)$, $\gamma = c/(r + b)$.

As in the passage from Bernoulli trials to the Poisson distribution, let drawings be made at the rate of one in time h and let $h \to 0$, $n \to \infty$ so that $np \to t$, $n\gamma \to at$. Show that in the limit (11.3) leads to (11.1). Show also that the Polya distribution V(2.3) passes into (11.2).

9. *Linear growth.* If in the process defined by (5.7) $\lambda = \mu$, and $P_1(0) = 1$, then

$$(11.4) \qquad P_0(t) = \frac{\lambda t}{1 + \lambda t}, \qquad P_n(t) = \frac{(\lambda t)^{n-1}}{(1 + \lambda t)^{n+1}}.$$

The probability of ultimate extinction is 1.

10. *Continuation.* Assuming a trial solution to (5.7) of the form $P_n(t) = A(t)B^n(t)$, prove that the solution with $P_1(0) = 1$ is

$$(11.5) \quad P_0(t) = \mu B(t), \qquad P_n(t) = \{1 - \lambda B(t)\}\{1 - \mu B(t)\}\{\lambda B(t)\}^{n-1}$$

with

$$(11.6) \qquad B(t) = \frac{1 - e^{(\lambda-\mu)t}}{\mu - \lambda e^{(\lambda-\mu)t}}.$$

11. *Continuation.* The generating function $P(s, t) = \Sigma P_n(t)s^n$ satisfies the partial differential equation

$$(11.7) \qquad \frac{\partial P}{\partial t} = \{\mu - (\lambda + \mu)s + \lambda s^2\} \frac{\partial P}{\partial s}.$$

12. *Continuation.* Let $M_2(t) = \Sigma n^2 P_n(t)$ and $M(t) = \Sigma n P_n(t)$ (as in section 5). Show that

$$(11.8) \qquad M'_2(t) = 2(\lambda - \mu)M_2(t) + (\lambda + \mu)M(t).$$

Deduce that when $\lambda > \mu$ the *variance* of $\{P_n\}$ is given by

$$(11.9) \qquad e^{2(\lambda-\mu)t}\{1 - e^{(\mu-\lambda)t}\}(\lambda + \mu)/(\lambda - \mu).$$

13. For the process (7.2) the generating function $P(s, t) = \Sigma P_n(t)\, s^n$ satisfies the partial differential equation

$$(11.10) \qquad \frac{\partial P}{\partial t} = (1 - s)\left\{-\lambda P + \mu \frac{\partial P}{\partial s}\right\}.$$

Its solution is

$$P = e^{-\lambda(1-s)(1-e^{-\mu t})/\mu}\{1 - (1 - s)e^{-\mu t}\}^i.$$

For $i = 0$ this is a Poisson distribution with parameter $\lambda(1 - e^{-\mu t})/\mu$. *As $t \to \infty$, the distribution $\{P_n(t)\}$ tends to a Poisson distribution with parameter λ/μ.*

14. For the process defined by (7.26) the generating function for the steady state $P(s) = \Sigma p_n s^n$ satisfies the partial differential equation

$$(11.11) \qquad (\mu + \lambda s)\frac{\partial P}{\partial s} = a\lambda P,$$

with the solution $P = \{(\mu + \lambda s)/(\lambda + \mu)\}^a$.

15. In the "simplest trunking problem," example (7.a), let $Q_n(t)$ be the probability that starting from E_n the system will reach E_0 before time t. Prove the validity of the differential equations

$$(11.12) \qquad \begin{aligned} Q'_n(t) &= -(\lambda + n\mu)Q_n(t) + \lambda Q_{n+1}(t) + n\mu Q_{n-1}(t), \qquad (n \geq 2) \\ Q'_1(t) &= -(\lambda + \mu)Q_1(t) + \lambda Q_2(t) + \mu \end{aligned}$$

with the initial conditions $Q_n(0) = 0$.

16. *Continuation.* Consider the same problem for a process defined by an arbitrary system of forward equations. Show that the $Q_n(t)$ satisfy the corresponding *backward equations* (for fixed k) with $P_{0k}(t)$ replaced by 1.

17. Show that the transition probabilities of the pure birth process and those of the birth and death process satisfy the Chapman-Kolmogorov equation (9.1).

18. Let $P_{ik}(t)$ satisfy the Chapman-Kolmogorov equation (9.1). Supposing that $P_{ik}(t) > 0$ and that $S_i(t) = \sum_k P_{ik}(t) \leq 1$, prove that either $S_i(t) = 1$ for all t or $S_i(t) < 1$ for all t.

19. *Ergodic properties.* Consider a stationary process with finitely many states; that is, suppose that the system of differential equations (9.9) is finite and that the coefficients c_j and p_{jk} are constants. Prove that the solutions are linear combinations of exponential terms $e^{\lambda(t-\tau)}$ where the real part of λ is negative unless $\lambda = 0$. Conclude that the asymptotic behavior of the transition probabilities is the same as in the case of *finite* Markov chains except that the periodic case is impossible.

Answers to Problems

CHAPTER I

1. (a) $\frac{3}{5}$; (b) $\frac{3}{5}$; (c) $\frac{3}{10}$.

2. The events S_1, S_2, $S_1 \cup S_2$, and $S_1 S_2$ contain, respectively, 12, 12, 18, and 6 points.

4. The space contains the two points HH and TT with probability $\frac{1}{4}$; the two points HTT and THH with probability $\frac{1}{8}$; and generally two points with probability 2^{-n} when $n \geq 2$. These probabilities add to 1, so that there is no necessity to consider the possibility of an unending sequence of tosses. The required probabilities are $\frac{15}{16}$ and $\frac{2}{3}$, respectively.

9. $\mathbf{P}\{AB\} = \frac{1}{6}$, $\mathbf{P}\{A \cup B\} = \frac{23}{36}$, $\mathbf{P}\{AB'\} = \frac{1}{3}$.

12. $x = 0$ in the events (a), (b), and (g).
$x = 1$ in the events (e) and (f).
$x = 2$ in the event (d).
$x = 4$ in the event (c).

15. (a) A; (b) AB; (c) $B \cup (AC)$.

16. Correct are (c), (d), (e), (f), (h), (i), (k), (l). The statement (a) is meaningless unless $C \subset B$. It is in general false even in this case, but is correct in the special case $C \subset B$, $AC = 0$. The statement (b) is correct if $C \supset AB$. The statement (g) should read $(A \cup B) - A = A'B$. Finally (k) is the correct version of (j).

17. (a) $AB'C'$; (b) ABC'; (c) ABC; (d) $A \cup B \cup C$;
(e) $AB \cup AC \cup BC$; (f) $AB'C' \cup A'BC' \cup A'B'C$;
(g) $ABC' \cup AB'C \cup A'BC = (AB \cup AC \cup BC) - ABC$;
(h) $A'B'C'$; (i) $(ABC)'$.

18. $A \cup B \cup C = A \cup (B - AB) \cup \{C - C(A \cup B)\} =$
$$= A \cup BA' \cup CA'B'.$$

CHAPTER II

1. (a) 26^3; (b) $26^2 + 26^3 = 18{,}252$; (c) $26^2 + 26^3 + 26^4$. In a city with 20,000 inhabitants either some people have the same set of initials or at least 1748 people have more than three initials.

2. $64 \cdot 14 = 896$. For a chess board with n^2 fields the formula is $n^2(2n - 2)$.

3. $2(2^{10} - 1) = 2046$.

4. $\binom{n}{2} + n = \frac{n(n + 1)}{2}$.   **5.** (a) $\frac{1}{n}$; (b) $\frac{1}{n(n - 1)}$.

6. (a) $p_1 = 0.01$, $p_2 = 0.27$, $p_3 = 0.72$.

(b) $p_1 = 0.001$, $p_2 = 0.063$, $p_3 = 0.432$, $p_4 = 0.504$.

7. $p_r = (10)_r 10^{-r}$. For example, $p_3 = 0.72$, $p_{10} = 0.00036288$. Stirling's formula gives $p_{10} = 0.0003598 \ldots$.

8. (a) $(9/10)^k$; (b) $(9/10)^k$; (c) $(8/10)^k$; (d) $2(9/10)^k - (8/10)^k$; (e) AB and $A \cup B$.

9. $\binom{n}{2} n! n^{-n}$.   **10.** $9 \div \binom{12}{8} = \frac{1}{55}$.

11. The probability of exactly r trials is $(n-1)_{r-1} \div (n)_r = n^{-1}$.

12. (a) $1/1 \cdot 3 \cdot 5 \cdots (2n-1) = 2^n n!/(2n)!$;   (b) $(n!)/1 \cdot 3 \cdots (2n-1) =$

$= 2^n / \binom{2n}{n}$.

13. On the assumption of randomness the probability that all of twelve tickets come either on Tuesdays or Thursdays is $(\frac{2}{7})^{12} = 0.0000003 \ldots$

There are only $\binom{7}{2} = 21$ pairs of days, so that the probability remains extremely small even for any two days. Hence it is reasonable to assume that the police have a system.

14. Assuming randomness, the probability of the event is $(\frac{6}{7})^{12} = \frac{1}{6}$ appr. No safe conclusion is possible.

15. $(90)_{10} \div (100)_{10} = 0.330476 \ldots$.

16. $25!(5!)^{-5} 5^{-25} = 0.00209 \ldots$.

17. $\dfrac{2(n-2)_r(n-r-1)!}{n!} = \dfrac{2(n-r-1)}{n(n-1)}$.

18. (a) $\frac{1}{216}$; (b) $\frac{83}{3888}$.

19. The probabilities are $1 - (\frac{5}{6})^4 = 0.517747 \ldots$ and $1 - (\frac{35}{36})^{24} =$ $= 0.491404 \ldots$.

20. (a) $(n-N)_r \div (n)_r$. (b) $(1 - N/n)^r$. For $r = N = 3$ the probabilities are (a) $0.911812 \ldots$; (b) $0.912673 \ldots$. For $r = N = 10$ they are (a) 0.330476; (b) $0.348678 \ldots$.

21. (a) $(1 - N/n)^{r-1}$.   (b) $(n)_{Nr} \div ((n)_N)^r$.

22. $(1 - 2/n)^{2^r - 2}$; for the median $2^{r+1} = 0.7n$, approximately.

23. On the assumption of randomness, the probabilities that three or four breakages are caused (a) by one girl, (b) by the youngest girl are, respectively, $\frac{13}{64} \approx 0.2$ and $\frac{13}{256} \approx 0.05$.

24. (a) $12!/12^{12} = 0.000054$.   (b) $\binom{12}{2}(2^6 - 2)12^{-6} = 0.00137 \ldots$.

25. $\dfrac{30!}{2^6 6^6} \binom{12}{6} 12^{-30} \approx 0.00035 \ldots$.

26. (a) $\binom{n}{2r} 2^{2r} \div \binom{2n}{2r}$; (b) $n \binom{n-1}{2r-2} 2^{2r-2} \div \binom{2n}{2r}$;

(c) $\binom{n}{2} \binom{n-2}{2r-4} 2^{2r-4} \div \binom{2n}{2r}$.

27. $\binom{N-3}{r-1} \div \binom{N-1}{r-1}.$

28. $p = \binom{2N}{N}^2 \div \binom{4N}{2N} \approx \{2/(N\pi)\}^{\frac{1}{2}}.$

29. $p = \dfrac{\binom{4}{k}\binom{48}{13-k}\binom{39}{13}\binom{26}{13}}{\binom{52}{13}\binom{39}{13}\binom{26}{13}} = \dfrac{\binom{4}{k}\binom{48}{13-k}}{\binom{52}{13}}.$

30. Cf. problem 29. The probability is

$$\binom{13}{m}\binom{39}{13-m}\binom{13-m}{n}\binom{26+m}{13-n} \div \binom{52}{13}\binom{39}{13}.$$

31. $\binom{4}{k}\binom{48}{26-k} \div \binom{52}{26}.$

32. $\dfrac{\binom{13}{a}\binom{39}{13-a}\binom{13-a}{b}\binom{26+a}{13-b}\binom{13-a-b}{c}\binom{13+a+b}{13-c}}{\binom{52}{13}\binom{39}{13}\binom{26}{13}}.$

33. (a) $24p(5, 4, 3, 1)$; (b) $4p(4, 4, 4, 1)$; (c) $12p(4, 4, 3, 2)$.

34. $\dfrac{\binom{13}{a}\binom{13}{b}\binom{13}{c}\binom{13}{d}}{\binom{52}{13}}.$ (Cf. problem 33 for the probability that the

hand contains a cards of some suit, b of another, etc.)

35. $p_0(r) = (52 - r)_4 \div (52)_4$; $p_1(r) = 4r(52 - r)_3 \div (52)_4$; $p_2(r) = 6r(r - 1)(52 - r)_2 \div (52)_4$; $p_3(r) = 4r(r - 1)(r - 2)(52 - r) \div (52)_4$; $p_4(r) = (r)_4 \div (52)_4$.

36. The probabilities that the waiting times for the first, ..., fourth ace exceed r are $w_1(r) = p_0(r)$; $w_2(r) = p_0(r) + p_1(r)$; $w_3(r) = p_0(r) + p_1(r) + p_2(r)$; $w_4(r) = 1 - p_4(r)$. Next $f_i(r) = w_i(r) - w_i(r + 1)$. The medians are 8, 20, 32, 44.

37. (a) $\binom{4}{k}\binom{4-k}{k}\binom{48}{r-k}\binom{48-r+k}{r-k} \div \binom{52}{r}\binom{52-r}{r},$

with $k \le 2$; (b) $\left\{\binom{4}{k}\binom{48}{r-k} \div \binom{52}{r}\right\}^2$, with $k \le 4$.

39. $\binom{r_1 + n - 1}{r_1}\binom{r_2 + n - 1}{r_2}.$ **40.** $\binom{r_1 + 5}{5}(r_2 + 1).$

41. $\dfrac{(r_1 + r_2 + r_3)!}{r_1!r_2!r_3!}.$ **42.** $(49)_4 \div (52)_4.$

43. $\mathbf{P}\{(7)\}$ $\qquad = 10 \cdot 10^{-7}$ $\qquad\qquad = 0.000\,001.$

$\mathbf{P}\{(6, 1)\}$ $\qquad = \dfrac{10!}{8!1!1!} \cdot \dfrac{7!}{1!6!} \cdot 10^{-7}$ $\qquad = .000\,063.$

$\mathbf{P}\{(5, 2)\}$ $\qquad = \dfrac{10!}{8!1!1!} \cdot \dfrac{7!}{2!5!} \cdot 10^{-7}$ $\qquad = .000\,189.$

$\mathbf{P}\{(5, 1, 1)\}$ $\qquad = \dfrac{10!}{7!2!1!} \cdot \dfrac{7!}{1!1!5!} \cdot 10^{-7}$ $\qquad = .001\,512.$

$\mathbf{P}\{(4, 3)\}$ $\qquad = \dfrac{10!}{8!1!1!} \cdot \dfrac{7!}{3!4!} \cdot 10^{-7}$ $\qquad = .000\,315.$

$\mathbf{P}\{(4, 2, 1)\}$ $\qquad = \dfrac{10!}{7!1!1!1!} \cdot \dfrac{7!}{1!2!4!} \cdot 10^{-7}$ $\qquad = .007\,560.$

$\mathbf{P}\{(4, 1, 1, 1)\}$ $\qquad = \dfrac{10!}{6!3!1!} \cdot \dfrac{7!}{1!1!1!4!} \cdot 10^{-7}$ $\qquad = .017\,640.$

$\mathbf{P}\{(3, 3, 1)\}$ $\qquad = \dfrac{10!}{7!2!1!} \cdot \dfrac{7!}{1!3!3!} \cdot 10^{-7}$ $\qquad = .005\,040.$

$\mathbf{P}\{(3, 2, 2)\}$ $\qquad = \dfrac{10!}{7!2!1!} \cdot \dfrac{7!}{2!2!3!} \cdot 10^{-7}$ $\qquad = .007\,560.$

$\mathbf{P}\{(3, 2, 1, 1)\}$ $\qquad = \dfrac{10!}{6!2!1!1!} \cdot \dfrac{7!}{1!1!2!3!} \cdot 10^{-7}$ $\qquad = .105\,840.$

$\mathbf{P}\{(3, 1, 1, 1, 1)\}$ $\qquad = \dfrac{10!}{5!4!1!} \cdot \dfrac{7!}{1!1!1!1!3!} \cdot 10^{-7}$ $\qquad = .105\,840.$

$\mathbf{P}\{(2, 2, 2, 1)\}$ $\qquad = \dfrac{10!}{6!3!1!} \cdot \dfrac{7!}{1!2!2!2!} \cdot 10^{-7}$ $\qquad = .052\,920.$

$\mathbf{P}\{(2, 2, 1, 1, 1)\}$ $\qquad = \dfrac{10!}{5!3!2!} \cdot \dfrac{7!}{1!1!1!2!2!} \cdot 10^{-7}$ $\qquad = .317\,520.$

$\mathbf{P}\{(2, 1, 1, 1, 1, 1)\}$ $\qquad = \dfrac{10!}{4!5!1!} \cdot \dfrac{7!}{1!1!1!1!1!2!} \cdot 10^{-7} = .317\,520.$

$\mathbf{P}\{(1, 1, 1, 1, 1, 1, 1)\} = \dfrac{10!}{3!7!} \cdot 7! \cdot 10^{-7}$ $\qquad = .060\,480.$

44. Letting S, D, T, Q stand for simple, double, triple, and quadruple, respectively, we have

$\mathbf{P}\{22S\}$ $\qquad = \dfrac{365!}{22!343!} \cdot 365^{-22}$ $\qquad = 0.524\,30.$

$\mathbf{P}\{20S + 1D\}$ $\qquad = \dfrac{365!}{20!1!344!} \cdot \dfrac{22!}{20!2!} \cdot 365^{-22}$ $\qquad = .352\,08.$

$\mathbf{P}\{18S + 2D\}$ $\qquad = \dfrac{365!}{18!2!345!} \cdot \dfrac{22!}{18!2!2!} \cdot 365^{-22}$ $\qquad = .096\,95.$

$\mathbf{P}\{16S + 3D\}$ $\qquad = \dfrac{365!}{16!3!346!} \cdot \dfrac{22!}{16!2!2!2!} \cdot 365^{-22}$ $\qquad = .014\,29.$

$$\mathbf{P}\{19S + 1T\} = \frac{365!}{19!1!345!} \cdot \frac{22!}{19!3!} \cdot 365^{-22} = .006\ 80.$$

$$\mathbf{P}\{17S + 1D + 1T\} = \frac{365!}{17!1!1!346!} \cdot \frac{22!}{17!2!3!} \cdot 365^{-22} = .003\ 36.$$

$$\mathbf{P}\{14S + 4D\} = \frac{365!}{14!4!347!} \cdot \frac{22!}{14!2!2!2!2!} \cdot 365^{-22} = .001\ 24.$$

$$\mathbf{P}\{15S + 2D + 1T\} = \frac{365!}{15!2!1!347!} \cdot \frac{22!}{15!2!2!3!} \cdot 365^{-22} = .000\ 66.$$

$$\mathbf{P}\{18S + 1Q\} = \frac{365!}{18!1!346!} \cdot \frac{22!}{18!4!} \cdot 365^{-22} = .000\ 09.$$

45. Let $q = \binom{52}{5} = 2{,}598{,}960.$ The probabilities are:

(a) $4/q$; (b) $13 \cdot 12 \cdot 4 \cdot q^{-1} = \frac{1}{4165}$; (c) $13 \cdot 12 \cdot 4 \cdot 6 \cdot q^{-1} = \frac{6}{4165}$;

(d) $9 \cdot 4^5 \cdot q^{-1} = \frac{768}{216580}$; (e) $13 \cdot \binom{12}{2} 4 \cdot 4^2 \cdot q^{-1} = \frac{88}{4165}$;

(f) $\binom{13}{2} \cdot 11 \cdot 6 \cdot 6 \cdot 4 \cdot q^{-1} = \frac{198}{4165}$; (g) $13 \cdot \binom{12}{3} \cdot 6 \cdot 4^3 \cdot q^{-1} = \frac{1760}{4165}.$

CHAPTER IV

1. 99/323.   **2.** 0.21 ....   **3.** 1/4.   **4.** $7/2^6$.
5. 1/81 and $31/6^6$.
6. If A_k is the event that (k, k) does not appear, then from (1.5)

$$1 - p_r = 6 \left(\frac{35}{36}\right)^r - \binom{6}{2}\left(\frac{34}{36}\right)^r + \binom{6}{3}\left(\frac{33}{36}\right)^r - \binom{6}{4}\left(\frac{32}{36}\right)^r + 6\left(\frac{31}{36}\right)^r - \left(\frac{30}{36}\right)^r.$$

7. Put $p^{-1} = \binom{52}{13}$.   Then $S_1 = 13\binom{48}{9}p$; $S_2 = \binom{13}{2}\binom{44}{5}p$;

$S_3 = 40 \cdot \binom{13}{3} \cdot p$. Numerically, $P_{[0]} = 0.9658$; $P_{[1]} = 0.0341$; $P_{[2]} = 0.0001$,

approximately.

8. $u_r = \sum_{k=0}^{N} (-1)^k \binom{N}{k} \left(1 - \frac{k}{n}\right)^r.$

9. $p_r = \sum_{k=0}^{N} (-1)^k \binom{N}{k} \frac{(n-k)_r}{(n)_r}.$ See II(12.18) for a proof that the two

formulas agree.
10. The general term is $a_{1k_1}a_{2k_2} \ldots a_{Nk_N}$, where $(k_1, k_2, \ldots, k_N)$ is a permutation of $(1, 2, \ldots, N)$. For a diagonal element $k_\nu = \nu$.

12. $u_r = \sum_{k=0}^{n} (-1)^k \binom{n}{k} \frac{(ns - ks)_r}{(ns)_r}.$

14. Note that, by definition, $u_r = 0$ for $r < n$ and $u_n = n!s^n/(ns)_n$.

15. $u_r - u_{r-1} = \sum\limits_{k=1}^{n} (-1)^{k-1} \binom{n-1}{k-1} \dfrac{(ns - ks)_{r-1}}{(ns - 1)_{r-1}} \rightarrow$

$$\rightarrow \sum_{k=0}^{n-1} (-1)^k \binom{n-1}{k} \left(1 - \frac{k+1}{n}\right)^{r-1}.$$

16. $\binom{N}{2}^{-r} \binom{N}{m} \sum\limits_{k=2}^{m} (-1)^{m-k} \binom{m}{k} \binom{k}{2}^r.$

17. Use $\binom{52}{5} S_k = \binom{4}{k} \binom{52 - 13k}{5}.$

$P_{[0]} = 0.264$, $P_{[1]} = 0.588$, $P_{[2]} = 0.146$, $P_{[3]} = 0.002$, approximately.

18. Use $\binom{52}{13} S_k = \binom{4}{k} \binom{52 - 2k}{13 - 2k}.$

$$P_{[0]} = 0.780217, \quad P_{[1]} = 0.204606, \quad P_{[2]} = 0.014845,$$

$$P_{[3]} = 0.000330, \quad P_{[4]} = 0.000002, \text{ approximately.}$$

19. $m!N!u_m = \sum\limits_{k=0}^{N-m} (-1)^k (N - m - k)!/k!.$

20. Cf. the following formula with $r = 2$.

21. $(rN)!x = \binom{N}{2} r^2(rN - 2)! - \binom{N}{3} r^3(rN - 3)! + - \ldots +$

$$+ (-1)^N r^N (rN - N)!.$$

24. $P_{[m]} = \dfrac{\binom{n}{m}}{\binom{n+r-1}{r}} \sum\limits_{k=0}^{n-m} (-1)^k \binom{n-m}{k} \binom{n-m+r-1-k}{r}.$

25. Use II(12.16) and (12.4).

26. Put $U_N = A_1 \cup \ldots \cup A_N$ and note that $U_{N+1} = U_N \cup A_{N+1}$ and $U_N A_{N+1} = (A_1 A_{N+1}) \cup \ldots \cup (A_N A_{N+1})$.

CHAPTER V

1. $1 - \dfrac{(5)_3}{(6)_3} = \dfrac{1}{2}.$ **2.** $p = 1 - \dfrac{10 \cdot 5^9}{6^{10} - 5^{10}} = 0.61 \ldots.$

3. (a) $\binom{35}{13} \div \binom{39}{13} = 0.182 \ldots.$ The probability of exactly one ace is

$4 \cdot \binom{35}{12} \div \binom{39}{13} = 0.411 \ldots.$ (b) $1 - 0.182 - 0.411 = 0.407$, approximately.

4. (a) $2 \cdot \dfrac{\binom{23}{10}}{\binom{26}{13}} = \dfrac{11}{50};$ (b) $2 \cdot \dfrac{\binom{23}{12}}{\binom{26}{13}} = \dfrac{13}{50}.$

6. $\frac{125}{345}$; $\frac{140}{345}$; $\frac{80}{345}$.   **7.** $\frac{20}{21}$.   **9.** $(\frac{5}{6})^2$.   **10.** $1 - (\frac{5}{6})^2$.

12. $\dfrac{p}{2-p}$.   **13.** (b) $\frac{3}{5}$; (c) $2^n \cdot (1 + 2^n)^{-1}$.

14. (d) Put $a_n = x_n - \frac{4}{7}$, $b_n = y_n - \frac{1}{7}$, $c_n = z_n - \frac{2}{7}$. Then $|a_n| + |b_n| + |c_n| = \frac{1}{2}\{|a_{n+1}| + |b_{n+1}| + |c_{n+1}|\}$.   Hence $|a_n| + |b_n| + |c_n|$ increases geometrically.

15. $p = (1 - p_1)(1 - p_2) \cdots (1 - p_n)$.

16. Use $1 - x < e^{-x}$ for $0 < x < 1$ or Taylor's series for $\log(1 - x)$; cf. II(8.12).

18. $\dfrac{b+c}{b+c+r}$.

19. If the statement is true for the nth drawing regardless of b, r, and c, then the probability of black at the $(n+1)$st trial is

$$\frac{b}{b+r} \cdot \frac{b+c}{b+r+c} + \frac{r}{b+r} \cdot \frac{b}{b+r+c} = \frac{b}{b+r}.$$

20. The preceding problem states that the assertion is true for $m = 1$ and all n. For induction, consider the two possibilities at the first trial.

23. Use II(12.9).

26. From (5.2) $2v = 2p(1 - p) \le \frac{1}{2}$.

28. (a) u^2; (b) $u^2 + uv + v^2/4$; (c) $u^2 + (25uv + 9v^2 + vw + 2uw)/16$.

33. $p_{11} = p_{32} = 2p_{21} = p$, $p_{12} = p_{33} = 2p_{23} = q$, $p_{13} = p_{31} = 0$, $p_{22} = \frac{1}{2}$.

CHAPTER VI

1. $\frac{5}{16}$.   **2.** The probability is $0.02804 \ldots$.   **3.** $(0.9)^x \le 0.1$, $x \ge 22$.

4. $q^x \le \frac{1}{2}$ and $(1 - 4p)^x \le \frac{1}{2}$ with $p = \dbinom{48}{9} \div \dbinom{52}{13}$.   Hence $x \ge 263$ and $x \ge 66$, respectively.

5. $1 - (0.8)^{10} - 2(0.8)^9 = 0.6242 \ldots$.

6. $\{1 - (0.8)^{10} - 2(0.8)^9\}/\{1 - (0.8)^{10}\} = 0.6993 \ldots$.

7. $\dbinom{26}{2}\dbinom{26}{11} \div \dbinom{52}{13} = 0.003954 \ldots$, and $\dbinom{13}{2}\dfrac{1}{2^{13}} = 0.00952 \ldots$.

8. $\dbinom{12}{2}\{6^{-6} - 2 \cdot 12^{-6}\}$.

9. True values: $0.6651 \ldots$, $0.40187 \ldots$, and $0.2009 \ldots$; Poisson approximations: $1 - e^{-1} = 0.6321 \ldots$, $0.3679 \ldots$, and $0.1839 \ldots$.

10. $e^{-2} \sum\limits_{4}^{\infty} 2^k/k! = 0.143 \ldots$.   **11.** $e^{-1} \sum\limits_{3}^{\infty} 1/k! = 0.080 \ldots$.

12. $e^{-x/100} \le 0.05$ or $x \ge 300$.

13. $e^{-1} = 0.3679 \ldots$, $1 - 2 \cdot e^{-1} = 0.264 \ldots$.

14. $e^{-x} \le 0.01$, $x \ge 5$.   **15.** $1/p = 649{,}740$.

16. $1 - p^n$ where $p = p(0; \lambda) + \ldots + p(k; \lambda)$.

18. q^3 for $k = 0$; pq^3 for $k = 1, 2, 3$; and $pq^3 - pq^6$ for $k = 4$.

19. $\displaystyle\sum_{k=0}^{n} \binom{n}{k}^2 2^{-2n} = \binom{2n}{n} 2^{-2n} \approx \left(\frac{1}{\pi n}\right)^{\frac{1}{2}}$ for large n.

20. $\displaystyle\sum_{k=a}^{a+b-1} \binom{a+b-1}{k} p^k q^{a+b-1-k}$. This can be written in the alternative

form $p^a \displaystyle\sum_{k=0}^{b-1} \binom{a+k-1}{k} q^k$, where the kth term equals the probability that

the ath success occurs directly after $k \leq b - 1$ failures.

21. $x_r = \dbinom{2N - 1 - r}{N - 1} \cdot 2^{-2N + r + 1}$.

22. (a) $x = \displaystyle\sum_{r=1}^{N} x_r 2^{-r-1} = 2^{-2N} \sum_{r=1}^{N} \binom{2N - 1 - r}{N - 1}$;   (b) Use II(12.6).

23. $k_i \approx np_i$, $k_{12} \approx np_{12}$ whence $n \approx k_1 k_2 / k_{12}$.

24. $\dbinom{n}{n_1} \cdot \dbinom{n - s_1}{n_2} \cdots \dbinom{n - s_{r-1}}{n_r} \cdot q^{s_r} p^{(rn - s_1 - \cdots - s_r)}$

where $s_i = n_1 + \ldots + n_i$.

25. $p = p_1 q_2 (p_1 q_2 + p_2 q_1)^{-1}$.

31. By the Taylor expansion for the logarithm

$$b(0; n, p) = q^n = (1 - \lambda/n)^n < e^{-\lambda} = p(0; \lambda).$$

The terms of each distribution add to unity, and therefore it is impossible that *all* terms of one distribution should be greater than the corresponding terms of the other.

32. There are only finitely many terms of the Poisson distribution which are greater than ϵ, and the remaining ones dominate the corresponding terms of the binomial distribution.

CHAPTER VII

1. Proceed as in section 1.   **2.** Use (1.7).   **3.** $\Phi(-\frac{32}{30}) = 0.143 \ldots$.
4. 0.99.   **5.** 500.   **6.** 66,400.

7. Most certainly. The inequalities of chapter VI suffice to show that an excess of more than eight standard deviations is exceedingly improbable.

8. $(2\pi n)^{-1}\{p_1 p_2 (1 - p_1 - p_2)\}^{-\frac{1}{2}}$.

CHAPTER VIII

1. $\beta = 21$.

2. $x = pu + qv + rw$, where u, v, w are solutions of

$$u = p^{\alpha-1} + (qv + rw)\frac{1 - p^{\alpha-1}}{1 - p}, \qquad v = (pu + rw)\frac{1 - q^{\beta-1}}{1 - q}$$

$$w = pu + qv + rw = x.$$

3. $u = p^{\alpha-1} + (qv + rw)\dfrac{1 - p^{\alpha-1}}{1 - p}$

$$v = (pu + rw)\dfrac{1 - q^{\beta-1}}{1 - q} \qquad w = (pu + qv)\dfrac{1 - r^{\gamma-1}}{1 - r}.$$

4. Note that $\mathbf{P}\{A_n\} < (2p)^n$, but

$$\mathbf{P}\{A_n\} > 1 - (1 - p^n)^{2^n/2n} > 1 - e^{-(2p)^n/2n}.$$

If $p = \frac{1}{2}$, the last quantity is $\sim \frac{1}{2}n$; if $p > 1$, then $\mathbf{P}\{A_n\}$ does not even tend to zero.

CHAPTER IX

1. The possible combinations are $(0, 0)$, $(0, 1)$, $(0, 2)$, $(1, 0)$, $(1, 1)$, $(2, 0)$, $(2, 1)$, $(3, 0)$. Their probabilities are 0.047539, 0.108883, 0.017850, 0.156364, 0.214197, 0.321295, 0.026775, 0.107098.

2. (a) The joint distribution takes on the form of a six-by-six matrix. The main diagonal contains the elements $q, 2q, \ldots, 6q$ where $q = \frac{1}{36}$. On one side of the main diagonal all elements are 0, on the other q. (b) $\mathbf{E}(\mathbf{X}) = \frac{7}{2}$, $\mathrm{Var}(\mathbf{X}) = \frac{35}{12}$, $\mathbf{E}(\mathbf{Y}) = \frac{161}{36}$, $\mathrm{Var}(\mathbf{Y}) = \frac{2555}{1296}$, $\mathrm{Cov}(\mathbf{X}, \mathbf{Y}) = \frac{105}{72}$.

3. In the joint distribution of $\mathbf{X}$, $\mathbf{Y}$ the rows are 32^{-1} times $(1, 0, 0, 0, 0, 0)$, $(0, 5, 4, 3, 2, 1)$, $(0, 0, 6, 6, 3, 0)$, $(0, 0, 0, 1, 0, 0)$; of $\mathbf{X}$, $\mathbf{Z}$: $(1, 0, 0, 0, 0, 0)$, $(0, 5, 6, 1, 0, 0)$, $(0, 0, 4, 6, 1, 0)$, $(0, 0, 0, 3, 2, 0)$, $(0, 0, 0, 0, 2, 0)$, $(0, 0, 0, 0, 0, 1)$; of $\mathbf{Y}$, $\mathbf{Z}$: $(1, 0, 0, 0)$, $(0, 5, 6, 1)$, $(0, 4, 7, 0)$, $(0, 3, 2, 0)$, $(0, 2, 0, 0)$, $(0, 1, 0, 0)$. Distribution of $\mathbf{X} + \mathbf{Y}$: $(1, 0, 5, 4, 9, 8, 5)$ all divided by 32, and the values of $\mathbf{X} + \mathbf{Y}$ ranging from 0 to 6; of $\mathbf{XY}$: $(1, 5, 4, 3, 8, 1, 6, 0, 3, 1)$ all divided by 32, the values ranging from 0 to 9. $\mathbf{E}(\mathbf{X}) = \frac{5}{2}$, $\mathbf{E}(\mathbf{Y}) = \frac{3}{2}$, $\mathbf{E}(\mathbf{Z}) = \frac{31}{16}$, $\mathrm{Var}(\mathbf{X}) = \frac{5}{4}$, $\mathrm{Var}(\mathbf{Y}) = \frac{3}{8}$, $\mathrm{Var}(\mathbf{Z}) = \frac{303}{256}$.

4. $\mathbf{P}\{\mathbf{Z} = i, \mathbf{X} = j\} = q^{i+j}p^2$ if $i > j$ and $= (1 - q^{i+1})q^i p$ if $i = j$; no other values are possible. $\mathbf{P}\{\mathbf{Z} = i\} = 2q^i p - q^{2i}p - q^{2i+1}p$.

8. The distribution of $\mathbf{V}_n$ is given by (3.5), that of $\mathbf{U}_n$ follows by symmetry.

9. $\mathbf{P}\{\mathbf{X} \le r, \mathbf{Y} \ge s\} = \left(\dfrac{r - s + 1}{N}\right)^n \qquad$ for $r \ge s$;

$$\mathbf{P}\{\mathbf{X} = r, \mathbf{Y} = s\} = N^{-n}\{(r - s + 1)^n - 2(r - s)^n + (r - s - 1)^n\}.$$

if $r > s$, and $= N^{-n}$ if $r = s$.

10. $x = \dfrac{r^{n-2} - (r - 1)^{n-2}}{r^n - (r - 1)^n} \qquad$ if $j < r$ and $k < r$.

$x = \dfrac{r^{n-2}}{r^n - (r - 1)^n} \qquad$ if $j \le r$ and $k = r$, or $j = r$ and $k \le r$.

$x = 0 \qquad$ if $j > r$ or $k > r$.

11. $\sigma^2 \approx \dfrac{nN^2}{(n + 1)^2(n + 2)}.$

12. $\mathbf{P}\{\mathbf{N} = n, \mathbf{K} = k\} = \dbinom{n}{k} p^{n-k}(qq')^k \cdot qp'.$

$\mathbf{P}\{\mathbf{N} = n\} = (1 - qp')^n qp'.$

$\mathbf{P}\{\mathbf{K} = k\} = (qq')^k qp' \Sigma \dbinom{-k-1}{\nu}(-p)^\nu = p'q'^k.$

13. $E\left(\dfrac{K}{N+1}\right) = \Sigma k p_{k,n}/(n+1) = q^z p'q' \displaystyle\sum_{n=1}^{\infty}\left(1 - \dfrac{1}{n+1}\right)(p+qq')^{n-1}$

$$= \dfrac{qq'}{1-qp'} - \dfrac{q^2 p'q'}{(1-qp')^2}\log\dfrac{1}{qp'}.$$

$$E(K) = \dfrac{q'}{p'}; \quad E(N) = \dfrac{(1-qp')}{qp'}; \quad \text{Cov}(K, N) = \dfrac{q'}{qp'^2}.$$

$$\rho(K,N) = \left\{\dfrac{q'}{(1-qp')}\right\}^{\frac{1}{2}}.$$

14. $p_k = p^k q + q^k p; \quad E(X) = pq^{-1} + qp^{-1}; \quad \text{Var}(X) = pq^{-2} + qp^{-2} - 2.$
15. $q_k = p^2 q^{k-1} + q^2 p^{k-1}; \quad P\{X = m, Y = n\} = p^{m+1}q^n + q^{m+1}p^n$ with $m, n \geq 1; \quad E(Y) = 2; \quad \sigma^2 = 2(pq^{-1} + qp^{-1} - 1).$

17. $\dbinom{n}{k} 364^{n-k}365^{1-n}.$

18. (a) $365\{1 - 364^n \cdot 365^{-n} - n364^{n-1} \cdot 365^{-n}\}$; (b) $n \geq 28.$
19. (a) $\mu = n, \sigma^2 = (n-1)n$; (b) $\mu = (n+1)/2, \sigma^2 = (n^2-1)/12.$
20. $E(X) = np_1; \quad \text{Var}(X) = np_1(1 - p_1); \quad \text{Cov}(X, Y) = -np_1 p_2.$
21. $-n/36.$ This is a special case of 20.

25. $E(Y_r) = \displaystyle\sum_{k=1}^{r}\dfrac{N}{r-k+1}; \quad \text{Var}(Y_r) = \displaystyle\sum_{k=1}^{r}\dfrac{N(N-r+k-1)}{(r-k+1)^2}.$

26. (a) $1 - q^k$; (b) $E(X) = N\left\{1 - q^k + \dfrac{1}{k}\right\}$; (c) $\dfrac{dE(X)}{dk} = 0.$

27. $\Sigma(1 - p_j)^n.$ Put $X_j = 1$ or 0 according as the jth class is not or is pre-represented.

28. $E(X) = \dfrac{r_1(r_2+1)}{r_1+r_2}; \quad \text{Var}(X) = \dfrac{r_1 r_2(r_1-1)(r_2+1)}{(r_1+r_2-1)(r_1+r_2)^2}.$

30. $E(S_n) = \dfrac{nb}{b+r}; \quad \text{Var}(S_n) = \dfrac{nbr\{b+r+nc\}}{(b+r)^2(b+r+c)}.$

33. $E\left(\dfrac{r}{X}\right) = r\displaystyle\sum_{k=r}^{\infty} k^{-1}\dbinom{k-1}{r-1} p^r q^{k-r}$

$$= \displaystyle\sum_{k=1}^{r-1}(-1)^{k-1}\dfrac{r}{r-k}\left(\dfrac{p}{q}\right)^k + \left(\dfrac{-p}{q}\right)^r r\log p.$$

To derive the last formula from the first, put $f(q) = r\Sigma k^{-1}\dbinom{k-1}{r-1}q^k.$
Using II(12.4), we find that $f'(q) = rq^{r-1}(1-q)^{-r}.$ The assertion now follows by repeated integrations by part.

CHAPTER XI

1. $sP(s)$ and $P(s^2).$
2. (a) $(1-s)^{-1}P(s)$; (b) $(1-s)^{-1}sP(s)$; (c) $\{1 - sP(s)\}/(1-s)$; (d) $p_0 s^{-1} + \{1 - s^{-1}P(s)\}/(1-s)$; (e) $\frac{1}{2}\{P(s^{\frac{1}{2}}) + P(-s^{\frac{1}{2}})\}.$
3. $U(s) = pqs^2/(1-ps)(1-qs).$ Mean $= 1/pq,$ Var $= (1-3pq)/p^2 q^2.$

6. A zero is the first, second, third, ... zero and therefore $U(s) = \Sigma F^k(s)$.

7. The generating function is $\{1 - F(s)\}(1 - s)^{-1} = (1 + s)U(s)$.

8. The generating function is $\Sigma\{\tfrac{1}{2}F(s)\}^k = 2F(s)\, s^{-2} - 1$.

9. Same generating function.

10. The kth zero must occur at a trial number $2r \leq n$ and the ensuing $n - 2r$ trials must not produce a zero.

11. Use an obvious analogue to (1.6) for the case where $P(1) < 1$.

12. Using the generating function for the geometric distribution of $\mathbf{X}_\nu$ we have without computation

$$P_r(s) = s^r \left(\frac{N-1}{N-s}\right)\left(\frac{N-2}{N-2s}\right)\cdots\left(\frac{N-r+1}{N-(r-1)s}\right).$$

13. $P_r(s)\{N - (r-1)s\} = P_{r-1}(s)(N - r - 1)s$.

14. $P_r(s) = \dfrac{s}{N - (N-1)s} \cdot \dfrac{2s}{N - (N-2)s} \cdots \dfrac{rs}{N - (N-r)s}$.

15. $\mathbf{S}_r$ is the sum of r independent variables with a common geometric distribution. Hence

$$P_r(s) = \left(\frac{q}{1 - ps}\right)^r, \qquad p_{r,k} = q^r p^k \binom{r+k-1}{k}.$$

16. $\mathbf{P}\{\mathbf{R} = r\} = \sum_{k=0}^{\nu-1}\mathbf{P}\{\mathbf{S}_{r-1} = k\}\mathbf{P}\{\mathbf{X}_r \geq \nu - k\} =$

$$= \sum_{k=0}^{\nu-1} q^{r-1}p^k \binom{r+k-2}{k} p^{\nu-k} = p^\nu q^{r-1}\binom{r+\nu-2}{\nu-1}.$$

$$\mathbf{E}(\mathbf{R}) = 1 + \frac{q\nu}{p}, \qquad \mathrm{Var}(\mathbf{R}) = \frac{\nu q}{p^2}.$$

21. $u_n = q^n + \sum_{k=3}^{n}\binom{k-1}{2} p^3 q^{k-3}u_{n-k}$ with $u_0 = 1,\ u_1 = q,\ u_2 = q^2,\ u_3 = p^3 + q^3$. Using the fact that this recurrence relation is of the convolution type,

$$U(s) = \frac{1}{1 - qs} + \frac{(ps)^3}{(1 - qs)^3}\, U(s).$$

22. $u_n = pw_{n-1} + qu_{n-1},\ v_n = pu_{n-1} + qv_{n-1},\ w_n = pv_{n-1} + qw_{n-1}$. Hence $U(s) - 1 = psW(s) + qsU(s);\ V(s) = psU(s) + qs\cdot V(s);\ W(s) = psV(s) + qsW(s)$.

CHAPTER XIII

1. It suffices to show that for all roots $s \neq 1$ of $F(s) = 1$ we have $|s| \geq 1$, and that $|s| = 1$ is possible only in the periodic case.

2. $u_{2n} = \left\{\binom{2n}{n} 2^{-2n}\right\}^r \sim (\pi n)^{-\frac{1}{2}r}$. Hence $\mathcal{E}$ is persistent only for $r = 2$.

For $r = 3$ the tangent rule for numerical integration gives

$$\sum_{n=1}^{\infty} u_{2n} \sim \pi^{-\frac{3}{2}} \int_{\frac{1}{2}}^{\infty} x^{-\frac{3}{2}}\, dx = \left(\frac{2}{\pi}\right)^{\frac{3}{2}} \approx \frac{1}{2}.$$

Hence by (3.5) the probability of $\mathcal{E}$ ever occurring is, approximately, $x = \frac{1}{3}$. A more precise evaluation of the sum is 0.47 and leads to $x = 0.32$.

3. $\mathbf{S}_n = 0$ is possible whenever $n = k(a + b)$, and the binomial distribution shows that for such n we have $\mathbf{P}\{\mathbf{S}_n = 0\} \sim (a + b)^{\frac{1}{2}}(2\pi abk)^{-\frac{1}{2}}$. The series diverges.

4. From $\Sigma f_k + \mathbf{P}\{\mathbf{X}_1 > 0\} \leq 1$ conclude that $f < 1$ unless $\mathbf{P}\{\mathbf{X}_1 > 0\} = 0$. In this case all $\mathbf{X}_k \leq 0$ and $\mathcal{E}$ occurs at the first trial or never.

5. Let $u_1, \ldots, u_N$ be given and $u_n = p_1 u_{n-1} + p_2 u_{n-2} + \ldots + p_N u_{n-N}$ for $n > N$. Then

$$\lim u_n = \frac{u_1 p_N + u_2(p_N + p_{N-1}) + \ldots + u_N(p_1 + p_2 + \ldots + p_N)}{p_1 + 2p_2 + 3p_3 + \ldots}.$$

If $p_k = N^{-1}$ then $\lim u_n = \dfrac{2}{N(N+1)}(u_1 + 2u_2 + \ldots + Nu_N)$.

6. $U_1(s) = \frac{1}{2} + \frac{1}{2}U(s)$, $\qquad F_1 = \sum\limits_{k=1}^{\infty}(\frac{1}{2}F)^k = s^{-2}F^2(s)$.

7. $F_2(s) = \frac{1}{2}s\{1 + F_1(s)\} = s^{-1}F(s)$.

8. $U_2(s) = \{1 - F_2(s)\}^{-1} = \frac{1}{2} + \frac{1}{2}(1 + s)(1 - s^2)^{-\frac{1}{2}}$. This shows the probability of a first passage at time $2n$ through a *positive* point to equal $\frac{1}{2}$ the probability of $S_{2n} = 0$.

9. (a) $F(s) = qs(1 - ps^r)^{-1}$, $\mu = 1 + rpq^{-1}$, $\sigma^2 = r^2pq^{-2}$; (b) $\mathbf{Z}_n = $ smallest integer $\geq (\mathbf{N} - n)/r$; then $\mathbf{E}(\mathbf{Z}_n) \sim np/(q + pr)$, $\quad \mathrm{Var}(\mathbf{Z}_n) \sim npq/(q + pr)^3$.

10. $U(s) = 1 + qs + \ldots + q^{r-1}s^{r-1} + q^r s^r(1 - s)^{-1}$, $\mu^{-1} = q^r$.

11. $\mathbf{N}_n^* \approx (\mathbf{N}_n - 714.3)/22.75$; $\quad \Phi(\frac{2}{3}) - \Phi(-\frac{2}{3}) \approx \frac{1}{2}$.

12. $r_n = r_{n-1} - \frac{1}{4}r_{n-2} + \frac{1}{8}r_{n-3}$ with $r_0 = r_1 = r_2 = 1$; $R(s) = (8 + 2s^2)(8 - 8s + 2s^2 - s^3)^{-1}$; $\quad r_n \sim 1.444248(1.139680)^{-n-1}$.

14. If a_n is the probability that an A-run of length r occurs at the nth trial, then $A(s)$ is given by (7.5) with p replaced by α and q by $1 - \alpha$. Let $B(s)$ and $C(s)$ be the corresponding functions for B- and C-runs. The required generating functions are $F(s) = 1 - U^{-1}(s)$, where in case (a) $U(s) = A(s)$; in (b) $U(s) = A(s) + B(s) - 1$; in (c) $U(s) = A(s) + B(s) + C(s) - 2$.

15. Use a straightforward combination of the method in example (8.b) and problem 14.

17. $u_n = Np$, $v_k(\infty) = Npq^k$.

19. Note that $1 - F(s) = (1 - s)Q(s)$ and $\mu - Q(s) = (1 - s)R(s)$, whence $Q(1) = \mu$, $2R(1) = \sigma^2 - \mu + \mu^2$. The power series for $Q^{-1}(s) = \Sigma(u_n - u_{n-1})s^n$ converges for $s = 1$.

CHAPTER XIV

1. The probability of ruin is still given by (2.4) with $p = \alpha(1 - \gamma)^{-1}$, $q = \beta(1 - \gamma)^{-1}$. The expected duration of the game is $\mathbf{D}_z(1 - \gamma)^{-1}$ with $\mathbf{D}_z$ given by (3.4) or (3.5).

2. The boundary conditions (2.2) are replaced by $q_0 - \delta q_1 = 1 - \delta$, $q_a = 0$. To (2.4) there corresponds the solution

$$q_z = \{(q/p)^a - (q/p)^z\}(1 - \delta) \div \{(q/p)^a (1 - \delta) + \delta q/p - 1\}.$$

The boundary conditions (3.2) become $\mathbf{D}_0 = \delta \mathbf{D}_1$, $\quad \mathbf{D}_a = 0$.

3. To (2.1) there corresponds $q_z = pq_{z+2} + qq_{z-1}$, and $q_z = \lambda^z$ is a particular solution if $\lambda = p\lambda^3 + q$, that is, if $\lambda = 1$ or $\lambda^2 + \lambda = qp^{-1}$. The probability of ruin is

$$q_z = \left\{ \left(\frac{1}{4} + \frac{q}{p} \right)^{\frac{1}{2}} - \frac{1}{2} \right\}^z \qquad \begin{array}{l} 1 \qquad \text{if} \quad q \geq 2p \\[4pt] \text{if} \quad q \leq 2p. \end{array}$$

5. $w_{z,n+1}(x) = pw_{z+1,n}(x) + qw_{z-1,n}(x)$ with the boundary conditions (1) $w_{0,n}(x) = w_{a,n}(x) = 0$ for $n \geq 1$; (2) $w_{z,0}(x) = 0$ for $z \neq x$ and $w_{x,0}(x) = 1$.
6. Replace (1) by $w_{0,n}(x) = w_{1,n}(x)$ and $w_{a,n}(x) = w_{a-1,n}(x)$.

10. $\mathbf{P}\{\mathbf{M}_n < z\} = \sum_{x=1}^{\infty} (v_{x-z\,n} - v_{x+z\,n})$

$\mathbf{P}\{\mathbf{M}_n = z\} = \mathbf{P}\{\mathbf{M}_n < z+1\} - \mathbf{P}\{\mathbf{M}_n < z\}.$
11. The first passage through x must have occurred at a time $k \leq n$, and the particle returned from x to x in the following $n - k$ steps.

CHAPTER XV

1. P has rows $(p, q, 0, 0)$, $(0, 0, p, q)$, $(p, q, 0, 0)$, and $(0, 0, p, q)$. For $n > 1$ the rows are (p^2, pq, pq, q^2).
2. (a) The chain is irreducible and ergodic; $p_{jk}^{(n)} \to \frac{1}{3}$ for all j, k. (Note that P is doubly stochastic.) (b) The chain has period 3, with G_1 containing E_1 and E_2; the state E_4 forms G_2, and E_3 forms G_3. We have $u_1 = u_2 = \frac{1}{2}$, $u_3 = u_4 = 1$. (c) The states E_1 and E_3 form a closed set S_1, and E_4, E_5 another closed set S_2, whereas E_2 is transient. The matrices corresponding to the closed sets are two-by-two matrices with elements $\frac{1}{2}$. Hence $p_{jk}^{(n)} \to \frac{1}{2}$ if E_j and E_k belong to the same S_r; $p_{j2}^{(n)} \to 0$; finally $p_{2k}^{(n)} \to \frac{1}{2}$ if $k = 1, 3$, and $p_{2k}^{(n)} \to 0$ if $k = 2, 4, 5$. (d) The chain has period 3. Putting $a = (0, 0, 0, \frac{1}{3}, \frac{1}{3}, \frac{1}{3})$, $b = (1, 0, 0, 0, 0, 0)$, $c = (0, \frac{1}{2}, \frac{1}{2}, 0, 0, 0)$, we find that the rows of $P^2 = P^5 = \ldots$ are a, b, b, c, c, c, those of $P^3 = P^6 = \ldots$ are b, c, c, a, a, a, those of $P = P^4 = \ldots$ are c, a, a, b, b, b.
3. $p_{jj}^{(n)} = (j/6)^n$, $p_{jk}^{(n)} = (k/6)^n - ((k-1)/6)^n$ if $k > j$, and $p_{jk}^{(n)} = 0$ if $k < j$.
4. $x_k = (\frac{3}{4}, \frac{1}{2}, \frac{1}{4}, \frac{1}{2})$, $y_k = (\frac{1}{4}, \frac{1}{2}, \frac{3}{4}, \frac{1}{2})$.
6. Put $\mu = \Sigma n p_n$. The states are null states if $\mu = \infty$. Stationary distribution: $u_k = \mu^{-1}(p_k + p_{k+1} + \ldots)$.
7. Ergodic if $\Sigma(1 - q_0)(1 - q_1) \ldots (1 - q_{n-1}) < \infty$. Stationary distribution proportional to the terms of the series.
8. $u_r = (p/q)^r(q - p)/p$.
9. $u_r = \{1 - p/q\}(p/q)^{r-1} \div \{1 - (p/q)^a\}$.
10. $p_{jj} = 2j(N - j)/N^2$, $p_{j,j+1} = (N - j)^2/N^2$, $p_{j,j-1} = j^2/N^2$,

$$u_k = \binom{N}{k}^2 \div \binom{2N}{N}.$$

13.
$$P = \begin{bmatrix} q & p & & & \cdots & 0 & 0 \\ 0 & 0 & 1 & & \cdots & 0 & 0 \\ 0 & 0 & 0 & 1 & \cdots & 0 & 0 \\ \cdot & \cdot & \cdot & \cdot & \cdot & \cdot & \cdot & \cdot \\ 0 & 0 & 0 & 0 & \cdots & 0 & 1 \\ q & p & 0 & 0 & \cdots & 0 & 0 \end{bmatrix}.$$

14. Note that the matrix is doubly stochastic; use example (6.b).

15. Put $p_{k,k+1} = 1$ for $k = 1, \ldots, N-1$, and $p_{Nk} = p_k$.

16. $\Sigma u_j p_{jk} = u_k$, then $U(s) = u_0(1 - s)\{P(s) - s\}^{-1}$. For ergodicity it is necessary and sufficient that $P'(1) < 1$.

23. Let M be the maximum of x_j. Consider the states E_r for which $x_r = M$.

26. If $N \geq m - 2$, the variables $X^{(m)}$ and $X^{(n)}$ are independent, and hence the three rows of the matrix $p_{jk}^{(m,n)}$ are identical with the distribution of $\mathbf{X}^{(n)}$, namely, $(\frac{1}{4}, \frac{1}{2}, \frac{1}{4})$. For $n = m + 1$ the three rows are $(\frac{1}{2}, \frac{1}{2}, 0)$, $(\frac{1}{4}, \frac{1}{2}, \frac{1}{4})$, $(0, \frac{1}{2}, \frac{1}{2})$.

CHAPTER XVII

3. $\mathbf{E}(\mathbf{X}) = ie^{\lambda t}$; $\mathrm{Var}(\mathbf{X}) = ie^{\lambda t}(e^{\lambda t} - 1)$.

4. $P'_n = -\lambda n P_n + \lambda(n + 1)P_{n+1}$.

$$P_n = \binom{i}{n} e^{-i\lambda t}(e^{\lambda t} - 1)^{i-nt} \qquad (n \leq i).$$

$$\mathbf{E}(\mathbf{X}) = ie^{-\lambda t}; \qquad \mathrm{Var}(\mathbf{X}) = ie^{-\lambda t}(1 - e^{-\lambda t}).$$

5. $P'_n(t) = -(\lambda + n\mu)P_n(t) + \lambda P_{n-1}(t) + (n + 1)\mu P_{n+1}(t)$ for $n \leq N-1$ and $P'_N(t) = -N\mu P_N(t) + \lambda P_{N-1}(t)$.

6. Birth and deaths process with $\lambda_n = \lambda$, $\mu_n = \mu$.

19. The standard method of solving linear differential equations leads to a system of linear equations. Cf. the hint contained in footnote 3 of chapter XVI.

Index